Pres

I

The
GUIDE

to Selecting Plays for performance

90th Edition (January 2000-December 2002)

Samuel French Ltd
52 Fitzroy Street London W1P 6JR

ISBN 0 573 09143 9

Contents

Contents—continued

Introduction

Sections of *The Guide*

Welcome to the 90th edition of *The Guide*, which will remain current until December 2002.

The plays are divided into four main sections: Section A, full length plays; Section B, one act plays (both sections include mixed cast, all-female and all-male cast titles); Section C, plays for children and young people; Section D, pantomimes and seasonal plays.

All plays new to this edition of the Guide are denoted by a bullet mark next to the title and the authors' indexes join the classified indexes at the beginning of Sections A and B (these are printed on yellow paper for Section A, blue for Section B).

For the first time in Section C the plays are listed alphabetically in one section with marginal marks to indicate the approximate playing time of the individual titles and suggestions as to whether they are for performance by children, young people or adults to children. In addition to the classified index at the beginning of this section there is now an authors' index. For details of the marginal markings please see page 458.

Cast Descriptions

The cast breakdown for each play gives the male/female ratio and the playing range of ages only, together with a note of any ethnic roles involved. Contemporary casting often has actors playing roles outside their actual age range and the change in details in our Guide reflects this.

Thus

M5 (18, 20s-50s)

indicates there are five male roles — aged eighteen and ranging in age from the twenties to the fifties.

Similarly

F5 (18, 20s (1 Asian), 40, 50)

indicates five women's roles — one aged eighteen, and the other four roles being for two in their twenties (one of whom is an Asian) one aged forty and one aged fifty.

Updating *The Guide*

To keep your copy of *The Guide* up to date please see page 23 for details of our mailing list and web site.

Licences to Perform French's Plays

Licences to perform are issued by:

UK and Overseas Agents

SAMUEL FRENCH LTD, 52 Fitzroy Street, London W1P 6JR and their authorized Agents as follows:

Nottingham	*"The Sign of Four"*, *Royal Centre*
Republic of Ireland and Northern Ireland	Drama League of Ireland, *Unit 2208, Richmond Business Campus, Nth Brunswick Street, Dublin 7*
Australia	Dominie Pty Ltd, *8 Cross Street, Brookvale, NSW 2100*
East Africa	Phoenix Players Ltd, *P.O. Box 52383, Nairobi, Kenya*
India	Jagdish Raja, *The Artistes' Repertory Theatre, Jagriti Farm, Whitefield, Bangalore 560 066*
Malta	Dingli Co. International Ltd, *18/2 South Street, Valetta*
New Zealand	Play Bureau (NZ) Ltd, *P.O. Box 420, New Plymouth*
South Africa (and Namibia, Swaziland, Botswana, Lesotho)	D.A.L.R.O. (Pty) Ltd, *P.O. Box 31627, Braamfontein 2017, Johannesburg*
Zimbabwe	National Theatre Organization, *P.O. Box 2701, Harare*

SAMUEL FRENCH Inc., 45 West 25th Street, New York, NY 10010, U.S.A.
SAMUEL FRENCH Inc., 7623 Sunset Boulevard, Hollywood, CA 90046, U.S.A.
SAMUEL FRENCH (Canada) Ltd, 100 Lombard Street, Lower Level, Toronto, Ontario, M5C 1M3, Canada

Fees

The fees quoted in this catalogue were correct at the time of going to press. They relate to performances within the United Kingdom only and may be subject to revision during the period in which this Guide remains current. If you are in any doubt as to the correct current fee, please apply to Samuel French London, or to one of our authorized agents, for a quotation.

Prices

The current prices of play copies can be found in our price list, published separately.

Restrictions

Please read the Notice on page xiii concerning restrictions on Amateur Rights.

Samuel French Ltd in Ireland

Thomas J. Mooney

Sadly, in 1999 we announced the death of Thomas J. Mooney. For many years he was the agent for Samuel French Ltd in Ireland and Northern Ireland.

New Agent for Ireland and Northern Ireland

The Drama League of Ireland has been appointed as Samuel French Ltd's agent for Ireland and Northern Ireland and can be contacted as follows:

> Drama League of Ireland
> Unit 2208
> Richmond Business Campus
> Nth Brunswick Street
> Dublin 7
>
> Telephone: 00 353 1 809 0478
> Fax: 00 353 1 807 2425
> Cellular phone: 086 852 4532
> e-mail: dli@eircom.net

Restrictions

From time to time it may be necessary for us to withdraw or restrict the Amateur Rights of Performance of certain plays. In their own interests, therefore, societies should always apply for written permission before committing themselves to a production.

Important Notice

Public Performances

Protection against unlawful performances of plays is afforded to dramatic authors by means of copyright. Under the Copyright Law no public performance or reading of a protected play may be given, either in its entirety or in the form of excerpts, without the prior consent of the owner of the copyright. The majority of plays in this Guide are copyright, and as agents for the copyright owners we issue licenses for performances on payment of a fee. The fees quoted in this Guide are subject to contract and subject to variation at the sole discretion of Samuel French Ltd. Fees for performances given in premises seating 400 or more persons will be subject to negotiation.

Private and Domestic Performances

The precise stage at which a reading or other representation of a play ceases to be a public performance and becomes a private and domestic one will depend entirely upon circumstances. Performances that take place in one's own home — and under certain conditions in hospitals and institutions — can be domestic; but it is not safe to assume that they are invariably so. It is always advisable to furnish us with the full facts of each individual case, and to apply for a free licence before any performance or reading takes place.

Charity Performances

Because it is intended to give a performance in aid of charity the owner of the copyright will not consent to reduce, or waive claim to, the usual fee. The writing of plays is a means of livelihood, and every performance reduces the potential audience — and therefore the earning capacity of the play. The cause of charity does not excuse infringement of the author's rights.

Performances Overseas

The plays listed in this Guide are generally available for performances by amateurs in the British Isles. There may be restrictions on the performance of certain plays overseas. Amateurs intending production overseas must, in their own interest, make application to us before starting rehearsals or booking a theatre or hall.

Prior Consent

It is important that the consent of the copyright owner should be obtained before any performance of a play is given. Willingness to pay the fee and obtain the licence after the event would not render those organizing, and those taking part in, the play any less liable for infringement of the copyright.

Restrictions

From time to time it may be necessary for us to withdraw or restrict the Amateur Rights of Performance of certain plays. In their own interests, therefore, societies should always apply for written permission before committing themselves to a production.

Copyright Information

Copyright Protection in Written Works

The titles in this catalogue are fully protected under the Copyright Laws of the British Commonwealth of Nations, the United States of America and all countries of the Berne and Universal Copyright Conventions.

All rights, including Stage, Motion Picture, Radio, Television, Public Reading, and Translations into Foreign Languages, are strictly reserved.

No part of these works may lawfully be reproduced in ANY form or by any means — photocopying, typescript, recording (including video-recording), manuscript, electronic, mechanical, or otherwise — or be transmitted or stored in a retrieval system, without prior permission.

Changes in UK Copyright Laws

Copyright now subsists in the work of a writer until the end of the seventieth year following his or her death, rather than the end of the fiftieth year as hitherto and works which were considered to be out of copyright have been brought back into protection and become liable for royalty payment when performed if the author has been dead for less than seventy years. Thus, a number of writers whose work was in the public domain are affected.

It is not safe to assume that a work is out of copyright. Therefore, be sure to check very carefully the availability of rights and royalty requirements. We are always prepared to help you in this respect.

Video-recordings

The copyright laws governing video-recording are extremely complex and it should not be assumed that any play may be video-recorded *for whatever purpose* without first obtaining the permission of the appropriate agents. The fact that a play is included in the Samuel French Ltd catalogue does not indicate that video rights are available or that Samuel French Ltd controls such rights. Our Performing Rights Department will be happy to give advice on this point.

Another Century — Another Millennium

Samuel French Ltd cannot claim to have been here throughout the past Millennium (although we do publish *1066 — And All That* and have a number of other plays set during the Gothic period) but we aim to be here to serve the theatre for the next thousand years!

Theatre is an enormously important part of our lives on many levels and it is a matter of continuing distress and shame that successive governments throughout the English speaking world do not appear to acknowledge this in essential financial terms. In so many instances the professional theatre is struggling for survival and it is frequently to the amateurs that the public turns for the dramatic experience.

This means, of course, that the public turns to us, because 'French's' and 'plays' have become synonymous. We have been publishing plays since 1830 and although our work (as in this catalogue) is directed to the amateur theatre we have a very secure niche in the professional world as well.

In 1830 one Thomas Hailes Lacy began to publish plays in London to meet the increasing market for amateur acting which was becoming a popular hobby. A few years later, across the Atlantic, one Samuel French began to do the same in New York. Within a few years each had appointed the other as his transatlantic agent and eventually Samuel French came to London, for health reasons, and later bought Lacy's Plays.

Our reputation has been built on staying abreast of modern writing and we continue to publish plays by new writers each year as well as keeping available the works of many of our great traditional playwrights.

Although the following pages list plays which are available for amateur production in the British Isles, it is our wish and hope that this catalogue will find its way wherever someone is looking for ideas for a play to perform or information on a play's vital statistics.

When you are in London come and visit us in our comfortable and well-stocked showroom and bookshop — which is now also open on Saturdays. Details of our opening hours and other access to us (our telephone, fax and e-mail) appear on page xxvii of *The Guide* and if you cannot visit us in person we are on-line at —

www.samuelfrench-london.co.uk

Latest Acquisitions

Please note that the following titles without an asterisk are not yet released for amateur performance. Those marked with an asterisk are released for amateur performance and full details will be given in the first supplement to the Guide (to be published Spring 2000). Please enquire for further details.

FULL LENGTH PLAYS

'Allo 'Allo	Jeremy Lloyd and David Croft
Art	Yasmina Reza, translated by Christopher Hampton
The Beauty Queen of Leenane	Martin McDonagh
Blinded by the Sun	Stephen Poliakoff
The Blue Room	David Hare, freely adapted from *La Ronde* by Arthur Schnitzler
Body Language	Alan Ayckbourn
The Boy Who Fell Into a Book	Alan Ayckbourn
Brief Lives	Patrick Garland
*Carpe Jugulum	Terry Pratchett, adapted for the stage by Stephen Briggs
Le Cid	Pierre Corneille, adapted by David Bryer
Cleo, Camping, Emmanuelle and Dick	Terry Johnson
Closer	Patrick Marber
Coarse Acting Strikes Back	Michael Green
Comic Potential	Alan Ayckbourn
Copenhagen	Michael Frayn
Darkness Falls	Jonathan Holloway
Disposing of the Body	Hugh Whitemore
The End of the Affair	Graham Greene, adapted by Rupert Goold and Caroline Butler
Equally Divided	Ronald Harwood
Fatal Encounter	Francis Durbridge
*Feed	Tom Elliott
Fred and Madge	Joe Orton
Funny About Love	Terence Frisby
Garden	Alan Ayckbourn
The Garden Party	Jimmie Chinn and Hazel Wyld
Ghost Writer	David Tristram
The Gift of the Gorgon	Peter Shaffer
Gym and Tonic	John Godber
Haunting Julia	Alan Ayckbourn
House	Alan Ayckbourn
In Flame	Charlotte Jones
It Started with a Kiss	John Godber
The Judas Kiss	David Hare
Life of Galileo	Bertolt Brecht, translated by David Hare
Life is a Dream	Calderón de la Barca, translated by Gwynne Edwards
Like a Virgin	Gordon Steel
The Lion, the Witch and the Wardrobe	C.S. Lewis, dramatized by Adrian Mitchell
The Lonesome West	Martin McDonagh

Latest Acquisitions — continued

Love in the Title	Hugh Leonard
The Memory of Water	Shelagh Stephenson
Misery	Stephen King. Adapted for the stage by Simon Moore
The Mousetrap	Agatha Christie
Mr Wonderful	James Robson
Nabokov's Gloves	Peter Moffatt
The Nativity	David Farr
Never Land	Phyllis Nagy
Nobody's Perfect	Simon Williams
Perfect Pitch	John Godber
Pullin' the Wool	Frank Vickery
Quartet	Ronald Harwood
Rose	Martin Sherman
Rosie and the Bad, Bad Apples	Valerie Hall. Music by Paul Whittington
The Secret Garden	Frances Hodgson Burnett, adapted by Neil Duffield
The Secret Lives of Henry and Alice	David Tristram
A Skull in Connemara	Martin McDonagh
*Sparkleshark	Philip Ridley
Surgeon of Honour	Calderón de la Barca, translated by Gwynne Edwards
Sweet Panic	Stephen Poliakoff
*Three Sisters	Anton Chekhov, in an adaptation by Samuel Adamson
Three Judgements in One	Calderón de la Barca, translated by Gwynne Edwards
The Twits	Roald Dahl, adapted for the stage by David Wood
The Unexpected Man	Yasmina Reza, translated by Christopher Hampton
Unleashed	John Godber
The Visitor	Joe Orton
The Woman in Black	Adapted by Stephen Mallatratt from the book by Susan Hill

ONE ACT PLAYS

The Bear	Anton Chekhov, adapted by Bernard Lawrence
Crossing	Reza de Wet, translated by Steven Stead
*Figuring Things	Michael Fosbrook
*Melons at the Parsonage	Nick Warburton
Missing	Reza de Wet, translated by Steven Stead

MUSICALS

Large As Life	Richard Harris, Keith Strachan
Boyband	Peter Quilter
A Day in Hollywood/A Night in the Ukraine	Book and lyrics by Dick Vosburgh and Frank Lazarus
The Demon Headmaster	Based on the novel by Gillian Cross. Music by Eric Angus and Cathy Shostak. Lyrics by Iain Halstead and Paul James. Book by Paul James
Peter Pan	J. M. Barrie. Lyrics by Carolyn Leigh, Betty Comden and Adolph Green. Music by Mark Charlap and Jule Styne

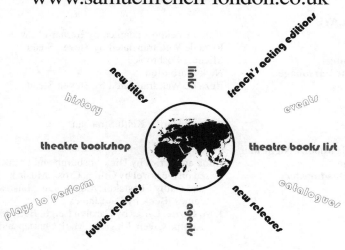

Keeping Up to Date

You can keep your *Guide* up to date either by joining our mailing list or visiting our web site which is constantly updated to give details of all new and future releases as they become available.

Mailing List

In Spring and Autumn we publish a supplement to *The Guide* which details all new and future releases and which is available free to all those on our mailing list. To obtain your copy please contact:

Sales Department
Samuel French Ltd
52 Fitzroy Street
London W1P 6JR

Telephone: 020 7387 9373
Fax: 020 7387 2161
e-mail: theatre@samuelfrench-london.co.uk

Web Site

If you have access to the world wide web (local libraries often have internet facilities) you may like to visit our site:

http://www.samuelfrench-london.co.uk

and obtain the supplement to *The Guide* online (available on our **New Releases** page).

In addition, we aim to provide regular updates on new French's publications, new releases available for amateur performance, details of theatre books on a wide range of topics available from our bookshop, and much more. The site includes:

- ◆ **New Releases**. Plays released for amateur performance with a link to the individual page giving full details of the title—casting, synopsis, fee code, set, etc.
- ◆ **Future Releases**. Plays released for amateur performance from the date given. Each title is linked to give full details of the play.
- ◆ **New Titles**. Newly published French's acting editions. (Please note that these titles, although available on sale, may not be available for amateur performance.)

FOR THE TIMES WHEN THE PERFORMANCE REALLY SETS THE THEATRE ON FIRE

CALL 020 7247 0023

When you are insuring a theatre or amateur production, the last thing you want to worry about is the policy.

But if you're not properly insured you could be liable.

Which is why you need First Night.

It's a policy specifically designed for amateur societies.

And coming from Gordon and Co, leading insurance brokers to the entertainment world, there's no better coverage, or more competitive rate.

So call us on 020 7247 0023 and if something catches fire, you won't get burnt.

Gordon & Co
Insurance Brokers
Freepost, 41-43 London Fruit Exchange,
Brushfield Street, London E1 6BR Fax. 020 7375 1286

Don't let your first night be your last

How to Order Your Books

Retail Mail Order

RETAIL MAIL ORDER

Unless you already have an Account with us, pre-payment is required for ALL orders, either

a) by cheque or postal order made out to Samuel French Ltd

OR

b) by credit/debit card when the number and expiry date of the registered card MUST be quoted.

Please send your order to:

Mail Order Department
Samuel French Ltd
52 Fitzroy Street
London W1P 6JR

Or you may telephone your order on 020 7255 4300 or fax on 020 7387 2161 and quote your credit/debit card number.

Credit/debit card orders may also be left on our telephone answering service outside office hours. Please leave a daytime telephone number should we need to contact you during office hours (Monday to Friday 9.30 a.m. to 5.30 p.m.).

Please ensure when ordering by credit/debit card that your card number is correctly quoted, together with the date of expiry and the address of the registered card owner.

Trade Customers

TRADE CUSTOMERS

Please enquire for trade terms and conditions.

The current prices of the plays in this Guide, together with postage rates for inland and overseas customers, can be found in our Price List, issued separately.

Orders for books may also be addressed to our authorized agents whose names and addresses appear on page ix of this Guide.

French's Theatre Bookshop

Our bookshop, situated in the heart of London, stocks:

- ◆ books on every aspect of theatre (16 categories, free lists available)
- ◆ plays in all editions in the English language currently in print
- ◆ theatre magazines
- ◆ greetings cards
- ◆ sound effect CDs
- ◆ theatre tokens
- ◆ and much more ...

Opening Hours

Monday to Friday 9.30 a.m. to 5.30 p.m.
Saturday 11.00 a.m. to 5.00 p.m.

Mail Order

If you can't visit us in person, we have a world-wide mail order service and accept all major credit and debit cards. For details of how to place your order please see page xxv.

Telephone

020 7255 4300 (Bookshop)

020 7387 9373 (general enquiries;
answering service outside office hours)

Fax

020 7387 2161 (24 hours)

e-mail

theatre@samuelfrench-london.co.uk

For details of books new to the bookshop, visit our web site at:

www.samuelfrench-london.co.uk

the
Musical
Plays Catalogue

A 136-page catalogue giving details of all
Musicals and Plays with Music handled by
Samuel French Ltd

Section I   Full scale musicals, with full synopsis etc.
Section II   Plays with music
Section III Plays with music for children and young people
Section IV Pantomimes with published scores

Please enquire!

SECTION A
Full Length Plays

CONTENTS

A

Classified Index

Titles arranged according to number of characters

ONE PERSON PLAYS

M1
Anorak of Fire
Brief Lives
Moscow Stations
One Fine Day

F1
Female Parts
Shirley Valentine

TWO CHARACTERS

COMEDIES

M1 F1
April In Paris
Different Way Home
Elsie and Norm's 'Macbeth'
Owl and the Pussycat
Same Time, Next Year
They're Playing Our Song
Two (*min. cast*)

M2
Mystery of Irma Vep

PLAYS

M1 F1
Conjugal Rites
Educating Rita
Happy Jack
Intimate Exchanges
Laughing Wild
Separation
September in the Rain
Stuttgart (*see* State of Affairs)
Two of Us

M2
Staircase

F2
Vita and Virginia

SERIOUS PLAYS

M1 F1
Duet for One
Gin Game
Old-World
Retreat
When the Wind Blows

M2
Not About Heroes

DRAMAS

M1 F1
Deceptions
Double Double
Killing Time
Man with Connections
Mysterious Mr Love
Petition

M2
Sleuth
Who Killed 'Agatha Christie'?

THREE CHARACTERS

COMEDIES

M1 F2
Decorator
Old Times
Teechers (*min. cast*)

M2 F1
Kingfisher
Maintenance Man
Ruffian on the Stair
Speed-the-Plow

PLAYS

M1 F2
Commitment (*see* State of Affairs)
Consequences (*see* State of Affairs)
Crystal Clear
Just the Three of Us

A

Maintenance Man
Moment of Weakness
Painting Churches
Stevie
Women on the Verge of HRT

M2 F1
Best of Friends
Betrayal
Mixed Doubles
Rattle of a Simple Man
Star-Spangled Girl
To Meet Oscar Wilde
Treats
Weekend Breaks

M3
American Buffalo
Caretaker
Life in the Theatre

SERIOUS PLAYS

M1 F2
Summit Conference
Tissue

M2 F1
Death and the Maiden (Dorfman)
Holidays
Kingdom of Earth
Massage

F3
Low Level Panic

DRAMAS

M2 F1
Business of Murder
Dangerous Obsession
Faith Healer
Final Twist (*min. cast*)
Inside Job
Playing Sinatra
Promise
Skylight
Tilting Ground

M3
Orphans
Someone Who'll Watch Over me

F3
Agnes of God
Mrs Klein
Skirmishes

FOUR CHARACTERS

FARCE

M2 F2
Alarms and Excursions (*min. cast*)

COMEDIES

Travels With My Aunt (*variable, min. cast*)

M1 F3
Last of the Red Hot Lovers
On the Verge, or the Geography of Yearning

M2 F2
About Alice
Born in the Garden
Butterflies Are Free
California Suite
Easy Terms
Groping for Words
Lovers Dancing
Lunatic View
Me and Mamie O'Rourke
On Approval
One for the Road
Opposite Sex
Relatively Speaking
Say Who You Are
Two of a Kind
You Say Tomatoes

M3 F1
Entertaining Mr Sloane
Hysteria
Knack
My Fat Friend

M4
Neville's Island

F4
Killing of Sister George

PLAYS

M1 F3
When I Was a Girl, I Used to Scream and
  Shout ...

M2 F2
Accommodations
Benefactors
Breaking the String
Cocktail Hour
Collaborators
Come As You Are
Flesh and Blood
Good Grief
Happy Family
Love Forty
Lucky Sods (*min. cast*)
Playing the Wife
Shades
Small Change
Things We Do For Love

M3 F1
Golden Pathway Annual
Making It Better
Passionate Woman

M4
Brothers of the Brush

F4
If We Are Women

SERIOUS PLAYS

M1 F3
Children
Extremities
Winter Wife

M2 F2
Ashes
Brimstone and Treacle
Exorcism
Glass Menagerie
Last Gamble
Me and My Friend
Real Estate
Retreat From Moscow
Who's Afraid of Virginia Woolf?

M3 F1
After Darwin (*min. cast*)
Hollow Crown
In Praise of Love
Insignificance
Tom and Clem

DRAMAS

M1 F3
Blood Money
Dead Guilty
Deadly Embrace

M2 F2
Anastasia File
Dead of Night
Hard Times (*min. cast*)
I'll Be Back Before Midnight!
Late Edwina Black
Murder Game
Murderer
Nightmare: The Fright of Your Life
Suspicions
Threat!
Veronica's Room

M3 F1
Final Twist
It's Ralph
Murder By Misadventure
Passionate Woman
Stage Struck
Who Saw Him Die?

F4
Bold Girls
My Mother Said I Never Should
My Sister In This House

FIVE CHARACTERS

COMEDIES

M1 F4
Cemetery Club
Farndale Avenue/*Chase Me Up*
Farndale Avenue/*A Christmas Carol*
Farndale Avenue/*Murder Mystery*
They Came From Mars ...

A

M2 F3
Abigail's Party
Baby with the Bathwater (*min. cast*)
Don't Misunderstand Me
Falling Off a Log
Good Doctor
Happy Birthday
Henceforward ...
Imaginary Lines
Lettice and Lovage
Life Goes On
Look Who's Talking!
Loose Ends
Office Suite
Pastimes
Perfect Party
Private Lives
Secretary Bird
Touch and Go
We Found Love ... Aboard the SS Farndale Avenue

M3 F2
Bedside Manners
Birthday Suite
Cat in the Bag
Confusions
Dead Funny
Don't Lose the Place!
Erogenous Zones
Gasping (*min. cast*)
Greetings!
Inspector Drake and the Perfekt Crime
Man Most Likely To ...
Marking Time
Other People's Money
Plaza Suite
Second from Last in the Sack Race (*min. cast*)
Silly Cow
Theft
Time and Time Again
Why Not Stay for Breakfast?

M4 F1
Bedwinner
Corpse!

F5
Kiss on the Bottom (*min. cast*)

PLAYS

M1 F4
Fall
Understanding

M2 F3
Actor's Nightmare (*see* Sister Mary Ignatius ...)
Anna's Room
Biting the Bullet
Blood, Sweat and Tears
I Love My Love
Just Between Ourselves
Loose Ends
Pizzazz
Something To Remember You By
Trouble With Old Lovers
Under The Stars

M3 F2
Can You Hear Me at the Back?
Carving a Statue
Day of the Dog (*see* State of Affairs)
Goose-Pimples
I Thought I Heard a Rustling
Jeffrey Bernard Is Unwell
Lent
Murder by the Book
Natural Causes
Piece of My Mind
Smelling a Rat
Sting in the Tale
Sufficient Carbohydrate

M4 F1
Clouds

M5
Waiting for Godot

F5
Effect of Gamma Rays on Man-in-the-Moon Marigolds
New Anatomies (*min. cast*)
Playhouse Creatures

SERIOUS PLAYS

M1 F4
Stages

M2 F3
Kennedy's Children
Mail Order Bride

M3 F2
Another Time
Clocks and Whistles
Five Finger Exercise
Heritage

A

Home
Letter of Resignation
Look Back in Anger

M4 F1
Killing Game
Next Time I'll Sing to You
Portraits (*min. cast*)

M5
Rents (*min. cast*)

DRAMAS

M2 F3
Being of Sound Mind
Caravan
Gaslight
March on Russia

M3 F2
Checkmate
Choice
Day in the Death of Joe Egg
Dead-Lock
Deathtrap
In for the Kill
In the Bar of a Tokyo Hotel
Kidnap Game
Present from the Past
Suspects
Taste of Honey
That Good Night

M4 F1
Accounts
Dial 'M' for Murder
Undertaking

F5
Thriller of the Year

SIX CHARACTERS

FARCES

M3 F3
Don't Dress for Dinner
Murder Room

M4 F2
Taking Steps

M5 F1
Accidental Death of an Anarchist

COMEDIES

M1 F5
Haunted Through Lounge ... Farndale Castle

M2 F4
All's Fair
Aspern Papers
Haywire
Look, No Hans!
Prisoner of Second Avenue
Romantic Comedy
Visiting Hour (*min. cast*)
When the Cat's Away

M3 F3
Absent Friends
Absurd Person Singular
Anyone For Breakfast?
Communicating Doors
Don't Dress for Dinner
Englishman's Home
Fly In The Ointment
Gingerbread Lady
Good and Faithful Servant
Happy Event
How the Other Half Loves
It Could Be Any One of Us
Just the Ticket!
Love in a Mist
My Friend Miss Flint
Norman Conquests
Salt of the Earth (*min. cast*)
Situation Comedy
Ski Whizz
Strike Up the Banns
Time Was
Toe in the Water
Two and Two Make Sex
Up and Running
Why Me?

M4 F2
Barefoot in the Park
Beyond Therapy
Heatstroke
Mixed Feelings
Pocket Dream
She Was Only an Admiral's Daughter
Torch Song Trilogy
Unoriginal Sin
What the Butler Saw
Wife Begins at Forty

A

M5 F1
End of the Food Chain
It Can Damage Your Health
Kafka's Dick
Loot
Rough Crossing

F6
Bazaar and Rummage

PLAYS

M1 F5
Come Back for Light Refreshments After the
    Service

M2 F4
Crimes of the Heart
Day After the Fair
House on the Cliff
Leaving Home
Lovers
My Heart's a Suitcase
Positive Hour
Relative Strangers
You Should See Us Now

M3 F3
Action Replay
Adam Bede
Amy's View
Anniversary
Close to the Wind
Dining Room (*min. cast*)
Grace Note
Hard Feelings
No One Sees the Video
Prin
Rise and Fall of Little Voice
Roots and Wings
Sister Mary Ignatius Explains It All for You
Whoops-a-Daisy

M4 F2
Audience Called Edouard
Broadway Bound
Chasing the Moment
Elton John's Glasses
Haunted
Not Quite Jerusalem
Some Sunny Day
Spokesong
Valued Friends

M5 F1
Building Blocks
Common Pursuit

SERIOUS PLAYS

Fen (*varied cast*)

M2 F4
Aurelia
Ballerina
Delicate Balance
Messiah
Remembrance
Secret Rapture

M3 F3
Bloody Poetry
Icecream
Kennedy's Children
Loved
Month of Sundays (Larbey)
Old Country
Sweet Panic

M4 F2
Birthday Party
I Have Been Here Before
Knuckle
Light Shining In Buckinghamshire
Taking Sides
Traps

M5 F1
After Darwin
Homecoming
Single Spies

DRAMAS

M2 F4
Power of the Dog (Dryden)
Time to Kill
Turn of the Screw
Wolfsbane

M3 F3
Anagram of Murder
Anybody for Murder?
Britannicus
Dead Man's Hand
Dining Room (*min. cast*)
Edge of Darkness
Exit the King
Fatal Attraction
Gone Up in Smoke
House of Secrets

Party to Murder
Portrait of Murder
Sad Hotel
September Tide

M4 F2
Interpreters
Lenz
Local Murder
Madhouse in Goa
Making History
Murder Assured
Murder by Appointment
Paddywack
Silhouette (*min. cast*)

M6
Birdy
Choice
Dealers
Our Boys

F6
Steel Magnolias

SEVEN CHARACTERS

FARCES

M2 F5
Blithe Spirit

M3 F4
Big Bad Mouse
Kindly Keep It Covered

M4 F3
Pull the Other One

M5 F2
Who's Under Where?

M6 F1
For Whom the Bell Chimes

COMEDIES

M1 F6
Caramba's Revenge

M2 F5
Gigi

M3 F4
Children's Day
Come Blow Your Horn
Every Other Evening
Family Planning
Fish Out of Water (*revised*)
Fringe Benefits
Key for Two
Month of Sundays (Savory)
Not With a Bang
Partners
Spanish Lies
Way Upstream
Will You Still Love Me in the Morning?

M4 F3
And a Nightingale Sang
Bedfull of Foreigners
Holiday Snap
Laugh? I Nearly Went to Miami!
Lost In Yonkers
Night on the Tiles
Party Piece
Passion Killers (*min. cast*)
Patrick Pearse Motel
Philanthropist
Ring Sisters
Rise and Fall of Little Voice
Rise in the Market
Straight and Narrow
There's a Girl in My Soup
Two and Two Together
Will You Still Love Me in the Morning?

M5 F2
Dead Ringer
Earl and the Pussycat
Foreigner
God's Favorite
I'm Not Rappaport
Nerd
Page 3 Murder
Sunshine Boys

M6 F1
Up 'n' Under

F7
Kiss on the Bottom

PLAYS

M1 F6
Steaming

M2 F5
Before the Party
Harvest
Island
Stars in the Morning Sky

M3 F4
Brighton Beach Memoirs
Cuckoo
84 Charing Cross Road
Mother Tongue
Take Away the Lady
Thickness of Skin

M4 F3
All Things Considered
Alphabetical Order
Brideshead Revisited
Butley
City Sugar
Cloud Nine
Dresser
Family Dance
Getting On
Lost In Yonkers
Our Song
Real Thing
Sneeze (*min. cast*)
Sylvia's Wedding
Time of My Life

M5 F2
Abducting Diana
Blue Murder
Blue Remembered Hills
Borders of Paradise
Breaking the Silence
Hand Over Fist
Otherwise Engaged
Quartermaine's Terms

M6 F1
Artist Descending a Staircase

SERIOUS PLAYS

M1 F6
Ask for the Moon

M3 F4
Children of a Lesser God
Dark Lucy
Pains of Youth

M4 F3
Architect
Holy Terror (*min. cast*)
Inspector Calls
Moonlight
Road (*min. cast*)

M5 F2
Animal Farm (adapt. Bond)
Lion in Winter
Single Spies

M6 F1
Portraits

M7
Glengarry Glen Ross

F7
Top Girls (*min. cast*)

DRAMAS

M2 F5
Death and the Maiden (Reid)
Living Room
Positive Hour

M3 F4
Dangerous Corner
Death Walked In
Doll's House
Experiment with an Air Pump
Hedda Gabler
Little Photographer
Maiden Stone
Miss Roach's War (*min. cast*)
New England
Nightmare
Restoration of Arnold Middleton
Tess of the D'Urbervilles (*min. cast*)
They Call It Murder
Turn of the Screw

M4 F3
Father
Murder in Neighbourhood Watch
Party to Murder
Red in the Morning
Scarlet Letter
Shock!
Silas Marner (*min. cast*)

M5 F2
Man and Boy
Murder in Mind
My Cousin Rachel
Talented Mr Ripley

M6 F1
Hothouse
Never the Sinner

M7
Class Enemy

EIGHT CHARACTERS

Gasping (*variable cast*)

FARCE

M4 F4
Amorous Ambassador

COMEDIES

M1 F7
Winter Glory

M2 F6
Fool's Paradise
Odd Couple (*female version*)

M3 F5
Billy Liar
Breath of Spring
Bride and the Bachelor
Clerical Errors
Fools Rush In
Kindly Leave the Stage
Murder In Play
Reluctant Debutante
So What Do We Do About Henry?

M4 F4
Bed Before Yesterday
Bedroom Farce
Beyond a Joke
Busybody
Caught on the Hop
Darling, I'm Home!
High Profiles
Holiday Snap

Home Is Where Your Clothes Are
Increased Difficulty of Concentration
Lady Audley's Secret
Late Mrs Early
Lend Me a Tenor
Period of Adjustment
Spring and Port Wine
Unvarnished Truth
Wildest Dreams
Woman in Mind

M5 F3
Enter a Free Man
False Admissions
Lloyd George Knew My Father
Marvellous Party (*min. cast*)
Serious Money (*min. cast*)
Successful Strategies
Travesties

M6 F2
Balmoral
Funny Money
Odd Couple
Run for Your Wife
School for Wives

PLAYS

M1 F7
Day of Reckoning

M2 F6
Waiting for Yesterday

M3 F5
Because of the Lockwoods
Curtain Up on Murder
Curtains
84 Charing Cross Road
Happy Families
Lovers
Rose
Same Old Moon (*min. cast*)
Winter Guest

M4 F4
Bed
Family Circles
Joking Apart
Life
Lucky Sods
Semi-Detached
Sisters Rosenzweig
Summer
Village Fête

M5 F3
Da
Editing Process
Goldhawk Road
Grace of Mary Traverse
Inconstant Couple
Rehearsal
Victor's Island
Wasted

M6 F2
Bad Company

M7 F1
Bacchae
Hapgood
Night and Day

SERIOUS PLAYS

M2 F6
Gut Girls (*min. cast*)

M3 F5
Find Me
Inadmissable Evidence
Pack of Lies

M4 F4
And a Little Love Besides
Doll's House
Fighting Chance
Map of the Heart
Neighbour
Now You Know
Rutherford and Son
Sacred Flame

M5 F3
Deep Blue Sea
Elephant Man
Handyman
Hidden Laughter
Robin Redbreast
Strangeness of Others (*min. cast*)

M6 F2
Progress
Walk On, Walk On

DRAMAS

M2 F6
Lights Are Warm and Coloured

M3 F5
Dancing at Lughnasa
John Gabriel Borkman
Little Photographer
Miss Roach's War
When She Danced

M4 F4
Charlatan
Frankenstein
House Guest
Jekyll and Hyde
Light of Heart
Morning Star
Murder in Company
New England
Suddenly at Home
Wind of Heaven
Year After the Fair

M5 F3
Dark River
Disappeared
Entertainer
Far from the Madding Crowd (*min. cast*)
Rough Justice
Silhouette
Small Hours
What I Did in the Holidays

M6 F2
Gentle Hook
Rope
Wait Until Dark
Who Killed Santa Claus?

M8
Long and the Short and the Tall
Thyestes

NINE CHARACTERS

Blue Heart (*variable cast*)
Fanshen (*variable cast*)
Inspector Drake and the Time Machine
    (*variable cast*)

FARCES

M3 F6
Darling Mr London

M4 F5
Fish Out of Water (*original*)
I'll Get My Man

A

Panic Stations
Pardon Me, Prime Minister
Rumours (British Version)

M5 F4
Don't Just Lie There, Say Something
Keeping Down with the Joneses
Running Riot

M6 F3
See How They Run
When Did You Last See Your Trousers?

COMEDIES

M2 F7
No Time for Fig Leaves

M3 F6
Bums on Seats (*min. cast*)
Flying Feathers
House of Blue Leaves

M4 F5
Constant Wife
Cut and Run
East Lynne
Hay Fever
Lessons and Lovers
Little Boxes
Local Affairs
No Love Lost
Out of Sight ... Out of Murder
Passion Killers
Popcorn
Sailor, Beware!
Three Birds Alighting on a Field
Weekend

M5 F4
Cracked Pot
Dolphins Rampant!
Importance of Being Earnest (3 act version)
Late Christopher Bean
Milk Train Doesn't Stop Here Any More
Season's Greetings

M6 F3
All Things Bright and Beautiful
Circle
Corpsing
Erpingham Camp
Laburnum Grove
Real Story of Puss in Boots (*min. cast*)
Shut Your Eyes and Think of England

M7 F2
Biloxi Blues
Picasso at the Lapin Agile
Robin Hood, the Truth Behind the Green
  Tights
Touch of Spring
Up 'n' Under II

F9
Ladies of Spirit

PLAYS

M1 F8
Come Back to the 5 & Dime, Jimmy Dean

M2 F7
Chalk Garden
Chance Visitor

M3 F6
Happy Families

M4 F5
Albert Make Us Laugh
Cripple of Inishmaan
Dearly Beloved
Word from Our Sponsor

M5 F4
Breezeblock Park
Cider With Rosie
Cracks
Hotel in Amsterdam
Moving (Leonard)
Outside Edge
Semi-Detached

M7 F2
Mummy's Tomb
Shadowlands

M8 F1
Donkey's Years

SERIOUS PLAYS

Vinegar Tom (*variable cast*)

M3 F6
Bitter Sanctuary
Heiress

M4 F5
Give Me Your Answer, Do!
They Came to a City
Wings

M5 F4
Roots
Equus

M6 F3
Aristocrats
Fashion
When the Barbarians Came

M7 F2
Dame of Sark

DRAMAS

M3 F6
Les Liaisons Dangereuses

M4 F5
Jekyll and Hyde
Night Must Fall
Someone Waiting
Trespass
Trojan Women

M5 F4
Far from the Madding Crowd
Living Quarters
Night Watch
Steward of Christendom
Touch of Danger
Uncle Vanya

M6 F3
Murder with Love
Sweet Revenge
Temptation

M7 F2
Breaking the Code
Count Dracula
Scent of Flowers
Small Craft Warnings

M9
Boys in the Band
Observe the Sons of Ulster Marching Towards
    the Somme
Seagulls Over Sorrento

F9
Watcher in the Shadow

TEN CHARACTERS

FARCES

M4 F6
Continental Quilt
Gypsy's Revenge
On the Verge

M5 F5
Gypsy's Revenge
Off the Hook
Wild Goose Chase

M6 F4
Cash on Delivery
Charley's Aunt
No Sex, Please — We're British!
Noises Off
Tons of Money
Who Goes Bare?

M8 F2
Dirty Linen and Newfoundland

COMEDIES

M1 F9
Stepping Out

M2 F8
Autumn Manoeuvres
Baby with the Bathwater

M3 F7
Farndale Avenue/*Macbeth*
Ladies Who Lunch
Play On!
Rape of the Belt

M4 F6
Bird in the Hand
I'll Leave It to You
Mystery at Greenfingers
Tiptoe Through the Tombstones
Tomb with a View
Wedding of the Year
What Are Little Girls Made Of?

M5 F5
Comfort and Joy (*min.cast*)
Goodnight Mrs Puffin
Lord Arthur Savile's Crime
Relative Values
Sisterhood
Two Into One

M6 F4
House of Frankenstein!
Man of the Moment
Out of Order
Zack

M7 F3
Fools
French Without Tears
My Three Angels
Whodunnit

M8 F2
Misanthrope
Return of A. J. Raffles

PLAYS

M4 F6
Beulah
Female Transport
Loves of Cass McGuire
Odd Women
Soft September Air
Strippers
Time and the Conways
Trivial Pursuits

M5 F5
Alfie
Number One
La Ronde

M6 F4
Jack the Lad
Mick and Mick
Play On!
Ten Times Table
Venus Observed

M8 F2
Parasol

M10
Another Country

SERIOUS PLAYS

M3 F7
Brezhnev's Children

M5 F5
Accrington Pals
Diary of Anne Frank
Eccentricities of a Nightingale
Gioconda Smile

M6 F4
Accolade
Edmond
Killers

M7 F3
Holy Terror
Redevelopment

M8 F2
Close the Coalhouse Door

M10
Rent

F10
Whale Music

DRAMAS

M3 F7
Restless Evil

M4 F6
Black Widow
House of Mirth
Jane Eyre (adapt. Vance)
Murder Has Been Arranged
Slaughterhouse

M5 F5
Forsyte Saga
Hound of the Baskervilles
Vieux Carré

M6 F4
Cat and the Canary
Deadly Nightcap
Uncle Vanya
Verdict
Wuthering Heights

A

M7 F3
Cat on a Hot Tin Roof
Translations
Unexpected Guest

ELEVEN CHARACTERS

FARCES

M6 F5
Cat on the Fiddle
Shock Tactics
Thark

M5 F6
Rookery Nook

COMEDIES

M3 F8
Play It Again, Sam

M4 F7
Midsummer Mink
Sing On
Surprise Package

M5 F6
Brush with a Body
Dear Brutus
Make Way for Lucia
Present Laughter
Ten Tiny Fingers, Nine Tiny Toes

M6 F5
House of Dracula
Stags and Hens

M7 F4
All in Good Time
Falling Short
Importance of Being Earnest (4 act)
Inspector Drake's Last Case
Laughter in the Dark
Lunatic View
Mr Whatnot
Real Story of Puss in Boots
What Every Woman Knows

M8 F3
Pope and the Witch
Servant of Two Masters
She Stoops to Conquer

PLAYS

M1 F10
After September

M4 F7
Little Women
Waltz of the Toreadors

M5 F6
After October
Salt of the Earth

M6 F5
Filumena
Habeas Corpus

M7 F4
Katherine Howard

M9 F2
Forget Herostratus!

M10 F1
Privates on Parade

M11
Comedians

SERIOUS PLAYS

M3 F8
Separate Tables

M7 F4
Rain
Winslow Boy

M8 F3
Hiawatha
Racing Demon

DRAMAS

Mad Forest (*variable cast*)

M10 F1
Savages

M3 F8
Bonaventure

M4 F7
Jane Eyre (adapt. Vance)

M6 F5
Forsyte Saga
Potting Shed
Woman in White

M7 F4
August
Flare Path
Our Country's Good
Second Mrs Tanqueray
Total Eclipse
Towards Zero

M8 F3
Lady's Not For Burning
Léocadia
Rebecca
Spider's Web
Sweeney Todd
Warrior

M9 F2
Hadrian the Seventh

M10 F1
Crucifer of Blood
Green Fingers
Normal Heart (*min. cast*)

M11
Bent

F11
House of Bernarda Alba

TWELVE CHARACTERS

FARCES

M6 F6
Post Horn Gallop
Uproar in the House

M7 F5
Court in the Act!

COMEDIES

M6 F6
Comfort and Joy

M7 F5
After The Ball Is Over
Hobson's Choice
House of Dracula
Inspector Drake's Last Case
It's Later Than You Think
It Runs In The Family
June Moon

M8 F4
Aren't We All?
Imaginary Invalid
Inspecting Carol
Rivals
Sisterly Feelings
Tartuffe (Malleson)

M10 F2
Inside Trading (*min. cast*)

PLAYS

M4 F8
Last Tango in Whitby

M7 F5
Canterbury Tales
Happy Wizard
Month in the Country (Friel)
Seagull
Sleeping Prince

M8 F4
Arcadia

M9 F3
Yard of Sun

F12
Princess Ascending

SERIOUS PLAYS

M2 F10
Enquiry

M5 F7
This Happy Breed

M6 F6
Streetcar Named Desire

M7 F5
Made in Bangkok

A

M8 F4
When the Barbarians Came

M9 F3
Largo Desolato

DRAMAS

M4 F8
Jane Eyre (adapt. Hall)

M5 F7
Cards on the Table
Murder Is Announced

M6 F6
Hollow
Wayward Spirit

M7 F5
Cat on a Hot Tin Roof
Ivanov

M8 F4
Antigone (Anouilh)
Fall and Redemption of Man (*min. cast*)
Ghost Train

M9 F3
After the Rain
And Then There Were None

M10 F2
Prisoner of Zenda

M11 F1
Crucifer of Blood

THIRTEEN CHARACTERS AND OVER·

FARCES

Alarms and Excursions
Amphibious Spangulatos
Cat Among the Pigeons (Feydeau)
Flea in Her Ear
Happiest Days of Your Life
Hotel Paradiso
Inner Voices
Keep an Eye on Amélie
Little Hotel on the Side
Magistrate
Man Alive!
Matchmaker

On the Razzle
One Way Pendulum

COMEDIES

Admirable Crichton
Black Snow
Bone-Chiller
Bums on Seats
Celebration
Chorus of Disapproval
Curse of the Werewolf
Cyrano de Bergerac
Darling Buds of May
Dear Octopus
Dogg's Hamlet, Cahoot's Macbeth
Don't Drink the Water
Drunkard
Enjoy
Forty Years On
Fosdyke Saga
Fur Coat and No Knickers
I Have Five Daughters
Inside Trading
It Was a Dark and Stormy Night
Joseph Andrews
Laughter in the Dark
London Cuckolds
Miser
Mr Quigley's Revenge
Murder of Maria Marten
Northanger Abbey
Nude With Violin
On Monday Next
Once a Catholic
Once in a Lifetime
One O'Clock from the House
Peer Gynt
Prodigious Snob
Revengers' Comedies
Robin Hood (Blamire)
Robin Hood (Wood)
Rosencrantz and Guildenstern Are Dead
Royal Pardon
Rumpelstiltzkin
Scapino!
Sea
Seagull
Second from Last in the Sack Race
The Secret Diary of Adrian Mole
    Aged 13¾
Serious Money
Servant of Two Masters
Small Family Business
Spring 1600
Suicide

Sweeney Todd
Sweeney Todd, the Barber
Sweeney Todd, the Demon Barber of Fleet
    Street
Tartuffe (Hampton)
Tom Jones
Travels With My Aunt
Trelawny of the 'Wells'
Twelfth Man
When We Are Married
Wild Honey

PLAYS

Adam Bede
Adventures of Huckleberry Finn
After Liverpool
Albert Make Us Laugh
Alfie
Anne of Green Gables
Bottom's Dream
Brideshead Revisited
Business of Good Government
Camino Real
Candleford
Canterbury Tales
Child's Christmas in Wales
Chinchilla
Christmas Carol
Cider With Rosie
Close the Coalhouse Door
Cold Comfort Farm
Come As You Are
Corn is Green
Daisy Pulls It Off
Dreaming
Epsom Downs
Games
Golden Pathway Annual
Grand Magic
Happy Wizard
Home Before Dark
I Remember Mama
Indian Ink
Invention of Love
Invisible Man
Jack the Ripper
Jumpers
Lark Rise
Life and Death of Almost Everybody
Make and Break
Mansfield Park
Maskerade
Memorandum
Men Should Weep
Mummy's Tomb

Murder on the Nile
Napoli Milionaria
National Health
No More Sitting on the Old School Bench
Philadelphia, Here I Come!
Pickwick Papers
Pied Piper
Pinocchio
Ring Round the Moon
Same Old Moon
Saturday, Sunday, Monday
Scarlet Pimpernel
Scottish Play
Shadowlands
Tales from Hollywood
Tales of King Arthur
Thieves' Carnival
Three Musketeers
Treasure Island
Two Planks and a Passion
Under Milk Wood
Voyage Round My Father
Waiting in the Wings
Was He Anyone?
When Five Years Pass
Women
Wind in the Willows
Zigger Zagger

SERIOUS PLAYS

Abelard and Heloise
Absolute Hell
Adventure Story
Animal Farm (adapt. Hall)
Battle of Angels
Becket
Break of Day
Business of Good Government
Cause Célèbre
Cavalcade
Cherry Orchard
Christmas Carol
Destiny
Elephant Man
Edmond
Equus
Fen
Few Good Men
Francis
Freedom of the City
Gentle Island
Ghetto
Hadrian the Seventh
Heart of a Dog

Heil, Caesar!
Hostage
Icecream
Lark
Light Shining in Buckinghamshire
Luther
Madness of George III
Man for All Seasons
Miracle Worker
Misha's Party
Mistress of Novices
Murmuring Judges
Mysteries
Nana
Night of the Iguana
One Flew Over the Cuckoo's Nest
Our Town
Physicists
Prime of Miss Jean Brodie
Red Devil Battery Sign
Roses of Eyam
Royal Hunt of the Sun
Skin of Our Teeth
Son of Man
State of Revolution
Temptation
Three Sisters
Twelve Angry Men
Vinegar Tom
Vivat! Vivat Regina!
Whose Life Is It Anyway?
Widows

DRAMAS

After Easter
Amadeus
Anastasia
Antigone (Brecht)
Baal
Beyond Reasonable Doubt
Black Coffee
Blood Wedding
Camille
Cards on the Table
Caucasian Chalk Circle
Christmas Truce
Clothes for a Summer Hotel
Coriolanus (Brecht)
Curtmantle
Dark Is Light Enough
Daughters of Venice
David Copperfield
Days of the Commune
Devils

Dining Room
Disorderly Women
Don Juan
Doña Rosita the Spinster
Dreaming
Drums in the Night
Entertaining Strangers
Fall and Redemption of Man
Fathers and Sons
Fears and Miseries of the Third Reich
Fifteen Streets
Firstborn
Front Page
Fuente Ovejuna
Germinal
Good Person of Sichuan
Good Person of Szechwan (Good Woman of Setzuan)
Great Expectations
Hamp
Ion
In the Jungle of the Cities (In the Cities' Jungle)
Jane Eyre
Journey's End
Juno and the Paycock
Life of Galileo
Little Like Drowning
Local Authority
Lorna Doone
Love of the Nightingale
Mad Forest
Man Is Man (Man Equals Man)
Mariana Pineda
Medea
Month in the Country
Mother
Mother Courage and Her Children
Mr Puntilla and his Man Matti
Murder at the Vicarage
Not About Nightingales
Oedipus at Colonus
Oedipus the King
Oliver Twist
Orpheus Descending
Our Country's Good
Picture of Dorian Gray
Plough and the Stars
Prisoner of Zenda
Quare Fellow
Resistible Rise of Arturo Ui
Richard of Bordeaux
Rose Tattoo
Ross
Roundheads and Peakheads (Rich and Rich)

Royal Baccarat Scandal
Sarcophagus
Schweyk in the Second World War
Silas Marner
Slapstick Tragedy
St Joan of the Stockyards
Strange Case of Dr Jekyll and Mr Hyde
Summer and Smoke
Sweet Bird of Youth
Tale of Two Cities
Tess of the D'Urbervilles
Tower
Trumpets and Drums
Turandot
Tutor
Visions of Simone Machard
Visit
Webster
Wild Duck
Witness for the Prosecution
Wolf at the Door
Woyzeck
Yerma

Titles arranged according to period and/or type of play

A

THE CLASSICS

Britannicus
Cyrano de Bergerac
False Admissions (Les Fausses Confidences)
Imaginary Invalid (Malade Imaginaire)
Importance of Being Earnest
Misanthrope
Miser
Prodigious Snob (Bourgeois Gentilhomme)
Rivals
School for Wives (L'École des Femmes)
She Stoops to Conquer
Sisterhood (Les Femmes Savantes)
Successful Strategies (L'Heureux Stratagème)
Tartuffe

COSTUME PLAYS

(Dates are given in round figures as an
approximate guide)

Ancient Greek
Adventure Story
Bacchae
Ion
Love of the Nightingale
Medea
Oedipus at Colonus
Oedipus the King
Rape of the Belt
Thyestes
Trojan Women

Ancient Roman
Britannicus

Biblical
Business of Good Government
Firstborn
Mysteries
Son of Man

Arthurian
Tales of King Arthur

Gothic 1100-1450
Abelard and Heloise
Becket
Canterbury Tales
Curtmantle
Francis
Lady's Not For Burning

Lark
Lion in Winter
Richard of Bordeaux
Robin Hood (Blamire)
Robin Hood (Wood)
Robin Hood, the Truth Behind the Green
   Tights
Tower
Two Planks and a Passion

Renaissance 1450-1500
Dreaming

Tudor 1500-1550
Katherine Howard
Luther
Man for All Seasons
Princess Ascending
Royal Hunt of the Sun

Elizabethan 1550-1620
Bottom's Dream
Devils
Making History
Rosencrantz and Guildenstern Are Dead
Spring 1600
Vinegar Tom
Vivat! Vivat Regina!
Webster

Civil War
Cyrano de Bergerac
Light Shining in Buckinghamshire

Restoration 1660-1700
Brief Lives
London Cuckolds
Lorna Doone
Messiah
Mother Courage and Her Children
Playhouse Creatures
Roses of Eyam
Three Musketeers

Louis XIV 1660 onwards
Imaginary Invalid
Inconstant Couple
Miser
Prodigious Snob
Scarlet Letter (USA)
School for Wives
Servant of Two Masters
Tartuffe

Georgian 1714-1750
Daughters of Venice
False Admissions
Joseph Andrews
Successful Strategies
Tom Jones
Warrior

Late Georgian 1750-1800
Amadeus
Charlatan
Grace of Mary Traverse
Lenz
Les Liaisons Dangereuses
Madness of George III
Our Country's Good
Rivals
She Stoops to Conquer
Tale of Two Cities (Francis)
Trumpets and Drums
Warrior

Directoire and 1st Empire 1790-1810
I Have Five Daughters
Northanger Abbey
Scarlet Pimpernel

Regency 1810-1820
Bloody Poetry
Cracked Pot
Frankenstein
Maiden Stone
Mansfield Park

Romantic 1820-1840
David Copperfield
Great Expectations
Mariana Pineda
Murder of Maria Marten
Peer Gynt
Pickwick Papers
Silas Marner (to 1860)

Early Victorian 1840-1865 (Crinoline)
Adam Bede
Camille
Christmas Carol
Dark Is Light Enough
Doña Rosita the Spinster
Drunkard
East Lynne
Entertaining Strangers
Gypsy's Revenge
Fathers and Sons
Hard Times
Heiress
Jane Eyre

Jekyll and Hyde
Lady Audley's Secret
Little Women
Mistress of Novices
Month in the Country
My Cousin Rachel
On the Razzle
Sweeney Todd
Sweeney Todd the Barber
Sweeney Todd, the Demon Barber of Fleet
    Street
Tale of Two Cities (Fitzgibbon)
Translations
Treasure Island
Trelawny of the 'Wells'
Virtue Triumphant
Woman in White
Wuthering Heights

Late Victorian 1865-1900 (Bustle)
Adventures of Huckleberry Finn
Aspern Papers
August
Candleford
Charley's Aunt
Cherry Orchard
Corn Is Green
Count Dracula
Crucifer of Blood
Day After the Fair
Days of the Commune
Doll's House
Elephant Man
Far from the Madding Crowd
Father
Female Transport
Fools
Forsyte Saga (to 1920)
Gaslight
Germinal
Hedda Gabler
Hobson's Choice
Hound of the Baskervilles
Importance of Being Earnest
Invention of Love (to 1936)
Ivanov
Jack the Ripper
John Gabriel Borkman
Lark Rise
Lord Arthur Savile's Crime
Magistrate
Mask of Moriarty
Matchmaker
Miracle Worker
Nana
New Anatomies
Odd Women

A

Oliver Twist
Parasol
Picture of Dorian Gray
Playing the Wife
Royal Baccarat Scandal
Seagull
Second Mrs Tanqueray
Strange Case of Dr Jekyll and Mr Hyde
Tess of the d'Ubervilles
Total Eclipse
Turn of the Screw
Uncle Vanya
Wild Duck
Wild Honey
Wind of Heaven
Wolf at the Door
Year After the Fair

Edwardian 1900-1910
Absolute Turkey
Admirable Crichton
Anne of Green Gables
Because of the Lockwoods
Black Widow
Cat Among the Pigeons (Feydeau)
Cavalcade (to 1930)
Court in the Act!
Death and the Maiden (Reid)
Edge of Darkness
Fifteen Streets
Flea in Her Ear
Fosdyke Saga
Gigi
Gut Girls
Hotel Paradiso
House of Mirth
I Remember Mama
Keep An Eye On Amélie
Lights are Warm and Coloured
Little Hotel on the Side
Little Photographer
My Three Angels
Picasso at the Lapin Agile
Prisoner of Zenda
Return of A. J. Raffles
La Ronde
Scarlet Ribbon
Sea
Seagull
Summer and Smoke
To Meet Oscar Wilde
Watcher in the Shadow
What Every Woman Knows
When We are Married
Winslow Boy

1910s
Accrington Pals
Breaking the Silence
Eccentricities of a Nightingale
Fifteen Streets
Hamp
In the Jungle of the Cities
Inspector Calls
Journey's End
Mother
Mysterious Mr Love
Not About Heroes
Observe the Sons of Ulster ...
Plough and the Stars
Ross
Rutherford and Son
Sleeping Prince
State of Revolution
Travesties

1920s
Aren't We All?
Black Snow
Blood Wedding
Breaking the Silence
Brideshead Revisited
Cider With Rosie
Daisy Pulls It Off
Front Page
Ghost Train
Hay Fever
I'll Leave It To You
June Moon
Juno and the Paycock
Never the Sinner
On Approval
Once in a Lifetime
Pains of Youth
Rain
Rookery Nook
Sacred Flame
Shadow of a Gunman
Suicide
Thark
This Happy Breed (1919-1937)
Time and the Conways (1919-1937)
Tons of Money
Vita and Virginia (1922-1941)
When She Danced
Winter Wife
Zack

1930s
After You with the Milk
Anastasia
Another Country
Balmoral

Bed Before Yesterday
Bent
Birdy (and 1946)
Brighton Beach Memoirs
Cause Célèbre
Cold Comfort Farm
Corpse!
Cripple of Inishmaan
Cuckoo
Dancing at Lughnasa
Dark River
Fears and Miseries of the Third Reich
Hysteria
Lend Me a Tenor
Men Should Weep
Mrs Klein
My Sister In This House
Night Must Fall
Not About Nightingales
Once in a Lifetime
Prime of Miss Jean Brodie
Private Lives
Rough Crossing
Roundheads and Peakheads
Second from Last in the Sack Race (to 1950s)
Steward of Christendom
Tales from Hollywood (to 1950s)
Tutor
Vieux Carré
Whodunnit

1940s
Absolute Hell
After October
All's Fair
And a Nightingale Sang
Biloxi Blues
Blue Remembered Hills
Breaking the Code
Brideshead Revisited
Broadway Bound
Caucasian Chalk Circle
Dame of Sark
Diary of Anne Frank
Dresser
Filumena
Flare Path
Ghetto
Glass Menagerie
Golden Pathway Annual (to late 1960s)
Happiest Days of Your Life
Home Before Dark (to 1964)
Long and the Short and the Tall
Lost In Yonkers
Men Should Weep
Miss Roach's War
Morning Star

Napoli Millionara
Next Time I'll Sing to You
Night of the Iguana
Orpheus Descending
Passing Out Parade
Privates on Parade
Promise
Rebecca
Schweyk in the Second World War
See How They Run
Some Sunny Day
Summit Conference
Taking Sides
Tom and Clem
Trespass

1950s
Accolade
Albert Make Us Laugh
All Things Bright and Beautiful
Billy Liar
Bonaventure
Cat Among the Pigeons (Greenwood)
Collaborators
Come Back to the 5 & Dime (to 1970s)
Darling Buds of May
Deep Blue Sea
Five Finger Exercise
Insignificance
Lent
Marvellous Party
Once a Catholic
Pack of Lies
Portraits
Roots
September Tide
Single Spies (to 1960s)
Shades
Shadowlands
Someone Waiting
Stevie
Talented Mr Ripley
Taste of Honey
Twelve Angry Men

1960s
Alfie
Bitter Sanctuary
Blue Murder
Dolphins Rampant
Kingdom of Earth
Knack
Letter of Resignation
Misanthrope (Harrison)
Quartermaine's Terms
Sad Hotel
Savages

A

Spring and Port Wine
What I Did in the Holidays

1970s
Aristocrats
Cracks
Epsom Downs
Freedom of the City
Rents
Why Not Stay for Breakfast?

Modern and Period
After Darwin
Amy's View
Anastasia File
Another Time
Arcadia
Artist Descending a Staircase
Ask for the Moon
Child's Christmas in Wales
Chinchilla
Cloud Nine
84 Charing Cross Road
Experiment with an Air Pump
Happy Families
Indian Ink
Kafka's Dick
Lessons and Lovers
Life
Little Like Dancing
Love Forty
Moving (Leonard)
Mummy's Tomb
On the Verge, or the Geography of Yearning
Portraits
Rehearsal
Salt of the Earth
Same Old Moon
Spokesong
Thurday's Ladies
Veronica's Room
When I was a Girl, I Used to Scream and Shout

HISTORICAL PLAYS

Ancient Greece
Adventure Story
Ion

Ancient Rome
Britannicus

12th Century
Abelard and Heloise
Becket

Curtmantle
Lion in Winter

13th Century
Francis

14th Century
Richard of Bordeaux

15th Century
Dreaming
Lark

16th Century
Katherine Howard
Luther
Man for All Seasons

Tudor
Royal Hunt of the Sun

Elizabethan
Devils
Making History
Vivat! Vivat Regina!

Stuart and Protectorate
Light Shining In Buckinghamshire
Roses of Eyam

Late Georgian
Madness of George III

Victorian
Miracle Worker
Mistress of Novices

Edwardian
Terra Nova

1940s
Diary of Anne Frank
Taking Sides
Tom and Clem

1960s
Letter of Resignation

Modern Costume
Business of Good Government
Fall and Redemption of Man
Florence Nightingale
Hollow Crown

DRAMATIZED NOVELS AND STORIES

Adam Bede
Adventures of Huckleberry Finn
Alan Turing: The Enigma (*see* Breaking the Code)
Animal Farm
Anne of Green Gables
Aurelia
Aspern Papers
Because of the Lockwoods
Birdy
Brideshead Revisited
Canterbury Tales
Cards on the Table
Christmas Carol
Cider With Rosie
Coat of Varnish
Cold Comfort Farm
Dame Aux Camélias (*see* Camille)
David Copperfield
Devils
Diary of Anne Frank
Dr Jekyll and Mr Hyde (*see* Strange Case of Dr Jekyll and Mr Hyde)
Dracula (*see* Count Dracula)
East Lynne
84 Charing Cross Road
Fanshen
Far from the Madding Crowd
Fathers and Sons
Fifteen Streets
Frankenstein
Forsyte Saga
George and Mildred (*TV series, see* When the Cat's Away)
Germinal
Good Grief
Great Expectations
Hadrian the Seventh
Hard Times
Hiawatha
In Their Wisdom (*see* Case in Question)
Jane Eyre
Jekyll and Hyde
Joseph Andrews
Lark Rise to Candleford (*see* Candleford and Lark Rise)
Lenz
Little Photographer
Little Women
Lord Arthur Savile's Crime
Lorna Doone
Lost In Yonkers
Lucia novels by E. F. Benson (*see* Make Way for Lucia)
Mansfield Park

Maskerade
Miss Thompson (*see* Rain)
Moscow to Petushki (*see* Moscow Stations)
My Cousin Rachel
Nana
Northanger Abbey
Now You Know
Odd Women
Oliver Twist
On the Western Circuit (*see* Day After the Fair)
One Flew Over the Cuckoo's Nest
Only When I Laugh (*TV series see* It Can Damage Your Health)
Our Song
Picture of Dorian Gray
Pied Piper
Pinocchio
Playmaker (*see* Our Country's Good)
Popcorn
Posthumous Papers of the Pickwick Papers (*see* Pickwick Papers)
Pride and Prejudice (*see also* I Have Five Daughters)
Prime of Miss Jean Brodie
Prime Pretender (*see* Dead Ringer)
Prisoner of Zenda
Rebecca
Royal Baccarat Scandal
Scarlet Letter
Scarlet Pimpernel
Second From Last in the Sack Race
Sign of Four (*see* Crucifer of Blood)
Silas Marner
Slaves of Solitude (*see* Miss Roach's War)
Sneeze
Tale of Two Cities
Talented Mr Ripley
Tess of the d'Urbervilles
Three Years (*see* Parasol)
Tom Jones
Travels With My Aunt
Turn of the Screw
Washington Square (*see* Heiress)
Wind in the Willows
Woman in White
Women's Decameron (*see* Brezhnev's Children)
Wuthering Heights

SOCIAL PLAYS
(Plays with a Social Interest)

Absolute Hell
After Darwin
All Things Bright and Beautiful
All Things Considered

Animal Farm
Ashes
Ask for the Moon
Bad Company
Ballerina
Barnaby and the Old Boys
Bazaar and Rummage
Benefactors
Bitter Sanctuary
Breezeblock Park
Children of a Lesser God
Choice
Crystal Clear
Curtains
Day in the Death of Joe Egg
Duet for One
Elephant Man
Enjoy
Enquiry
Equus
Exorcism
Fighting Chance
Find Me
Gasping
Groping for Words
Gut Girls
Handyman
Hard Feelings
Home
Inspector Calls
Killers
Look Back in Anger
Low Level Panic
Mad Forest
Made in Bangkok
Massage
Me and My Friend
Miracle Worker
Month of Sundays (Larbey)
Murmuring Judges
National Health
Neighbour
No More Sitting on the Old School Bench
Normal Heart
Not Quite Jerusalem
Not With a Bang
Now You Know
Odd Women
One Fine Day
One Flew Over the Cuckoo's Nest
Other People's Money
Pains of Youth
Physicists
Progress
Racing Demon
Real Estate
Rents

Road
Sarcophagus
Savages
Serious Money
Skin of Our Teeth
Strangeness of Others
Strippers
Sweet Panic
Taste of Honey
That Good Night
They Came to a City
Thickness of Skin
Tissue
Tom and Clem
Undertaking
Valued Friends
Wasted
Whose Life Is It Anyway?
Why Me?
Widows
Winslow Boy

PLAYS WITH COURTROOM SCENES

Beyond Reasonable Doubt
Cause Célèbre
Cracked Pot
Few Good Men
Magistrate
Murmuring Judges
Never the Sinner
One Way Pendulum
Rough Justice
Royal Baccarat Scandal
Twelve Angry Men
Witness for the Prosecution

PLAYS SET IN CONVENTS

Agnes of God
Bonaventure
Daughters of Venice
Devils
Mistress of Novices
Once a Catholic
Wayward Spirit

MILITARY PLAYS
(Plays with a Military Interest)

Accrington Pals
Biloxi Blues
Birdy
Dame of Sark

Few Good Men
Flare Path
Hamp
Journey's End
Killing Game
Long and the Short and the Tall
Not About Heroes
Observe the Sons of Ulster ...
Our Boys
Our Country's Good
Privates on Parade
Ross
Translations

NAVAL PLAYS
(Plays with a Naval Interest)

Rough Crossing
Sailor Beware!
Seagulls Over Sorrento
Watch it Sailor!
Winslow Boy

PLAYS WITH A SCHOLASTIC SETTING

After September
All Things Considered
Another Country
Butley
Daisy Pulls It Off
Donkey's Years
Educating Rita
Forty Years On
Gone Up in Smoke
Groping for Words
Happiest Days of Your Life
Ladies of Spirit
Lent
Marking Time
No More Sitting on the Old School Bench
Ostrich
Person Unknown
Prime of Miss Jean Brodie
Prin
Quartermaine's Terms
Rose
Shadowlands
Teechers
Translations

PLAYS SET IN HOSPITALS

Brezhnev's Children
Clothes for a Summer Hotel
Cut and Run
It Can Damage Your Health
It Runs in the Family
Kiss on the Bottom
National Health
Old-World
One Flew Over the Cuckoo's Nest
Our Boys
Roots and Wings
Sarcophagus
Visiting Hour
Wayward Spirit
What the Butler Saw
Wings
Whose Life Is It Anyway?

PLAYS SET IN SHOPS

American Buffalo
Come Back to the 5 & Dime, Jimmy Dean
84 Charing Cross Road
Hobson's Choice
Imaginary Lines
Laughing Wild
Man Alive
Orpheus Descending
Staircase
Spokesong
What Are Little Girls Made Of?

PLAYS WITH A THEATRICAL INTEREST

Actor's Nightmare (*see* Sister Mary Ignatius ...)
Amy's View
Bums on Seats
Chorus of Disapproval
Corpsing
Curtain Up on Murder
Dresser
Entertainer
Inspecting Carol
Invisible Man
Killing of Sister George
Life in the Theatre
Maiden Stone
Marvellous Party
Murder Has Been Arranged
Murder in Company

A

Murder In Play
Noises Off
On Monday Next
Our Country's Good
Play On!
Playing the Wife
Pocket Dream
Real Thing
Rehearsal
Royal Pardon
Scottish Play
Spring, 1600
Stage Struck
Trelawny of the 'Wells'
Trivial Pursuits
Under the Stars
Webster

PLAYS WITH A NATIONAL OR REGIONAL SETTING OR INTEREST

AMERICAN

Accommodations
Adventures of Huckleberry Finn
American Buffalo
Amorous Ambassador
Barefoot in the Park
Battle of Angels
Beyond Therapy
Biloxi Blues
Birdy
Bone-Chiller
Brighton Beach Memoirs
Broadway Bound
Butterflies Are Free
California Suite
Cat on a Hot Tin Roof
Cemetery Club
Clothes for a Summer Hotel
Cocktail Hour
Come Back to the 5 & Dime, Jimmy Dean
Come Blow Your Horn
Cracks
Crimes of the Heart
Deathtrap
Delicate Balance
Dining Room
Disappeared
Don't Drink the Water
Eccentricities of a Nightingale
Edmond
Extremities
Effect of Gamma Rays ...
Fatal Attraction

Few Good Men
Foreigner
Front Page
Gin Game
Gingerbread Lady
Glass Menagerie
Glengarry Glen Ross
God's Favorite
Greetings!
Heiress
Hiawatha
House of Blue Leaves
House of Mirth
I Remember Mama
If We Are Women
I'm Not Rappaport
In the Bar of a Tokyo Hotel
Insignificance
Inspecting Carol
Invisible Man
It Was a Dark and Stormy Night
June Moon
Kingdom of Earth
Last of the Red Hot Lovers
Laughing Wild
Lend Me a Tenor
Lights Are Warm and Coloured
Lost In Yonkers
Matchmaker
Me and Mamie O'Rourke
Miracle Worker
Murder Room
Nerd
Never the Sinner
New England
Night of the Iguana
Night Watch
Normal Heart
Not About Nightingales
Odd Couple
Odd Couple (female)
On the Verge, or the Geography of Yearning
Once in a Lifetime
One Flew Over the Cuckoo's Nest
Orphans
Orpheus Descending
Other People's Money
Our Town
Out of Sight ... Out of Murder
Owl and the Pussycat
Painting Churches
Party to Murder
Perfect Party
Period of Adjustment
Play It Again, Sam
Play On!
Plaza Suite

A

Popcorn
Prisoner of 2nd Avenue
Red Devil Battery Sign
Resistable Rise of Arturo Ui
Romantic Comedy
Rose Tattoo
Sad Hotel
Scarlet Letter
Sing On!
Skin of Our Teeth
Same Time, Next Year
Sisters Rosenweig
Slapstick Tragedy
Small Craft Warnings
Speed-the-Plow
Steel Magnolias
Streetcar Named Desire
Summer and Smoke
Sunshine Boys
Sweet Bird of Youth
Talented Mr Ripley
Tales from Hollywood
They're Playing Our Song
Tilting Ground
Torch Song Trilogy
Veronica's Room
Vieux Carré
Who's Afraid of Virginia Woolf?
You Say Tomatoes

CANADIAN
Anne of Green Gables

FRENCH

Camille
Don't Dress for Dinner
Every Other Evening
Germinal
Gigi
Nana
Number One
Picasso at the Lapin Agile
Rehearsal
Rise in the Market
Tower
Visions of Simone Machard
Wolf at the Door
(*See also* Feydeau, Marivaux, Molière)

IRISH

Comedies
Patrick Pearse Motel
Suburb of Babylon
Time Was

Costume
Making History
Translations

Plays
Brothers of the Brush
Cripple of Inishmaan
Da
Life
Lovers
Loves of Cass McGuire
Mick and Mick
Moving (Leonard)
Philadelphia, Here I Come!
Pizzazz
Same Old Moon
Spokesong
Summer
Women on the Verge of HRT

Serious Plays
After Easter
Aristocrats
Bold Girls
Dancing at Lughnasa
Faith Healer
Freedom of the City
Gentle Island
Give Me Your Answer, Do!
Hostage
Juno and the Paycock
Living Quarters
Paddywack
Quare Fellow
Plough and the Stars
Remembrance
Steward of Christendom
Suburb of Babylon

INDIAN
Indian Ink

ITALIAN

Accidental Death of an Anarchist
Filumena
Grand Magic
Inner Voices
Local Authority
Pope and the Witch
Saturday, Sunday, Monday
Scapino
Talented Mr Ripley
That Good Night
Yard of Sun

RUSSIAN

Black Snow
Breaking the Silence
Brezhnev's Children
Chance Visitor
Cherry Orchard
Fathers and Sons
Fools
Heart of a Dog
Ivanov
Misha's Party
Month in the Country
Moscow Stations
Parasol
Promise
Sarcophagus
Seagull
Sneeze
Stars in the Morning Sky
State of Revolution
Three Sisters
Uncle Vanya

SPANISH

Blood Wedding
Doña Rosita the Spinster
Mariana Pineda
Yerma

SCOTS

Costume
Maiden Stone
What Every Woman Knows

Plays
Men Should Weep
Shades
When I Was a Girl, I Used To Scream and
    Shout ...
Winter Guest

Serious
Rents

WELSH
(in English)

All's Fair
August
Biting the Bullet
Child's Christmas In Wales
Corn Is Green
Easy Terms
Kiss on the Bottom
Loose Ends

Roots and Wings
Small Change
Trivial Pursuits
Under Milk Wood
Wind of Heaven

NORTH COUNTRY

Accrington Pals
All in Good Time
And a Nightingale Sang
Because of the Lockwoods
Beulah
Billy Liar
Caravan
Cat Among the Pigeons (Greenwood)
Close the Coalhouse Door
Cracked Pot
Different Way Home
Fifteen Streets
Fur Coat and No Knickers
Happy Families
Happy Jack
Hobson's Choice
Home Before Dark
Last Tango in Whitby
Mail Order Bride
Not With a Bang
Road
Rutherford and Son
Salt of the Earth
Second From Last in the Sack Race
September in the Rain
Up 'n' Under
Up 'n' Under II
When We Are Married

RURAL

Adam Bede
Candleford
Cider with Rosie
Cold Comfort Farm
Cracked Pot
Darling Buds of May
Flesh and Blood
Lark Rise
Tess of the d'Urbervilles
What I Did in the Holidays

MYSTERY AND SUSPENSE PLAYS

Anagram of Murder
And Then There Were None
Anybody for Murder?
Being of Sound Mind

Black Coffee
Blood Money
Bonaventure
Bone-Chiller
Business of Murder
Busybody
Cards on the Table
Checkmate
Corpse!
Crucifer of Blood
Curtain Up on Murder
Dangerous Obsession
Dead Guilty
Dead Man's Hand
Dead of Night
Dead on Nine
Dead Ringer
Dead-Lock
Deadline
Deadly Embrace
Deadly Nightcap
Death and the Maiden (Reid)
Death Walked In
Deathtrap
Dial 'M' for Murder
Double Double
Edge of Darkness
Edwina Black
Fatal Attraction
Final Twist
Gaslight
Gentle Hook
Ghost Train
Gioconda Smile
Gone Up In Smoke
Hollow
Hound of the Baskervilles
House Guest
House of Secrets
House on the Cliff
I'll Be Back Before Midnight!
In for the Kill
Inside Job
It Could Be Any One of Us
Jekyll and Hyde
Kidnap Game
Killing Time
Lady Audley's Secret
Last Gamble
Local Murder
Murder Assured
Murder at the Vicarage
Murder by Appointment
Murder by Misadventure
Murder by the Book
Murder Game
Murder Has Been Arranged

Murder in Company
Murder in Mind
Murder in Neighbourhood Watch
Murder in Play
Murder is Announced
Murder of Maria Marten
Murder on the Nile
Murder Room
Murder With Love
Murderer
Mysterious Mr Love
Mystery at Greenfingers
Mystery of Irma Vep
Natural Causes
Night Watch
Nightmare
Nightmare: The Fright of Your Life
Out of Sight.....Out of Murder
Page 3 Murder
Party to Murder
Portrait of Murder
Red in the Morning
Robin Redbreast
Rope
Shock!
Silhouette
Slaughterhouse
Sleuth
Small Hours
Spider's Web
Star Spangled Girl
Sting in the Tale
Suddenly at Home
Suspects
Suspicions
Sweet Revenge
Talented Mr Ripley
Take Away the Lady
That Good Night
Theft
Threat!
Tilting Ground
Time to Kill
Touch of Danger
Towards Zero
Unexpected Guest
Verdict
Veronica's Room
Wait Until Dark
Who Lies There?
Who Killed Santa Claus?
Who Saw Him Die?
Whodunnit
Witness for the Prosecution
Wolfsbane

A

PLAYS CONCERNING GHOSTS, WITCHCRAFT AND THE SUPERNATURAL

Blithe Spirit
Bride and the Bachelor
Clothes for a Summer Hotel
Curse of the Werewolf
Dear Brutus
Duet for Two Hands
Exorcism
Gypsy's Revenge
Haunted
I Have Been Here Before
Inspector Calls
Invisible Man
Late Mrs Early
Laughter in the Dark
Man Alive
Murder Has Been Arranged
Mystery of Irma Vep
Robin Redbreast
Salonika
Trespass
They Came to a City
Wind of Heaven

VERSE PLAYS

Cracked Pot
Curtmantle
Cyrano de Bergerac
Dark is Light Enough
Firstborn
Hiawatha
Lady's Not For Burning
Peer Gynt
Roundheads and Peakheads
Venus Observed
Village Fête
Yard of Sun

NON-ROYALTY PLAYS

Charley's Aunt
Importance of Being Earnest (3 act)
Rivals
She Stoops to Conquer

PLAYS WITH MUSIC

And a Nightingale Sang
Animal Farm
Baal
Canterbury Tales
Caucasian Chalk Circle
Child's Christmas in Wales
Close the Coalhouse Door
Curse of the Werewolf
Days of the Commune
Drunkard (Burton)
East Lynne (Burton)
Fear and Misery of the Third Reich
Fosdyke Saga
Ghetto
Good Doctor
Good Person of Szechwan
Happy Wizard
Hiawatha
Hollow Crown
House of Blue Leaves
Invisible Man
Jack the Lad
Jack the Ripper
June Moon
Lady Audley's Secret (Burton)
Lend Me a Tenor
Life of Galileo
Man Is Man
Mother
Mother Courage
Mr Puntila and his Man Matti
Mummy's Tomb
Murder of Maria Marten (Burton)
Pied Piper
Privates on Parade
Prodigious Snob
Resistable Rise of Arturo Ui
Robin Hood
Rough Crossing
Roundheads and Peakheads
Schweyk in the Second World War
Secret Diary of Adrian Mole Aged $13\frac{3}{4}$
Sing On!
Spokesong
St Joan of the Stockyards
Sweeney Todd the Barber (Burton)
Tess of the d'Urbervilles
They're Playing Our Song
Thieves' Carnival
Trumpets and Drums
Turandot
Under Milk Wood
Vinegar Tom
Wind in the Willows

Women on the Verge of HRT
Word from Our Sponsor

RELIGIOUS AND MORALITY PLAYS

Easter
Son of Man

Biblical
Firstborn

Morality
Fall and Redemption of Man
Inspector Calls

Religious Interest
Abelard and Heloise
Agnes of God
And a Little Love Besides
Becket
Bonaventure
Clerical Errors
Devils
Exit the King
Francis
God's Favorite
Hadrian the Seventh
Lark
Life and Death of Almost Everybody
Man for All Seasons
Messiah
Mistress of Novices
Our Town
Physicists
Potting Shed
Racing Demon
Royal Hunt of the Sun
Skin of Our Teeth
They Came to a City
Two Planks and a Passion
Waiting for Godot
Wayward Spirit
Wind of Heaven

ALL FEMALE

Agnes of God
Bazaar and Rummage
Bold Girls
Effect of Gamma Rays ...
Female Parts
House of Bernarda Alba
If We Are Women
Killing of Sister George
Kiss on the Bottom

Ladies of Spirit
Low Level Panic
Mrs Klein
My Mother Said I Never Should
My Sister In This House
New Anatomies
Playhouse Creatures
Princess Ascending
Shirley Valentine
Skirmishes
Steaming
Steel Magnolias
Thriller of the Year
Top Girls
Vita and Virginia
Watcher In The Shadow
Whale Music
Women

ALL MALE

American Buffalo
Anorak of Fire
Another Country
Bent
Birdy
Boys In The Band
Brief Lives
Brothers of the Brush
Caretaker
Class Enemy
Comedians
Dealers
Glengarry Glen Ross
Hamp
Journey's End
Life in the Theatre
Long and the Short and the Tall
Moscow Stations
Mystery of Irma Vep
Neville's Island
Not About Heroes
Observe the Sons of Ulster ...
One Fine Day
Orphans
Our Boys
Quare Fellow
Rents
Ross
Sleuth
Someone Who'll Watch Over Me
Staircase
Thyestes
Treasure Island
Twelve Angry Men
Waiting for Godot

A

Authors' Index

Entries in italics refer to novels by well-known authors which have been dramatized either under their own name or under another title which is given in parenthesis.

Abbot, Rick
Play On!
Sing On!

Ackland, Rodney
Absolute Hell
After October
Dark River

Adamson, Samuel
Clocks and Whistles
Grace Note

Albee, Edward
Delicate Balance
Who's Afraid of Virginia Woolf?

Alcott, Louisa M
Little Women

Allen, Jay Presson
Prime of Miss Jean Brodie

Allen, Woody
Don't Drink the Water
Play It Again, Sam

Anouilh, Jean
Antigone
Becket
It's Later Than You Think
Lark
Léocadia
Number One
Rehearsal
Ring Round the Moon
Thieves' Carnival
Waltz of the Toreadors

Antrobus, John
(*see* Galton, Ray)

Arbuzov, Aleksei
Chance Visitor
Old-World
Promise

Archer, Jeffrey
Beyond Reasonable Doubt

Arden, John
Royal Pardon

Ardito, Carlo
Grand Magic (trans.)
Local Authority (trans.)

Arthur, Dave and Toni
(*see* Wood, David)

Aron, Geraldine
Same Old Moon

Ashby, Sylvia
Anne of Green Gables (adapt.)

Atkins, Eileen
Vita and Virginia

Aubrey, John
Brief Lives

Austen, Jane
Mansfield Park
Northanger Abbey
Pride and Prejudice (see also *I Have Five
    Daughters*)

Ayckbourn, Alan
Absent Friends
Absurd Person Singular
Bedroom Farce
Chorus of Disapproval
Communicating Doors
Confusions
Family Circles
Henceforward ...
How the Other Half Loves
Intimate Exchanges
It Could Be Any One of Us
Joking Apart
Just Between Ourselves
Man of the Moment
Mr Whatnot
Norman Conquests
Relatively Speaking
Revengers' Comedies
Season's Greetings
Sisterly Feelings
Small Family Business
Taking Steps
Things We Do for Love
Time and Time Again
Time of My Life
Ten Times Table
Tons of Money (revisor)
Way Upstream
Wildest Dreams
Wolf at the Door (adapt.)
Woman in Mind
Word from Our Sponsor

Bagnold, Enid
Chalk Garden

Bannerman, Kay
(*see* Brooke, Harold)

Barnes, Peter
Corpsing
Dreaming

Barret, Earl
(*see* Sultan, Barret, Cooney)

Barrie, J. M.
Admirable Crichton
Dear Brutus
What Every Woman Knows

Barry, Sebastian
Steward of Christendom

Barton, John
Hollow Crown

Bates, H. E.
Darling Buds of May

Batson, George
House on the Cliff

Beckett, Samuel
Waiting For Godot

Becque, Henry
Les Corbeaux (*see* Wolf at the Door)

Beevers, Geoffrey
Adam Bede (adapt.)
Silas Marner (adapt.)

Beghel, Larry
Page 3 Murder

Behan, Brendan
Hostage
Quare Fellow

Benfield, Derek
Anyone for Breakfast?
Bedside Manners
Beyond a Joke
Bird in the Hand
Caught on the Hop
Don't Lose the Place!
Fish Out of Water
Fly In The Ointment
Flying Feathers
In for the Kill
Look Who's Talking!
Off the Hook

Panic Stations
Post Horn Gallop
Running Riot
Toe in the Water
Touch and Go
Two and Two Together
Up and Running
Wild Goose Chase

Bennett, Alan
Enjoy
Forty Years On
Getting On
Habeas Corpus
Kafka's Dick
Madness of George III
Office Suite
Old Country
Single Spies
Wind in the Willows

Benson, E.F.
(see *Make Way for Lucia*)

Bent, Simon
Bad Company
Goldhawk Road
Wasted

Bentley, Eric
(*see* Schnitzler, Arthur and Brecht, Bertolt)

Bettinson, Rob
Fifteen Streets (adapt.)

Bill, Stephen
Curtains

Birch, Michael
Second From Last in the Sack Race

Blackmore, R.D.
Lorna Doone

Blackwell, Vera
Increased Difficulty of Concentration (trans.)
Memorandum (trans.)
Vanek Plays (trans.)

Blakeman, Helen
Caravan

Blamire, Larry
Robin Hood

Bleasdale, Alan
No More Sitting on the Old School Bench

A

Bloomfield, Robert
Portrait of Murder

Bogdanov, Michael
Hiawatha

Bolt, R. R.
Resistible Rise of Arturo Ui (trans.)
Sisterhood

Bolt, Robert
Man for All Seasons
State of Revolution
Tiger and the Horse
Vivat! Vivat Regina!

Bolton, Guy
Anastasia (adapt.)

Bond, Edward
Sea

Bond, C. G.
Sweeney Todd

Bond, Nelson
Animal Farm (adapt.)

Bowen, John
After the Rain
Disorderly Women
Fall and Redemption of Man
Florence Nightingale
Heil, Caesar!
Inconstant Couple
Little Boxes
Robin Redbreast

Bradbury, Malcolm
Inside Trading (adapt.)

Bradbury, Parnell
(*see* King and Bradbury)

Braddon, Mary
Lady Audley's Secret

Bradley, Alfred
(*see* Whitmore and Bradley)

Bray, Barbara
Antigone (trans.)

Brecht, Bertolt
Antigone
Baal
Caucasian Chalk Circle

Coriolanus
Days of the Commune
Don Juan
Drums in the Night
Fears and Miseries of the Third Reich
Good Person of Szechwan (Good Woman of
    Setzuan, Good Person of Sichuan)
In the Jungle of the Cities (In the Cities' Jungle)
Life of Galileo
Man Is Man (Man Equals Man)
Mother
Mother Courage and her Children
Mr Puntilla and his Man Matti
Resistible Rise of Arturo Ui
Roundheads and Peakheads (Rich and Rich)
Schweyk in the Second World War
St Joan of the Stockyards
Trumpets and Drums
Turandot
Tutor
Visions of Simone Machard

Brenton, Howard
Bloody Poetry
Epsom Downs

Brett, Simon
Mr Quigley's Revenge
Murder In Play
Silhouette

Brewer, Elly and Toksvig, Sandi
Pocket Dream

Brighouse, Harold
Hobson's Choice
Zack

Briggs, Raymond
When the Wind Blows

Briggs, Stephen
Maskerade (adapt.)

Brittney, Lyn
Pickwick Papers (adapt.)

Brock, Jeremy
Oliver Twist

Brontë, Charlotte
Jane Eyre

Brontë, Emily
Wuthering Heights

Brooke, Harold and Bannerman, Kay
Earl and the Pussycat
She Was Only An Admiral's Daughter

Brooks, Jeremy and Mitchell, Adrian
Child's Christmas in Wales

Brown, Ben
All Things Considered

Browne, E. Martin
Mysteries

Broughton, Pip
Tutor (trans)

Bruckner, Ferdinand
Pains of Youth

Buchner, Georg
Woyzeck

Bulgakov, Mikhail
Black Snow
Heart of a Dog

Burke, Stewart
Murder in Neighbourhood Watch
Party to Murder
(*see also* Chase, Olive)

Burrows, John
(*see* Harding, John)

Burton, Brian J.
Being of Sound Mind
Drunkard
East Lynne
Lady Audley's Secret
Murder of Maria Marten
Sweeney Todd the Barber

Byrne, John
London Cuckolds (adapt.)

Caddy, Leonard H.
Jekyll and Hyde

Camoletti, Marc
Don't Dress for Dinner
Happy Birthday

Campton, David
Life and Death of Almost Everybody
Lunatic View

Cargill, Patrick
Don't Misunderstand Me

Carmichael, Fred
Out of Sight, Out of Murder

Cartwright, Jim
Bed
Rise and Fall of Little Voice
Road
Two

Cary, Falkland L. and King, Philip
Big Bad Mouse
Sailor, Beware!

Chambers, John
Tales of King Arthur

Chapman, John
Kindly Leave the Stage

Chapman, John and Freeman, Dave
Key for Two

Chapman, John and Lloyd, Jeremy
Keeping Down with the Joneses

Chapman, John and Marriott, Anthony
Shut Your Eyes and Think of England

Chapman, John and Pertwee, Michael
Holiday Snap
Look, No Hans!

Chappell, Eric
Haunted
Haywire
Heatstroke
It Can Damage Your Health
Natural Causes
Theft

Charles, Moie and Toy, Barbara
Murder at the Vicarage

Chaucer, Geoffrey
Canterbury Tales

Chekhov, Anton
Cherry Orchard
Ivanov
Three Years (see *Parasol*)
Seagull
Three Sisters
Uncle Vanya
(*see also* August)
Wild Honey
(*see also* Sneeze)

Chernomirdik, Vlada
Uncle Vanya (trans.)

Chervinsky, Alexander
Heart of a Dog

Chinn, Jimmie
After September
Albert Make Us Laugh
Different Way Home
Home Before Dark
Something To Remember You By
Straight and Narrow
Sylvia's Wedding
Take Away the Lady

Christie, Agatha
And Then There Were None
Black Coffee
Cards on the Table
Hollow
Murder at the Vicarage
Murder is Announced
Murder on the Nile
Spider's Web
Towards Zero
Unexpected Guest
Verdict
Witness for the Prosecution

Christopher-Wood, John
Elsie and Norm's "Macbeth"

Churchett, Stephen
Heritage
Tom and Clem

Churchill, Caryl
Blue Heart
Cloud Nine
Fen
Icecream
Light Shining In Buckinghamshire
Mad Forest
Serious Money
Thyestes (trans.)
Top Girls
Traps
Vinegar Tom

Churchill, Donald
Decorator
Mixed Feelings
Moment of Weakness
(*see also* Yeldham, Peter)

Clapham, Peter
Little Women (adapt.)

Clark, Brian
Can You Hear Me at the Back?
Petition
Whose Life is it Anyway?

Clayton, Tony
Murder Assured

Clemens, Brian
Edge of Darkness
Inside Job
Shock!

Clemens, Brian and Spooner, Dennis
Anybody for Murder?
Sting in the Tale
Will You Still Love Me in the Morning?

Clepper, P.M.
Joseph Andrews

Coburn, D.L.
Gin Game

Cogo-Fawcett, Robert and Murray, Braham
Court in the Act! (trans.)
Keep An Eye on Amélie (trans.)

Coke, Peter
Autumn Manoeuvres
Breath of Spring
Fool's Paradise
Midsummer Mink
What are Little Girls Made Of?
Winter Glory

Cole, Giles
Suspects

Colette
Gigi

Colley, Peter
I'll Be Back Before Midnight!

Collins, Wilkie
Woman in White

Colton, John and Randolph, Clemence
Rain

Conan Doyle, Arthur
Hound of the Baskervilles
Sign of Four (*see* Crucifer of Blood)

Connolly, H.
Twelfth Man

Cooke, Brian
(*see* Mortimer, Johnnie)

Cookson, Catherine
Fifteen Streets

Cooney, Michael
Cash on Delivery

Cooney, Ray
Funny Money
It Runs in the Family
Out of Order
Run for Your Wife
Two into One
(*see* Stone, Gene)
(*see* Sultan, Barret, Cooney)

Cooper, Giles
Happy Family

Coward, Noël
Blithe Spirit
Cavalcade
Hay Fever
I'll Leave it to You
Nude with Violin
Present Laughter
Private Lives
Relative Values
This Happy Breed
Waiting in the Wings

Cowper, Trevor
Relative Strangers

Cox, Constance
Because of the Lockwoods (adapt.)
Lord Arthur Savile's Crime
Murder Game
Woman in White

Crane, Richard
Under The Stars

Crimp, Martin
No One Sees the Video

Crisp, N. J.
Dangerous Obsession
Fighting Chance
Suspicions
That Good Night

Cross, Beverley
Happy Birthday (adapt.)
Scarlet Pimpernel (adapt.)

Crowley, Mart
Boys In The Band

Curry, Neil
Bacchae (trans.)
Trojan Women (trans.)

Dale, Jim
Scapino!

Daniels, Sarah
Gut Girls

Darbon, Leslie
Cards on the Table (adapt.)
Murder is Announced (adapt.)
Time to Kill
(*see also* Harris and Darbon)

D'Arcy, Margaretta
(*see* Arden, John)

Davies, Andrew
Prin
Rose

Daviot, Gordon
Richard of Bordeaux

Day, Julie
Come Back for Light Refreshments After the
    Service

De Angelis, April
Playhouse Creatures
Positive Hour

de Fillipo, Eduardo
Filumena
Grand Magic
Inner Voices
Local Authority
Napoli Milionaria
Saturday, Sunday, Monday

De Marne, Denis
(*see* Pember, Ron)

Deegan, Denise
Daisy Pulls it Off

Delaney, Sheila
Taste of Honey

Desvalliere, Maurice
(*see* Feydeau and Desvalliere)

Devlin, Anne
After Easter

Dewhurst, Keith
Black Snow (adapt.)
Candleford
Lark Rise

Dickens, Charles
Christmas Carol
David Copperfield
Great Expectations
Hard Times
Oliver Twist
Posthumous Papers of the Pickwick Club (see
    Pickwick Papers)
Tale of Two Cities

Dighton, John
Happiest Days of Your Life
Man Alive!

Dinner, William and Morum, William
Late Edwina Black

Dinsdale, Stephen
Anorak of Fire

Dole, John
Cat on the Fiddle
Shock Tactics

Donoghue, Mary Agnes
Me and Mamie O'Rourke

Dorfman, Ariel
Death and the Maiden
Widows (with Tony Kushner)

Doust, Paul
Amphibious Spangulatos
Cold Comfort Farm (adapt.)

Downing, Martin
House of Dracula
House of Frankenstein!

Dryden, Ellen
Anna's Room
Harvest
Power of the Dog

Dudzick, Tom
Greetings!

du Maurier, Daphne
Little Photographer
My Cousin Rachel
Rebecca
September Tide

Dumas
La Dame aux Camélias (see *Camille*)
Three Musketeers
Tower

Dunai, Frank
Parasol (adapt.)

Dunlop, Frank
Scapino!

Dunn, Nell
Steaming

Durang, Christopher
Baby with the Bathwater
Beyond Therapy
Laughing Wild
Sister Mary Ignatius Explains It All For You
    and Actor's Nightmare

Durbridge, Francis
Deadly Nightcap
Gentle Hook
House Guest
Murder With Love
Small Hours
Suddenly at Home
Sweet Revenge
Touch of Danger

Dürrenmatt, Friedrich
Physicists
Visit

Dyer, Charles
Lovers Dancing
Rattle of a Simple Man
Staircase

Edgar, David
Entertaining Strangers
Strange Case of Dr Jekyll and Mr Hyde

Edleston, Kathleen
Happy Wizard

Edwards, Gwynne
Blood Wedding (trans.)
Doña Rosita the Spinster (trans.)
Mariana Pineda (trans.)

Elice, Eric and Rees, Roger
Double Double

Eliot, George
Adam Bede
Silas Marner

Elliott, Alistair (trans.)
Medea

Elton, Ben
Gasping
Popcorn
Silly Cow

Emery, Ed
Pope and the Witch (trans.)

Erdman, Nikolai
Suicide

Euripides
Bacchae
Ion
Medea
Trojan Woman

Evan, Thomas
(*see* Cherrett, Don)

Evans, Will and Valentine
Tons of Money

Everett, Richard
Close to the Wind
Hand Over Fist
Happy Event
Present from the Past

Farr, David
Elton John's Glasses

Fauchois, Renée
Prenez Garde à la Peinture (*see* Late
    Christopher Bean)

Feely, Terence
Murder in Mind
Who Killed Santa Claus?

Ferriere, Jean-Paul
Aurelia

Ferris, Monk
Bone-Chiller

Feydeau, Georges
Cat Among the Pigeons
Flea in Her Ear
Keep an Eye on Amélie

Feydeau, Georges and Desvalliere, Maurice
Hotel Paradiso
Little Hotel on the Side

Fielding, Henry
Joseph Andrews
Tom Jones

Fierstein, Harvey
Torch Song Trilogy

Fillinger, Johan
Peer Gynt (trans.)

Firth, Tim
End of the Food Chain
Neville's Island

Fitzgibbons, Mark
Tale of Two Cities

Fletcher, Lucille
Night Watch

Fo, Dario
Abducting Diana
Accidental Death of an Anarchist
Pope and the Witch

Fo, Dario and Rame, Franca
Female Parts

Foley, David
Sad Hotel

Foot, Alistair
(*see* Marriott, Anthony)

Foxton, David
Real Story of Puss in Boots

Francis, Matthew
Adventures of Huckleberry Finn
David Copperfield
Northanger Abbey
Prisoner of Zenda (adapt.)
Tale of Two Cities (adapt.)

Franks, Alan
Mother Tongue

Frayn, Michael
Alarms and Excursions
Alphabetical Order
Balmoral
Benefactors
Cherry Orchard (trans.)
Clouds
Donkey's Years
Make and Break
Noises Off
Now You Know
Number One (trans.)
Sneeze (trans., adapt.)
Two of Us
Wild Honey (trans.)

Freeman, Dave
Bedfull of Foreigners
Kindly Keep It Covered
(*see also* Chapman, John)

Friel, Brian
Aristocrats
Dancing at Lughnasa
Faith Healer
Fathers and Sons
Freedom of the City
Gentle Island
Give Me Your Answer, Do!
Living Quarters
Lovers
Loves of Cass McGuire
Making History
Month in the Country (trans.)
Philadelphia, Here I Come!
Three Sisters (trans.)
Translations
Uncle Vanya (trans.)

Frisby, Terence
Rough Justice
There's a Girl in My Soup

Fry, Christopher
Curtmantle
Cyrano de Bergerac (trans.)
Dark is Light Enough
Firstborn
Lady's Not For Burning
Lark (trans.)
Venus Observed
Yard of Sun

Michael, Fry
Tess of the d'Ubervilles (adapt.)

Galantière, Lewis
Antigone (trans.)

Galin, Alexander
Stars in the Morning Sky

Galsworthy, John
Forsyte Saga

Galton, Ray and Antrobus, John
When Did You Last See Your Trousers?

Gaminara, William
Germinal

Gardner, Herb
I'm Not Rappaport

Garland, Patrick
Brief Lives (adapt.)

Gates, Tudor
Aurelia
Kidnap Game
Ladies Who Lunch
Who Saw Him Die?

Gee, Shirley
Ask For The Moon
Warrior

Gelman, Alexander
Man With Connections (trans.)
(*see* Nelson, Richard)

Gems, Pam
Camille

Gershe, Leonard
Butterflies Are Free

Gibbons, Stella
Cold Comfort Farm

Gibson, William
Miracle Worker

Gill, Peter
Small Change

Giovanni, Paul
Crucifer of Blood

Gissing, George
Odd Women

Glass, Joanna McClelland
If We Are Women

A

Glenny, Michael
Forget Herostratus! (trans.)
Heart of a Dog (trans.)
Sarcophagus (trans.)
Stars in the Morning Sky (trans.)

Glenville, Peter
Hotel Paradiso (adapt.)

Godber, John
April In Paris
Blood Sweat and Tears
Happy Families
Happy Jack
Lucky Sods
Passion Killers
Salt of the Earth
September in the Rain
Teechers
Up 'n' Under
Up 'n' Under II
Weekend Breaks

Goetz, Ruth and Augustus
Heiress

Goldman, James
Lion in Winter

Goldoni, Carlo
Servant of Two Masters

Goldsmith, Oliver
She Stoops to Conquer

Gooch, Steve
Female Transport

Goodrich, Frances
(*see* Hackett, Albert and Goodrich, Frances)

Gorin, Grigory
Forget Herostratus!

Gourlay, Logan
Prime Pretender (*see* Dead Ringer)

Graczyck, Ed
Come Back to the 5 and Dime, Jimmy Dean,
    Jimmy Dean

Graham, John
(*see* Taylor, Edward)

Grahame, Kenneth
Wind in the Willows

Gray, Simon
Butley
Close of Play
Common Pursuit
Hidden Laughter
Holy Terror
Just the Three of Us
Otherwise Engaged
Quartermaine's Terms
Stage Struck

Greene, Graham
Carving a Statue
For Whom the Bell Chimes
Living Room
Potting Shed
Return of A. J. Raffles
Travels With My Aunt

Greening, Joan
Continental Quilt

Greenwood, Duncan
Cat Among the Pigeons
Waiting for Yesterday

Greenwood, Duncan and King, Robert
Murder by the Book
No Time for Fig Leaves

Greenwood, Duncan and Parkes, Derek
Surprise Package

Greig, David
Architect

Griffiths, Trevor
Comedians

Gubaryev, Vladimir
Sarcophagus

Guare, John
House of Blue Leaves

Gurney, A. R.
Cocktail Party
Dining Room
Perfect Party

Hackett, Albert and Goodrich, Frances
Diary of Anne Frank

Hall, Lee
Mr Puntila and His Man Matti (adapt.)

Hall, Nick
Accommodations

A

Hall, Peter
Animal Farm (adapt.)

Hall, Roger
Conjugal Rites

Hall, Willis
Jane Eyre (adapt.)
Long and the Short and the Tall
Mansfield Park (adapt.)
Three Musketeers
Walk On, Walk on
(*see* Waterhouse and Hall)

Hamilton, Patrick
Gaslight
Rope
Slaves of Solitude (see *Miss Roach's War*)

Hampton, Christopher
Doll's House
Hedda Gabler
Les Liaisons Dangereuses
Philanthropist
Savages
Tales from Hollywood
Tartuffe (trans.)
Treats
Wild Duck

Hanna, Gillian
Accidental Death of an Anarchist (trans.)

Hanff, Helene
84 Charing Cross Road

Harding, John and Burrows, John
Golden Pathway Annual

Harding, Mike
Comfort and Joy
Fur Coat and No Knickers
Last Tango In Whitby
Not With a Bang

Hardy, Thomas
Far from the Madding Crowd
On the Western Circuit (see *Day After the Fair*)
Tess of the d'Urbervilles

Hare, David
Amy's View
Fanshen
Ivanov (adapt.)
Knuckle
Mother Courage and her Children (adapt.)
Murmuring Judges

Racing Demon
Secret Rapture
Skylight

Harling, Robert
Steel Magnolias

Harris, Richard
Business of Murder
Dead Guilty
Local Affairs
Maintenance Man
Outside Edge
Partners
Party Piece
Stepping Out
Visiting Hour

Harris, Richard and Darbon, Leslie
Two and Two Make Sex
Who Goes Bare?

Harrison, John
Holidays

Harrison, Tony
Misanthrope (trans./adapt.)
Mysteries

Hart, Moss
(*see* Kaufmann, George)

Harvey, Frank
Day After the Fair

Harwood, Ronald
Another Time
Dresser
Handyman
Interpreters
Taking Sides

Hastings, Charlotte
Bonaventure
Dolphins Rampant
Enquiry
Restless Evil
So What Do We do About Henry?
Soft September Air
Wayward Spirit

Havel, Vaclav
Increased Difficulty of Concentration
Largo Desolato
Memorandum
Redevelopment
Temptation
Vanek Plays

Havergal, Giles
Travels With My Aunt

Hawdon, Robin
Birthday Suite
Don't Dress for Dinner (adapt.)

Hawthorne, Nathaniel
Scarlet Letter

Hayes, Catherine
Skirmishes

Hayman, Ronald
Playing The Wife

Heather Brothers
Blood Money

Hecht, Ben and MacArthur, Charles
Front Page

Henley, Beth
Crimes of the Heart

Hennequin, Maurice and Veber, Pierre
Court in the Act!

Hibbert, Guy
Tilting Ground

Highsmith, Patricia
Talented Mr Ripley

Hill, Lucienne
Becket (trans.)
It's Later Than You Think (trans.)
Thieves' Carnival (trans.)

Hill, Ken
Curse of the Werewolf
Invisible Man
Mummy's Tomb

Hinton, William
Fanshen

Hoddinott, Derek
Little Photographer

Hoddinott, Derek and Pat
Forsyte Saga

Hodges, Adrian
Life Goes On

Hodges, Alan
Alan Turing: the Enigma (see Breaking the Code)

Holland, Norman
Princess Ascending
To Meet Oscar Wilde
Watcher In The Shadow

Holland, Vyvyan (adapt.)
Importance of Being Earnest (4 act version)

Holliday, Graham
Scottish Play

Home, William Douglas
After the Ball is Over
Dame of Sark
Kingfisher
Lloyd George Knew My Father
Portraits
Reluctant Debutante
Secretary Bird

Hope, Anthony
Prisoner of Zenda

Horne, Kenneth
Fools Rush In
Love in a Mist

Horsler, Peter
Cut and Run
On the Verge

Howe, Tina
Painting Churches

Hughes, Doug
(*see* Kash, Marcia)

Husson, Albert
Cuisine des Anges (see My Three Angels)

Huth, Angela
Understanding

Huxley, Aldous
Gioconda Smile
Devils of Loudun (see Devils)

Hyem, Jill
Lorna Doone (adapt.)

Ibsen, Henrik
Hedda Gabler

Kopit, Arthur
Wings

Kops, Bernard
Playing Sinatra

Kramer, Larry
Normal Heart

Kushner, Tom
(*see Ariel Dorfman*)

Lambe, Michael
Gypsy's Revenge

Lan, David
Ghetto (trans.)
Ion (trans.)

Lapworth, Paul
(*see* Turner, David)

Larbey, Bob
Building Blocks
Month of Sundays

Lardner, Ring
(*see* Kaufman, George)

Laurence, Charles
About Alice
My Fat Friend
Ring Sisters

Leach, Karoline
Mysterious Mr Love

Lee, Laurie
Cider With Rosie

Leigh, Mike
Abigail's Party
Goose-Pimples
Great Expectations (adapt.)
Smelling a Rat

Leonard, Hugh
Da
Great Expectations
Life
Mask of Moriarty
Mick and Mick
Moving
Patrick Pearse Motel
Pizzazz
Suburb of Babylon
Summer
Time Was

Levin, Ira
Deathtrap
Veronica's Room

Levy, Benn, W.
Rape of the Belt

Lewis, Jonathan
Our Boys

Lloyd, Jeremy
(*see* Chapman, John)

Logan, John
Never the Sinner

Lomas, Derek
Night of the Vixen

Lonsdale, Frederick
Aren't We All?
On Approval

Loos, Anita: and Colette
Gigi

Lorca, Federico García
Blood Wedding
Doña Rosita The Spinster
House of Bernada Alba
Mariana Pineda
Yerma

Lovegrove, Arthur
Goodnight Mrs Puffin

Lucas, Victor
Laughter in the Dark

Luce, Clare Booth
Women

Lucie, Doug
Fashion
Hard Feelings
Progress

Ludlam, Charles
Mystery of Irma Vep

Ludwig, Ken
Lend Me A Tenor

Luke, Peter
Hadrian the Seventh
Yerma (trans.)

Lumborg, Dennis
One Fine Day

Macalpine, Joan
Tom Jones

MacArthur, Charles
(*see* Hecht, Ben)

MacDonald, Robert David
Britannicus (adapt.)
Chinchilla
Summit Conference
Webster

Macdonald, Sharman
Borders of Paradise
Shades
When I Was Girl, I Used to Scream and
   Shout …
Winter Guest

MacDonald, Stephen
Not About Heroes

MacIlwraith, Bill
Anniversary
Last Gamble

Mackendrick, John
Woyzeck (trans)

Macnamara, Margaret
I Have Five Daughters

Madgwick, Donald
Year After the Fair

Magee, Daniel
Paddywack

Mallatratt, Stephen
Englishman's Home

Malleson, Miles
Imaginary Invalid (adapt.)
Miser (adapt.)
Prodigious Snob (adapt.)
School for Wives (adapt.)
Tartuffe (adapt.)

Mamet, David
American Buffalo
Cherry Orchard (adapt.)
Edmond
Glengarry Glen Ross
Life In The Theatre

Speed-the-Plow
Uncle Vanya (adapt.)

Manhoff, Bill
Owl and the Pussycat

Manktelow, Bettine
Curtain Up on Murder
Death Walked In
They Call it Murder

Marber, Patrick
Dealer's Choice

Marcus, Frank
Killing Of Sister George

Marivaux
Les Fausses Confidences (*see* False
   Admissions)
L'Heureux Stratagème (*see* Inconstant Couple
   and Successful Strategies)

Marriott, Anthony and Chapman, John
Shut Your Eyes and Think of England

Marriott, Anthony and Foot, Alistair
No Sex, Please — We're British!
Uproar in the House

Marriott, Anthony and Grant, Bob
Darling Mr London
Home is Where Your Clothes Are
(*see* also Chapman, John)

Martin, Steve
Picasso at the Lapin Agile

Mastrosimone, William
Extremities

Matthews, Seymour
Anagram of Murder
Dead Man's Hand

Maugham, Somerset
Circle
Constant Wife
Miss Thompson (see *Rain*)
Sacred Flame

Maurette, Marcelle
Anastasia

McDonagh, Martin
Cripple of Inishmaan

McGillivray, David and Zerlin Jr, Walter
Chase Me Up Farndale Avenue
Farndale Avenue/*A Christmas Carol*
Farndale Avenue/*Macbeth*
Farndale Avenue/*Murder Mystery*
Haunted Through Lounge … Farndale Castle
They Came from Mars …
We Found Love … SS Farndale Ave

McGuinness, Frank
Observe The Sons of Ulster ...
Someone Who'll Watch Over Me

McIntyre, Clare
Low Level Panic
My Heart's a Suitcase
Thickness of Skin

McKelvey, Peter
House of Secrets

McLoughlin, Maurice
Brush with a Body

Medoff, Mark
Children of a Lesser God

Mellor, Kay
Passionate Woman

Menchell, Ivan
Cemetery Club

Meyer, Michael
Odd Women

Miles, Bernard; Coe, P and Wilson, J
Treasure Island

Millar, Ronald
Abelard and Heloise
Bride and the Bachelor

Minghella, Anthony
Little Like Drowning
Made in Bangkok
Two Planks and a Passion
Whale Music

Mitchell, Adrian
Francis
Fuente Ovejuna (adapt.)
(*see also* Brooks, Jeremy)

Mitchell, Julian
Another Country
August

Molière
Bourgeois Gentilhomme (*see* Prodigious
  Snob)
L'École des Femmes (*see* School for Wives)
Les Femmes Savantes (*see* Sisterhood)
Malade Imaginaire (*see* Imaginary Invalid)
Misanthrope
Miser
Tartuffe

Molnar, Ferenc
Rough Crossing

Montgomery, L. M.
Anne of Green Gables

Moon, Gerald
Corpse!

Moone, Daphne
Pains of Youth (trans.)

Morgan, Diana
My Cousin Rachel

Morley, John
Pinocchio
Wind in the Willows

Morrison, Blake
Cracked Pot (adapt.)

Mortimer, John
Bells of Hell
Cat among the Pigeons (trans.)
Christmas Carol (adapt.)
Collaborators
Come As You Are
Flea in Her Ear (trans.)
Little Hotel on the Side (trans.)
Voyage Round My Father

Mortimer, Johnnie
Situation Comedy
When the Cat's Away

Morum, William
(*see* Dinner, William)

Moss, Roger S
Nightmare: The Fright of Your Life

Mulrine, Stephen
Man with Connections (trans.)
Moscow Stations (trans.)

A

Munro, Rona
Bold Girls
Maiden Stone

Murphy, Jimmy
Brothers of the Brush

Murray, Braham
(*see* Cogo-Fawcett, Robert)

Nagy, Phyllis
Disappeared
Scarlet Letter (adapt.)
Talented Mr Ripley

Naughton, Bill
Alfie
All in Good Time
Spring and Port Wine

Neilson, David
Robin Hood, Truth Behind the Green Tights

Nelson, Richard
New England

Nelson, Richard and Gelman, Alexander
Misha's Party

Nestroy, Johann
Einen Jux will er sich machen
(see *On the Razzle*)

Nichols, Peter
Blue Murder
Born in the Gardens
Day in the Death of Joe Egg
National Health
Piece of My Mind
Privates on Parade

Nicholson, William
Katherine Howard
Map of the Heart
Shadowlands

Nicolaeff, Ariadne (trans.)
Chance Visitor
Old-World
Promise

Nield, Maureen
(*see* Chase, Olive)

Nobbs, David
Second From Last in the Sack Race

Norfolk, William
Caramba's Revenge
Charlatan
Lights Are Warm and Coloured

Norris, Pat
Virtue Triumphant

Oakes, Meredith
Editing Process
Neighbour

Obey, André
Noah

O'Casey, Sean
Juno and the Paycock
Plough and the Stars

Oliver, Reggie
Imaginary Lines

O'Malley, Mary
Once A Catholic

Orczy, Baroness
Scarlet Pimpernel

Orton, Joe
Entertaining Mr Sloane
Erpingham Camp
Funeral Games
Good and Faithful Servant
Loot
Ruffian on the Stair
What the Butler Saw

Orwell, George
Animal Farm

Osborne, John
End of Me Old Cigar
Entertainer
Epitaph for George Dillon
Father (adapt.)
Hedda Gabler (adapt.)
Hotel in Amsterdam
Inadmissble Evidence
Look Back in Anger
Luther
Picture of Dorian Grey

Osment, Philip
Dearly Beloved
Flesh and Blood
Undertaking
What I Did In The Holidays

Overmyer, Eric
On the Verge, or the Geography of Yearning

Page, Louise
Real Estate
Tissue

Paice, Eric
Deadly Embrace

Palin, Michael
Weekend

Parker, Michael
Amorous Ambassador

Parker, Stewart
Spokesong

Parkes, Derek
Threat!
(*see also* Greenwood and Parkes)

Parsley, Roger
Brideshead Revisited (adapt.)

Patrick, Robert
Kennedy's Children

Pember, Ron and De Marne, Denis
Jack the Ripper

Pernak, Adam
Killers

Pertwee, Michael
Don't Just Lie There, Say Something
(*see also* Chapman, John)

Pielmeier, John
Agnes of God

Pinero, Arthur W.
Magistrate
Second Mrs Tanqueray
Trelawny of the 'Wells'

Pinter, Harold
Betrayal
Birthday Party
Caretaker
Homecoming
Hothouse
Moonlight
Old Times

Plater, Alan
And a Little Love Besides
Close the Coalhouse Door
I Thought I Heard A Rustling

Plater, Alan and Tidy, Bill
Fosdyke Saga

Plowman, Gillian
Me and My Friend

Poliakoff, Stephen
Breaking the Silence
City Sugar
Sweet Panic

Pomerance, Bernard
Elephant Man

Poole, Alan
Bottom's Dream

Popplewell, Jack
Busybody
Darling, I'm Home!

Porter, Cathy
Stars in the Morning Sky (trans.)

Potter, Dennis
Blue Remembered Hills
Brimstone and Treacle
Son of Man
Sufficient Carbohydrate

Pratchett, Terry
Maskerade

Price, Stanley
Moving
Why Me?

Priestley, J. B.
Dangerous Corner
I Have Been Here Before
Inspector Calls
Laburnum Grove
Mystery at Greenfingers
They Came to a City
Time and the Conways
When We Are Married

Pritchard, Emlyn
(*see* Bateman, Geoff)

Racine
Britannicus

Rame, Franca
(*see* Fo, Dario)

Randolph, Clemence
(*see* Colton and Randolph)

Rattigan, Terence
Adventure Story
Cause Célèbre
Deep Blue Sea
Flare Path
French Without Tears
In Praise of Love
Man and Boy
Ross
Separate Tables
Sleeping Prince
Winslow Boy

Ravenscroft, Edward
London Cuckolds

Rayburn, Joyce
Man Most Likely To …

Rayment, Mark (adapt.)
September Tide

Redgrave, Michael
Aspern Papers (adapt.)

Rees, Roger
(*see* Elice, Eric)

Reid, Georgina
Clerical Errors
Death and the Maiden
Falling Off a Log
Gone Up in Smoke
Ladies of Spirit
Wolfsbane

Reid, Graham
Remembrance

Richards, Gavin
Accidental Death of an Anarchist (trans.)

Ridley, Arnold
Ghost Train

Robinson, Rony
No Love Lost

Robbins, Norman
Late Mrs Early
Nightmare

Pull the Other One
Rumpelstiltzkin
Slaughterhouse
Tiptoe Through the Tombstones
Tomb with a View
Wedding of the Year

Robson, James
Beulah
Falling Short
Mail Order Bride

Rolfe, Frederick
Hadrian the Seventh

Roose-Evans, James
Cider With Rosie (adapt.)
84 Charing Cross Road

Rose, Reginald
Twelve Angry Men

Ross, Charles
Dead Ringer

Rosser, Austin
Sweeney Todd, the Demon Barber of Fleet Street

Rudkin, David
Ashes

Rostand, Edmond
Cyrano de Bergerac

Russell, Willy
Breezeblock Park
Educating Rita
One for the Road
Shirley Valentine
Stags and Hens

Ryton, Royce
Anastasia File
Royal Baccarat Scandal
Unvarnished Truth

Sackville-West, Vita
Vita and Virginia

Sams, Jeremy
Rehearsal (trans.)

Sands, Leslie
Checkmate

Saunders, James
After Liverpool
Fall
Games
Island
Making It Better
Next Time I'll Sing to You
Redevelopment (trans.)
Retreat
Scent of Flowers

Savory, Gerald
Month of Sundays

Schnitzler, Arthur
La Ronde

Seneca
Thyestes

Shaffer, Anthony
Murderer
Sleuth

Shaffer, Peter
Amadeus
Equus
Five Finger Exercise
Lettice and Lovage
Royal Hunt of the Sun

Sharkey, Jack
Murder Room
Who's on First?

Shelley, Mary
Frankenstein

Shepherd, Jack
Chasing The Moment

Sheridan, R. Brinsley
Critic
Rivals

Sherman, Martin
Bent
Cracks
Madhouse in Goa
Messiah
Some Sunny Day
When She Danced

Sherriff, R. C
Journey's End

Shue, Larry
Foreigner
Nerd

Simon, Neil
Barefoot in the Park
Biloxi Blues
Brighton Beach Memoirs
Broadway Bound
California Suite
Come Blow Your Horn
Fools
Gingerbread Lady
God's Favorite
Good Doctor
Last of the Red Hot Lovers
Lost In Yonkers
Odd Couple
Odd Couple (female)
Plaza Suite
Prisoner of 2nd Avenue
Rumours (British version)
Star Spangled Girl
Sunshine Boys
They're Playing Our Song

Simpson, N. F.
Inner Voices (trans.)
One Way Pendulum
Was He Anyone?

Sisson, Rosemary Anne
Bitter Sanctuary

Skouen, Arne
Ballerina

Slade, Bernard
Fatal Attraction
Romantic Comedy
Same Time, Next Year
You Say Tomatoes

Smith, Dodie
Dear Octopus

Smith, Stevie
Stevie

Snelgrove, Michael
Bums on Seats
Marking Time

Sobel, Joshua
Ghetto

A

Sophocles
Oedipus at Colonus
Oedipus the King

Sorkin, Aaron
Few Good Men

Sowerby, Githa
Rutherford and Son

Spark, Muriel
Prime of Miss Jean Brodie

Spewack, Sam and Bella
My Three Angels (adapt.)

Spooner, Dennis
(see Clemens, Brian)

Stace, Christopher
Oedipus at Colonus (trans.)
Oedipus the King (trans.)

Stenning, Stephen
Abducting Diana (adapt.)

Stephenson, Shelagh
Experiment with an Air Pump

Sterner, Jerry
Other People's Money

Stevenson, Robert Louis
Jekyll and Hyde (see also Strange Case of ...)
Treasure Island

Stewart, Ena Lamont
Men Should Weep

Stocks, Bryan
Victor's Island

Stockwell, Richard
Killing Time

Stoker, Bram
Dracula (see *Count Dracula*)

Stone, Gene and Cooney, Ray
Why Not Stay For Breakfast?

Stoppard, Tom
Arcadia
Artist Descending a Staircase
Dirty Linen and Newfoundland
Dogg's Hamlet, Cahoot's Macbeth
Enter a Free Man

Hapgood
Indian Ink
Invention of Love
Jumpers
Largo Desolato (trans.)
Night and Day
On the Razzle
Real Thing
Rosencrantz and Guildenstern are Dead
Rough Crossing
Seagull (trans.)
Travesties

Storey, David
Home
March on Russia
Restoration of Arnold Middleton
Stages

Stott, Mike
Lenz

Strindberg, August
Father

Sullivan, Daniel
Inspecting Carol

Sultan, Arne; Barret, Earl and Cooney, Ray
Wife Begins at Forty

Sutton, Shaun
Christmas Carol (adapt.)

Swannell, Graham
State of Affairs

Taylor, C. P.
And a Nightingale Sang

Taylor, Don
Daughters of Venice
Exorcism
Retreat from Moscow
Roses of Eyam
When The Barbarians Came

Taylor, Edward
Murder by Misadventure
Rise in the Market

Taylor, Edward and Graham, John
Pardon Me, Prime Minister

Taylor, Samuel
Touch of Spring

A

Tegel, Peter
Suicide (trans.)

Terson, Peter
Pied Piper
Strippers
Zigger Zagger

Thain, Paul
Black Widow

Theiner, George
Temptation (trans.)

Thomas, Brandon
Charley's Aunt

Thomas, Dylan
Child's Christmas in Wales
Under Milk Wood

Thomas, Evan
(*see* Cherrett, Don)

Thomas, Robert
Aurelia

Thompson, Flora
Candleford
Lark Rise

Tidy, Bill
(*see* Plater and Tidy)

Tiller, Ted
Count Dracula

Tinniswood, Peter
Napoli Milionaria (adapt.)
Village Fête
You Should See Us Now

Toksvig, Sandi and Brewer, Elly
Pocket Dream

Tomalin, Claire
Winter Wife

Townsend, Sue
Bazaar and Rummage
Groping for Words
Queen and I
Secret Diary of Adrian Mole Aged $13\frac{3}{4}$
Ten Tiny Fingers, Nine Tiny Toes

Toy, Barbara
(*see* Charles and Toy)

Travers, Ben
Bed Before Yesterday
Rookery Nook
Thark

Tredinnick, Miles
Laugh? I Nearly Went to Miami!

Tristram, David
Inspector Drake and the Perfekt Crime
Inspector Drake and The Time Machine
Inspector Drake's Last Case
Opposite Sex
Unoriginal Sin

Turgenev, Ivan
Fathers and Sons
Month in the Country

Turner, David
Semi-Detached

Turner, David and Lapworth, Paul
Servant of Two Masters

Twain, Mark
Adventures of Huckleberry Finn

Valentine
(*see* Evans and Valentine)

Valentine, Pam
Day of Reckoning

van Druten, John
I Remember Mama
Make Way for Lucia (adapt.)

Vance, Charles
Jane Eyre (adapt.)
Wuthering Heights (adapt.)

Veber, Pierre
(*see* Hennequin, Maurice)

Vega, Lope de
Fuente Ovejuna

Vickery, Frank
All's Fair
Biting the Bullet
Breaking the String
Easy Terms
Erogenous Zones

Family Planning
Kiss On The Bottom
Loose Ends
Love Forty
Night on the Tiles
One O'Clock From the House
Roots and Wings
Spanish Lies
Trivial Pursuits

Vozneskaya, Julia
Women's Decameron
(*see* Brezhnev's Children)

Walker, David
Wolf at the Door (trans.)

Wallace, Naomi
Birdy (adapt.)

Ward, David
Strangeness of Others

Wasserman, Dale
One Flew Over the Cuckoo's Nest

Wasserstein, Wendy
Sisters Rosenweig

Waterhouse, John
Just the Ticket!

Waterhouse, Keith
Jeffrey Bernard Is Unwell
Our Song

Waterhouse, Keith and Hall, Willis
All Things Bright and Beautiful
Billy Liar
Celebration
Children's Day
Filumena (adapt.)
Good Grief
Saturday, Sunday, Monday (adapt.)
Say Who You Are
Whoops-A-Daisy

Watson, Donald
Exit the King (trans.)

Waugh, Evelyn
Brideshead Revisited

Weldon, Fay
Action Replay
I Love My Love

Wells, H. G
Invisible Man

Wertenbaker, Timberlake
After Darwin
Break of Day
False Admissions (trans.)
Grace of Mary Traverse
Léocadia (trans.)
Love of the Nightingale
New Anatomies
Our Country's Good
Successful Strategies (trans.)
Three Birds Alighting on a Field

Wesker, Arnold
Roots

Whalley, Peter
Dead of Night
Local Murder

Wharton, Edith
House of Mirth
Roman Fever
(*see* Pizzazz)

Wharton, William
Birdy

Wheeler, Paul
Deceptions

Whelan, Peter
Accrington Pals

Whipple, Dorothy
Because of the Lockwoods

White, Matthew
Far from the Madding Crowd (adapt.)

Whitemore, Hugh
Best of Friends
Breaking the Code
It's Ralph
Letter of Resignation
Pack of Lies
Stevie

Whitmore, Ken
La Bolshie Vita
Turn of the Screw

Whitmore, Ken and Bradley, Alfred
Final Twist

Whiting, John
Devils

Wilcox, Michael
Accounts
Green Fingers
Lent
Massage
Rents

Wilde, Oscar
Importance of Being Earnest
Lord Arthur Savile's Crime
Picture of Dorian Gray

Wilder, Thornton
Matchmaker
Our Town
Skin of Our Teeth

Willard, John
Cat and the Canary

Williams, Clifford
Rebecca (adapt.)

Williams, Emlyn
Accolade
Corn is Green
Cuckoo
Late Christopher Bean (adapt.)
Light of Heart
Month in the Country (trans.)
Morning Star
Murder Has Been Arranged
Night Must Fall
Someone Waiting
Spring 1600
Trespass
Wind of Heaven

Williams, Frank
Murder by Appointment

Williams, Nigel
Class Enemy

Williams, Tennessee
Battle of Angels
Camino Real
Cat on a Hot Tin Roof
Clothes for a Summer Hotel
Eccentricities of a Nightingale
Glass Menagerie
In the Bar of a Tokyo Hotel
Kingdom of Earth

Milk Train Doesn't Stop Here Any More
Night of the Iguana
Not About Nightingales
Orpheus Descending
Period of Adjustment
Red Devil Battery Sign
Rose Tattoo
Slapstick Tragedy
Small Craft Warnings
Streetcar Named Desire
Summer and Smoke
Sweet Bird of Youth
Vieux Carré

Wilson, John
Hamp

Wood, Charles
Tower (adapt.)

Wood, David, and Arthur, Dave and Toni
Jack the Lad
Robin Hood

Wood, Mrs Henry
East Lynne

Woods, Phil
Canterbury Tales

Woolf, Virginia
Vita and Virginia

Wright, Nicholas
John Gabriel Borkman (trans.)
Mrs Klein

Wyatt, Woodrow
High Profiles

Wymark, Olwen
Brezhnev's Children (adapt.)
Female Parts (adapt.)
Find Me
Lessons and Lovers
Loved
Nana (adapt.)
Strike Up the Banns

Wynne-Tyson, Jon
Marvellous Party

Yeldham, Peter and Churchill, Donald
Fringe Benefits
My Friend Miss Flint

A

Yerofeev, Venedikt
Moscow Stations

Young, Phil
Crystal Clear

Zerlin Jnr, Walter
(*see* McGillivray, David)

Zindel, Paul
Effect of Gamma Rays On Man-in-the-Moon
    Marigolds

Zola, Emile
Germinal
Nana

THEATRE BOOKS LISTS

SAMUEL FRENCH THEATRE BOOKS LISTS

FREE LISTS ARE AVAILABLE OF THEATRE BOOKS STOCKED IN OUR BOOKSHOP

- ACTING
- AUDITION MATERIAL
- CIRCUS, MAGIC, COMEDY, CLOWNS AND PANTOMIME
- COSTUME
- CRITICISM
- DRAMA IN EDUCATION AND DRAMA TRAINING
- MAKE-UP, MIME, MOVEMENT AND DANCE
- MUSICAL INTEREST
- PRODUCTION, STAGE MANAGEMENT AND LIGHTING
- PUPPETRY
- SHAKESPEARE
- SPEECH TRAINING
- STAGECRAFT AND DESIGN
- THEATRE BIOGRAPHY
- THEATRE
- WRITING, TELEVISION AND RADIO

PLEASE ENQUIRE!

A

the

Musical
Plays Catalogue

A 136-page catalogue giving details of all
Musicals and Plays with Music handled by
Samuel French Ltd

Section I   Full scale musicals, with full synopsis etc.
Section II   Plays with music
Section III Plays with music for children and young people
Section IV Pantomimes with published scores

Please enquire!

Full Length Plays

Abducting Diana. Play. Dario Fo adapted by Stephen Stenning
M5 F2. An apartment, a warehouse. Fee code M

Millionaire media boss, Diana Forbes-McKaye, is kidnapped — but the ruthless magnate proves more resourceful than her clumsy abductors. Are things what they seem? Who masterminded the abduction? Who has the television rights to this premier media event? Into this cocktail of chaos, Fo adds a gun-toting priest, a deranged altar boy, a kidnapper hiding in the fridge, pyromania and an explosive climax. This adaptation was presented at the Edinburgh Festival in 1994.

Abelard and Heloise. Play. Ronald Millar
M12 F9. Extras. Multiple skeleton set. Fee code J

The famous love story of Abelard, the renowned teacher who fell in love with Heloise, a girl half his age, had a child by her, married her, was cruelly punished and was eventually received into the Church, is told in flashback. Throughout looms the presence of the Church, the monasteries and convents of twelfth-century France, with the monks and nuns who watch and silently comment on the action. Keith Michell and Diana Rigg starred in the original production at London's Wyndham's Theatre.
ISBN 0 573 01013 7

Abigail's Party. Play. Devised by Mike Leigh
M2 (30s) F3 (30s, 40). A living-room and kitchen. Fee code M

First performed at Hampstead Theatre, London, and subsequently produced for BBC TV, this sharply wicked social satire on lower-middle-class suburbia starred Alison Steadman in an award-winning role as the formidable hostess, Beverly, entertaining new neighbours. The evening's initial good-will, clichés and fatuous small-talk only serve to create a rising tension which finally snaps with a dramatic denouement.
ISBN 0 573 11016 6

◆ **About Alice**. Play. Charles Laurence
M2 (31, 60) F2 (30s). A sitting-room. Fee code M

Alice, the second wife of a famous sculptor, has indomitable humour and a lusty spirit that never let her down. So, when Peggy, a businesslike publisher, arrives with a sexy young gigolo in tow and a proposal to publish the renowned sculptor's memoirs, Alice has no trouble in dispatching the publisher but retaining the young man. That is, until Peggy returns with some news which will stun Alice. An ingenious comedy thriller which twists and turns and maintains the suspense until the very end.
ISBN 0 573 62632 4

Absent Friends. Play. Alan Ayckbourn
M3 (young, middle-age) F3 (20s, 30s). A living-room. Fee code M

Colin's friends are determined to comfort him in his grief over the death of his fiancée — a girl they have never met. They arrange a tea-party for him and are understandably on edge wondering what to say to him as they await his arrival. Their unease, however, has deeper roots as they are all kept together by a mixture of business and cross-marital emotional ties and by the time Colin arrives their tension contrasts dramatically with his cheerfully relaxed air.
ISBN 0 573 01331 4

Absolute Hell. Play. Rodney Ackland
M11 F10. Extras. A drinking club. Fee code M

This fascinating evocation of Bohemian life in London in 1945 was presented at the Orange Tree, Richmond, in 1988 and is a revision of the play *The Pink Room* originally staged at the Lyric Theatre, Hammersmith, in 1952. A world-weary hostess runs a drinking-club where the members gather to drink and, variously, escape, dream, seek, bitch, mock and destroy. 'This is not only an archaeologist's treasure, but is among the most convincing, moving pieces to hit London yet this year.' *Independent*

Absurd Person Singular. Play. Alan Ayckbourn
M3 (30s, 40s) F3 (30s, 40s). Three kitchen settings. Fee code M

We visit three couples in their three kitchens on the Christmas Eves of three successive years: the lower-class Hopcrofts; their bank manager and his wife and their architect neighbour with a suicidal wife. Running like a darker thread through the wild comedy of behind-the-scenes disasters at Christmas parties is the story of the advance of the Hopcrofts and the declines of the others. ISBN 0 573 01023 4

◆**Accidental Death of an Anarchist**. Farce. Dario Fo, adapted by Gavin Richards from a translation by Gillian Hanna
M5 F1. Two offices. Fee code M

Dario Fo has always put a premium on entertainment and this sharp and hilarious satire on police corruption in Italy is no exception. This translation and adaptation was first seen in 1979 and enjoyed a very successful run at Wyndham's Theatre, London, in 1980. 'The brothers Marx, Karl and Groucho, have been working in unison ... when broad farce and social protest miscegenate the offspring is a real cracker.' *Guardian*

Accolade. Play. Emlyn Williams
M5 (20-50) F4 (20s-40s) 1 boy (13). A study. Fee code M

William Trenting, a successful novelist and Nobel Prize winner, encountered early criticism of his works which were labelled 'indecent'. Now accepted as an *enfant terrible* he is knighted in the 1950's Honours List. But his sordid past, on which his novels were based, comes back to haunt him on the day of his investiture and he finds himself facing a very serious charge.

Accommodations. Comedy. Nick Hall
M2 (young, 30s) F2 (young, 30s). An apartment room. Fee code L

Lee decides to leave her husband and suburban home for six weeks to assert her independence and moves into a New York apartment with two roommates. One is an aspiring actress, never out of character or costumes; the other, due to an agency mix-up is a serious, young, graduate student called Tracy — but male! The ensuing complications make for an hysterical evening. ISBN 0 573 60560 2

◆**Accounts**. Play. Michael Wilcox
M4 F1. Various simple interior and exterior settings. Fee code L

Mary, a widow, and her two sons have moved to a new farm in the Scottish Borders where, for the first time, they are landowners. The play's action is spread over the first year in the new place and details the family's daily routine, their attempts to make the farm pay, Mary coming to terms with widowhood, the boys growing up without a father and the exploration of their own awakening sexuality — in the case of Donald, emerging homosexuality.

A

The Accrington Pals. Play. Peter Whelan
M5 (teenage, 30s) F5 (20s, 30s). Simple settings on an open stage. Fee code M

This lyrical, absorbing play, premièred by the RSC, is set in Accrington during 1914-16. The 'Pals' are the men from the local volunteer battalion who march high-spiritedly off to the Great War with their experiences in the trenches contrasted with those of the women left behind. At times funny, at times sad, it paints a moving and powerful picture of the changes in civilian life during wartime.
ISBN 0 573 11009 3

Action Replay. Play. Fay Weldon
M3 F3. A flat and elsewhere. Fee code L

This is a study of the shifting inter-relationships between three young couples, following the developments with sympathy and a certain ironic humour, through a span of twenty-five years. The 'Action Replay' technique of television sporting coverage is here used to present the characters in different lights and situations by repeating the action, sometimes in quite brief scenes, with subtle and often radical differences, in order to examine a vast part of the male/female relationship.
ISBN 0 573 11001 8

Adam Bede. Play. Geoffrey Beevers, adapted from the novel by George Eliot
Flexible cast of up to 30 characters, can be played by a miniumum of M3 F3. Various interior and exterior settings. Fee code M

In this rich and humorous portrayal of eighteenth-century rural life, Geoffrey Beevers remains true to George Eliot's original novel. Adam Bede, a young carpenter of integrity, loves Hetty Sorrel, a pretty and self-centred dairymaid, who herself dreams of Arthur Donnithorne, the young squire. Arthur cannot resist seducing her, and their passion has tragic consequences for the whole community.
ISBN 0 573 11049 2

The Admirable Crichton. Fantastic comedy. J. M. Barrie
M13 F12. Two interiors, one exterior. Fee code M

The time-honoured classic comedy of the butler Crichton and his eccentric aristocratic master, Lord Loam, marooned on a desert island.
ISBN 0 573 01002 1

Adventure Story. Play. Terence Rattigan
M12 F5. Four interiors, two exteriors. Fee code H

The Pythia had warned Alexander that only self-conquest could fit a man to conquer the world. Sure of his destiny, Alexander pursues his vision of a world living in a united concord under his rule. He captures the enormous empire of Darius of Persia, but the demon that forces him to press on to Bactria and then India corrupts his purpose and his vision. He grows despotic, suspicious and ruthless, killing all who question his divinity. He dies at thirty-one, having achieved his conquests but brutally aware of their futility. Period Ancient Greek
ISBN 0 573 01003 X

◆ The Adventures of Huckleberry Finn. Play. Adapted by Matthew Francis from the novel by Mark Twain
M22 F8 (doubling possible). Various interior and exterior settings. Fee code M

Huckleberry Finn's adventurous journey along the Mississippi is skilfully captured in Matthew Francis' superb adaptation of Mark Twain's classic novel. First produced at the Greenwich Theatre, this exciting approach to Twain's epic thrives on the use of minimal set and prop devices to illustrate the many locations. A truly imaginative, both moral and humorous, tale of discovery with flexible casting opportunities. Period 19th century
ISBN 0 573 01779 4

◆ After Darwin. Play. Timberlake Wertenbaker
M5 F1 or M3 F1. Simple settings. Fee code M

It's 1831 and the naturalist Charles Darwin is to travel with Robert FitzRoy into uncharted waters off the coast of South America aboard *The Beagle*. So far, so factual. But for Millie, Ian and Tom, getting to grips with a 1998 stage version of events includes uncovering the polarities both in and between their own lives. The exploration of nineteenth-century philosophical tensions, with the staunch solidity of FitzRoy's Christian ideals sparring with Darwin's slowly dawning radical vision, provokes unsuspected emotions in the present-day director and actors.

After Easter. Play. Anne Devlin
M7 (20s, 30s, old) F7 (30s, old). Various simple settings. Fee code M

Greta, married to a Marxist and living in Oxford, has turned her back on her Catholic Belfast background. Suffering post-natal depression, she goes to stay with her sister Helen in London, where she reveals she is experiencing religious visions. When their father suffers a heart attack they are called back to the family home in Belfast and all the old grievances and jealousies are bared. Greta finds herself confronting the identity that she has wilfully excluded for so long.

After Liverpool. Play. James Saunders
Any number of characters. Fee code F. (Published with *Games*.) Playing time one to one and a half hours according to use made of material

A note on *After Liverpool* by the Author: '*After Liverpool* is not a play but a suite of pieces, to be performed by one or more actors and one or more actresses. The order in which the pieces are played is not specified. Using a musical analogy the script gives some themes, within and between which any number of variations are possible.'
ISBN 0 573 02501 0

◆ After October. Play. Rodney Ackland
M5 F6. A living-room. Fee code M

After October is Ackland's most autobiographical play. It shows a feckless family in the grip of poverty, with a young playwright, Clive, scenting the possibilities of escape to affluence and extravagance. But Clive's play is a failure and his beloved Frances opts for his rival Brian. A loan helps Clive until his novel will be completed and everything will be all right 'after October'. The mood lightens — only the creditors are heavy.

After September. Play. Jimmie Chinn
M1 (middle-age) F10 (20s-60s). A school staffroom. Fee code L

The staff of the Gwendolen Kyte School for Girls are an odd assortment of social misfits and eccentric types. Returning for a new term they face a catalogue of catastrophe and tension reaches breaking point when a government inspector arrives with anonymous letters defaming the school as outmoded, old-fashioned and unsafe, and the staff as unqualified. Who could have betrayed them? And if the school is closed down, where will they go? A warm and touching depiction of female relationships, with several excellent roles for older actresses.
ISBN 0 573 01716 6

After the Ball Is Over. Comedy. William Douglas Home
M7 (20s, middle-age, elderly) F5 (20s, middle-age, elderly). A sitting-room and gallery. Fee code M

This delightful comedy was seen at the Old Vic in 1985 starring Patrick Cargill and Anthony Quayle. The annual Drayton Castle Hunt Ball is held on the very night that the Bill outlawing fox-hunting passes through the House of Lords. This inauspicious start to the evening only serves to herald further confusion and disaster! 'He [William Douglas Home] loves his characters, knows their world intimately and he sends you away with a warm regard for their eccentricities.' *Spectator*
ISBN 0 573 01624 0

After the Rain. Play. John Bowen
M9 F3. A bare stage. Fee code M

The time is '200 years after the Rain of 1969' and the action is a paraphrase of the Bible, commencing with the ark and the flood and ending with the sacrifice of the god-figure. A vital youth and a girl are introduced to the rituals of the community led by Arthur, who believes himself divine. Another man becomes his priest and establishes a ritual — ablutions, confession, audiences, sacrifices, etc. But Arthur is disabused of his godly notions and convinced that he was only possessed by God and was only his vicar. It is he who must be sacrificed.

Agnes of God. Play. John Pielmeier
F3 (21, middle-age). An open stage. Fee code M. For further details of the music apply to Samuel French Ltd

Dr Livingstone, a court-appointed psychiatrist, is asked to determine the sanity of a nun accused of murdering her own baby. The Mother Superior seems bent on protecting Sister Agnes from Livingstone whose suspicions are immediately aroused. In searching for solutions to various mysteries Livingstone forces all of them to face some harsh realities in their own lives. This powerful drama was an outstanding success on Broadway and was filmed with Jane Fonda and Anne Bancroft.
ISBN 0 573 63022 4

♦ **Alarms and Excursions**. Eight short plays. Michael Frayn
M16 F14 can be played by M2 (35, 45) F2 (35, 45). Various simple settings. Fee code M

These eight plays examine the difficulties modern technology has added to life — with hilarious results. **Available 1st September 2000**

Alarms. Fee code D
Two couples embark on a dinner party which is doomed to failure as labour-saving devices and furniture become hostile.

Doubles. Fee code E
Two couples in adjacent hotel rooms have similar problems to those in *Alarms*.

Leavings. Fee code B
The dinner-party is revisited.

Look Away Now. Fee code A
Passengers ignore their airliner's safety lecture.

Heart to Heart. Fee code A
Deals with the impossibility of communication at a noisy drinks party.

Glassnost. Fee code A
Presents us with a political speech sabotaged by a harassed autocue operator.

Toasters. Fee code A
Shows the problems of trying to eat and work standing up at a function.

Immobiles. Fee code C
This is acted out entirely over the phone, as a couple try to decide where they should be meeting their German guest.
ISBN 0 573 01808 1

Albert Make Us Laugh. Play. Jimmie Chinn
M6 F8 or M4 F5 (with doubling). Various simple interior and exterior settings. Fee code M

Some would say Albert Nuttall, aged eleven, is backward — but he is special. He is a poet and a visionary who, as he grows into manhood, inspires unexpected depths of emotion in other people, notably his classmate Primrose, whose glorious future as an actress fails to materialize, and the lost and lonely young schoolteacher, Janet Partington. This strange, touching and uplifting story — written to be enacted *entirely* by adults — is engaging and theatrically innovative. Period 1940s-1950s.
ISBN 0 573 01719 0

Alfie. Play. Bill Naughton
M9 (30s, 40s, 65) F9 (20s, 30s, 50). Composite setting. Fee code M

With sublime amorality Alfie swaggers and philosophizes his way through the play, chattily allowing the audience to eavesdrop as he goes from one 'bird' to another, trying hard to communicate his own brand of determined hedonism and carefully rejecting anyone or anything that might touch him too deeply. Premièred at London's Duchess Theatre, the stage play was later successfully filmed with Michael Caine in the role of the ebullient Cockney Alfie.
ISBN 0 573 01008 0

A

All in Good Time. Comedy. Bill Naughton
M7 (20s, 40s, 50s) F4 (20s-50). Three interiors, one exterior. Fee code H

This robustly humorous play centres on the sensitive Arthur and his new bride forced by economic circumstances to live with his good-hearted but rough-tongued father. The lack of privacy is so inhibiting that Arthur is unable to consummate the marriage, and gradually word gets around. But fortunately Arthur becomes so humiliated and enraged — he loses his inhibitions ...! Filmed as *The Family Way* with Hywel Bennett and Hayley Mills.
ISBN 0 573 01011 0

All Things Bright and Beautiful. Comedy. Keith Waterhouse and Willis Hall
M6 (20s-40s, 70) F3 (19, 40s). A kitchen/living-room, a yard. Fee code M

An exuberant and racy comedy which is yet a sad commentary on twentieth-century bureaucracy. The Hesseltines are living in property well overdue for demolition and are looking forward to being re-housed in more beautiful and salubrious surroundings. The crisis comes when they find that, far from a house with a little bit of garden, they are to live in a warrenous block of flats.
ISBN 0 573 11012 3

◆ **All Things Considered**. Play. Ben Brown
M4 (49, middle-age) F3 (young, late 20s, 40s). A living-room. Fee code M

David Freeman, a Professor of Philosophy about to reach fifty, is tired of life. His only desire now is to control the timing and manner of his death. His plans for 'self-deliverance', however, are disrupted by the earthly demands of people around him. Alone at last he carries out his plan, but is saved by the college electrician. Returning from hospital, David hears news that may change his mind — yet ultimately the vagaries of chance would have it otherwise.
ISBN 0 573 01720 4

All's Fair. Play. Frank Vickery
M2 (20s) F4 (14, 20s, middle-age). A living-room. Fee code L

This poignant comedy is set in the wartime Rhondda and captures perfectly the claustrophobic yet protective and supportive atmosphere of life in the Welsh Valleys in 1942. The two central characters — Dilys, in love with an American GI and Sophie, frustrated at being unmarried and happy to settle for Dilys's dull brother — are contrasted and astutely observed, as are the other members of the household — Mother, nearing the end of her years and precocious Brenda, trembling on the brink of adolescence.
ISBN 0 573 01675 5

Alphabetical Order. Play. Michael Frayn
M4 (30s-60s) F3 (20s, 30s, 50s). A library. Fee code M

The library office of a provincial newspaper is a scene of utter confusion — the cluttered chaos of the room matching the lives of its staff. It is also a scene of warmth and light-heartedness. In comes Leslie, a new young assistant with a passion for organization who transforms the office and the lives of its inhabitants into something orderly and neat — and also arid and colourless. An announcement that the paper is to close leads to a struggle between chaos and order.
ISBN 0 573 01600 3

Amadeus. Play. Peter Shaffer
M12 (30s-70) F3 (20s, 30s). Extras. Interior and exterior settings. Fee code M

In old age, Salieri recalls his successful career as Court Composer, his hatred of Mozart, and how he contrived the brilliant young composer's demise. A musical genius, Mozart died neglected and impoverished while the mediocre Salieri lived in a blaze of fame and praise. Period 1823 Vienna and in recall, 1781-1791. First presented at the Royal National Theatre.
ISBN 0 573 11015 8

American Buffalo. Drama. David Mamet
M3 (young, 40s). A junk shop. Fee code M

In a Chicago junk shop three small-time crooks plot to rob a man of his coin collection which came to light when the collector found a valuable 'buffalo nickel' in the shop. The three plotters fancy themselves as businessmen pursuing the genuine concerns of free enterprise. In reality, they are Donny, the stupid junk shop owner; Bobby, a spaced-out young junkie Donny has befriended; and Teacher, a violent, paranoid braggart. But their plans come to naught and are futile, vulgar verbal exercises.

◆ **The Amorous Ambassador**. American farce. Michael Parker
M4 (20-30, 25-45, 50+, 45-65) F4 (20-25, 25-40, 50+). A living-room. Fee code M

When Harry Douglas, the new American Ambassador to Great Britain, tells his family he is going to Scotland to play golf, his wife Lois and daughter Debbie announce plans of their own. Their newly hired butler, Perkins, watches stoically as each leaves and secretly returns for a romantic rendezvous in the empty house. In the wake of a bomb threat, the Embassy is sealed off — with hilarious results.
ISBN 0 573 67040 4

Amphibious Spangulatos, or Newt on Your Nellie! Farce. Paul Doust
M13 F21. Doubling possible. A sports changing-room in a village hall. Fee code L

Cherry Hellingsworth is fulfilling her Community Service stint by working at a Village Hall as the Functions Manager. But she's not terribly good at it. On one evening she manages to to hire out the hall to the Village Drama Society, the Cricket team, a Singing Telegram and a Country and Western group called the Southern Fried Chickens. A frenzied, door-slamming farce, suitable for adults or youth groups.
ISBN 0 573 01717 4

◆ **Amy's View**. Play. David Hare
M3 (20s, early 50s) F3 (23-39, 49-66, late 70s, mid 80s). A living-room, a dressing-room. Fee code M

1979. Esme Allen is a well-known West End actress at just the moment when the West End is ceasing to offer actors a regular way of life. The visit of her daughter, Amy, with a new boyfriend sets in train a series of events which only find their shape sixteen years later. David Hare mixes love, death and the theatre in a heady and original way. Period: 1979, 1995. **Available (British Isles only) 1st January 2001**

A

Anagram of Murder. Thriller. Seymour Matthews
M3 (40s, 50s) F3 (20s-40s). A living-room. Fee code L

This tense, dramatic thriller contains plenty of twists to keep your audience guessing. Beautiful Veronica plots to murder her writer husband, Gus, but becomes alarmed when Gus discusses the plot of his new novel, which is uncomfortably close to her murder plans. She presses ahead, however, but things do not run entirely smoothly. Next day the police report the finding of a body — but is it Gus? The final denouement contains several surprises before the guilty are brought to justice.
ISBN 0 573 11487 0

Anastasia. Play. Marcelle Maurette. Adapted by Guy Bolton
M8 (30s-50s, elderly) F5 (30s, 40s, 70, 84). A room in a mansion. Fee code M

Berlin hums with a rumour that the Tzar's youngest daughter had escaped the bullets at Ekaterinburg in 1918. Prince Bounine, intent on exploiting the fortune and nostalgia of the Russian exiles, finds an amnesiac waif on the point of suicide. She is carefully groomed for the part and makes a convincing impersonation, then suddenly turns her back on the fortune and the past to live anonymous but free. Period 1930
ISBN 0 573 60529 7

The Anastasia File. Play. Royce Ryton
M2 F2. Various simple settings. Fee code M

Did the Grand Duchess Anastasia actually die with the rest of the Imperial family at Ekaterinburg in 1918? Using only four characters — Mrs Manahan, a police Inspector and an actor and actress (playing between them forty parts) — this brilliantly structured drama presents in flashback the life of the lady found in an asylum in 1920. Is Anastasia genuine? Why did some of the closest relatives reject her? Your audience will be held by his compelling play until the final surprising twist.
ISBN 0 573 01642 9

And a Little Love Besides. Play. Alan Plater
M4 F4. Single setting. Fee code J

The Friday Fellowship is a religious group that meets with prayers and hymns to organize the activities of their parish. During one meeting when Mr Briggs reports on a recent Youth Club outing, another member mentions an unfortunate 'physical incident': Mr Briggs, in fact, 'touched' a young girl. This revelation brings about surprising results, one of the most surprising being the reaction of the Vicar. Semi-realistic in treatment, the play is written for the simplest style of production.
ISBN 0 573 01025 0

And a Nightingale Sang. Play. C. P. Taylor
M4 (20s, 30s, 50s, 70) F3 (22, 30s, 50s). An open stage. Fee code M

This play follows the course of World War II as experienced by a working-class family in Newcastle, each scene being opened by a member of the family addressing the audience or singing a song of the period. In wartime there are no public worries, only private worries, and this story of the family's personal relationships, preoccupations, troubles and joys suggests, perhaps, the reason why — with all the perils and troubles besieging it — the human race will continue to survive.
ISBN 0 573 11020 4

And Then There Were None. Play. Agatha Christie
M9 (20s, 30s, middle-age, elderly) F3 (25, middle-age). A living-room. Fee code M

Ten people are invited by unknown hosts to a lonely house on a remote island. A mysterious voice indicts each of them of murder. First one and then another dies, and the tension grows as they realize that the killer is one of themselves. With only two people remaining, it becomes apparent that one of the deaths was feigned; the real killer appears and they are able to outwit him.
ISBN 0 573 01441 8

Animal Farm. Fable. Adapted by Nelson Bond from the book by George Orwell
M5 F2. No setting. Fee code M. NB. This is a staged reading version.

Orwell's biting satire is a fable with a sting, revealing how an idealistic Communist dream was converted into a nightmare. This simply staged dramatic reading begins with the creatures who have emancipated themselves from their cruel human masters, only to find themselves subjected to even more ruthless autocrats: the greedy, cunning pigs. Eventually, the animals numbly accept that 'All animals are equal but some are more equal than others.'
ISBN 0 573 60538 6

Animal Farm. George Orwell, adapted by Peter Hall, with lyrics by Adrian Mitchell and music by Richard Peaslee
M9 F6, 1 boy. Extras. Various simple settings. Fee code M

This much-acclaimed dramatization of George Orwell's classic, allegorical novel was first seen at the National Theatre in 1984. The play starts with a schoolboy sitting down to read the novel by a toy farmyard. As he reads, the farmyard comes to life around him, enacting the animals' rebellion. The dialogue is complemented by Mitchell's witty lyrics and Peaslee's music, jaunty at first, but increasingly threatening and dissonant.

Anna's Room. Play. Ellen Dryden
M2 (young, 30s) F3 (20s-30s, middle-age). An attic room. Fee code M
ISBN 0 573 01601 1

Anne of Green Gables. Play. Sylvia Ashby, from the novel by L.M. Montgomery
M4 (30s, middle-age). F5 (20s, middle-age). 3 boys, 4 girls (12). Some doubling possible. Various interior and exterior settings. Fee code L

Mathew Cuthbert and his sister Marilla decide to adopt a boy to work on their farm, Green Gables, but the orphanage sends a girl by mistake — the young, befreckled, warm, witty and charitable Anne Shirley — and their lives are changed forever. This concise yet detailed adaptation is humorous and bittersweet; a refreshing, contemporary telling of a classic story.

The Anniversary. Play. Bill MacIlwraith
M3 (20s, 30s) F3 (19, 30s, 50s). A living-room. Fee code M

Mother keeps a tight hold on all three of her sons with gifts, threats and ruthless exploitation of their weaknesses. But as the family is unwillingly brought together to celebrate Mum's wedding anniversary (regardless of deceased Dad), revolt is in the air. One son gathers the courage to tell Mum he is moving to Canada; another breaks the news of his impending marriage. Mum finds her long ascendancy is broken at last. The play was filmed starring Bette Davis and Sheila Hancock.
ISBN 0 573 11007 7

A

◆ **Anorak of Fire**. The Life and Times of Gus Gascoigne, Trainspotter. Play. Stephen Dinsdale
M1 (20s). A railway station platform. Fee code H

'I was born a spotter.' Thus we are introduced to Gus Gascoigne, young, spotty, perpetually cheerful
and completely bemused by anything that isn't involved with his sole interest — trainspotting.
Touching, ironic and consistently hilarious, *Anorak of Fire*, which enjoyed a long run at London's
Arts Theatre, after the Edinburgh Fringe, is a guaranteed audience-pleaser. Running time
approximately one hour.
ISBN 0 573 14201 7

Another Country. Play. Julian Mitchell
M9 (17, 40s). 1 boy. A public school library, study, dormitory, cricket field. Fee code M

Julian Mitchell's much-acclaimed play is set in an English public school in the early 1930s. The
two central characters are outsiders: Guy Bennett, coming to terms with homosexuality, and Tommy
Judd, a committed Marxist. 'In this subtle, absorbing and deceptive play, Julian Mitchell
persuasively examines the seeds of tribal snobberies sown in the pre-war heyday of the British
public school and reaped today in a harvest of spy scandals in top places.' *Daily Mail*

Another Time. Play. Ronald Harwood
M3 F2 (some characters age over 35 years). A pentagonal hall of a small ground-floor flat, a
recording studio. Fee code M

In early 1950s Sea Point Town, Ike and Belle live with their son, Leonard, already a brilliantly
gifted pianist who needs to study in Europe. When Ike dies, Belle is determined to further Leonard's
studies whatever the cost. In Act II it is thirty-five years later in London where Leonard is a
famous concert pianist. Belle and her brother and sister have travelled to London to see him, but
Leonard has some shattering news for Belle.

Antigone. Play. Jean Anouilh. Translated by Lewis Galantière
M8 (20s, middle-age, 60s) F4 (19, 20s, 60s). An open space. Fee code M

This play was first performed in German-occupied France and its theme is resistance to oppression.
It is based on the Greek tragedy of Antigone, who tried to bury her brother's corpse against the
diktat of her uncle, Creon. Creon is a dictator, but defends his position on practical grounds. In
spite of her love for Creon's son, she chooses her part: to bury her brother and die.

Antigone. Play. Jean Anouilh. Translated by Barbara Bray

For cast, synopsis and setting details see synopsis above. Fee code M

Antigone. Play. Bertolt Brecht
Translations: K. I. Porter
               Robert Cannon
Fee code M

A prologue set in 1945 Berlin shows two sisters whose brother has deserted from the German
army and is found hanged: should they risk being seen by the SS cutting his body down? In the
play itself Creon becomes a brutal aggressor, who has attacked Argos for the sake of its iron ore.
Tiresias, instead of prophesying the future, becomes a pessimistic analyst of the present; while the
chorus of elders, always reserved in its attitude, eventually turns against Creon too.

Anybody for Murder? Play. Brian Clemens and Dennis Spooner
M3 (30s, 40s) F3 (30s, 40s). A converted farmhouse on a Greek island. Fee code M

Max and his lover Suzy have concocted a plot to kill Max's wife Janet, with ten thousand pounds insurance money as an added bonus. Their plan is for Janet to have a sailing 'accident'. Then two unexpected visitors arrive, in the shape of George and Mary Ticklewell, who have an eye on the money, with murder plans of their own. Thus begins an intriguing round of plot and counter-plot, with a final, unexpected twist.
ISBN 0 573 01713 1

Anyone for Breakfast? Comedy. Derek Benfield
M3 (20, 40s) F3 (20, 40s) A living-room. Fee code L

In this merry comedy of marital mishaps the scene is set for an evening and morning of riotous misunderstandings and mistaken identities as the guilty parties in question try desperately to keep their romantic secrets secret! Your audience will be kept on a roar for two hours and at the end of the play we realize that the complications and confrontations — far from ending — are only just beginning ...
ISBN 0 573 01715 8

April in Paris. Comedy. John Godber
M1 (30s) F1 (30s). Various simple settings. Fee code M

Bet and Al lead a quiet, humdrum life in their small Yorkshire home until Bet wins a 'Romantic Breaks' competition in a magazine. The prize, a holiday in Paris, represents their first experience abroad and has profound effects on the way they look at the world around them once they return home. They sort out French cuisine, wrestle with their phrase book, and fend off would-be muggers on the Métro in this hilarious depiction of the English abroad. **Available 1st September 1997**
ISBN 0 573 01714 X

♦ **Arcadia**. Play. Tom Stoppard
M8 (15, 20s, 30s, middle-age) F4 (teenage, 30s). A room. Fee code M

In 1809 at Sidley Park, the orderly classicism of Lady Croom's Capability Brown grounds is being turned into picturesque romantic chaos, as fashion dictates. In a Regency room overlooking the work is Lady Croom's brilliant adolescent daughter, Thomasina Coverly, with her tutor. They are interrupted by, among others, the amorous Lady Croom and Ezra Chater, a cuckold and minor poet, determined on satisfaction. 180 years later, in the same room, a corresponding group try to unravel the events of 1809 — with spectacularly wrong results.
ISBN 0 573 01718 2

The Architect. Play. David Greig
M4 (20s, 40s, 50s) F3 (20s, 40s, 50s). Various simple settings. Fee code M

Leo Black was an architect of his time, a builder of buildings, an idealistic designer, but these days he has an executive role in designing car parks. Has he really sunk so low? His family are falling apart and his buildings are falling down, leaving Leo struggling with the grubby reality of his once magnificent visions. The play was premièred at Edinburgh's Traverse Theatre in 1996.

Aren't We All? Comedy. Frederick Lonsdale
M8 (young, 30s, middle-age, 59) F4 (20s, middle-age). Two drawing-rooms. Fee code M

Willie is a devoted husband but falls prey to the charms of a beautiful young woman while his wife, Margot, is on holiday. Margot is furious when she discovers the affair, but becomes terrified when Willie's father finds out about her own holiday romance. Eventually she realizes that Willie still loves her and confesses her infidelity. Forgiveness is mutual.
ISBN 0 573 61987 5

Aristocrats. Play. Brian Friel
M6 (30s, 50s, 70s) F3 (20s, 30s). A lawn and a small room. Fee code M

Set in the mid-1970s in a crumbling Georgian mansion in County Donegal, this is a portrait of an upper-class Catholic family which, over four generations, has declined from a position of social power to one of genteel poverty. The characters find themselves attending the patriarch's funeral, and sit about the lawn drinking and quarrelling. ' ... sad, enchanting play ... a heartaching world of crushed hopes and futile longings.' *Evening Standard* ' ... Friel's eloquence and piquant irony speaks volumes.' *Time Out*

Artist Descending a Staircase. Play. Tom Stoppard
M6 (20s, 70s) F1 (22). An attic studio, a room, in the open air. Fee code M

Donner, Beauchamp and Martello, three elderly avant-garde artists, have co-existed for over fifty years. The play opens with Beauchamp and Martello accusing each other of the murder of Donner. In a series of flashbacks from 1972 to 1914, the bickering trio are contrasted with their young counterparts. The pivot is Sophie, loved by each of them in different ways. In the play's final moments, the reality of Donner's death is revealed.
ISBN 0 573 01687 9

Arturo Ui . See **Resistible Rise of Arturo Ui**

Ashes. Play. David Rudkin
M1 F1. 10 other characters played by M1 F1. Composite set. Fee code L

First seen at the Open Space Theatre in 1974, this is a sensitive study of a childless couple and the various indignities they have to endure in the search to find out why they are childless after two years of trying for a family. Filled with much wry humour this is a delicate treatment of a difficult subject and as such is suitable for advanced societies, University and College groups.
ISBN 0 573 01707 7

Ask for the Moon. Play. Shirley Gee
M1 (40s) F6 (16, 20s (1 Asian), 40s (1 West Indian), elderly). Split set: Victorian cottage and modern sweat-shop. Fee code M

A moving play, first seen at Hampstead, showing the plight of women workers in the rag trade, separated by almost 150 years but still sharing a tragic fate. In a split setting we see the Victorian cottage where the lace-makers work in appalling conditions and also the modern-day sweat shop where goods are made on piece work. Times have not changed much — everyone must still keep up or face the sack.

The Aspern Papers. Comedy of Letters. Adapted by Michael Redgrave from the story by Henry James
M2 (40s) F4 (40s, 55, old). The sala of a Venetian house. Fee code H. ISBN 0 573 01028 5

August. Play. Julian Mitchell, adapted from *Uncle Vanya* by Anton Chekhov
M7 (middle-age, old) F4 (20s, old). A terrace, a dining-room, a drawing-room, a bedroom. Fee code M

Chekhov's eloquent study of languid Russian landowners has been transposed by Julian Mitchell to Victorian north Wales in this stunning adaptation, which dispenses with many of the alienating Russian principles — confusing patronymics — and theatrical clichés — birch forests and samovars — that characterize most modern British productions. Anthony Hopkins played Ieuan Davies in the acclaimed original production for Theatr Clwyd in 1994.

Aurelia. Robert Thomas, after the novel by, and in collaboration with, Jean-Paul Ferriere, adapted by Tudor Gates
M2 (20, 35) F4 (24, 30s, 50, 60). A drawing-room. Fee code K
ISBN 0 573 01593 7

Autumn Manoeuvres. Comedy. Peter Coke
M2 (30s, 70s) F8 (30s, middle-age, elderly), doubling possible. A drawing-room. Fee code K

This sequel to *Breath of Spring* and *Midsummer Mink* sees Dame Beatrice — and her lodgers Nan, Hattie and the Brigadier — embarking on a series of 'operations' to acquire funds to purchase a flat. Their complicated but well-planned manoeuvres succeed so well that by the end of this gentle comedy they are well on their way to obtaining a second flat, proving, as Bea says, that in their case age certainly isn't limiting!
ISBN 0 573 11010 7

Baal. Play. Bertolt Brecht
Translations: Peter Tegal
                        Christopher Logue
                        William E. Smith and Ralph Manheim
M18 F12. Extras. Interior and exterior settings. Fee code M (for play), code A (for music)

Baal, a poet and singer, drunk, lazy, selfish and ruthless, seduces (among others) a disciple's seventeen-year-old mistress, who drowns herself. He mixes with tramps and drivers and sings in a cheap nightclub. With his friend the composer Ekart he wanders through the country, drinking and fighting. Sophie, pregnant by him, follows them and likewise drowns herself. Baal seduces Ekart's mistress, then kills him. Hunted by the police and deserted by the woodcutters, he dies alone in a forest hut.

Baby with the Bathwater. Comedy. Christopher Durang
M2 F8 or M2 F3. Composite set. Fee code H

This bitingly satiric black comedy, which enjoyed a long off-Broadway run, begins with Helen and John deciding their newly born child is a girl and naming it Daisy — which leads to all manner of future emotional and personality problems because Daisy is actually a boy. Brilliantly theatrical and wildly hilarious, the play charts the saga of Daisy's struggle to establish his identity.

The Bacchae. Play. Euripides, translated by Neil Curry
M7 F1, chorus of women. An open stage. Fee code J

A lively, modern English translation of Euripides' last and greatest play which depicts the turbulent arrival of the Dionysiac religion in Greece.

Bad Company. Play. Simon Bent
M6 (20s) F2 (20s). Various simple scenes. Fee code M

A group of twentysomethings hangs out on the seafront of a northern resort at the end of the summer season, finding little to relieve the futility and boredom of their lives: they gamble in amusement arcades, bicker in cafés, lust on the beach ... Casual sex, mindless violence and comic clashes of outlook permeate this entertaining, contemporary and humane play which paints a believable, touching portrait of modern youth.
ISBN 0 573 01723 9

Ballerina. Play. Arne Skouen
M2 (25, 50s) F4 (18, 20s, 40, 50s). An hotel room. Fee code M
ISBN 0 573 11018 2

Balmoral. Comedy. Michael Frayn
M6 (20s, 50s, 60) F2 (20, 40). A room in Balmoral Castle. Fee code M

It is 1937. Twenty years earlier the Revolution took place in Britain instead of Russia and the Soviet Republic of Great Britain is at the height of the purges. The royal residence of Balmoral is now a State Writers' Home with Godfrey Winn, Warwick Deeping, Enid Blyton and Hugh Walpole among its current inmates. Upon this very entertaining premise, Michael Frayn has constructed a witty, ingenious farce which was presented at the Bristol Old Vic in 1987.

Barefoot in the Park. Comedy. Neil Simon
M4 (26, 30, 58, 60) F2 (young, 60). New York apartment. Fee code M

Corrie and Paul are newly-weds who have just moved into their cold eyrie of an apartment. Corrie is starry-eyed, Paul less so after staggering up five flights. Their house seems to be populated by unusual people, the most bohemian being Victor whom Corrie finds entertaining. Corrie tries matchmaking between Victor and her lonely mother but after a disastrous dinner party she learns that walking barefoot in the park may not necessarily denote *joie de vivre* — in February it is simply silly!
ISBN 0 573 01551 1

Battle of Angels. Play. Tennessee Williams
M11 F11. Fee code M

As in its later, and substantially re-written version (entitled *Orpheus Descending*) the play deals with the arrival of a virile young drifter, Val Xavier, in a sleepy, small town in rural Mississippi. Taking a job in a store his smouldering animal magnetism draws out the latent sexual passion in the love-starved store keeper, whilst her husband lies dying upstairs. A sense of inevitable tragedy grows and there is a denouement of overwhelming and chilling intensity.

Bazaar and Rummage. Comedy. Sue Townsend
F6 (20s, 30s, middle-age). A multi-purpose church hall. Fee code J

Gwenda, an ex-agoraphobic, leads a self-help group of three who have been unable to leave their homes for a variety of reasons. She forces them to help at a local bazaar, enlisting the support of Fliss, a trainee social-worker. While sorting through the rummage their individual fears erupt but calm is restored by the ever-sensible Fliss. As they leave the hall it is apparent their agoraphobia is not cured but they have made the effort.

Because of the Lockwoods. Play. Constance Cox from the novel by Dorothy Whipple
M3 (20s, 50) F5 (18, 20, 40, 50). A room in a provincial house. Fee code L

Set in Lancashire in 1902 this play deals with the Hunter family who are obliged to live in the poorer district of town. The Lockwoods' former neighbours prove patronizing but the Hunters are saved from despair by the help of Oliver Read, a young junk dealer whose cheerfulness and acumen assists them to a much brighter future. This play has moments of great comedy and is simple to dress and set.
ISBN 0 573 01722 0

Becket, or The Honour of God. Play. Jean Anouilh. Translated by Lucienne Hill
M34 F5. Composite setting. Fee code H

As he waits to be scourged for his part in Becket's murder, King Henry II retraces his entire relationship with the saint, once his dearest friend and mentor. His catastrophic mistake was to create Becket Archbishop out of political expediency for Becket found a fulfilment lacking in his hitherto luxurious life and therefore guarded the honour of God as once he had, as Henry's Chancellor, once guarded the honour of his King. Period 12th century
ISBN 0 573 01034 X

Bed. Play. Jim Cartwright
M4 F4. A giant bed. Fee code M

Seven elderly people share a vast bed, to dream, remember and reflect on a long past. The play, with a running time of 90 minutes, was acclaimed at the Royal National Theatre. 'Cartwright writes better about old people than anyone I know, except perhaps Beckett. This is an odd, harrowing and hilarious piece, entirely without sentimentality, sturdy but moving.' *Sunday Times*. 'Sophisticated of structure and mature in content ... brims with the confidence of a craftsman who can work as happily with surrealism as naturalism ...' *City Limits*

The Bed Before Yesterday. Comedy. Ben Travers
M4 (young, 35-50) F4 (21, 40s, 50). A living-room. Fee code M

Alma, a rich but physically far from lovely widow, has had no sexual experience since the sole occasion on her wedding night twenty years ago. She marries impoverished Victor on the understanding that their marriage will be based on friendship. But intervention from Victor's son, his unconventional girlfriend and Alma's free-and-easy cousin warm up her long-cooled fires with unexpected results. Period 1930
ISBN 0 573 01596 1

A Bedfull of Foreigners. Comedy. Dave Freeman
M4 (30s, middle-age) F3 (20s, 30s). An hotel bedroom. Fee code M

On the eve of a local festival in a French village Stanley and Brenda, on a motoring trip, think themselves lucky to obtain a hotel room. But in less than an hour Stanley finds himself lowering an attractive girl, stark naked, from the window. The girl's husband arrives and by the second hour almost everybody is in the wrong bed, figures dressed as nuns and monks rush in and out, seductions and confrontations run rampant!
ISBN 0 573 11104 3

Bedroom Farce. Comedy. Alan Ayckbourn
M4 (young, 60) F4 (young, 50s). Three bedrooms in one set. Fee code M

Three bedrooms are presented simultaneously on stage and the action between three households flows in and out from one to the other during this hectic night. There are Ernest and Delia celebrating an anniversary with pilchards on toast after a disastrous meal out; Malcolm and Kate preparing a house-warming party and Nick and Jan, the former resting his injured back in bed. The marital disasters of Trevor and Susannah weave in out and out of the bedrooms.
ISBN 0 573 11047 6

Bedside Manners. Comedy. Derek Benfield
M3 (young, middle-age) F2 (young). A reception room and two bedrooms represented by the same set. Fee code L

Ferris is looking after his sister's seedy hotel. Two young couples arrive. Roger has arranged an assignation with Sally, leaving his wife Helen at home, but Helen and Geoff, Sally's husband, have also made plans for a naughty weekend together — at the same hotel. The mischievous Ferris discovers their guilty secrets and tries (at some financial reward to himself) to prevent the inevitable meeting of husbands, wives and lovers in assorted compromising situations.
ISBN 0 573 11030 1

Being of Sound Mind. Play. Brian J. Burton
M2 (40s) F3 (30s). A farmhouse kitchen. Fee code L

Susan is particularly looking forward to her usual holiday in a rented cottage in France as she is recovering from a nervous breakdown. John leaves her to go to the local shop and a stranger turns up purporting to be John and thus begins a series of confusing and terrifying events for Susan. It transpires that Susan will inherit her father's money if she is 'of sound mind' but John, and Judy her sister, wish to prevent her from doing so.
ISBN 0 573 11022 0

Benefactors. Play. Michael Frayn
M2 F2. A bare stage. Fee code M

Michael Frayn's highly-acclaimed play was premièred at London's Vaudeville Theatre and won the *Standard*, *Plays and Players* and Laurence Olivier awards for the Best Play of 1984. Spanning fifteen years this complex, well-structured play traces the story of the destruction of David's architectural dream by the embittered Colin and Colin's marriage to the inept Sheila, contrasting those who help and those who are helped; those who create and those who destroy. '... a beautifully crafted play, economically written.' *Time Out*
ISBN 0 573 01643 7

Bent. Play. Martin Sherman
M11 (20s, 30s) with doubling. Various simple interior and exterior settings. Fee code M

In 1930s Berlin Max and his lover/flatmate Rudy begin a nightmare odyssey through Nazi Germany, which placed homosexuals on a lower scale than Jews. Max refuses to abandon Rudy and soon they're caught. *En route* to Dachau, Rudy is killed and Horst, another homosexual prisoner, warns Max to deny Rudy, which he does. Max opts for the label 'Jew' rather than 'queer' but he and Horst are attracted to each other; when Horst is callously killed Max declares himself before committing suicide.

The Best of Friends. Play. Hugh Whitemore, adapted from the letters and writings of Dame Laurentia McLachlan, Sir Sydney Cockerell and George Bernard Shaw
M2 F1. A sitting-room, a conservatory, a study. Fee code M

In 1924, when George Bernard Shaw was 68, his friend Sydney Cockerell, then Director of the Fitzwilliam Museum in Cambridge, introduced him to a Benedictine nun at Stanbrook Abbey in Worcestershire. Dame Laurentia McLachlan, later to be elected Abbess, enjoyed a lively friendship with both Shaw and Cockerell for over twenty-five years. Whitemore's play is based upon the letters and writings of the three friends.

Betrayal. Play. Harold Pinter
M2 (40s) F1(30s). Extra 1M. Various simple settings. Fee code M

Jerry is a literary agent; Emma runs an art gallery; Robert is a publisher. Emma and Robert are married and Jerry is Robert's best friend, but Emma and Jerry have had a seven-year affair. The play opens with Emma and Jerry meeting for lunch in 1977, two years after the affair has finished and by a brilliant device the relationship of the three is traced backwards nine years to the evening when it all began. First presented at the National Theatre in 1978.

Beulah. Play. James Robson
M4 (teenage, 40, 67, 70) F6 (40s, 60s). A living-room. Fee code M

Dad and Mam Ling live in sheltered accommodation in a Yorkshire town. Dad is nearing death, and so the family congregate to see him through his final days. Displayed on the wall of the living-room is a picture of 'Beulah', the farm which the Lings worked for many years. As Dad's health diminishes, he remembers his happy times as a Dalesman, and his children are reminded of their youth at 'Beulah'.
ISBN 0 573 01726 3

Beyond a Joke. Comedy. Derek Benfield
M4 (young, 50) F4 (20, 40s, 50). A drawing-room and a garden. Fee code L

Six times fatalities have occurred in Jane and Andrew's country house. When daughter Sally's new young man, Geoff, arrives for the weekend he mistakenly gets the idea that the occurrences were due to something more sinister than 'accident'. When a visiting vicar passes peacefully away in the garden Andrew and Jane try to remove the body. Events are further confused by the unexpected arrival of Geoff's parents who are unaware that the body has been stowed in their car boot!
ISBN 0 573 11027 1

Beyond Reasonable Doubt. Play. Jeffrey Archer
M11 F3. The Central Criminal Court, a London house. Fee code M

Accused of the wilful murder of his terminally ill wife, Sir David Metcalf finds himself locked in legal combat with his old rival, Anthony Blair-Booth QC. After a tense and gripping courtroom scene, Act I ends just as we are about to hear the jury's verdict. Act II takes us back in time to the fateful night of Lady Metcalfe's death and ends with a surprising twist. This play enjoyed a successful run in London's West End, with Frank Finlay and Wendy Craig in the leading roles. 'I loved it ... it's much more than a courtroom drama. It's a compelling love story and it's got the lot — laughter, tears and tension ...' *TV-am*.
ISBN 0 573 01676 3

Beyond Therapy. Comedy. Christopher Durang
M4 (30) F2 (29, middle-age). Various interiors, may be simply suggested. Fee code M

Prudence's therapist is urging her to be more assertive; while Bruce's therapist urges him to meet someone of the opposite sex by placing a personal ad, not realizing that Bruce has a male lover named Bob. Having met each other Bruce doesn't know how to handle nervous Prudence; and Prudence doesn't know what to make of decidedly unpredictable Bruce. How they sort it all out is the story of this delightful comedy. '*Beyond Therapy* offers the best therapy of all: guaranteed laughter.' *Time*

Big Bad Mouse. Farce. Philip King and Falkland Cary. From an idea by Ivan Butler
M3 (19, 40, 50) F4 (18, 50). An office. Fee code M

In the Orders Office of Chunkibix Ltd, it is Mr Price-Hargreaves who gives the orders and Mr Bloome who obeys them. Until, that is, Mr Bloome is one day accused of chasing a young female person across Wandsworth Common making him the hero of every woman and girl in the office not least Miss Spencer. So glorious is Bloome's transformation, in fact, that when the young person in question discovers she has made a mistake in her identification, Bloome is the reverse of pleased, and determines to keep her quiet.
ISBN 0 573 01532 5

Billy Liar. Comedy. Keith Waterhouse and Willis Hall
M3 (19, 50s) F5 (17-19, 40s, 80s). A composite set. Fee code M

Less than dedicated to his job as undertaker's clerk, bored with his North Country family background, Billy Fisher takes refuge in his own invented world. For Billy, an energetic imagination makes life tolerable but well-nigh intolerable for all around him. He lies his way into and out of every situation, producing any explanation and making any promise that will extricate him from his present predicament, and thereby creating ever more tortuous entanglements for the immediate future.
ISBN 0 573 11142 1

Biloxi Blues. Comedy. Neil Simon
M7 (18-20) F2. Various interior and exterior settings. Fee code M

This sequel to *Brighton Beach Memoirs* won the 1985 Tony Award for Best Play and received its British première at the Library Theatre, Manchester, in 1991. When we last met Eugene, he was coping with adolescence in the 1930s in Brooklyn. Now it is 1943 and the saga of Eugene Morris Jerome, *alter ego* of the youthful Neil Simon, continues with him as a young army recruit during the Second World War. 'Joyous and unexpectedly rewarding.' *New York Times*
ISBN 0 573 69040 5

A Bird in the Hand. Comedy. Derek Benfield
M4 (37, 40s, 50) F6 (18, 30, 40s). A flat. Fee code K

When Sylvia returns only twenty-four hours after walking out, her husband Max isn't exactly overjoyed. Nor is three times divorced Harry who has set the wheels in motion to recapture the romantic successes of their youthful days of bachelorhood and it's too late to stop the young ladies arriving! Sylvia watches with much amusement as her hapless husband tries, and fails, to appreciate the delights of freedom and finally decides that the bonds of matrimony are preferable.

◆ **Birdy**. Play. Naomi Wallace, based on the novel by William Wharton
M6 (16,17, 21, 22, 50). Various simple settings. Fee code M

Naomi Wallace has skilfully transformed William Wharton's novel into a compelling, intimate piece of theatre. This is the journey of Birdy and his friend Al who are seen both as young men in Philadelphia in the years just before World War Two and as wounded soldiers bearing the mental and physical scars of war. Period 1930s, 1946 '… ingeniously conveys the essence of the book's attraction.' *Evening Standard*

The Birthday Party. Play. Harold Pinter
M4 (35, 50, 65) F2 (25, 65). A living-room. Fee code M

Goldberg and McCann arrive at a seaside boarding house where Meg and Petey live with their guest Stanley. They inquire about Stanley: we soon find out that McCann and Goldberg have a job to do. Learning it is his birthday they give Stanley a party at which Stanley is verbally bludgeoned into submission. The next day Stanley is removed. It is the collective impact of the dialogue which welds the seemingly inexplicable actions of Goldberg and McCann into a menacing whole. ISBN 0 573 01042 0

Birthday Suite. Comedy. Robin Hawdon
M3 (30, 40) F2 (30). Two adjoining hotel rooms. Fee code M

Geoff Tippet has arranged a special birthday treat for his old friend, Bob. The treat is a hotel room for the night, a double-bed which folds up into the wall and an attractive girl called Mimi. Add a shy Kate who anxiously awaits her computer agency date — Dick, who has been shown into the wrong room; Bob's wife Liz, who believes she is dining with Geoff, and a connecting door between the two rooms and you have the recipe for a fast-moving and hilarious comedy.
ISBN 0 573 11509 5

◆ **Biting the Bullet**. Play. Frank Vickery
M2 (late 20s, 55) F3 (young, middle-age, 58). A living-room. Fee code M

Ted, undergoing a mid-life crisis, leaves the house he and home-loving wife Beryl have shared for thirty-two years. At first Beryl is shattered, but gradually works back from the edge of despair, helped by her exuberant daughter Angie and down-to-earth neighbour Dawn. A holiday abroad, a complete make-over — not to mention a platonic friendship with the young handyman, who gives her new ways of looking at life — rescue her from the nightmare of separation.
ISBN 0 573 01920 7

Bitter Sanctuary. Play. Rosemary Anne Sisson
M2 (30s) F5 (20s-40) 1 boy (12) 1 girl (9). A refugee camp hut. Fee code L

Stefan and Tanya are determined to prevent themselves and their children from sinking into degradation. In their cramped, bare space in a displaced persons' camp, they try to create a home, to teach their children, and above all, to retain their dignity. Emigration and escape is their only hope, thus Tanya's greatest sacrifice must be to send her husband and children away to Australia even though she is barred from the country by having TB. This is a play that can inspire great affection and love, not just for itself, but for the whole human condition. Period 1960s
ISBN 0 573 01514 7

Black Coffee. Play. Agatha Christie
M10 (30s, 60s) F3 (20s, 50s). A library. Fee code M

Lucia, wife of Sir Claude Amory's son Richard, Dr Carelli and Barbara are all having coffee when Sir Claude announces that a new explosive formula has been stolen from his safe and that he has sent for Hercule Poirot. To enable the thief to replace the formula he orders the lights to be turned out but when they are switched on again and as Poirot enters, Sir Claude is found poisoned. Poirot sets about his investigation, foils the murderer in a second attempt and cleverly tricks him into betraying himself.
ISBN 0 573 61885 2

Black Snow. Play. Keith Dewhurst, adapted from the novel by Mikhail Bulgakov
Large cast may be played by M10 F5 with extras. Various interior settings. Fee code M

This bitingly funny adaptation of Bulgakov's modern Russian classic novel of 1936 was premièred at the Royal National's Cottesloe Theatre in 1991. Set between 1924 and 1925 it is an hilarious send-up of Stanislavsky's famous 'Method' and the acting profession in general and was based on fact — the mutilation of Bulgakov's play *Molière*, for which Bulgakov blamed Stanislavsky. '... the funniest and cleverest new play I have seen for a very long time.' *Financial Times*

Black Widow. Play. Paul Thain
M4 (any age, 30s, 60s) F6 (teens, 30s-60s). Doubling possible. A bare stage. Fee code M

Lord Arlington is dead, poisoned by a corned beef sandwich. His daughter Emily, obsessed by *Hamlet*, becomes convinced that her mother Cressida and old family friend Richard Harker are responsible for Lord Arlington's death, and she sets out to exact a terrible revenge. Madness, murder, passion, ghosts and retribution are all themes of this complex and compelling drama, set in the Edwardian era but with a very modern sensibility.
ISBN 0 573 01727 1

Blithe Spirit. Improbable Farce. Noël Coward
M2 (40, middle-age) F5 (young, 45, middle-age). A living-room. Fee code M

Charles Condomine, whose first wife Elvira has been dead for seven years, has been reasonably happy with his second wife Ruth. After he invites Madame Arcati, a local medium, to conduct a seance at their home, Elvira returns from the dead. Determined to get Charles to herself forever, she arranges several 'accidents', one of which culminates in Ruth joining Elvira. Now plagued by *two* jealous squabbling spirits, Charles bids them both farewell and his two wives are left petulantly tearing the house apart.
ISBN 0 573 01044 7

♦ **Blood Money**. Thriller. The Heather Brothers
M1 (40s) F3 (20s-40s). 1F extra. 1M 2F voices only. A lounge. Fee code M

Seven years ago, Mike Mason, star of TV's 'Bargain Basement', and his wife Liz killed young Carol Mitchell in a hit-and-run car accident — and now it seems they have at last been found out. A mysterious telephone caller claims to be Carol Mitchell and her name appears in blood on the wall; Liz is certain she has been followed; then a car draws up outside the house and shots soon ring out ...
ISBN 0 573 01753 0

Blood Sweat and Tears. Play. John Godber
M2 (30s, 40s) F3 (20s). Composite set on 2 levels: a burger bar, a judo hall. Fee code M

Louise Underwood's life revolves around the hamburger restaurant where she works, and a night club: then she discovers judo. This inspiring play charts Louise's progress to Black Belt. Her personal journey involves numerous sacrifices, crises of confidence and battles with more experienced players who think she has no chance of success. A play about the opportunities given to ordinary people to be something special.
ISBN 0 573 01725 5

Blood Wedding. Play. Federico García Lorca. Translated by Gwynne Edwards
M9 F11. Various simple settings. Fee code M

A young couple from rival clans plans to marry, much to the distress of the bridegroom's mother whose husband and other son have previously been murdered through clan rivalry. As the wedding day draws nearer the tension mounts and after the bride meets and elopes with former lover Leonardo, who is also married, the bridegroom's mother is caught in a dilemma of conscience, wondering whether she should cry for vengeance and bloodshed or protect the life of her remaining son. In a violent ambush Leonardo and the bridegroom are killed leaving the bridegroom's mother, the bride and Leonardo's wife united in their grief.

Bloody Poetry. Play. Howard Brenton
M3 (20-30s) F3 (18-20s). A bare stage. Fee code M

Staged to critical acclaim in both New York and London, first at the Hampstead Theatre in 1984 and subsequently in a revival at the Royal Court Theatre in 1988, this is a portrayal of the lives of Shelley, Mary Shelley and Claire Clairemont. Set between the summers of 1816 and 1822 the play opens with their flight from England to Switzerland and Italy where, for the first time, they encounter Lord Byron.

♦ **Blue Heart**
A double bill by Caryl Churchill. M2 F7, with doubling. Child extras. Fee code M as a double bill. For separate fee codes see below

Two related short plays, both teasingly entertaining and brilliantly executed, one about a father and daughter, the other about a mother and son. In *Heart's Desire*, a family await the return of their daughter after a long sojourn in Australia. In *Blue Kettle* a middle-aged man and his girlfriend are involved in a con trick, making elderly women believe they are the man's long-lost mother. But neither play is what it seems. Something catastrophic is happening which disrupts and destroys them.

Heart's Desire
M2 F4 with doubling. Child extras. A kitchen. Fee code E if performed separately

Blue Kettle
M2 F6. Various simple settings. Fee code E if performed separately

◆ **Blue Murder**. Double bill. Peter Nichols
M5 F2. FOREIGN BODIES: composite set: a study, a sitting-room A GAME OF SOLDIERS: an elegant room. Fee code M

Subtitled 'a play or two', Blue Murder opens with *Foreign Bodies*, where Swinging London meets bourgeois Shrewsbury in 1963 and the drinks are laced with cyanide. The second half, *A Game of Soldiers*, is a Whitehall farce taking place in St James's Palace. A dramatist has brought his completed play to be censored but the Lord Chamberlain's Men have a few shameful secrets of their own ... Period 1963 and 1967

Blue Remembered Hills. Play. Dennis Potter
M5 F2. Composite setting: wood, field, barn. Fee code M

This apparently simple tale relates the activities of seven-year-olds on a summer afternoon during World War II. The children (all played by adult actors) and their world become a microcosm of adult interaction. Willie tags along as burly Peter bullies Raymond and is challenged by fair-minded John. Audrey is over-shadowed by Angela's prettiness and wreaks her angry frustrations on the boys. All of them gang up on the terrified 'Donald Duck' who, abused by his mother and ridiculed by his peers, plays his own dangerous game of pyromania which ends in tragedy.
ISBN 0 573 01699 2

Bold Girls. Play. Rona Munro
F4 (young, middle-age). A kitchen, a night club, a hilltop. Fee code M

The dramas of everyday life in Belfast are but off-stage events in this stirring play about the lives of three women whose men have been killed or imprisoned for their political activities, but where bread must still be bought between explosions. In spite of its chilling theme there are many humorous and heart-warming moments — a play about people, not politics, which offers excellent acting opportunities. Rona Munro received the *Evening Standard* Most Promising Playwright Award for 1991 for *Bold Girls*.
ISBN 0 573 13006 X

Bonaventure. Play. Charlotte Hastings
M3 (young, 35, 40) F8 (20-50, elderly). Two interiors. Fee code M

A flood in the Fen country has trapped two prison officials and their prisoner, Sarat Carn, who is on her way to the gallows for the murder of her brother. In spite of the evidence, Sister Mary Bonaventure is certain of Sarat's innocence. She uncovers a hitherto unknown connection between Sarat's friend Dr Jeffries and a woman for whose death Sarat's brother had been responsible. Just before the police launch arrives, a confession is forced from the real murderer. Period 1950s
ISBN 0 573 01046 3

Bone-Chiller. Comedic Mystery-Thriller. Monk Ferris
M5 (20s, 30s, elderly) F8 (18, 20s, 30s, middle-age). Can also be M4 F9, or M6 F7. A parlour/
library. Fee code M

On Friday the 13th, thirteen people gather for the reading of the late Josiah Travers's will. The will
consists of a rebus which offers the lucrative estate to *anyone* who can solve the puzzle. To make
things tougher, the lights keep going out and people keep being murdered. This is not only a very
funny farce, it is also a superbly-crafted mystery.
ISBN 0 573 61985 9

♦ **Borders of Paradise**. Play. Sharman Macdonald
M5 (young) F2 (young). A beach. Fee code M

Ellen and Rose have arrived from Scotland and set up their tent on a Devonshire cliff top. Down
on the beach Rob, David, Charlie, Cot and John are enjoying a surfing break. A touching and
humorous piece with seven excellent roles for young actors. 'No-one writes about the mysteries
of young adulthood with more truth … combines warm and funny naturalism with an appropriate
touch of the mystic.' *The Times*

Born in the Gardens. Play. Peter Nichols
M2 (45, 50) F2 (35, 70s). A living-room. Fee code M

Maud, a decidedly eccentric woman, lives in a dilapidated mock-Tudor Victorian house with her
son Mo. The other children, Hedley, an ineffectual Labour MP, and Queenie, an expatriate in
America, arrive and try to persuade Maud to go to a modern 'duplex' in London, and Mo to join
Queenie in California, but both prefer to remain as they are. Not all of us, Mo says, 'want freedom.
Captivity has its points as well.'
ISBN 0 573 11045 X

Bottom's Dream. Play. Alan Poole
M8 F6. Children: M or F5. Various simple settings on an open stage. Fee code K

Who dreamt the Midsummer Night's Dream? What were the reactions of the Artisans' relatives to
their play-acting activities? The author considers the play from the point of Bottom — and the
women as members of the audience. Bottom and his wife are discovered settling down for the
night — as twelve o'clock strikes, Bottom dreams a 'most rare vision'. All the Artisan scenes are
preserved intact — but here the women also have their say.
ISBN 0 573 12026 9

The Boys in the Band. Play. Mart Crowley
M9 (20s-30s, 1 Black). An apartment. Fee code M

Michael, a homosexual, has invited a number of friends to his birthday party. A 'straight' friend of
his, Alan, rings up and wants to see him. Though anxious about the outcome, Michael agrees to
his joining them. Alan's presence acts as a catalyst to the emotions — never far from the surface
— of those at the party. The result is a mixture of bitter humour and physical violence. Alan goes,
leaving behind him the debris of the party.
ISBN 0 573 64004 1

The Break of Day. Play. Timberlake Wertenbaker
M8 (20, 40s, 80, old) F5 (20s, 40) (with doubling). Various simple settings. Fee code M

Tess, Nina and April are old friends reunited one hot summer weekend to celebrate Tess's fortieth birthday. With their partners in tow, a feeling of dissatisfaction and unease seizes the group. Is it too late to have children? Were they wrong to focus so much on work? The second act finds Tess and Robert resorting to the fertility industry to conceive, while Nina and Hugh become embroiled in the corrupt bureaucracy of an East European country as they try to adopt a baby.

Breaking the Code. Play. Hugh Whitemore, based on the book *Alan Turing: The Enigma* by Alan Hodges
M7 (17, 20s, 40s, 60s) F2 (20s-50s, 60s). An open space. Fee code M

This compassionate play is the story of Alan Turing, who broke the code in two ways: he cracked the German Enigma code during World War II (for which he was decorated by Churchill) and also shattered the English code of sexual discretion with his homosexuality (for which he was arrested on a charge of gross indecency). Whitemore's play, shifting back and forth in time, seeks to find a connection between the two events.
ISBN 0 573 01656 9

Breaking the Silence. Play. Stephen Poliakoff
M5 (teenage, 20s-50s) F2 (30s, 40s). A railway carriage. Fee code M

Stephen Poliakoff's intriguing and moving play is inspired by his own family's experience in Russia. Father spends his time (and government money) in trying to record sound on to film. With the death of Lenin, however, the research must be abandoned and the family is forced to flee. The play follows the material and spiritual adjustments the upper-middle-class Pesiakoff family have to make when forced to live for years in a railway carriage.
ISBN 0 573 01617 8

Breaking the String. Play. Frank Vickery
M2 (20s, middle-age) F2 (20s, middle-age). A sitting-room. Fee code L

To add to her own and her family's problems, Iris nurtures an intensely possessive love for her only child, Simon. Simon comes home, accompanied by a girlfriend, Deryn, and Iris's joy quickly turns to jealousy and suspicion. Confronted with an increasingly difficult situation Simon finally announces that he and Deryn are married and expecting a baby. Iris cannot be reconciled to the news and the play closes with Iris alone, her world shattered, unable to acknowledge her own folly.
ISBN 0 573 01728 X

Breath of Spring. Comedy. Peter Coke
M3 (young, middle-age, elderly) F5 (20s, middle-age). A living-room. Fee code M

Dame Beatrice houses a collection of middle-aged 'guests', plus Lily her maid. To repay Dame Beatrice for giving her a job despite her criminal past, Lily presents her with a mink stole filched from the next flat. The Brigadier deploys his 'troops' to return the fur. The whole campaign is so invigorating that they decide to retain this excitement in their lives by pinching furs and giving the proceeds to charities.
ISBN 0 573 01053 6

Breezeblock Park. Play. Willy Russell
M5 (young, middle-age) F4 (young, middle-age). Two split-level sets: living-room and kitchen. Fee code M

Three married couples, 'superior' council-house dwellers, regard themselves as a close-knit family, a team, despite their generally concealed jealousies. When one of their daughters, Sandra, announces she is pregnant and intends to live unmarried with her student lover, Tim, the news explodes like an atom bomb. Tim himself is unhappy about the arrangement and tries to make Sandra realize she now has responsibilities, but she walks out on them all.
ISBN 0 573 11051 4

Brezhnev's Children. Play. Olwen Wymark, based on the novel *The Women's Decameron* by Julia Vozneskaya
M3 (40s) F7 (20s-40s). A maternity ward. Fee code M

It is International Women's Day in Moscow, 1985. Isolated in a run-down maternity hospital ward seven women tell their own violent and disturbing stories of rape, abuse and oppression. Despite the depressing nature of these stories, however, the enormous strength, vitality and humour of the women comes through. Finally overcoming the patriarchal, authoritative hospital system, their escape is set against the wider background of Gorbachev coming to power in this moving play.
ISBN 0 573 01729 8

The Bride and the Bachelor. Farcical Comedy. Ronald Millar
M3 (32, middle-age, 50s) F5 (16, 24, 40s, 50). A lounge hall. Fee code H

On the eve of her wedding, Serena Kilpatrick is having cold feet. Among her wedding presents is a magic bowl which can bring aid to a distressed bride. The aid turns out to be Sir William Benedick Barlow, lately dead, but earthbound until he can soothe a troubled bride. He discovers that Serena, abandoned as a baby, is really his own daughter, while her mother arrives from Heaven to settle matters.
ISBN 0 573 01054 4

Brideshead Revisited. Play. Evelyn Waugh, adapted for the stage by Roger Parsley
M14 (late teens, 20s, middle-age) F8 (late teens, middle-age, elderly). M4 F3 with doubling. Characters age over 20 years. Various simple settings. Fee code M

This portrait of the interweaving relationships and fortunes of a desperately charming, if eccentric, aristocratic family and their influences upon Charles Ryder has been faithfully adapted for the stage, preserving all the sharp wit and candid social commentary of Waugh's narrative. Period 1943, and in flashback to the 1920s. (**Availability restricted**)
ISBN 0 573 01730 1

Brief Lives. John Aubrey. Adapted for the stage by Patrick Garland
M1 (71), M and F voices only. A Jacobean chamber. Fee code M. Typescript on hire

John Aubrey (1626-97) has come to be recognized as England's first serious biographer. Patrick Garland's adaptation of Aubrey's writings represents a day in the latter part of Aubrey's life. 'It is as if one is paying a visit to the house of an old man, who makes up for the absence of friends by bringing to life reminiscences of people, remembering them and telling stories about them.'

A

Brighton Beach Memoirs. Play. Neil Simon
M3 (teenage, 40) F4 (teenage, 30s, 40s). Various interior and exterior settings. Fee code M

This portrait of the writer as a Brooklyn teenager in 1937, living with his family in crowded, lower-middle-class circumstances, was first presented in London at the National Theatre in 1986. Eugene (the young Neil Simon) is the narrator and central character. The play's scenes consist of a few days in the life of a struggling Jewish household, of whom two have heart disease, one has asthma and two at least temporarily lose jobs needed to keep the straitened family afloat. It is a deeply appealing play that deftly mixes drama with comedy.
ISBN 0 573 61941 7

Brimstone and Treacle. Play. Dennis Potter
M2 (young, middle-age) F2 (young, middle-age). A living-room. Fee code M

A clever and highly controversial play about the intrusion of a slick, satanic young man into the lives of a humdrum couple whose only deviation from the appalling norm to which they steadfastly adhere is that they have an attractive only daughter, reduced to a vegetable after a car accident. 'Dennis Potter is a mass of contradictions as a writer and in *Brimstone and Treacle* ... we see all his paradoxical drives coming fruitfully together.' *Guardian*
ISBN 0 573 01626 7

♦ **Britannicus.** Play. Racine. A new version by Robert David Macdonald
M3 F3. Extras. A room. Fee code M

In his great neo-classical plays, Jean Racine reached the peak of sophistication in French tragedy. *Britannicus* addresses power and politics with the action centring essentially on the politics seething within the young Emperor Nero's Court. Yet the play is as much about his mother, Aggripina, losing her hold on power as Nero turns against her. Although Racine does not draw a direct parallel with Louis XIV's Court, he regards those in power with an all-seeing, but not forgiving eye. Period: Ancient Rome

Broadway Bound. Play. Neil Simon
M4 (20s, 50, 75) F2 (50s). 2M 1F, voices only. Split set representing a house. Fee code M

Forming the third part of the famous Neil Simon autobiographical trilogy, this charming play about youthful ambition and parental regret is set in late 1940s Brooklyn. While their parents go through various conflicts which will ultimately end in divorce, Eugene and his brother Stanley struggle to become professional comedy writers. When a sketch based on their family life gets a radio broadcast it upsets the family but Eugene and Stan are now Broadway bound.
ISBN 0 573 69053 7

♦ **Brothers of the Brush**. Play. Jimmy Murphy
M4 (30, 40, 60) A basement room. Fee code M

Jimmy Murphy's 'subtle unsentimental lament for the working class' (*Irish Times*) tells how housepainters, patching over the cracks of an old house, misuse each other for their own advantage. In a world blighted by economic recession, with workers losing faith in old ideologies, this award-winning play demonstrates just how fragile allegiances are when personal interests are at stake. 'There is a new and remarkably realistic voice on the scene with the arrival of Jimmy Murphy ...' *Sunday Independent*

Brush with a Body. Play. Maurice McLoughlin
M5 (22, 30s, 50s) F6 (17-20s, 50s, 60s). A morning-room. Fee code K

In Sybil Walling's absence her children call in the chimney-sweep, whose brushes dislodge not only soot but a body. When Sybil returns she tells them that, just before he died twenty years ago, their father had killed a Soho gangster and had hidden the body in the chimney. The police descend in pursuit of an amorous patient of Sybil's son Henry, which leads to hilarious misunderstandings and surprises.
ISBN 0 573 01058 5

Building Blocks. Play. Bob Larbey
M5 (young, 30s, 40s-50s) F1 (30s). A garden. Fee code M

Jim and Mary Baxter are in the middle of one of life's major traumas — they are having an extension built on to their house. A great deal of their time is taken up with negotiating with the builder, the charming but evasive David. By turns hilarious and touching, this well-observed comedy will bring smiles and groans of recognition to all those who have ever been involved in this situation — and a few rueful warnings to those who have not!
ISBN 0 573 11086 7

♦ **Bums on Seats**. Comedy. Michael Snelgrove
M6 (20s, 40s-60s, any age) F10 (20s-40s, any age) can be played by M3 F6 with doubling. Extras. A stage, an auditorium

In a tatty provincial theatre, a new play, *Fecund*, is being staged. *Bums on Seats* introduces us to everyone involved in the production: in a series of hilarious scenes, linked by a chorus of usherettes, we meet the stage manager, the leading actors, the lecherous, unscrupulous author, and others. In the second act, set in the auditorium, attention focuses on the audience, an equally mixed and unharmonious group.
ISBN 0 573 01756 5

The Business of Murder. Play. Richard Harris
M2 (40s) F1 (20s). A first-floor flat. Fee code M

A psychological thriller on the theme of revenge centres on the interlocking triangular relationship between Dee, a successful TV playwright, Hallett, a detective superintendent and Stone, 'a humourless, rather prissy man', *The Business of Murder* had a very successful West End run. 'How refreshing to welcome that rarity of the West End: a well-written, skilfully crafted tale of mystery and suspense that pays dividends from start to finish.' *Sunday Express*
ISBN 0 573 11017 4

Busybody. Comedy. Jack Popplewell
M4 (young, 30s-50s) F4 (19, 30s, 48). An office. Fee code M

Detective Superintendent Harry Baxter is plagued by two busybodies — a corpse that vanishes and the officious office cleaner, Mrs Piper, who finds it. Motives for murder abound — all the office staff and the corpse's wife are suspect. His self-control snaps completely when the corpse himself walks in alive and well. But Mrs Piper still insists that there was a body, and it is she who finally identifies both corpse and murderer and actually obtains a confession.
ISBN 0 573 01515 5

A

Butley. Play. Simon Gray
M4 (young, 20s, 30s) F3 (young, 30s, 40s). A university lecturer's study. Fee code M

This play concerns a university lecturer, Ben Butley, who shares his office and his flat with a former star pupil, Joey, now also a teacher. On the day when the play takes place Butley faces both the ultimate breakdown of his marriage and of his intense friendship with Joey. Butley's painful discoveries are made against a background of petty university politics and unease about student dissent. He greets them with a blistering torrent of repartee and rhetoric.

Butterflies Are Free. Comedy. Leonard Gershe
M2 (young, 20s) F2 (19, middle-age). A one-room apartment. Fee code M

Don, a young bachelor in his first apartment, is escaping from an overprotective mother; his next-door neighbour is an actress who offers true friendship. We are well in to the play when we discover, with the actress, that Don is blind. Mother does not like the girl and succeeds in breaking up the match, but then realizes how demoralized her son is. Eventually the neighbour returns and the young people can together face up to life.
ISBN 0 573 60644 7

California Suite. Comedy. Neil Simon
M2 (40s) plus M3. F2 (30s, 40s) plus F3. A hotel suite. Fee code M

This four-part play is Neil Simon at his best. In *Chicago* two couples go on vacation together, but wind up miserable and hating each other. *London* concerns a British star who returns from the Academy Awards ceremony without an Oscar. *Philadelphia* is about a wife who arrives at the hotel suite before her husband can get rid of the drunken hooker in his bed. In *New York* a magazine writer is visited by her ex-husband.
ISBN 0 573 60664 1

Camille. Play. Pam Gems
M13 F6, a boy, M1(voice only), a pianist. Extras. Interior and exterior settings. Fee code M

Beautiful Marguerite Gautier, seduced at the age of fifteen by her Marquis employer, decides on a courtesan life. She meets Armand Duval, son of the Marquis, and the two fall desperately in love. Aware that she is in the initial stages of tuberculosis, Armand persuades her to settle in the country with him, but Marguerite is threatened by the Marquis and forced to return to Paris, dying and reviled by Armand. Period 1840s Paris
ISBN 0 573 01634 8

Camino Real. Play. Tennessee Williams
M21 F7. Extras. A plaza in a walled city. Fee code M

Aptly described both as an 'expressionist phantasmagoria' and 'an apocalyptic vision of the contemporary world', the play is set in a walled town in a police state from which various characters try to escape. Among the fictional people are famous literary and historical characters such as Don Quixote, Marguerite Gautier, Casanova and the mythical American Kilroy who 'was here'; they converse with one another in cryptic and soulful conversation in the midst of various extraordinary events happening around them.

Can You Hear Me at the Back? Play. Brian Clark
M3 (17, 40s) F2 (30s, 40s). A living-room, other small sets. Fee code M

Philip Turner, chief architect of Feltonly New Town, is disillusioned in the realization of what he has destroyed in planning and developing the town's sterile, inhuman tower and office blocks. He decides to plan nothing at all, to opt for spontaneity even in his private life. Margery, wife of his old friend, is willing to become his mistress, but Philip demurs. 'Can't you see you are just as ruthlessly planning spontaneity?' says his wife.

Candleford. Play. Keith Dewhurst, from the book by Flora Thompson
M12 F6, with doubling. An open stage. Fee code M. (In a volume with *Lark Rise*)

A sequel to *Lark Rise*, *Candleford* is also performed with audience and players freely mingling, re-enacting a meeting of the local hunt in mid-winter. It concentrates on events in the Oxfordshire village where Flora Thompson worked in the post office-cum-blacksmith, includes music and song, and ends with a flash forward to her own unhappy married life, after which Company and audience perform the Grand Circle Dance. Period 1880s
ISBN 0 573 10011 X

Canterbury Tales. Chaucer made modern by Phil Woods. Music by Chris Barnes
Large cast may be played by M7 F5. An open space. The music is available on hire from Samuel French Ltd. Fee code M (play), B (music)

Phil Woods has updated Chaucer to recreate for a modern audience the spectacle, humour and bawdiness of the fourteenth-century original. Set in the present the tales are told in the form of an annual 'Geoffrey Chaucer Canterbury Tales-telling Competition', with the audience invited on stage between tales. 'Colourful, boozy, good-spirited, compelling entertainment.' *Stage and Television Today*

◆ **Caramba's Revenge**. Play. William Norfolk
M1 (late 30s) F6 (20, late 60s, 70s). A living-room. Fee code L

A highly entertaining and ingenious black comedy. Four elderly ladies have been sharing their lives in Violet's rented house, pooling their pension books and sharing chores. After a mugging Violet dies, but Marge, Lottie and Doris omit to tell the authorities and leave Violet's body peacefully in the cemetery. However, Violet's granddaughter, Ronnie, arrives from Australia in search of her relative ...
ISBN 0 573 01771 9

◆ **Caravan**. Play. Helen Blakeman
M2 (20, 50) F3 (15, 19, 45) A caravan park. Fee code M

Fifteen-year-old Kim brings twenty-year-old Mick back to the family caravan where he rapes her and leaves her pregnant. Her older sister Kelly falls for the same man, and rushes into marriage when she too becomes pregnant, only to miscarry. The girls' widowed mother, Josie, is involved with striking docker, Bruce. Whilst Bruce faces redundancy, Mick seizes the job opportunity and is labelled a 'scab'. Lives and loves become increasingly entangled in this desperate search for a place to go. Period 1994-1996
0 573 01770 0

A

Cards on the Table. Play. Dramatized by Leslie Darbon from the novel by Agatha Christie M7 (30s-50s) F7 (20s, 30s, middle-age, 63) or M5 F7, with doubling. Two drawing-rooms, a surgery, a patio, a flat. Fee code M

A dramatization, first presented at London's Vaudeville Theatre starring Gordon Jackson and Margaret Courtenay, of a classic Agatha Christie tale of murder and mystery, involving a wealthy collector, four murderers and two crime specialists, Superintendent Battle of the Yard and Mrs Oliver the novelist.
ISBN 0 573 11540 0

The Caretaker. Play. Harold Pinter
M3 (25, 35, old). A shabby room. Fee code M

Into his derelict household shrine Aston brings Davies, a tramp — but a tramp with pretensions, even if to the world he may be a pathetic old creature. All that is left of his past now is the existence in Sidcup of some papers, papers that will prove exactly who he is and enable him to start again. Aston, too, has his dreams: he has always been good with his hands and there is so much to do in the house. Aston's hopes are tied to his flash brother Mick's; he has aspirations to live in a luxurious apartment. Human nature is a great spoiler of plans, however ...
ISBN 0 573 04002 8

Carving a Statue. Play. Graham Greene
M3 (teenage, middle-age, elderly) F2 (young). A studio. Fee code M

An untalented sculptor, Father has spent many years working on an enormous statue of God the Father, modelling the face on that of his own parent. Meanwhile life goes on at the base of the statue. He is looked after by his teenage son who becomes briefly involved with a sexy young girl, later seduced by the father. The son then brings a gentle deaf and dumb girl to the studio with tragic consequences.

◆ **Cash on Delivery**. Farce. Michael Cooney
M6 F4. A living-room. Fee code M

Michael Cooney's riotous farce has all the ingredients for rib-tickling hilarity and offers a colourful selection of character roles. Eric Swan (aided by his Uncle George and unbeknown to his wife, Linda) has pocketed thousands of pounds through fraudulent DSS claims. When Norman Bassett (the lodger) opens the door to Mr Jenkins, the DSS Inspector, deceptive mayhem follows — as do the undertaker, bereavement counsellor, psychiatrist, Norman's fiancée, a corpse, the ominous *Ms* Cowper and a rather rebellious washing-machine!
ISBN 0 573 01752 2

Cat Among the Pigeons. Farce. Georges Feydeau. Translated by John Mortimer
M13 F7. A drawing-room, a bedroom, an apartment. Fee code M

Feydeau's lady this time has two lovers: a ne'er-do-well who has secretly affianced himself to a baroness's daughter, and a flamboyant Spanish general who challenges anyone who comes near her. Complications arrive with an amateur composer of a bad song which he hopes the lady will sing in the theatre ... This translation was presented at Wyndham's Theatre. 'A triumph of ingenuity, gaiety, absurdity and laughter.' *Daily Telegraph*. Period early 1900s
ISBN 0 573 60683 8

The Cat and the Canary. Melodrama. John Willard by arrangement with Alan P. Twyman for the Rohauer Collection
M6 (30s, old) F4 (young, old, Black). A library, a room. Fee code J

The family of Ambrose West attend a reading of his will at midnight. Mr West feared that a touch of insanity ran in his family. Annabelle West is made sole heir of his estate, but if there is any indication of insanity another will should be opened and a different heir named. From then on the family attempts to frighten Annabelle, by murders, tales of lunatics and the like. One of the most successful of mystery melodramas.
ISBN 0 573 60684 6

Cat on a Hot Tin Roof. Play. Tennessee Williams
M7 (young, 60, 2 Black) F3 (young, 60). 2 small girls. Extras. A bedsitting-room. Fee code M

This award-winning play is set in a Mississippi plantation house where the family celebrate Big Daddy's birthday. '... a stunning drama ... It is the quintessence of life. It is the basic truth ... The tone is gay. But the mood is sombre. For a number of old evils poison the gaiety — sins of the past, greedy hopes for the future, a desperate eagerness not to believe in the truths that surround them ...' *New York Times*

Cat on the Fiddle. Farce. John Dole
M6 (20s, middle-age) F5 (young, middle-age). A living-room. Fee code H

As David's Italian penpal, Mario, is coming to stay, his wife Kate goes to her mother's so that they can practise their languages in peace. When the penpal turns out to be a shapely brunette named Maria David is in big trouble, not least because Maria has smuggled in a packet of diamonds. The flat is soon besieged with assorted gangsters, a lady plumber, a curate, the police and an angry Kate!
ISBN 0 573 11538 9

The Caucasian Chalk Circle. Play. Bertolt Brecht
Translations: W. H. Auden and James and Tania Stern
Ralph Manheim, music by Dessau
Eric Bentley, music by Durrent
John Holstrom, music by Griffiths
M38 F11 with doubling possible. Various simple settings. Fee code M (for play), code C (for music)

In this adaptation of an old Chinese legend, a cruel town governor is murdered. His wife escapes but abandons her baby, who is harboured by a kitchen-maid, Grusha. Later the governor's widow returns and a trial is ordered with the test: which woman can drag the child out of a chalk circle? In refusing to harm the child by pulling it, Grusha is ruled to be the 'true' mother. Period 1945

Caught on the Hop. Comedy. Derek Benfield. *Revised version*
M4 (30s, middle-age) F4 (20s, 37, middle-age). A sitting-room and patio. Fee code L

When Phil tells his friend George that he is leaving his wife, Maggie, to move in immediately with a girl he met on the top of a bus, George is appalled. However, George is persuaded to give a helping hand — thus setting in motion the most frenetic confusion of mistaken identities, plotting and counterplotting that ever erupted on one quiet summer's day.
ISBN 0 573 11066 2

Cause Célèbre. Play. Terence Rattigan
M15 (young, 18, middle-age, elderly) F5 (40, middle-age). 1 boy (9). Composite setting. Fee code M

When Alma Rattenbury, attractive wife of an elderly man, engages the handsome but uncouth Wood as odd-job boy it has tragic consequences, culminating in murder. The story follows the course of the trial, and also the lasting effect on a woman member of the jury. The play, first presented in London at Her Majesty's Theatre, was partly inspired by the facts of a well-known case. Period 1934-5
ISBN 0 573 11059 X

Cavalcade. Play. Noël Coward
M12 F16. 4 children. Extras. (Some of the characters age during the thirty-year span of the play.) Various interior and exterior settings. Fee code M

Written before the Second World War, this is the story of a family and a nation, with a message of faith in the future. Its grand procession of time and events opens with bells ringing in the twentieth century as the Marryots drink a toast to the year 1900 and follows the family and friends over the next thirty years, mingling their private ups and downs with more public events.

Celebration. Comedy. Keith Waterhouse and Willis Hall
M7 (19, 20s, 40s, middle-age) F7 (19, 20s, middle-age). A large room above a pub. Fee code M.
If performed separately *The Wedding* and *The Funeral* are each fee code F

The Wedding and *The Funeral* make up the two parts of this comedy in which we are introduced to the same family, first making preparations for a wedding and subsequently, six months later, returning from the funeral of their Uncle Arthur, a lovable personality who provides the link between the two plays.
ISBN 0 573 11251 7

The Cemetery Club. Play. Ivan Menchell
M1 (late 50s-early 60s) F4 (late 50s- early 60s). A living-room, a cemetery. Fee code M

Ida, Lucille and Doris are part of a club — the cemetery club. Every month they meet at Ida's New York house for tea, then trundle off to the cemetery to remember the good times and gossip with their late husbands. Sam, a butcher, meets the widows at the cemetery while he is visiting his wife's grave and changes their lives forever. This touching play about three superannuated, feuding Jewish women is funny, wise and gloriously witty.

The Chalk Garden. Play. Enid Bagnold
M2 (elderly) F7 (16, 40s, middle-age, elderly). A living-room. Fee code M

The chalk garden which totally defeats Mrs St Maugham's attempts to cultivate it is symbolic of her failure with her daughter and her granddaughter. Then Miss Madrigal, a hired companion, takes charge. 'We eavesdrop on a group of thorough-bred minds, expressing themselves in speech of an exquisite candour, building ornamental bridges of metaphor, tiptoeing across frail causeways of simile, and vaulting over gorges impassable to the rational soul.' Kenneth Tynan, *Observer*
ISBN 0 573 01064 1

Chance Visitor. Play. Aleksei Arbuzov, translated by Ariadne Nicolaeff
M2 (27, 45) F7 (20s-55, 70). A veranda/garden, an open-air restaurant, a roadside. Fee code M
ISBN 0 573 01623 2

The Charlatan. Play. William Norfolk
M4 (40, 50s) F4 (18, 50). Composite setting: a coffee house, a study, a parlour. Fee code M

Maria-Theresa Paradies is sent to Doctor Mesmer to cure her blindness. Mesmer's treatment is based on what he terms 'animal-magnetism'. Maria is asked to stay in his house for the duration of the treatment. Inevitably gossip follows and the treatment ends in scandal. Maria returns to her parents' home and resumes her career as a blind pianist while most of Vienna is convinced that Mesmer is nothing more than a charlatan. Period 1777 Vienna
ISBN 0 573 01731 X

Charley's Aunt. Farce. Brandon Thomas
M6 (20s, 40s, 51) F4 (young, middle-age). Two interiors, one exterior. No fee

This classic evergreen farce is set in Oxford during Commemoration Week in 1882. The imminent visit of Charles Wykeham's aunt from Brazil, Donna Lucia, provides an excuse for Charles and Jack to invite their young ladies to meet her. When a telegram arrives postponing Donna Lucia's visit, they persuade their amiable friend Babbs (since they must have a chaperone) to impersonate the aunt — and the fun begins.
ISBN 0 573 01067 6

Chase Me Up Farndale Avenue, S'Il Vous Plaît! Comedy. David McGillivray and Walter Zerlin Jnr
M1 F4 (late 20s, 40s-50s). Two adjoining rooms. Fee code K

Le farce français est arrivée! Bubbling comme une glasse de champagne, ces femmes formidables et leur chef d'étage, Gordon, fizz leur way avec panache entre un plot unintelligible, un plethora de portes, et un grand range de characteurs. Oo-la-la, le show-stopping moment de Thelma ... mais pour dire quelque chose else would spoilé le surprise — ah quelle surprise! — Vive les dames de Farndale Avenue Housing Estate Townswomen's Guild Dramatic Society!
ISBN 0 573 01732 8

Chasing the Moment. Play. Jack Shepherd
M4 (young, 1 Black, middle-age, old) F2 (young, 1 Black). A basement club. Fee code M

This could be the last gig for Les Padmore and his jazz band. Wes, the founder of the club, is on life-support and there are rifts between the players. Les looks back to a golden age of jazz and is suspicious of the younger, more progressive band members, who are all are seeking a balance to the chaos of their lives. This is a gritty play, full of wry philosophy.

Checkmate. Play. Leslie Sands
M3 (40s, middle-age) F2 (20s, 40s). 1F voice only. 1 extra. A living-room. Fee code M

Subtitled *A Play on Murder*, this is a witty and theatrical thriller. The career of famous TV actor Peter Conway is in the doldrums, his financial state is parlous, he has a drink problem and his long-suffering wife Stella has had enough. Secretly, he has been having an affair with Lori, an American actress, and Stella's death brings the police to his up-market London home. It looks an open and shut case but is what we see real or unreal?
ISBN 0 573 69481 8

A

The Cherry Orchard. Play. Anton Chekhov, translated by Michael Frayn
M9 (young, 20s, middle-age, 87) F5 (17, middle-age). A nursery, a drawing-room, open fields.
Fee code M

This translation of Chekhov's last and most elusive play was originally produced at the Naonal
Theatre in 1978, with Dorothy Tutin, Albert Finney, Robert Stephens and Ralph Richardson.
Michael Frayn revised this edition for the 1989 production at the Aldwych Theatre, with Judi
Dench, Ronald Pickup, Bernard Hill and Michael Gough. 'Frayn's translation, which strikes me
as splendidly lucid and alive ... will be acted again and again.' *New Statesman*

The Cherry Orchard. Play. Anton Chekhov, adapted by David Mamet
M9 F5. A nursery, a drawing-room, open fields. Fee code M

The Cherry Orchard is the story of a mortgage, with the grounds and beautiful trees of the proud
landowners going for sale at a public auction to pay off their debts to the boorish son of a peasant
who has risen in the world. Mme Ranevskaya's family departs to take up their lives anew, leaving
the old and forgotten Firs to die alone as the woodsmen's axes thud ironically against the cherished
trees.

Children of a Lesser God. Play. Mark Medoff
M3 (20s, 30s-40s) F4 (late teens, mid-20s, 30-40s). Various simple interior and exterior settings.
Fee code M

James joins a school for the deaf to teach lip-reading and meets the spirited Sarah, totally deaf
from birth and estranged from the world of hearing and from those who would compromise to
enter it. James tries to help Sarah, but gradually the two fall in love and marry. Discord develops
as Sarah militates for the rights of the deaf, but love and compassion hold the hope of reconciliation.

Children's Day. Play. Keith Waterhouse and Willis Hall
M3 (30s, 40s) F4 (19, youngish, 30s). A kitchen. Fee code M

A hectic children's birthday party provides a noisy background to a series of domestic crises.
Robin has left Emma and Emma has become friendly with her solicitor, Tom; both Tom and
Robin arrive for the celebrations. The mishaps of the party spill over into the kitchen situation, the
behaviour of the young visitors affecting the adults. By the end of the party however, things look
a little brighter for Robin and Emma.
ISBN 0 573 01561 9

A Child's Christmas in Wales. Christmas musical. Jeremy Brooks and Adrian Mitchell. Based
on the poem by Dylan Thomas
M15 F7. Extras. Various simple settings. Fee code M

This enchanting play with music uses a variety of carols and well-known Welsh songs to conjure
up the pure magic of Christmas for the enjoyment of an audience of all ages. The main course of
events takes place on Christmas Eve itself, when the Thomas family are host to their relatives.
Apart from a potentially major hiccup, when the turkey catches fire, the traditional Yuletide
celebrations are enjoyed by all.

Chinchilla. Play. Robert David MacDonald
M11 F5. Simple settings. Fee code M

Subtitled *Figures in a Classical Landscape with Ruins*, this takes us into the world of the Ballet Russe. On holiday in Venice, the impresario, Chinchilla, is longing for both love and money amid the backstage drama of dancers, choreographers, designers and hangers-on. Autocratic, splendid and world-weary, he is the creator and destroyer of what happens on his stage and to his company. The play is divided into scenes marked 'Present' (taking place on a single afternoon in June 1914) 'Past' and 'Future'.

The Choice. Play. Claire Luckham
M2 (30, 50s) F3 (30s, late 40s). A space. Fee code M

The choice is whether or not to abort a foetus after an amniocentesis test reveals that the unborn child has a chromosome deficiency. Sal, a journalist in her thirties, is the mother, and she must make the most difficult decision of her life in the midst of the conflicting opinions of those around her. Sally's story is framed within Claire Luckham's own personal tale — she grew up with a handicapped brother.

A Chorus of Disapproval. Play. Alan Ayckbourn
M7 (young, 30s-late 50s) F6 (young, 30s-50s). Extras. Various simple settings. Fee code M

Alan Ayckbourn skilfully draws parallels between John Gay's *The Beggar's Opera* and the day-to-day activities of the amateur dramatic society who are performing it, showing how painfully embarrassed are the British in the face of emotion and keeping us laughing in happy recognition. *A Chorus of Disapproval* played very successfully at the National Theatre in 1985. '... symmetrically shaped, psychologically acute and painfully, heartbreakingly funny ...' *Guardian*
ISBN 0 573 01620 8

A Christmas Carol. Play. Adapted by John Mortimer from the story by Charles Dickens.
Large mixed cast, doubling possible. Various simple settings. Fee code M

Charles Dickens' famous tale of Ebenezer Scrooge's transformation from embittered skinflint to generous benefactor has been dramatized by John Mortimer with typical flair and wit in this definitive adaptation, first performed by the Royal Shakespeare Company. Retaining Dickens' own ironic point of view through the use of a Chorus, Mortimer has created a panoramic view of Victorian London with all the much-loved characters in place. There is plenty of scope for imaginative doubling, and the staging requirements are flexible.
ISBN 0 573 01733 6

A Christmas Carol. Christmas Play. Adapted by Shaun Sutton from the story by Charles Dickens.
M24 F15. Three interiors, one exterior. Fee code K

This adaptation follows its well-loved original in tracing Scrooge's conversion from miserliness to benevolence. We first see him in the counting house berating his unfortunate clerk Bob Cratchit and then receiving the visitations of the Spirits of Past, Present and Future. He learns to feel compassion for Tiny Tim and remorse for his avarice. Some scenes are introduced that elaborate a Christmas play into a simple form of pantomime. Period early Victorian
ISBN 0 573 01070 6

A

Cider with Rosie. Laurie Lee. Adapted for the stage by James Roose-Evans
24 roles, may be played by M5 F4. Various simple settings. Fee code M

Poet Laurie Lee was born in 1914 in a small Cotswold village and grew up during a time of change when the rural traditions of past centuries were being swept aside in the path of twentieth-century progress. His autobiography *Cider with Rosie*, a poetic evocation of his childhood, has become a modern classic both in the United Kingdom and in America and is here imaginatively adapted for the stage by James Roose-Evans.
ISBN 0 573 01735 2

The Circle. Comedy. W. Somerset Maugham
M6 (young, 35, 60s, elderly) F3 (20s, 40, 50s). A drawing-room. Fee code M

Arnold Champion-Cheney has never forgotten or ceased to resent his mother's elopement. He is a politician with a beautiful young wife — Elizabeth — in whom he has a proprietory pride. Home from their long exile come his mother, Lady Kitty, and her lover. With Arnold's father living nearby, the visit seems fraught with embarrassment, but instead becomes extremely amusing ...
Period 1920s
ISBN 0 573 01071 4

City Sugar. Play. Stephen Poliakoff
M4 (17, young, 30s, middle-age) F3 (young). A sound studio, a supermarket, a bedroom. Fee code M

Leonard, a disc jockey, is becoming increasingly disgusted with the soul-destroying falsity of his job as he manipulates the fantasies of his teenage listeners. He tries to force Nicola, a contestant in an imbecilic competition, into a realization of the stupidity of the whole set-up. Nicola's fantasy world is shattered. Our last glimpse of her hints at the viciousness in which the inducement of such false dreams may result.
ISBN 0 573 11072 7

Class Enemy. Play. Nigel Williams
M7 (16, older). A schoolroom. Fee code M

In a decrepit, thoroughly vandalized, South London schoolroom a group of foul-mouthed boys are awaiting the arrival of a teacher who never seems likely to appear. A sort of tribal ritual is self-imposed by the group, forming a natural hierarchy, and events culminate in a fierce fight which is interrupted by the arrival of a master.
NB. The play contains explicit language.

Clerical Errors. Comedy. Georgina Reid
M3 (16, 30, 50) F5 (17, 27, middle-age, 65). A disused Methodist Chapel. Fee code L

James Martin's moral upbringing is suddenly shattered by the encampment of the Briggs family in his now disused Methodist chapel. Uncharacteristically, James decides to try their way of life by moving in with them. However, his attempts to solve the Briggs' problems have unexpected and often hilarious results! Young Julie Briggs' honest, if unconventional, appraisal of James' congregation forces him to reconsider his own career. A highly entertaining comedy, rich with comic pathos.
ISBN 0 573 01608 9

Clocks and Whistles. Play. Samuel Adamson
M3 (25, late 40s-early 50s) F2 (26, late 30s). Various simple settings. Fee code M

Henry watches. He watches Anne — who is helped or hindered by the older man in her life, the enigmatic Alec — as she tries to make it as an actor. And he watches Trevor, who hangs out in seedy clubs and his flat in Paddington, as he tries to make it as a poet. As the lives of the three interlock, they drift into a world of sexual and emotional confusion.

Close the Coalhouse Door. Musical Documentary. Alan Plater
M8 F2. Extras. Composite set. Fee code M

'A hymn of unqualified praise to the miners — a group of men who forged a revolutionary weapon without having revolutionary intent.' A golden wedding party of an old pitman and his wife forms a springboard into reminiscence and reflection about the past. Originally written for the Newcastle Playhouse this play is one of the outstanding documentary musicals to emerge from the regional theatre in recent years.

Close to the Wind. Play. Richard Everett
M3 (young, middle-age, elderly) F3 (young, middle-age, elderly). A living-room. Fee code M
ISBN 0 573 11082 4

Clothes for a Summer Hotel. Ghost Play. Tennessee Williams
M9-13 F7–14, doubling possible. An asylum. Fee code M

The play opens in an asylum where Zelda Fitzgerald is being treated for mental disorder. Her husband, Scott, visits her, and this leads to a series of flashbacks in which details of their lives, in particular those concerning Zelda's attempts to achieve self-expression, are enacted.

Cloud Nine. Play. Caryl Churchill
M4 F3. A veranda, a hut interior. Fee code M

Written for Joint Stock, this theatre company's workshop for the play was 'sexual politics', thus giving Caryl Churchill the idea for her parallel between colonial and sexual oppression. Act I takes place in Victorian Africa, whilst Act II is set in modern London. Much interplay is made of gender and colour: for example, Clive, the white settler, has a black servant, Joshua, who is played by a white because he wants to be what the whites want him to be. Hilarious and thought-provoking. ISBN 0 573 01668 2

Clouds. Play. Michael Frayn
M4 (30s, middle-age) F1 (30s). An open stage. Fee code M

The place is Cuba where two English journalists, Owen and Mara, find themselves on a fact-finding mission, researching a story for rival colour supplements. The play is a travel sketchbook of sharp and entertaining caricatures; the title is a metaphor for the characters who appear from nowhere, coalesce, form themselves into weird and extravagant shapes, drift and disappear. ISBN 0 573 11083 2

The Cocktail Hour. Comedy. A. R. Gurney
M2 (40s, 70s) F2 (40s, 60s). A living-room. Fee code M

With a mixture of gentle comic poignancy and dramatic tension, one of America's leading contemporary playwrights here examines the problems which arise when John, a leading playwright, returns home to ask his parents' permission to produce his latest work, a play about his family. *The Cocktail Hour* had a long and successful run in New York and successful tours in both the UK and Australia.
ISBN 0 573 01736 0

Cold Comfort Farm. Play. Paul Doust, adapted from the novel by Stella Gibbons
M9 (20s, middle-age) F6 (20s, middle-age, 60), doubling possible. Extras. A kitchen, an attic room, a garden. Fee code M

Orphan Flora Poste, heroine of Gibbons's tongue-in-cheek classic novel, likes everything to be tidy and comfortable so when she goes to live with her eccentric relatives at Cold Comfort Farm she tries to alter her surroundings and encourage others to greater things. But this proves difficult ... Period 1930s. 'Paul Doust's new adaptation embraces the book with a stylistic exuberance.' *Financial Times*
ISBN 0 573 01737 9

Collaborators. Play. John Mortimer
M2 (30s, age uncertain) F2 (young, 30s). A living-room. Fee code K. Period 1950s
ISBN 0 573 01558 9

Come As You Are. Four Playlets. John Mortimer
M2 F2 or M8 F7. A bedroom, a living-room, a basement apartment, a flat. Fee code M

The characters in all four plays are in their twenties to forties and can either be played by the same four artists or by separate casts. The first, *Mill Hill*, calls for 2 Men and 1 Woman, the remainder, *Bermondsey*, *Gloucester Road* and *Marble Arch*, call for 2 Men and 2 Women each. These four plays are linked by their themes of sexual entanglements and by their central or suburban London settings.
ISBN 0 573 01052 8

◆ **Come Back for Light Refreshments After the Service**. Play. Julie Day
M1 (any age) F5 (19, mid 30s, 40s, early 70s) Various simple interior and exterior settings. Fee code G

Beth is in the kitchen preparing food for her father's wake — real sandwiches, cakes, etc., that the audience are invited to partake of as they become the visiting mourners. After nursing her father for five years before he died, she plans to sell the house and go back-packing despite the disapproval of others. This play about relationships and understanding garnered rave reviews and an Edinburgh Fringe Award for excellence.
ISBN 0 573 60130 5

Come Back to the 5 & Dime, Jimmy Dean, Jimmy Dean. Comedy-drama. Ed Graczyck
M1 (17) F8 (17, 30s, middle-age). A five-and-dime store in Texas. Fee code M

In a small-town dime store in West Texas, the Disciples of James Dean, now middle-aged, gather for their twentieth reunion. The ladies' reminiscences mingle with flash-backs to their youth; then the arrival of a momentarily unrecognized woman sets off a series of upsetting and revelatory confrontations. The action takes place in 1975 and, in recall, 1955.
ISBN 0 573 60764 8

Come Blow Your Horn. Comedy. Neil Simon
M3 (21, 33, 60) F4 (20s-50s). A bachelor apartment. Fee code M

Harry Baker should be a happy man, but his sons are a daily trial. Alan is a playboy with a penchant for beautiful girls and now Buddy, formerly so timid and obedient, has joined his brother in dissipation, unsuccessfully experimenting with the fair sex while his parents become more mystified and irate. Alan suddenly redeems himself by settling down, and Buddy, having learned how to handle women, determines to take over Alan's role as the family playboy.
ISBN 0 573 60713 3

Comedians. Play. Trevor Griffiths
M11 (20 -50s, middle-age). A classroom. Fee code M

The setting is a schoolroom near Manchester where an evening class of budding comics congregate for a final briefing from their tutor before facing an agent's man from London. Telling jokes for money offers an escape from the building site or the milk round. But the humour is a deadly serious business that also involves anger, pain and truth. How and why are laughter engineered? What dark secrets within us trigger mirthful responses to shaped remarks about sex, ethnic groups and physical disabilities?

◆ **Comfort and Joy**. Comedy. Mike Harding
M6 (20s, 50s, elderly, 70s) F6 (late 20s-early 30s, 50s, elderly) or M5 F5 with doubling. A front room. Fee code M

It's Christmas. Relatives you hardly ever see and who are now very different from you arrive at your house for the festivities. No-one receives a present that is at all appropriate. Culinary disasters abound. Long-buried resentments rear their ugly heads as the alcohol flows and tongues are loosened. *Comfort and Joy,* Mike Harding's comedy, is painfully — but always amusingly — familiar.
ISBN 0 573 01772 7

The Common Pursuit. Play. Simon Gray
M5 F1 (all young, ageing 15 years). Various interior settings. Fee code M

A very English modern play, reeking of real tragedy, real humour and real life. *The Common Pursuit* chronicles the erosion of the ambitions of a smug, elitist group of Cambridge friends. Stuart is editor of a literary magazine and the pursuit of excellence is shown to be economically a bad proposition in this world. The magazine collapses and the characters' fates vary as the play proceeds. An ironic epilogue returns to the early days in Cambridge with the young people planning their futures.
ISBN 0 573 01696 8

Communicating Doors. Comedy. Alan Ayckbourn
M3 (30s-70) F3 (25-45). A hotel suite. Fee code M

An ingenious time-warp comedy which begins in the year 2014 when a prostitute, Poopay, is summoned to a deluxe London hotel suite by an infirm elderly businessman to witness a document detailing the murder of his two wives by his psychopathic business associate. Poopay finds herself in the year 1994 confronting Ruella, the second wife, and when Ruella finds herself in 1974 with the first wife she decides to rewrite the future!
ISBN 0 573 01740 9

Confusions. Five interlinked one-act plays. Alan Ayckbourn
M3 F2 (minimum cast). A living-room, a bar, a restaurant, a marquee, a park. Fee code M

These five short plays deal riotously, but with sharply pointed undertones, with the human dilemma of loneliness; a mother unable to escape from baby talk (*Mother Figure*), a disastrous fête (*Gosforth's Fête*), an unsuccessful seduction attempt (*Drinking Companion*), a fraught dinner encounter (*Between Mouthfuls*) and the final play, *A Talk In The Park*, sums up, with five self-immolated characters on park benches.
ISBN 0 573 11073 5

Conjugal Rites. Play. Roger Hall
M1 (late 40s) F1 (mid 40s). A bedroom. Fee code M

A middle-aged couple, Barry and Gen, are celebrating their twenty-first anniversary — in bed. It begins amiably enough — it's a time for reflection and celebration, after all. But the rewards of middle-aged married life are doubtful, and gradually, the picture darkens as they confront the spectres of death, physical decline and adultery that surround them. (*Restricted availability*)

The Constant Wife. Comedy. W. Somerset Maugham
M4 (40s) F5 (30s, 40, elderly). A drawing-room. Fee code M

When Mortimer Durham storms into the Middletons' home revealing that Constance's husband is having an affair with his wife, Constance refuses to create a scene. A year later, and financially independent, Constance feels entitled to sexual independence. She announces that she will, as John has done, take a short revivifying break by having a holiday with an early admirer, leaving John first outraged and then appreciative of his remarkable wife.
ISBN 0 573 01077 3

The Continental Quilt. Farce. Joan Greening
M4 (middle-age) F6 (22, 30s, 45). A living-room. Fee code K

Mike is looking forward to a pleasant stay with girlfriend Gloria. Scarcely has the curtain risen than a ring of the doorbell shatters his plans — his brother Dick seeking help after being thrown out by his wife, Marion, following her discovery of him in the bedroom with his neighbour Angela. There follows the most hectic evening of Mike's life and an even more hectic morning as he tries to sort everything out.
ISBN 0 573 11057 3

Coriolanus. Play. Bertolt Brecht. Translated by Ralph Manheim
M11 F3. Extras. Numerous settings on an open stage. Fee code M

Brecht writes of his adaptation of Shakespeare's tragedy, 'I don't believe the new approach to the problem would have prevented Shakespeare from writing a *Coriolanus*. I believe he would have taken the spirit of our time into account as much as we have done, with less conviction no doubt, but with more talent.' He follows the framework and shape of the play very closely, but adapts the general slant to his own purpose of commenting on the modern world.

The Corn Is Green. Play. Emlyn Williams
M10 (12-16, 40s) F5 (14, 30s-middle-age). Extras. A living-room. Fee code M

Miss Moffat settles in a remote Welsh mining village and starts a school for the local boys, one of whom, Morgan Evans, shows great promise. Miss Moffat determines to do everything to help Morgan's application for a scholarship to Oxford. But Morgan rebels against help from a woman and falls prey to the flashy charms of Bessie Watty. His chances of success are almost destroyed but Miss Moffat's courageous wisdom and her affection for him win the day and Morgan wins the scholarship. Period late nineteenth century

Corpse! Comedy thriller. Gerald Moon
M4 (middle-age) F1 (middle-age). A basement flat, an elegant flat. Fee code M

Evelyn, an out-of-work actor, engages Powell, with a shady past, to do away with his suave, sophisticated, moneyed twin. As with most 'fool-proof' plans things do not go as they should and people are not what they seem. *Corpse!* is not so much a whodunit as a whodunit to whom! 'If *The Mousetrap* is the thriller for the fifties; *Sleuth* for the sixties; *Deathtrap* for the seventies; *Corpse!* is surely the thriller for the eighties...' *Los Angeles Times*. Period 1936
ISBN 0 573 11014 X

Corpsing. Four one-act plays. Peter Barnes
M6 (20s-30s, elderly) F3 (20s-30s, elderly). Various simple settings. Fee code M

This collection of plays — three duologues and one three-hander — on a strong theatrical theme, may be presented individually (see the separate listings in Section B) or in one programme as a complete evening's entertainment under the title *Corpsing*. Together they encapsulate Peter Barnes' consummate skill of contrasting opposites and simultanously combining 'the absurdly tragic and the tragically absurd'.
ISBN 0 573 10006 3

Count Dracula. Play based on Bram Stoker's novel *Dracula*. Ted Tiller
M7 (young, 50) F2 (young, 40). Living quarters and crypt of an asylum for the insane. Fee code M

This is a new witty version of the classic story of a suave vampire whose passion is sinking his teeth into the throats of beautiful young women. There are many surprising but uncomplicated stage effects (full details are given) including secret panels, howling wolves, bats that fly over the audience, and Dracula vanishing in full view of the audience.
ISBN 0 573 60729 X

Court in the Act! Farce. Maurice Hennequin and Pierre Veber, translated and adapted by Robert Cogo-Fawcett and Braham Murray
M7 F5, with doubling. Extras. A drawing-room, an office, an hotel foyer. Fee code M

A

First performed at the Royal Exchange Theatre, Manchester, this brilliant, hilarious adaptation of the classic French farce went on to enjoy a successful run at London's Phoenix Theatre in 1987. No man can resist Mademoiselle Vobette, from a provincial Judge to the Minister of Justice himself and from her arrival in the backwoods town of Gray, Hennequin and Veber spin a series of seductions, cover-ups and mistaken identities which catch the characters well and truly in the act!

The Cracked Pot. Play. Blake Morrison. Translated and adapted from Heinrich von Kleist's *Der Zerbrochene Krug*
M5 F4. A courtroom. Fee code M

The Cracked Pot is more than a translation of Heinrich von Kleist's *Der Zerbrochene Krug*, as the action now takes place in Skipton, Yorkshire, in 1810, with Kleist's German verse transformed into tough Yorkshire dialect. Funny, earthy and satirical, the play concerns Judge Adam, Skipton's sole agent of justice, who is far from happy to be visited by the investigating magistrate Walter Clegg, seeking out signs of malpractice.
ISBN 0 573 01734 4

Cracks. Play. Martin Sherman
M5 (20s-40s) F4 (17, late 20s, 42). Composite setting: a living-room, study and garden. Fee code M

California, 1973. Rick, a musician and dancer, is shot dead. Was it Gideon, his drug-happy co-performer? Maggie, his older lover, an actress? Roberta, Rick's transsexual bodyguard? Or one of the other oddball guests? As Rick's friends investigate one murder follows another ... no-one is safe! With a host of hilarious, way-out characters, outspoken dialogue and a mystery that keeps the audience guessing until the last minute, *Cracks* is a truly entertaining *adult* comedy.
ISBN 0 573 11089 1

Crimes of the Heart. Comedy. Beth Henley
M2 (30) F4 (20s, 30). A kitchen. Fee code M

Three sisters have gathered in their small Mississippi hometown awaiting news of their grandfather who is dying in a local hospital; Lenny, unmarried, Meg, a failed singer and Babe, on bail having shot her husband. Their troubles, which are grave yet somehow hilarious, are highlighted by their cousin Chick, Doc Porter and Babe's lawyer who is trying to keep her out of jail while waging a personal vendetta against her husband. But the play ends on a joyful note with the three sisters re-united celebrating Lenny's birthday.

◆ **The Cripple of Inishmaan**. Play. Martin McDonagh
M5 F4. Various simple interior and exterior settings. Fee code M

Set on a remote island off the west coast of Ireland in 1934, this is a strange comic tale in the great tradition of Irish storytelling. As word arrives on Inishmaan that the Hollywood director Robert Flaherty is coming to the neighbouring island of Inishmore to film 'Man of Aran', the one person who wants to be in the film more than anybody is young Cripple Billy, if only to break away from the bitter tedium of his daily life.

The Crucifer of Blood. Play. Paul Giovanni, based on characters created by Sir Arthur Conan Doyle
M10 (20, 30, 50, black pygmy) F1, with doubling. Three exterior, two interior settings. Fee code M

A Sherlock Holmes pastiche based mainly on *The Sign of Four*, though with some fundamental differences (the lady in the case proves to be far from Dr Watson's true love), and bringing in elements from other stories. The action starts in India with the theft of the Agra Treasure, moves forward thirty years to deal with the exciting events resulting from the crime and concludes with a tantalizing hint of one of Watson's most famous unwritten adventures — 'The Giant Rat of Sumatra'. Period 1857 and 1887
ISBN 0 573 60757 5

Crystal Clear. Play devised by Phil Young in collaboration with Anthony Allen, Diana Barrett, Philomena McDonagh
M1(30) F2 (30). A flat. Fee code M

When Richard, who is partially sighted, meets blind Thomasina and subsequently loses the sight of his other eye, he and Thomasina are forced to confront the basic question of how successfully two blind people can live in a world made for the sighted. This beautiful and moving play enjoyed a successful run at Wyndham's Theatre in 1983, and won Phil Young *The Standard's* Drama Award for Most Promising Playwright (1983).
ISBN 0 573 11521 4

Cuckoo. Play. Emlyn Williams
M3 (30, 49) F4 (20, 35, 50). A living-room, a veranda. Fee code M

Spoiled and cossetted over the years by her devoted mother, Cuckoo's future is thrown into crisis by the death of Mam. But it's not just Cuckoo's future which then becomes doubtful — what of sister Lydia's plans to marry wealthy Jerome, and those of her aunt Madam, and the physically disabled Uncle Powell? First produced at Guildford with Rosemary Leach in the title role, this absorbing and touching play reveals the hidden depths in the woman who has always been treated as a child. '... there is plenty of cosy humour to give (it) charm ... very actable...' *Daily Telegraph*. Period 1935
ISBN 0 573 01649 6

The Curse of the Werewolf. Play. Ken Hill. Songs by Ian Armit and Ken Hill
M9 F3, 1 child, with doubling. Composite setting. Fee code L

Dr Bancroft has brought his wife, daughter Kitty and butler d'Arcy to visit a medical school chum, Steiner, at Walpurgisdorf Castle. Strange things happen when the moon is full — men change into werewolves. Then it transpires that Steiner is carrying out experiments on the various inmates of the castle, turning them into werewolves. His plan to mate Kitty and Martin to produce a natural werewolf is foiled by the return from the forest of the other male members of the party.
ISBN 0 573 11062 X

♦ **Curtain Up on Murder**. Thriller. Bettine Manktelow
M3 (35, 40, elderly) F5 (18, 20, 28, 40, 50s). A stage. Fee code L

An amateur drama company is rehearsing in the theatre at the end of the pier. Storms rage overhead and the doors are locked — they are trapped! Then a mysterious, ghostly presence passes across the stage, and when the Assistant Stage Manager falls to certain death through a trapdoor, the remaining actors are thrown into disarray. Their panic increases when one of the actresses is poisoned and it becomes evident that a murderer is in their midst ...
ISBN 0 573 01769 7

A

Curtains. Play. Stephen Bill
M3 (30, 48, 63) F5 (43, 50s, 70, 86). A living-room. Fee code M

It is Ida's eighty-sixth birthday — a milestone she would rather not have reached. Her family has gathered to celebrate with a birthday tea. After tea is cleared the family disperse leaving Katherine remembering a pact she made with Ida not to let her suffer into old age. She helps her out of her misery and into the next world. Returning to find a mercy-killer in the house the family proceed to reveal a panorama of English mores at their hilarious worst. This triple award-winning play was presented at London's Whitehall Theatre.
ISBN 0 573 01686 0

Curtmantle. Play. Christopher Fry
M24 F7. Extras, doubling possible. Various simple settings. Fee code M

The stage is William Marshal's mind, as though he were remembering King Henry's life. Though it follows chronologically it is not a chronicle play; its form is one of memory and contemplation. It adds up to no more than a sketch of Henry — whose character covers a vast field of human nature, as the thirty-five years of his reign contains a concentration of the human condition. Period 12th century

♦ **Cut and Run**. Comedy. Peter Horsler
M4 F5. A doctor's surgery. Fee code L

The young, altruistic Dr Glow is perturbed when his National Health Clinic is hired out to Dr Boxclever, a private consultant who extorts outrageous fees from his patients by prescribing unnecessary treatments and useless medicines. Boxclever persuades Dr Glow to impersonate an eminent specialist and so begins a slide into malpractice. The denouement, though, is not as straightforward as it would appear for, by another twist of the plot, all ends happily. This is an hilarious comedy painting large the dangers in private health care.
ISBN 0 573 01768 9

♦ **Cyrano de Bergerac**. Comedy. Edmond Rostand. Translated by Christopher Fry
Large cast. Various interior and exterior settings. Fee code M

Rostand's hero has become a figure of theatrical legend: Cyrano, with the nose of a clown and the soul of a poet, is by turns comic and sad, as reckless in love as in war, and never at a loss for words. Audiences immediately took him to their hearts, and since its triumphant opening night the play has never lost its appeal. Christopher Fry's acclaimed translation into 'chiming couplets' represents the homage of one verse dramatist to another. Period: 1640-1655

Da. Play. Hugh Leonard
M5 F3. A kitchen, hall and neutral areas. Fee code M

Charlie returns to his Dublin home to attend his father's funeral. As he is sorting out papers after the ceremony he is suddenly confronted by Da's very solid ghost. Thenceforward the play moves between past and present, between reality and imagination as passages in Charlie's life are enacted. Finally Charlie's very real warmth and regard for the old man shine through the dramas, confrontations and badinage, as the play leaves the two of them — the living and 'dead' — together.
ISBN 0 573 11065 4

Daisy Pulls It Off. Comedy. Denise Deegan
M2 F14, may be played by M2 F11. Extras. A school. Fee code M

Daisy Pulls it Off is about the attempts of Daisy Meredith to find acceptance in the snobby confines of Grangewood School for Young Ladies. After undergoing a number of tribulations all comes right in the end with Daisy saving the lives of her arch-enemies, discovering the treasure of Grangewood, scoring the winning goal at hockey and finding her long-lost father! This witty comedy enjoyed a long and very successful run in the West End at the Globe Theatre. Period 1927
ISBN 0 573 11117 0

The Dame of Sark. Play. William Douglas Home
M7 (young, middle-age, 50) F2 (50, middle-age). A drawing-room. Fee code M. Period Second World War.
ISBN 0 573 11093 X

Dancing at Lughnasa. Play. Brian Friel
M3 (30s, 53) F5 (26, 30s). Composite set: a kitchen and garden. Fee code M

Premièred at Dublin's Abbey Theatre, this multi-award-winning play is about five impoverished spinster sisters in a remote part of County Donegal in 1936. With them live Michael, seven-year-old son of the youngest sister, and Jack, the sisters' elder brother, a missionary priest newly returned from Africa. The events of that summer are narrated in recall by the adult Michael, unfolding a tender study of these women's lives.
ISBN 0 573 01742 5

Dangerous Corner. Drama. J. B. Priestley
M3 (25-40) F4 (20, 47). A drawing-room. Fee code M

Robert Caplan and his wife are entertaining her brother and sister-in-law. Because Robert insists on uncovering the truth about his brother Martin's 'suicide', many unpalatable revelations ensue which cause Robert to shoot himself. At this point, the opening scene is repeated, but this time they bypass the dangerous corner at which the truth is demanded, thus averting the disaster. Written in 1932 this forms one of the three 'time plays'.
ISBN 0 573 01088 9

Dangerous Obsession. Play. N. J. Crisp
M2 (30, 40) F1(20). A conservatory. Fee code M

John Barrett appears at the home of Sally and Mark Driscoll. It emerges that Barrett is 'dangerously obsessed' with pinning the blame for his wife's accident on someone. Barrett strips away the conflicting facets of the Driscolls' lives. As suddenly as he entered Barrett slips away leaving behind shattered faith, broken trust and a marriage that will never heal. This play had a very successful run in the West End starring Dinsdale Landen, Carol Drinkwater and Jeremy Bulloch.
ISBN 0 573 01682 8

The Dark Is Light Enough. Play. Christopher Fry
M13 F3. A room and a great staircase, stables. Fee code M

This verse play dramatizes an imaginary incident during the Hungarian Revolution of 1848-9. The elderly, kind Countess Rosmarin Ostenburg's daughter's former husband is a lazy Hungarian officer who alone seems impervious to the Countess's charm. As the play closes the Austrians are hammering at the door. He turns to escape but seeing the Countess dying turns to stand by her body as the knocking of the Austrians grows louder.

Dark Lucy. Play. Philip King and Parnell Bradbury
M3 (38, 50, 60) F4 (30, 47, 65). A vicarage living-room, a cottage living-room. Fee code J

When Carol, the highly-strung ex-actress wife of the Vicar, complains hysterically that she has been assaulted by 'Dark Lucy' — an unpleasant old village woman who lives in a dirty broken-down cottage — the doctor is inclined to put it down to hallucinations and she is believed by nobody. But when another young girl disappears Carol decides to investigate what goes on in the the old cottage. What she discovers exceeds her wildest nightmares.
ISBN 0 573 01110 9

♦ **The Dark River.** Play. Rodney Ackland
M5 F3 1 boy. A room in an old house. Fee code M

It is 1937; there are warning signs of World War Two. Catherine Lisle, recently divorced and with her hopes of a dancing career dashed, moves into the house of her old school-teacher. Like nearly everyone else in the house, Catherine is attempting to evade the present by living entirely in the past, and is hopelessly torn between her infantile ex-husband Chris and her lover Alan, who is passionately aware of the dangerous political situation surrounding them.

The Darling Buds of May. Comedy. H. E. Bates
M5 (15, 24, 40s, middle-age, 60) F6 (17, 19, 37, 45). 1 boy, 4 girls. A kitchen/living-room and yard. Fee code M

Pop Larkin, who makes a fortune from scrap-iron deals but has never paid income tax, lives in rural idyllic bliss with generous-hearted Ma and their six children. When a young, earnest tax official, Mr Charlton, turns up one hot May afternoon in 1957 to investigate he is bewitched immediately by eldest daughter Mariette and it isn't long before he succumbs to the boisterous Larkin family charm and largesse. Period 1950s
ISBN 0 573 01751 4

Darling, I'm Home! Play. Jack Popplewell
M4 (30, 40) F4 (young, 20, 40). A drawing-room. Fee code K

With Celia Johns growing more and more frustrated by staying at home, and her husband Rupert proving more and more inefficient as a businessman, it seems a good idea that they should change places: and indeed Celia soon starts Rupert's firm on a profit-making course, while Rupert runs the house with equal efficiency. Matters are brought to a head by the arrival of daughter Karen to take up residence — with two babies, but for the moment, no husband.
ISBN 0 573 01591 0

Darling Mr London. Farce. Anthony Marriott and Bob Grant
M3 (20-40) F6 (20, 30, 50). A living-room. Fee code L

Mild Edward works at the Continental Telephone Exchange and has been in the habit of chatting up his co-telephonists, all female, in various Continental exchanges. These affairs-by-proxy have caused no complications until the occasion of a Miss Europhone Contest brings the girls to London. Four of the most glamorous turn up at his home anxious to meet the flirtatious 'Mr London' in the flesh. The complications that ensue result in an evening he will never forget!
ISBN 0 573 11113 8

Daughters of Venice. Play. Don Taylor
M9 (20s-40s) F22 (teenage-40s). Extras. Various simple interior and exterior settings. Fee code M

Written for Chiswick Youth Theatre, this play of rich comedy and powerful drama has a large cast, with a preponderance of good female roles. The daughters are the young girls taken in as orphans and cared for by the Sisters of the Pietà. The convent is famous for its girls' orchestra under the direction of Vivaldi and the play follows the fortunes of three of the girls about to enter the harsh commercial world. Period 1720
ISBN 0 573 01741 7

♦ **David Copperfield.** Play. Matthew Francis, adapted from the novel by Charles Dickens
M19 F10. Extras. Minimum cast of 13. Various interior and exterior settings. Fee code M

Following the adventures of its eponymous hero from birth through three decades, this acclaimed stage adaptation presents a plethora of brilliant characters from the original novel: the Peggottys; 'umble Heep; eccentric Aunt Betsey and Steerforth, young David's champion. Two actors play David Copperfield: one the young David, the other David's older self, each interacting throughout. This clever device moves the play effortlessly from scene to scene, ensuring a vigorous momentum for the narrative. Period 1820s-1840s
ISBN 0 573 01775 1

The Day After the Fair. Play. Frank Harvey, from a short story by Thomas Hardy
M2 (young, 50s) F4 (young, 35, 60). A living-room and hall. Fee code K

Anna, a servant, meets an attractive stranger from London, Charles, a budding barrister, at the country town fair. Illiterate Anna persuades her mistress to carry on a correspondence with him on her behalf. In writing her servant's love letters, and reading out his replies, the mistress falls in love with Charles and he with her. Charles, innocent of the deception, proposes to Anna. Only when it is too late does he discover the real writer of the letters. On this shaky foundation the couple start their marriage, leaving the mistress desolate. Period late nineteenth century
ISBN 0 573 01554 6

A Day in the Death of Joe Egg. Play. Peter Nichols
M2 (30s) F3 (30s, 60s), 1 child (10, non-speaking). A living-room. Fee code M

Joe Egg is the name given by Bri and Sheila to their spastic child. To make their lives bearable they have evolved an elaborate series of fantasy games about Joe. Yet ten years of devotion to a human vegetable have created terrible strains on their marriage and when Bri sees an opportunity of allowing Joe to die, he takes it. The attempt fails; Joe's living death will continue. Although the theme is deeply serious the tone is one of biting, ironic comedy, giving the work enormous theatrical effectiveness and compassion.
ISBN 0 573 01084 6

♦ **Day of Reckoning**. Play. Pam Valentine
M1 (50s) F7 (20s-50s, 83). A village hall. Fee code L

A committee meets on a winter's night to arrange the summer village fête. As protocol gives way to bickering and gossip, the personalities of those present emerge — busybody Ethel; Pauline, the vicar's long-suffering wife; careworn Gloria; horsy Marjorie who is very attentive to the shy new teacher, Angela; elderly Mavis and Sally, the brisk Army wife. Six months on, the cathartic events of the fête are related with humour and pathos, and the upbeat ending affirms the enduring value of village life.
ISBN 0 573 01806 5

The Days of the Commune. Play. Bertolt Brecht
Translations: Clive Barker and Arno Reinfrank, music by Hanns Eisler
                Jean Benedetti
                Ray Herman
M42 F12, 2 children. Extras. Interior and exterior settings. Fee code M (for play), code C (for music)

The story of the Paris Commune is told through fictional Men in the Street grouped round a Montmartre café, and a number of historical personages. The Men in the Street resist Thier's attempt to disarm the National Guard and watch its Central Committee seize power at the Hôtel de Ville. The Men in the Street put up a barricade, on which they fight and die. Set in Paris between January-April 1871.

◆ **Dead Funny.** Comedy. Terry Johnson
M3 (36, 59) F2 (33, 39) A living-room. Fee code M

The death of Benny Hill provides the impetus for this award-winning comedy about impotence, sex therapy and the English sense of humour. Eleanor wants what her husband Richard won't give her. Richard wants to be left in peace. Benny would rather rest in peace, but for tonight at least, his fans won't let him. '... a shatteringly good play, as hilarious as it is heartbreaking ...' *Daily Telegraph*

◆ **Dead Guilty**. Play. Richard Harris
M1 (20s), F3 (30s, 40s-60s). 1 male voice A sitting-room. Fee code M

When John Haddrell dies of a heart attack at the wheel of his car, the woman at his side is not his wife Margaret but his lover, Julia. Recovering from the injuries she sustained in the ensuing crash, Julia is visited by Margaret, who apparently knows nothing of the affair. Events take a sinister turn when Margaret begins to encroach on Julia's life. Left alone in the house together, Julia and Margaret are locked in deadly combat ...
ISBN 0 573 01750 6

Dead Man's Hand. Thriller. Seymour Matthews
M3 F3. A lounge. Fee code L

This captivating thriller employs a play within a play theme in a singularly exciting manner. At first it seems to be the usual Agatha Christie-type play — two couples lured to a remote Italian villa to be murdered one by one. It is only when this play is well advanced that we learn we are watching actors rehearsing their own murder mystery. An intriguing final twist unravels the real reason for the whole charade.
ISBN 0 573 01618 6

Dead of Night. Thriller. Peter Whalley
M2 (30s, 40s) F2 (20s, 30s). A living-room. Fee code M

Jack has just been acquitted of manslaughter, and regales his girlfriend Maggie and their neighbours with a disparaging account of the trial. According to the evidence (most of it Jack's), the victim, Philip Mercer, had broken in late at night, and, on being confronted by Jack, produced a gun which Jack got hold of during the ensuing struggle and then used to kill Mercer. A clear case of self-defence. Or was it?
ISBN 0 573 01743 3

Dead Ringer. Comedy thriller. Charles Ross, adapted from *The Prime Pretender* by Logan Gourlay
M5 (50s) F2 (40s). A study. Fee code M

When the Prime Minister drops dead from an apparent heart attack on the eve of a General Election, two members of the Cabinet, fearing defeat without the charisma of the PM, hire an out-of-work actor, a 'dead ringer' for the deceased, to take his place until the election is won. However, the actor grows to like his role until he discovers the real PM was poisoned. Thereafter this thriller plunges us forcibly from the early amusing fantasy world into murder and dark plots.
ISBN 0 573 11534 6

Dead-Lock. Thriller. Hugh Janes
M3 (middle-age) F2 (30s, middle-age). A large country house. Fee code M

When her husband dies in a car crash, Diana is determined to succeed as the new head of his successful company. Her son Alec believes the position should be his, while her younger son demands more of the family fortune. When strange events start happening in the house and a voice haunts her, Diana's fears and uncertainties increase. Just as she feels she knows who is responsible, events take a dramatic turn as her real enemy is revealed.
ISBN 0 573 01744 1

Deadly Embrace. Thriller. Eric Paice
M1 (35) F3 (18, early 40s). Extras 1M 1F. A living-room with gallery bedroom. Fee code M

Angry and bitter after throwing out her unfaithful husband, Julia is only too ready to succumb to the good-looking Welshman who comes ostensibly to update her husband's computer. Julia enjoys playing games with the computer, particularly when it invites her to play the Murder Game and she can fantasize about how easy it would be to commit the perfect murder by computer with her errant husband as victim. However, stopping the program the next morning isn't so easy ...
ISBN 0 573 01745 X

Deadly Nightcap. Play. Francis Durbridge
M6 (30, 40, middle-age) F4 (young, 40s). A living-room. Fee code M

Murder and mystery abound in this ingenious play from the master of the genre. Initially the plot seems to concern a greedy husband plotting to kill his wife. Disposing first of his brother-in-law, Jack enlists the help of his girlfriend in his plan to murder Sarah. But his scheme goes horribly wrong and he, not his wife, ends up dead. There are so many possible suspects and motives that the truth eludes us all ... although Cliff seems to be on the right track.
ISBN 0 573 01627 5

♦**Dealer's Choice**. Play. Patrick Marber
M6 (20s-50s). A kitchen, restaurant, basement. Fee code M

Stephen, a restaurateur, has a weekly poker game in the basement. The stakes are high and the waiters often lose their paycheques. Stephen's son, Carl, is an obsessive gambler who has run up debts and when Ash, a professional gambler, threatens to kill Carl if he doesn't pay the £4000 he owes, Carl arranges for him to play in the weekly game. But Stephen can spot a professional and confronts Ash who asks where Carl acquired his addiction. Who is the real addict, Carl or Stephen?

Dear Brutus. Comedy. J. M. Barrie
M5 (young-old) F6 (young-60). A drawing-room, a wood. Fee code M
ISBN 0 573 60782 6

A

Dear Octopus. Comedy. Dodie Smith
M5 F12. Three interiors. Fee code M

From far and wide four generations of the family gather to celebrate Charles and Dora Randolph's golden wedding anniversary. It is largely Dora's loving wisdom that makes this momentous occasion a chance for a few of her scattered brood to regain, within the security of the home, a new strength of purpose. All join that evening in toasting 'The Family' — that dear octopus from whose tentacles we never quite escape nor, in our innermost hearts, ever quite wish to. First produced in 1938.
ISBN 0 573 01096 X

The Dearly Beloved. Play. Philip Osment
M4 (teenage, 40s) F5 (30s, 40s, 70). Simple interior and exterior settings. Fee code M

When Alaric, a successful London television producer, returns to his sleepy rural home town, his arrival heralds suffering and domestic turmoil in this sensitive, compelling depiction of a variety of family relationships. The play was critically acclaimed at Hampstead Theatre in 1993. '... exceptionally poignant, and there is no mistaking the overall richness of this play. Osment's penetrating observation of character and heartening generosity of spirit mark him out as a dramatist of exceptional and distinctive promise.' *Daily Telegraph*
ISBN 0 573 01746 8

Death and the Maiden. Play. Ariel Dorfman
M2 (45, 50) F1 (40). A dining/living-room. Fee code M

Set in a fragile new South American democracy, this piece concerns Paulina who, fifteen years ago, was picked up by the police, blindfolded and tortured. When Roberto stops to help Gerardo, whose car has broken down, and brings him home, Paulina is convinced he is one of her torturers. Husband and wife are caught in a gripping, passionate deadlock: one liberal and judicious, the other victimized and full of hatred, coming to grips with an oppressor. **NB. The text of the 1992 Broadway première must be used in all performances.**

Death and the Maiden. Play. Georgina Reid
M2 (young, 50) F5 (teenage, 40, 50, 70). A living-room. Fee code L

After twenty years abroad beautiful Sylvia returns to visit her mother and spinster sister, Mavis, bringing with her her daughter Rose whose plainness arouses in old Mrs Bell the same enmity that has led her to mistreat Mavis for so long. Rose shows spirit and humour in dealing with her grandmother, but when Mrs Bell is frightened almost to death, and the family are the only suspects, this gentle play develops sinister overtones, and surprising revelations about Mavis come to light. Period early twentieth century.
ISBN 0 573 11240 1

Death Walked In. Play. Bettine Manktelow
M3 (30, 60s) F4 (teens, 20, 30, 40). An hotel lounge. Fee code K

Celia, lonely and highly strung, is struggling to run her small country hotel. Her charming, rakish step-son, Rex, is no help. Joan and her tearaway sister, Eva, are staying at the hotel which represents something of a romantic pilgrimage for Joan who, after ten years, still believes herself in love with Rex. Events lead to a suicide (or is it murder?). The climax involves mistaken identity and mislaid cyanide!
ISBN 0 573 11127 8

Ira Levin's **Deathtrap**. Thriller
M3 (25, 50s) F2 (40, 50). A study. Fee code M

A hugely popular stage and screen success, this ingeniously constructed play offers a rare and skilful blending of two priceless theatrical ingredients — gasp-inducing thrills and spontaneous laughter. Unknown dramatist Clifford Anderson has sent his new thriller to award-winning Broadway author Sidney for comment — or has he? Without a success to his credit for some years, Sidney plots with his reluctant wife Myra about how best to plagiarize 'Deathtrap' and when Clifford turns up to discuss the play with the 'Master' events take a sinister turn.
ISBN 0 573 11121 9

Deceptions. Play. Paul Wheeler
M1 (early 20s) F1 (early 40s). A consulting room, a bedsitter. Fee code M

Julia Smythe is a psychiatrist. A mysterious young man comes into her Mayfair consulting rooms for treatment for impotence and a tendency towards compulsive lying. Quickly, the psychoanalyst becomes hooked on the case of this strange young man, curing him to the point where he seemingly stops lying and falls in love with her. We are plunged into a complex, perverse situation right, it seems almost, out of Jacobean drama. '... intriguing ... neatly structured and snappily written.' *Independent*
ISBN 0 573 69287 4

The Decision. See **The Measures Taken**

The Decorator. Comedy. Donald Churchill
M1 (53) F2. A flat. Fee code M

Marcia has a surprise visitor: Jane, the wife of the man with whom Marcia is having an affair, who has come to take her revenge by informing Marcia's husband of his wife's infidelity. Marcia is at her wits' end, then has a brilliant idea. It seems her housepainter is a part-time professional actor. Marcia hires him to impersonate her husband, Reggie, at the big confrontation later that day, when the wronged wife plans to return and spill the beans. From then on hilarity piles on hilarity ...
ISBN 0 573 69127 4

The Deep Blue Sea. Play. Terence Rattigan
M5 (young-50) F3 (young, 30, 50). A sitting-room. Fee code M

Hester Collyer's husband is a rich, talented lawyer; her lover, Freddie, is neither Hester's moral nor intellectual equal, but Hester loves him with an intensity that few, and especially not Freddie, are capable of matching. They are death to each other. Hester is driven to attempt suicide. Between the devil and the deep blue sea the latter looks very attractive. She is saved by Miller, a disbarred doctor, and through him learns how to transcend both hope and despair. Period 1950s
ISBN 0 573 01098 6

A Delicate Balance. Play. Edward Albee
M2 (60s) F4 (30-50s). A living-room. Fee code M

Agnes and Tobias are long married and remain together out of habit. Agnes' sister, Claire, lives with them and takes refuge from life's perils in alcohol and self-lacerating wit. One night Julia, Agnes and Tobias' daughter, comes home, escaping from her fourth marriage. They are visited by Edna and Harry, their oldest friends, who are deeply disturbed by a great shock they have had. The door is locked and Tobias' family is made to recognize how they have lost love through undervaluing it. This stimulating play is distinguished by the award of a Pulitzer Prize.

The Devils. Play. John Whiting from a book by Aldous Huxley
M17 F6. Composite setting. Fee code L

The nuns of St Ursula's Convent, led by the Prioress, Sister Jeanne, accused Urbain Grandier, Vicar of Loudon, of sorcery. He was tried, tortured and burned. On this baldly terrible foundation, Whiting has built a powerful, complex play, interweaving the personal dilemmas of Jeanne and Grandier with the political necessities of the time. Period 1623-34, although essentially it is no more a period play than Miller's *The Crucible*.
ISBN 0 573 01101 X

Dial 'M' for Murder. Play. Frederick Knott
M4 (30s, 45) F1 (20). A living-room. Fee code M

Tony had quite blatantly married Sheila for her money. When it seems likely that she is in love with Max, Tony begins to plot her murder. Lesgate, the hired killer, enters the flat while Tony establishes his own alibi. But Sheila defends herself so ably that it is Lesgate who is killed. Tony callously plants evidence to suggest that Sheila had killed Lesgate because he was blackmailing her. She is convicted but fortunately the Inspector continues his investgations ...
ISBN 0 573 01102 8

The Diary of Anne Frank. Play. Dramatized by Frances Goodrich and Albert Hackett
M5 (16, middle-age-elderly) F5 (teenage, 20s-40). An attic. Fee code M

Few more poignant true stories emerged from World War II than the diary of young Anne Frank. Published long afterwards by her father, the only family survivor, it records the minutiae of twenty-five months that two Jewish families spent in hiding from the Gestapo in an Amsterdam warehouse attic. The constant secrecy, growing hunger and friction of living in such cramped conditions could not dull Anne's vibrant personality or her passion for living.
ISBN 0 573 01104 4

♦ **A Different Way Home**. Play. Jimmie Chinn
M1 F1. A living-room. Fee code M

A deeply moving, astutely observed play which consists of two monologues from a middle-aged estranged brother and sister in a closely-knit, North of England town. Leslie, who has lived always with his mother, narrates the events leading up to his mother's death, unwittingly revealing the extent of his loss. From Maureen we hear that Leslie had succumbed to his grief, and we hear her side of the story: feeling rejected because she married a Jew, she also feels betrayed for not being asked to help.
ISBN 0 573 11092 1

The Dining Room. Play. A. R. Gurney
57 characters played by M3 F3 (minimum). A dining-room. Fee code M

Three men and three women portray a wide, diverse range of characters — from little boys to grandfathers, from giggling girls to housemaids — in this brilliantly structured play which enjoyed a very successful run off-Broadway and was given its British première at Greenwich Theatre in 1983. The action takes place in an upper middle-class American dining-room, the hub of social family life, comprising a mosaic of interrelated scenes, sometimes funny, sometimes touching, sometimes rueful, which together create a profound study of the decaying mores of the American WASP.
ISBN 0 573 11536 2

Dirty Linen and **New-Found-Land.** Two plays. Tom Stoppard
M8 (young, middle-age) F2 (young, middle-age). A committee room in the House of Commons. Fee code K

Dirty Linen concerns the investigation of a Select Committee into the moral standards of the House of Commons — a somewhat unconventional investigation, rendered not less so by the presence of an ultra-sexy secretary whose clothes have a trick of whisking off in the hands of various members. *New-Found-Land* is a duologue between two Home Office officials, with a tour-de-force speech on America by one of them.
ISBN 0 573 11109 X

Disappeared. Play. Phyllis Nagy
M5 (20s, any age, middle-age, 40s) F3 (25, 30s, middle-age). Various simple settings. Fee code M

This starkly modern play concerns Sarah Casey, a twenty-five-year-old travel agent who has never been outside New York City. She goes missing after leaving a bar, where the last person to see her was Elston Rupp, a man who works in a thrift shop and dresses in his clients' clothes to assume different identities. Was Sarah killed, or did she merely 'disappear' to escape her anonymous existence in a big, lonely city?
ISBN 0 573 01747 6

The Disorderly Women. Play. John Bowen
M6 F7. Composite set. Fee code J

One of the classical myths that the modern theatre has found to be more relevant to our time is that portrayed in *The Bacchae* of Euripides in which Pentheus, the King of Thebes, denies the god Dionysus and is then torn limb from limb by the 'dancing women', who are the god's followers. In this play the author presents the myth as a tragic story, in which a good man, attempting to perform good acts, is destroyed by his denial, both in himself and others, of what is instinctive, irrational and destructive.
ISBN 0 573 11105 7

Dogg's Hamlet, Cahoot's Macbeth. Double bill. Tom Stoppard
Up to 20 characters, much doubling possible. Fee Code M (when performed as a double bill). Fee code F when performed separately

Tom Stoppard explains that the comma between the two titles serves to unite the plays: 'the first is hardly a play at all without the second which cannot be performed without the first'. *Dogg's Hamlet* is a reworking of *Dogg's Our Pet*, an exercise in nonsense language which leads on to *The Fifteen Minute Hamlet* (published separately by Samuel French) which takes the most well-known lines from *Hamlet* and condenses them into 13 minutes. *Cahoot's Macbeth* ingeniously abbreviates Shakespeare and combines it with linguistic jokes, political comment and farce.

A Doll's House. Play. Henrik Ibsen, in a new version by Christopher Hampton
M3 (late 30s, 40s) F4 (30s, 35, old), 1 boy 1 girl (optional). A flat. Fee code M

Ibsen's classic play tells the story of Nora, beautiful, fragile wife of Torvald Helmer. Nora had secretly borrowed money for her husband by forging her father's signature. Krogstad, her creditor, threatens to ruin Helmer by exposing Nora's fraud. When Helmer finds out, he is not prepared to sacrifice his reputation to protect Nora; she realizes that she must close the door on her marriage and her husband to retain her self-respect.

Dolphins Rampant. Comedy. Charlotte Hastings
M5 (25, 40s) F4 (young, 40s, 60s). A living-room. Fee code L

George Dolphin, a rich, well-bred man, is so obsessed with making money that he fails to notice his wife's devotion to him or his daughter's serious feelings towards his young assistant. With the unexpected arrival from the States of his mother, a cheerful, generous and irrepressible humanist, his world is turned completely upside down. Period 1960s

Don Juan. Play. Bertolt Brecht, adapted from Molière. Translated by Ralph Manheim
M15 F6. Fee code M

In this adaptation Don Juan, the legendary lover, is regarded as a means to ridicule the hypocrisy and pretentiousness of the world as he pursues his amorous ways, dodges and outwits his enemies until, in the form of the Statue of the Commander, he meets his inevitable nemesis and is cast into hell fire. This is one of Brecht's less radical adaptations and one of those with which he apparently had least to do.

Doña Rosita the Spinster, or the Language of Flowers. Play. Federico García Lorca. Translated by Gwynne Edwards
M7 F12, a voice. Two rooms. Fee code M

A realistic social drama set in Granada between 1855 and 1911. The central character, Rosita, is an attractive and hopeful 20-year-old, in love with her cousin. Act II is set in 1900 and portrays the movement of Progress beyond Rosita's home whilst she waits for her cousin. The play ends dramatically with an anguished portrayal of Rosita as an ageing spinster. Lorca's treatment of Rosita is one of sympathy and understanding as he records her bitter humiliation.

Donkey's Years. Play. Michael Frayn
M8 F1. A college courtyard. Two studies. Fee code M

The occasion is a reunion dinner at a lesser college of an older university. Gathered together are a number of graduates now in their early forties and mostly in responsible, influential positions. All starts smoothly, with the usual conventional greetings, but as the night goes on the college port causes behaviour surprising in those positions of political, academic or spiritual authority. The play was seen at the Globe Theatre, London, with Peter Barkworth, Jeffrey Wickham and Penelope Keith.
ISBN 0 573 11097 2

A

◆ **Don't Dress for Dinner**. Farce. Marc Camoletti, adapted by Robin Hawdon
M3 (35, any age) F3 (30s). A living-room. Fee code M

Bernard is hoping to weekend in the country with his chic Parisian mistress Suzy. He has arranged for a cordon bleu cook, is in the process of packing his wife Jacqueline off to her mother, and has invited along his best friend Robert as a suitable alibi. It's foolproof. What could possibly go wrong? Well ... Hilarious confusion piles upon hilarious confusion as Bernard and Robert improvise at breakneck speed!
ISBN 0 573 01748 4

Don't Drink the Water. Comedy. Woody Allen
M12 F4. An embassy. Fee code M

This hilarious affair takes place in an American Embassy behind the Iron Curtain. An American tourist, caterer by trade, and his family, rush into the embassy two steps ahead of the police who suspect them of spying and picture-taking. But it is not much of a refuge as the ambassador is absent and his son, now in charge, has been expelled from a dozen different countries. Nevertheless they carefully and frantically plot their escape and the ambassador's son and the caterer's daughter even have time to fall in love.
ISBN 0 573 60817 2

Don't Just Lie There, Say Something. Farce. Michael Pertwee
M5 (30-old) F4 (20s). A town hall stage, a London flat. Fee code K
ISBN 0 573 01040 4

Don't Lose the Place! Comedy. Derek Benfield
M3 (young, late 30s, early 50s) F2 (young, 35). Composite setting: a sitting-room, patio and part of a kitchen. Fee code L

When Sylvia's boyfriend Robin walks out on her she decides on a rather unconventional method of finding a replacement. Determined not to be let down a second time, she has carefully arranged a timetable in order to 'try out' various assorted lovers and assess their suitability before making her final choice of a potential husband. But timetables have a way of going wrong ... A torrent of confusions and mistaken identities inevitably arise as Sylvia and her friend Jemma try, with unexpected and hilarious results, to prevent the final confrontation of the three trial husbands. A delightfully comic climax ensues.
ISBN 0 573 01749 2

Don't Misunderstand Me. Comedy. Patrick Cargill
M2 (40s) F3 (20, 40). A living-room. Fee code M

A light and frothy comedy relating the complications and misunderstandings that arise when Charles and Margery prepare to entertain Charles's brother Robert and his new wife, Jane, whom they have never met. Robert arrives, without Jane, and reveals that he had a brief *affaire* in America with Jaynie, but has covered his tracks by not giving her his English address. Minutes later Jaynie arrives! Confusions arise from wild deceptions as Charles and Robert struggle to keep Margery, Jaynie and a further young lady from revealing their true identities ...
ISBN 0 573 11150 2

Double Double. Play. Eric Elice and Roger Rees
M1 (40) F1 (30). A London apartment. Fee code M

Phillipa has picked up down-and-out Duncan. It is, she explains, purely a business arrangement based on Duncan's uncanny resemblance to her recently deceased husband, Richard, who stood to inherit a million-pound trust fund in a few weeks. All Duncan has to do for a half-share in the fund is impersonate Richard at a party. This clever thriller twists and turns until the stunning climax that leaves the audience gasping. 'A glossy romantic thriller — it should be seen to be believed.' *Sunday Times*
ISBN 0 573 01646 1

♦ **Dreaming.** Play. Peter Barnes
Large cast may be played by M11 F4. Various simple settings. Fee code M (play). Details of the music available from Samuel French Ltd

In the bloody aftermath of the Wars of the Roses, Captain John Mallory leads a band of renegades across a war-torn landscape on a breathtaking quest in search of a dream — a dream of home. An apocalyptic vision packed with ravishing images, *Dreaming* is a haunting and brutally funny story of heroism and human values. Period 1471

The Dresser. Play. Ronald Harwood
M4 (30, 40, 60, old) F3 (young, middle-age, 50s). Composite set. Fee code M

Sir, the last of the great, but dying, breed of English actor-managers, is in a very bad way tonight. As his dresser tries valiantly to prepare him to go on stage as King Lear, Sir is having great difficulty remembering who and where he is, let alone Lear's lines. With a Herculean effort on the part of Norman, the dresser, Sir does finally make it on stage, and through the performance. Period 1942. During its long West End run the play starred Tom Courtenay and Freddie Jones.

Drums in the Night. Drama. Bertolt Brecht
Translations: John Willett
                Gerhard Nellhaus
                Richard Beckley
                Frank Jones
M9 F6. Interior and exterior settings. Fee code M

The soldier Andreas returns from a prison camp to find his fiancée Anna just engaged to the prosperous Murk. Against sounds and reports of the Spartacists storming the newspaper offices, Andreas quarrels in a bar with Anna's parents and the now drunken Murk. Lost in the street, he follows the rioting; Anna follows him. In desperation Andreas leads the (partly drunken) company to the newspaper offices. In the early morning he and Anna meet in the streets. He refuses to return to the fighting and the two go home together.

The Drunkard or Down with Demon Drink! Melodrama. Brian J. Burton
M7 (20s, middle-age, 60s, elderly) F8 (11, young, middle-age, 60). Extras. Interior and exterior settings. Fee code L

Edward, the penniless heir of his kind-hearted father, is a virtuous man. One day the villain Squire Cribbs lures Edward to drink in an inn, and the effect is instantaneous; he becomes a drunkard and his poverty increases. It is his foster brother William who finds out what Cribb is up to, discovers Edward in the slums of London and finds the true will hidden by the villain. Period Victorian

Duet for One. Play. Tom Kempinski
M1 (60s) F1 (33). A consulting room. Fee code M

Stephanie, an eminent violinist struck down by multiple sclerosis, consults Dr Feldmann to help her adjust to her new life. Under Dr Feldmann's quiet, probing questions layers of protective pretence are stripped from her, revealing dangerous depths of resentment and despair. She becomes aggressive towards the psychiatrist and finally decides to give up the treatment, but his last word is to ask her if 'the same time' will be convenient for her next appointment.
ISBN 0 573 11091 3

The Earl and the Pussycat. Comedy. Harold Brooke and Kay Bannerman
M5 (16, young, middle-age, 60) F2 (young West Indian, middle-age). A drawing-room. Fee code M
ISBN 0 573 11119 7

East Lynne or Never Called Me Mother! Melodrama with music. Brian J. Burton, based on the novel by Mrs Henry Wood
M4 (20s, 30s, middle-age) F5 (young, 40s). 1 child (optional). A sitting-room. Fee code L

Lady Isabel is cunningly seduced by the villain into believing that the clandestine meetings of her husband and another woman are for romance rather than business. In despair, she abandons home and children, only to come back in later years disguised as a governess to her own children and to die in her husband's arms in heartbroken penitence and forgiveness. Period Victorian

♦ **Easy Terms**. Comedy. Frank Vickery
M2 (early 20s, early 30s) F2 (young, mid 50s) 1 girl (non-speaking). Various simple interior and exterior settings. Fee code M

A year ago Vi Davies suffered a stroke and her son Howard gave up his college course to nurse her. Vi is now capable of looking after herself but cannot let go of her son. Howard finds this situation extremely difficult, not least because he has a secret — he is gay, and has been seeing Bernard Fowler, Vi's insurance agent, for some time. A caravan holiday does nothing to relieve the tension ...
ISBN 0 573 01757 3

The Eccentricities of a Nightingale. Play. Tennessee Williams
M5 (young, middle-age, 60s) F5 (young, middle-age, 60s). A small square with fountain, three interiors. Fee code M

Hemmed in by her parents, Alma Winemiller, afraid that she will always remain a spinster, has set her heart on the young Dr Buchanan. Though attached to Alma, he is guided by his socially ambitious mother and by his own uncertainties. Neither of them can break free from the influences that pull them apart. Period shortly before World War I

The Edge of Darkness. Play. Brian Clemens
M3 (30s-50s) F3 (20s, 50s). Extra 1M. A living-room. Fee code L

After her disappearance several years ago, Emma finds that her memory is damaged; there is much she does not recognize or understand. Why does she appear familiar with certain Russian phrases; why has she such a horror of a harmless silver bell, of a portrait on the wall, of knives? Is she, in fact, Emma Cranwell? Behind these questions looms a menacing mystery which finally erupts into violence and horror. Period 1900
ISBN 0 573 11118 9

A

The Editing Process. Play. Meredith Oakes
M5 (20s, 30s, 60) F3 (20s, 50). Various offices. Fee code M

In publishing, little companies are often gobbled up by big ones. This scenario faces the staff of *Footnotes in History*, who find their old-fashioned magazine amalgamated into a large publishing consortium. What will happen to pedantic William, who has edited the magazine all his life? How does his long-suffering secretary feel about being 'rationalized'? And does the new company — satirically represented by designer 'image consultants' — really want William's magazine to continue?

Edmond. Play. David Mamet
M20 F8 (may be played by M6 F4). Simple interior and exterior settings. Fee code M

This is a brutal, probing, and controversial story of a man set morally adrift in a corrupt and violent world. Leaving a wife and marriage in which he finds no fulfilment, Edmond sets out to find sex, adventure and companionship but ultimately finds the meaning of his existence in a world where there seems to be no concern for others, only selfishness and self interest. What Edmond experiences is a nightmare odyssey through the underworld of New York City.
ISBN 0 573 60848 2

Educating Rita. Comedy. Willy Russell
M1 (middle-age) F1 (26). A first-floor room in a university. Fee code M

Frank is a tutor of English whose disillusioned outlook on life drives him to the bottle. Rita is a hairdresser hungry to find some meaning to life. With Frank as her tutor Rita embarks on an Open University course and her education process begins. The effects are both amusing and serious as her fresh, intuitive approach becomes clouded and stifled as she grapples with the problem of a formal education, while Frank also learns something — to believe in himself again.
ISBN 0 573 11115 4

Edwina Black. Play. William Dinner and William Morum
M2 (40s) F2 (30s, elderly). A lounge. Fee code M

The day before Edwina Black's funeral, Inspector Martin calls to interview her husband Gregory, her companion Elizabeth and her housekeeper, Ellen. Gregory has long endured the domination of his wealthy wife, but is in love with Elizabeth. It is revealed Edwina died from arsenic. Gregory and Elizabeth quarrel bitterly. However Ellen confesses that Edwina poisoned herself: with vindictive spite she devised a suicide which would serve to incriminate Gregory and Elizabeth and so destroy them.
ISBN 0 573 60853 9

The Effect of Gamma Rays on Man-in-the-Moon Marigolds. Play. Paul Zindel
F5, or 2 women, 3 girls. A living-room. Fee code M

Encouraged by her teacher, Matilda undertakes a gamma ray experiment with marigolds which wins her a prize at high school — and brings on the shattering climax of the play. Proud, jealous, too filled with her own hurts to accept her daughter's success, Beatrice can only maim when she needs to love, and deride when she wants to praise. Yet, as Matilda's experiment proves, something beautiful can emerge from even the most barren, afflicted soil.

84 Charing Cross Road. Helene Hanff. Adapted for the stage by James Roose-Evans
M3 F4 or 5. Extra 1M. Split set: an apartment and bookshop. Fee code M

In 1949 a struggling American writer started a correspondence with a firm of British antiquarian booksellers that was to last for twenty years. The warm, compassionate and very human exchange of letters was published as a book and is here skilfully and lovingly adapted for the stage. 'An evening of enchantment and charm the like of which is rarely encountered in the theatre.' *What's On in London*
ISBN 0 573 11005 0

The Elephant Man. Play. Bernard Pomerance
M5 F3, with doubling and trebling. Composite setting. Fee code M

The true story of John Merrick, treated first as a fairground freak because of his hideously, repulsively deformed body and later exploited more subtly by Victorian society. He is befriended by a young doctor who provides him with a home in the London Hospital where Merrick is shrewdly used for fund-raising. He is introduced to high society, and is trapped by Victorian values so incongruous to his reality. Even those who love him can't help him and he dies from his horrible affliction. Period 1884-90

Elsie and Norm's "Macbeth". Comedy. John Christopher-Wood
M1 (late middle-age) F1 (late middle-age). Extra 1M. A living-room. Fee code L

Elsie and Norm have decided to have a bit of a bash at culture by staging a production of *Macbeth* in their living-room. After a spot of judicious re-writing by Norm to make it snappier and more punchy, and undaunted by the large cast, Elsie and Norm set out to act 'one of the greatest pieces of literature what has ever been wrote in the English language', playing all the characters between them. The hilarious results set Shakespeare spinning in his grave!
ISBN 0 573 01754 9

◆ **Elton John's Glasses**. Play. David Farr
M4 (21, 24, 30s) F2 (16, 35). A room. Fee code M

Bill is a fanatical supporter of Watford F.C. Day after day he sits in his unfurnished flat, watching the 1984 Cup Final with an obsession verging on madness. The video replays the fatal moment when the Watford goalkeeper fumbles the ball and Everton take a two-nil lead. Bill blames the goalkeeper's mishap on the glare from Elton John's glasses. Reconciled to an agoraphobic existence, Bill laments the decline of his beloved team: 'It was there the dream died'.

End of Me Old Cigar. John Osborne. Copies available on hire only. Please enquire for further details.

The End of the Food Chain. Play. Tim Firth
M5 (20s) F1 (20s). Composite set: 3 levels of a grocery distribution depot, plus the roof. Fee code M

Welcome to the 'animal shift' at Kale Moor grocery distribution depot. Under the guidance of Bruce, work here is an endless round of sports and juvenile humour. But a change is due, for their new colleague is not a born games player and is — even worse — a woman. Wildly funny, sharply observed and peopled with vivid, likeable characters, this is another comic gem from the author of *Neville's Island*.
ISBN 0 573 01755 7

An Englishman's Home ... Play. Stephen Mallatratt
M3 (young) F3 (young). A living-room. Fee code K
ISBN 0 573 01595 3

A

Enjoy. Play. Alan Bennett
M6 (teenage, 20s, middle-age, 60s) M4 (non-speaking) F3 (20s, 60s). A living-room. Fee code M

Dad thinks everything will be better when the family moves. The social worker who calls to observe their lives turns out to be absent son Terry, idolized by Mam, in drag. Secretary daughter Linda, in reality a prostitute, breezes in, shattering Dad's illusions. The house is dismantled around them to be rebuilt in a park preserving the ideals of family life. Mam will be in a showcase whilst Dad is carted off to the geriatric ward.
ISBN 0 573 11129 4

The Enquiry. Play. Charlotte Hastings
M2 (20s, 50s) F10 (20s-70s). The Governor's office in an open prison. Fee code H

Kate, a prisoner sentenced for killing her very sick child, has been attacked and driven to attempt suicide. The prison authoritites discover that the attack was made by an inmate, Gow, who has a lesbian attachment to another prisoner, Valentine, and who is insanely jealous of Kate's innocent friendship with Valentine. The investigations also reveal that Kate's husband had killed the child and that Kate, herself innocent, is shielding the man she loves.
ISBN 0 573 01114 1

Enter a Free Man. Comedy. Tom Stoppard
M5 (young, 30s, 50s) F3 (18, 20s, 50s). Composite setting. Fee code M

George Riley refuses unemployment on the grounds that he is employed in inventing; unfortunately his inventions are slightly ahead of their time. Every Saturday he sweeps into his local declaring that he has left home to make his fortune. But this Saturday his long-suffering, pocket-money-providing daughter has had enough, and she too runs away, only to discover that her knight in shining motor-cycle gear is already married. Sunday finds them both back at home once again.

The Entertainer. Play. John Osborne
M5 (young, middle-age, 50s, 70s) F3 (young, 22, 60s). A living-room, a front cloth. Fee code M

Archie Rice is a failure as a comedian. News of his son's death while on military service arrives as the family is anticipating his return with a party. Archie tries to stage a comeback for his befuddled, has-been father who, mercifully, dies in the attempt. A prosperous brother offers to send the family to Canada but Archie cannot leave the decaying world of the music hall, where he is at home.
ISBN 0 573 11206 1

Entertaining Mr Sloane. Play. Joe Orton
M3 (young, elderly) F1 (middle-age). A room. Fee code M

A youth named Sloane comes in search of a room, and is then seduced by the landlady. Along comes her homosexual brother, who sets about capturing the affections of the youth for himself. Their father believes he witnessed the youth murder someone and, to silence him, Sloane kicks the old man to death. The landlady and her brother now have Sloane exactly where they want him: each of them will enjoy his company for six months of the year.

Entertaining Strangers. Play. David Edgar
59 characters. Various simple interior and exterior settings. Fee code M

Sarah Eldridge, a beer-brewing tradeswoman, embodies the free-thinking, bustling spirit of a community beginning to reap the rewards of the Industrial Revolution. The rise to commercial eminence runs parallel to the story of Reverend Henry Moule, a hardline fundamentalist who believes brewing to be a sinful trade. During the Dorchester cholera epidemic Moule, spiritually intolerant, proves socially altruistic, while self-interest keeps Sarah away from helping the infectious sick. Period Victorian

Epitaph for George Dillon. John Osborne. Copies available on hire only. Please enquire for further details.

Epsom Downs. Play. Howard Brenton
M31 F11 or M6 F2. The Downs. Fee code M

Commissioned and first performed by the Joint Stock Theatre Company in August 1977, this play takes place on Derby Day in Silver Jubilee Year. In the words of *The Times* critic, Irving Wardle, it explores 'a great public festival, held on common land and pulling in punters of every degree from the Aga Khan to the homeless family who are camping out in a Dormobile'. All in all *Epsom Downs* is a 'a marvel of expressive economy'.

Equus. Play. Peter Shaffer
M5 (17, middle-age) F4 (20s, middle-age). Extras M. An open stage. Fee code M

Martin Dysart, a psychiatrist, is confronted with Alan Strang, a boy who has blinded six horses, although his parents insist he has always adored horses. Dysart finds the psychological puzzle turns into something far more complex and disturbing — a confrontation with himself as well as with Alan, in which he comes to an inescapable view of man's need to worship and the distortions forced on that need by so-called civilized society.
ISBN 0 573 01566 X

Erogenous Zones. Play. Frank Vickery
M3 (20s, 30s). F2 (30s). Composite set: a kitchen, a bedroom-sitting room, a sitting-room. Fee code M

This ingeniously constructed play is set in three separate flats over a bank holiday weekend. Shifting backwards and forwards in time it depicts a triangle of relationships: Michael, a homosexual, who is in love with his flatmate Andrew, who in turn is having an affair with Lesley, whose husband Tom seeks respite from their disintegrating marriage in the arms of Alison.
ISBN 0 573 01759 X

The Erpingham Camp. Play. Joe Orton
M6 (middle-age) F3 (young, middle-age). A camp office and bare stage. Fee code F

This is a camp for grown-ups, not for children, and certainly not for fun. In the midst of the activities there is a fight, or rather a free-for-all, during which the headmaster falls through the floor on to the heads of the dancers below, killing several of them. The action concludes with an elegy.

A

Exit the King. Play. Eugene Ionesco. Translated by Donald Watson
M3 F3. A throne room. Fee code M

King Berenger has only the duration of the play to live. His kingdom has shrunk to the confines of his garden wall, his nation reduced to the six within his throne-room. Once, it seemed, he ruled over an immense empire; now he cannot command even the movements of his own body. Like Everyman, Berenger has lived from day to day, and there is now no more time.
ISBN 0 573 01123 0

The Exorcism. A Ghost Story. Don Taylor
M2 (38, 40) F2 (30s). A cottage. Fee code M

Dan and Margaret have come to spend Christmas with Rachel and Edmund in their renovated seventeenth-century labourer's cottage. Later, as Rachel plays the piano, she suddenly gets a sinister feeling of *déjà vu.* Shortly afterwards, the electricity fails and the phone is out of order too. It is the start of a series of macabre events which mount relentlessly to a bizarre and terrifying climax culminating in a tragic report coming from the TV into an empty brightly-lit room.
ISBN 0 573 11120 0

♦ **An Experiment with an Air Pump**. Play. Shelagh Stephenson
M3 F4. A room. Fee code M

1799 — On the eve of a new century, the house buzzes with scientific experiments, furtive romance and farcical amateur dramatics. 1999 — In a world of scientific chaos, cloning and genetic engineering, the cellar of the same house reveals a dark secret buried for 200 years. Shelagh Stephenson's daring and thoughtful play, inspired by the painting of Joseph Wright of Derby, was joint recipient of the 1997 Margaret Ramsay Award.

Extremities. Play. William Mastrosimone
M1 (young) F3 (young). The living-room of an old New Jersey farmhouse. Fee code M

Helen Mirren and Kevin McNally starred at the Duchess Theatre, London, in this drama about a young woman who is attacked in her own home by a rapist. She manages to overpower the man and imprisons him. When her roommates return, they have to try to talk the victim out of her ultimate revenge. (NB. This play contains violent scenes and explicit language.) '... all the tensions of the classic thriller ... an extraordinary humanity ...' *Daily Mail*
ISBN 0 573 60875 X

Faith Healer. Play. Brian Friel
M2 (middle-age, 50s) F1 (middle-age). Simple settings on a bare stage. Fee code M

This is now recognized as one of the masterpieces of Ireland's greatest living playwright. In the course of four monologues the stories unfold of the travelling healer Frank who has gone all over Wales and Scotland with his wife Grace, and his manager Teddy. Brian Friel weaves their versions of the healer's performance and a terrible event into haunting, magnificent art.

Fall. Play. James Saunders
M1 F4 (20s, 30s, 50s). A garden in late summer. Fee code M

On an Indian summer day three sisters, uncertain Kate, Marxist social worker Helen and flippant, carefree Ann, meet at the house of their mother Mary to await the death of their father. During the afternoon the three girls talk, sometimes bickering, gradually revealing the complexities of their lives. Their mother has the ability and clear sight to keep her worries in perspective. Throughout, Fox, as observer, provides comments which give depth and tone to the atmosphere.
ISBN 0 573 11076 X

The Fall and Redemption of Man. Play. John Bowen
57 characters, played by M8 F4 or M9 F3 (minimum) although more can be used. A bare stage. Fee code M

John Bowen's vibrant adaptation into modern English of the Mystery Plays of Chester, Coventry, Lincoln, Norwich, Wakefield and York is intended to show 'a group of young actors presenting a Mystery Play'. Dressed simply, donning or bringing on a small item to create a new character, and acting from a pageant wagon, history is played out from the creation of Adam and Eve to the death of Jesus Christ.
ISBN 0 573 11078 6

Falling Off a Log. Comedy. Georgina Reid
M2 (25, late 20s) F3 (young, late 20s, 40s). A veranda. Fee code L

When Mother unexpectedly plans a trip home from America, she is expecting to find her beloved garden in the state in which she left it. Her son Gerald's work on the garden has fallen short of her expectations, however, and the garden is now a jungle. Neighbour Pip comes to rescue Gerald with a brilliant idea; why not try a house-swap? Things seem to work out until a nosy reporter from *Happy Gardening* comes on the scene ...
ISBN 0 573 01684 4

Falling Short. Comedy. James Robson
M7 (mid 20s, 44, 55, 60s) F4 (25, 30s). 3 extras. An office. Fee code M

Tell the absolute truth for a day — a difficult task for an honourable man? Well, publisher Giles Short is honourable, but he is also kind, with a wife, a mistress and an appointment with an execrable, but very lucrative, author. And Giles has made a bet with a dubious, ruthless entrepreneur, staking everything he owns. The next twelve hours are likely to be something of a nightmare for Giles ... and those around him.
ISBN 0 573 01763 8

False Admissions. A translation of Marivaux's *Les Fausses Confidences* by Timberlake Wertenbaker
M5 F3. Interior settings. Fee code M

Marivaux's classic comedy is set among the pre-revolutionary French bourgeoisie and its satire on the manners of the time is biting. Here is a class for whom money speaks louder than love and even lechery must take a back seat if an inheritance is in the balance. The story hinges on unsuitable passion and how to consummate it against the odds, while its sub-text — servants controlling their masters — accounts for much of its post-revolutionary popularity.

A

Family Circles. Play. Alan Ayckbourn
M4 (20s, 30s, 60s) F4 (20s, 30s, 50s). A living-room. Fee code M

'We all marry the wrong people,' announces Edward Gray and, looking at his three daughters and their unsuitable partners, it is difficult to disagree. Edward's marriage to mousy Emma isn't much better— otherwise why would the daughters suspect they are trying to kill each other? Just as the plot is thickening, there comes Ayckbourn's *coup de théâtre* : the younger couples change partners — and then again! — so that every possible combination is shown to the audience.
ISBN 0 573 01764 6

Family Planning. Play. Frank Vickery
M3 (young, 21, 40s) F4 (teenage, 40s, old). Composite setting: a living-room, a bedroom, a hallway. Fee code L

When young Tracy discovers she is pregnant she doesn't know how to tell either her parents — solid, dependable Elsie and hypochondriac Idris — or her boyfriend, Bobby. Gran, permanently ensconced in bed (on stage), knows all and sees all, and helps to pave the way for her announcement. Unfortunately, Idris, overhearing Tracy and Elsie, jumps to the wrong conclusion and believes he has but a short time to live! An hilarious comedy!
ISBN 0 573 01685 2

Fanshen. Play. David Hare, based on the book by William Hinton
9 actors taking 30 parts. An open stage. Fee code M

This play is an accurate historical record of what once happened in one village four hundred miles south-west of Peking. Based on William Hinton's book it recounts in vividly dramatic form how the people of this village come to terms with Communism. The play should be performed by about nine actors, with no props, lighting cues or scenery.
ISBN 0 573 01703 4

♦ **Far from the Madding Crowd**. Play. Adapted by Matthew White from the novel by Thomas Hardy
M5 F3 or 4. Various simple settings. Fee code M (play), code A (music)

The passion, melodrama, earthy humour and strong, gripping plot of Thomas Hardy's novel *Far from the Madding Crowd* are vividly conveyed in Matthew White's fast-moving and admirably economical adaptation. Written to be performed with the simplest of settings and a relatively small cast, this is a powerfully intimate, concentrated theatrical experience. Period 1870s
ISBN 0 573 01769 7

The Farndale Avenue Housing Estate Townswomen's Guild Dramatic Society Murder Mystery. Comedy. David McGillivray and Walter Zerlin Jnr
M1 F4 (20s-50s). A drawing-room. Fee code L

Every drama group has experienced the horrors of what can go wrong on the night and the ladies of the F.A.H.E.T.G.D.S. are no different, with the possible exception that almost everything that could happen does. The scenery collapses, cues are missed, lines forgotten, as the ladies present their ambitious evening's entertainment with the cunning whodunit *Murder at Checkmate Manor.*
ISBN 0 573 11141 3

The Farndale Avenue Housing Estate Townswomen's Guild Dramatic Society's Production of *A Christmas Carol.* Comedy. David McGillivray and Walter Zerlin Jnr
M1 F4 (20s, 40s, 50s). M and F voices. Various simple settings. Fee code K

In festive mood, the F.A.H.E.T.G.D.S. ladies mount yet another assault on the classics with their stage version of *A Christmas Carol.* Enthusiasm their middle name, and with the virile support of stage-manager Gordon, the cast present a dizzy array of characters from the Dickensian favourite (and a few which aren't).
ISBN 0 573 01680 1

The Farndale Avenue Housing Estate Townswomen's Guild Dramatic Society's Production of *Macbeth.* Comedy. David McGillivray and Walter Zerlin Jnr
M3 F7 (20s-50s), with doubling. M1 F2 voices only. Simple settings. Fee code K

This uproarious comedy introduces the ladies of F.A.H.E.T.G.D.S., their producer, Plummer, and stage manager, Henry. Their startlingly original production of Macbeth should get them to the Welwyn Garden City Finals, but, under the carefully mascara'd eye of adjudicator George Peach, events conspire against them ...
ISBN 0 573 11269 X

Fashion. Play. Doug Lucie
M6 F3. An office, a kitchen/dining area. Fee code M

By the author of *Progress* and *Hard Feelings*, this play opened to critical acclaim at the RSC's The Other Place in April 1987, transferring to The Pit, London, in the same year. It starred Brian Cox as Cash, the successful advertising agent in Thatcherite Britain trying to land the Tory Party account.

Fatal Attraction. Thriller. Bernard Slade
M3 (35-50s) F3 (30s, 40s). A living-room. Fee code M

Blair is a famous actress about to be divorced from her second husband Morgan who has called at Blair's hideaway Nantucket beach-house to collect some of his paintings. A second visitor is Tony Lombardi, a photo-journalist who has dogged Blair for fifteen years and whom she has sued for harassment. His obsession with Blair certainly goes beyond professional interest but what motive does he have for murdering Morgan?
ISBN 0 573 69009 X

The Father. Play. August Strindberg. Adapted by John Osborne
M4 (20s, middle-age, 50) F3 (17, 40s, elderly). A living-room. Fee code M

John Osborne's adaptation of Strindberg's portrayal of the battle of the sexes presents a moving, incisive examination of marriage and parenthood. The Captain and his wife Laura struggle over the heart and mind of their only daughter, until Laura decides that she must completely destroy her husband in order to raise her child according to her own wishes. ' ... a scathing adaptation by John Osborne ... a natural Strindbergian for our times.' *Punch*. Period late nineteenth century

Fathers and Sons. Play. Brian Friel from the original novel by Ivan Turgenev
M10 (16, 19, 22, 40s, 60s) F5 (18, 20s, 50s, 70s). Various interior and exterior settings. Fee code M

Adapted from Turgenev's socio-political novel of rural Russia of the mid-nineteenth century, this passionate and powerful play's central topic is the confrontation of the old and the young, of liberals and radicals, romanticism and revolution.

Fear and Misery of the Third Reich. Play. Bertolt Brecht
Translations: John Willett, music by Hanns Eisler
                Eric Bentley
                Paul Kriwaczek
About 90 characters M and F. Interior and exterior settings. Fee code M for play, code C for music

The twenty-four scenes of this play could be regarded as separate playlets covering the years from 1933 to just before Hitler's entry into Vienna. Each is preceded and linked by a short verse, forming a sort of kaleidoscope of life under the Nazi dictatorship. The whole forms a horrifying picture of darkest tyranny, but is lightened by the occasional gleams of defiance.

Female Parts. One-woman plays. Dario Fo and Franca Rame. Adapted by Olwen Wymark
F1. An open stage. Fee code M for complete play. See individual titles below for fee codes if plays are performed separately

These four short plays were first performed in Italy in 1977. They were first performed in Olwen Wymark's English adaptation at the Royal National Theatre, London, in 1981 with Yvonne Bryceland playing the part of the woman in each.

In **Waking Up**, a young woman factory worker sleeps in late. In her anxious search for her house keys, she reconstructs the various phases of her day, demonstrating how trapped she is — by her husband, her baby, her work and her home. Fee code D
In **Woman Alone**, a housewife is locked up at home by her possessive husband — a paradoxical and comic interpretation of a woman used as a sexual object. Fee code D
The Same Old Story is a hilariously scatological fairy story. It describes the sexual relationship of a woman who is subordinate to the man and who refuses this subordination, while carrying the child she does not want. Fee code D
Medea takes its cue from the Euripidean tragedy, but here Medea kills her children in a howl of rage, in the painful awareness that children are the links of a chain which society hangs round the neck of women 'like a heavy wooden yoke that makes us easier to milk and easier to mount'. Fee code B

Female Transport. Play. Steve Gooch
M4 F6. Various simple settings. Fee code M

This is an account of six women in nineteenth century London, sentenced to be transported to a life of hard labour in Australia. During the six-month voyage, and while cramped below deck, they come to learn of the bias of a male-dominated society, represented in the play by the crew of the prison ship, that has lead to their sentence. 'A funny play, carried by racy vigour.' *Evening Standard* 'A compelling play.' *Financial Times*
ISBN 0 573 69185 1

Fen. Play. Caryl Churchill
22 characters, can be played by a cast of 6. Various simple interior and exterior settings. Fee code M

Fen tells the story of a poverty-stricken group of potato pickers working on a farm in the Fens. It traces the fortunes of one of the gang's workers, Val, and how she leaves her family for Frank, a farm labourer, against a general backdrop of greed and commercialism. '...will establish Miss Churchill without question as a playwright who expresses the complexities of the world through the lives of individual women brilliantly.' *Wall Street Journal*

◆ **A Few Good Men**. Play. Aaron Sorkin
M14 (wide range of ages) F1. Extras. Various simple settings. Fee code M

Two marines are on trial for their complicity in the death of a fellow marine. Their lawyer makes a valiant effort to defend his two clients and, in so doing, puts the whole US military mentality on trial because the defendants were following orders and are willing to go to jail if need be to maintain the marine honour code. Period 1986
ISBN 0 573 69200 9

The Fifteen Streets. Play. Adapted by Rob Bettinson from the novel by Catherine Cookson
M8 F8, with doubling. 2 boys 2 girls. Various simple interior and exterior settings. Fee code M

Set in 1910, this tells the story of one family's fight for physical and moral survival in the poverty and squalor of the dockland slums of Tyneside. At the centre is the apparently impossible love affair between rugged docker John O'Brien and Mary Llewellyn, a schoolteacher. With elements of tragedy, humour, intrigue and love, this simple tale affords plenty of scope for imaginative and evocative production.
ISBN 0 573 01688 7

Fighting Chance. Play. N. J. Crisp
M4 (40s, middle-age) F4 (30s). Basic set representing several interiors. Fee code M

Based on the author's own experiences, *Fighting Chance* is set in a residential rehabilitation centre for neurological patients, and charts the progress made by five patients over the course of eight weeks. The five demonstrate the humour, frustration, anger and pity of their situation, and help each other to progress, each to a different degree, through the course of this funny and ultimately optimistic play.
ISBN 0 573 01629 1

Filumena. Play. Eduardo de Filippo, adapted by Keith Waterhouse and Willis Hall
M6 F5. Extras. A dining-room. Fee code M

After twenty-five years Filumena is to be thrown over for a younger woman. She pretends to be dying, inveigling Domenico into a 'deathbed' marriage. When he proves the marriage null and void she informs him she has three grown sons — one of them his. After trying in vain to discover his son's identity he marries her. Filumena keeps the secret and as the play ends they are fully reconciled, with every promise of happiness before them. Period 1946
ISBN 0 573 11130 8

◆ **The Final Twist**. Play. Ken Whitmore and Alfred Bradley
M2 (30, 60s) or 3 F1 (23). A living-room. Fee code M

Charlie Nicholson has writer's block, but when he is offered a commission he sees a way to escape his debts. Merlin Foster, an actor, has specific needs: Charlie's script must contain the perfect method and alibi for the murder of Merlin's wife, only then can it be theatrically convincing. Eden, Merlin's young wife, is to remain in the dark so he can surprise her with the play ... A murderous and surprising tale.
ISBN 0 573 01765 4

Find Me. Play. Olwen Wymark
M3 F5 (variable). A bare stage. Fee code L

At the age of twenty Verity was charged by the police with damaging a chair by fire in the mental hospital where she was a patient. Later she was committed to Broadmoor 'from where she may not be discharged without permission of the Home Secretary'. Using a technique of multiple characterization, the play seeks to investigate in depth the personality of the young girl — to 'find her' — and at the same time studies the effects of her behaviour on those around her.
ISBN 0 573 11136 7

The Firstborn. Play. Christopher Fry
M10 F3. Pharoah's palace, Miriam's tent. Fee code M

The action takes place in Tanis, Egypt, during the period of the great plague. Its theme is the development to maturity of Moses as he confronts the Pharaoh, but it is the author's intention that the 'figure of life' which the latter's son, Rameses, presents should also be seen to take a central place. Period 1200 BC.

Fish Out of Water. (Original version.) Farce. Derek Benfield
M4 F5. An hotel lounge. Fee code K
ISBN 0 573 01654 2

Fish Out of Water (Revised version). Comedy. Derek Benfield
M3 (young, 40s, 50s) F4 (20, middle-age, 50s). An hotel lounge. Fee code K

The peaceful atmosphere of a hotel on the Italian Riviera is shattered by the arrival of Agatha, an outspoken widow, and her timid sister, Fiona. Agatha crushes all protests as she rounds up the guests into communal games, her unflagging spirit of togetherness invading the private lives of the other characters. All the ingredients of package holidays — late flights, double bookings, foreign food etc. — provide an evening of uproarious and innocent fun.
ISBN 0 573 11187 1

Five Finger Exercise. Play. Peter Shaffer
M3 (19, 20, 40s) F2 (14, 40). A weekend cottage. Fee code M

Walter, a sensitive young German, has been engaged as tutor to Pamela Harrington. He has fled to England from a Nazi father hoping to find a new home and nationality. His stay in the Harrington family begins propitiously, but the Harringtons are a desperately unhappy family. As Clive says, 'This isn't a family. It's a tribe of wild cannibals'. It takes a near tragedy to shock them into an awareness of their cruelty to each other. Period 1950s
ISBN 0 573 01132 X

Flare Path. Play. Terence Rattigan
M7 F4. An hotel lounge. Fee code M

Filmed as *The Way To The Stars* and set in the 1940s, Rattigan's famous play concerns Patricia's love for a film actor, despite her marriage to Flight-Lieutenant Teddy Graham. Going to the hotel to break with Teddy, followed by Peter, Pat encounters Doris, married to a Polish Count, who is one of two pilots not to return from a bombing raid. Hearing the Count's last letter, Pat realizes how much Teddy needs her, and gives Peter his dismissal.
ISBN 0 573 11128 6

A Flea In Her Ear. Farce. Georges Feydeau, translated by John Mortimer
M9 F5. A drawing-room, the Coq d'Or. Fee code M

Raymonde suspects her husband, Victor, of infidelity and she turns to her best friend, Lucienne, to help her gain proof. They concoct a ploy — based on a perfumed letter — to trap him at the Hotel Coq d'Or. In true Feydeau fashion the plan misfires; the plot is complicated by confused identities, revolving beds, a great many doors and the fact that the foolish hotel porter, Poche, is the exact double of Victor. Period early 1900s
ISBN 0 573 01148 6

Flesh and Blood. Play. Philip Osment
M2 (20s, 30s) F2 (20s, 30s). All age 30 years. A farm interior and exterior. Fee code M

Rose, Charles and William are reluctant partners in a remote farm. Charles wants his siblings to buy him out so he can settle down with Shirley, a local girl of dubious morals. Rose and William refuse. Shirley, pregnant, emigrates. Thirty years later the same trio are still marooned on the farm where time has done nothing to repair their jealousies and resentments. Shirley returns, forcing the family feuds to the surface and precipitating disaster. Period 1950s-1980s.

A Fly in the Ointment. Comedy. Derek Benfield
M3 (19, 50s) F3 (30s, 40s). A living-room. Fee code M

Why should Ron Corley MP, the Minister for the Environment, be searching the seaside bungalow of his ex-mistress Donna? And why does his virtuous wife, Louise, turn up at the same place on the same day? And what was a romantic doctor with a bunch of flowers doing in Sussex when his practice is in London? Add to these questions the presence of a frustrated policewoman and a devious pizza delivery boy ...
ISBN 0 573 01761 1

Flying Feathers. Comedy. Derek Benfield
M3 (40, middle-age, 60) F6 (young, 30, 50). A drawing-room. Fee code L

When Chief Constable Henry Potterton and his wife Sarah arrive at the country house of their late lamented brother Bernard, they are astonished to find several scantily-clad ladies wandering about, not knowing that Bernard's housekeeper has turned the place into a 'house of sin'. There are many hilarious comings and goings and when Bernard turns up, proving to be Henry's identical twin, the household is thrown into further confusion and chaos.
ISBN 0 573 01657 7

Fools. Comic fable. Neil Simon
M7 F3. A village square, a house. Fee code M

Leon Tolchinsky is ecstatic at landing a job as schoolteacher in the idyllic Ukrainian village of Kulyenchikov in 1890. But the village has been cursed with chronic stupidity for two hundred years and the desperate villagers have hired Leon hoping he can break the curse, which he must do in twenty-four hours or become stupid himself. Instead of leaving he falls in love, gets the girl and breaks the curse.
ISBN 0 563 60877 6

Fool's Paradise. Farcical comedy. Peter Coke
M2 (23, 50) F6 (20s, 40s, 50s, old). A drawing-room. Fee code M

Although surrounded by valuable antiques, Jane and Catherine live in debt, for their late husband, Basil, left house and property to them stipulating they could not sell any of it. Basil's sister has left them a spray of emeralds. If they prove valuable all their debts can be paid. Unfortunately Jane giddily accepts deposits on the emeralds from too many people and has to invent a third owner for them. As debts and troubles increase, she even accepts a deposit on Catherine's son!
ISBN 0 573 01137 0

Fools Rush In. Comedy. Kenneth Horne
M3 (young, 45, 50) F5 (20s, 40, elderly). A lounge-hall. Fee code J

On her wedding morning Pam is so appalled at the gravity of the promises she must make that she refuses to be married to Joe. Her doubts increase on meeting her father, Paul, long divorced from her mother. Pam was taught to think him an abandoned bounder, but finds him so charming she is convinced that if his marriage disintegrated then hers is bound to fail. Paul intervenes and incites Joe to elope with Pam whilst he himself enjoys a reconciliaton with his wife.
ISBN 0 573 01138 9

For Whom the Bell Chimes. Farce. Graham Greene
M6 F1. An apartment. Fee code J

The first chime ushers in to X a con-man supposedly collecting for charity. In a very short time X has changed clothes with him, covered his bald head with his own shockhaired wig, and walked off with his visitor's collecting case. Almost immediately the con-man discovers a dead girl, and from then on situations and surprises become increasingly frenetic.

The Foreigner. Play. Larry Shue
M5 F2. Extras. A fishing-lodge parlour. Fee code M

Trying to forget his marital problems, dull and doleful Charlie Baker takes a fishing-lodge holiday in the Deep South of America, and to avoid being pestered by the locals pretends that he is a foreigner who speaks no English. This leads him to become involved, at first unwillingly, in bizarre goings-on featuring a corrupt preacher, his pregnant girl-friend, her none-too-bright kid brother and the local branch of the Ku Klux Klan! The London production of this play starred Nicholas Lyndhurst.
ISBN 0 573 11282 7

The Forsyte Saga. Play. Pat and Derek Hoddinott, dramatized from the novels of John Galsworthy
M6 F5, M5 F5 with doubling. Extras 1M 1F. Various simple interior and exterior settings. Fee code M

Galsworthy's famous trilogy has been superbly adapted for the stage and achieved enormous acclaim following a national tour, starring Nyree Dawn Porter. Set between 1886 and 1920 with multiple locations cleverly contained within one set — a Victorian-style conservatory — requiring the minimum of props, the play centres on Soames and Irene and the stifling, destructive power of the Forsyte family, embodied in the cold hauteur of Soames.
ISBN 0 573 01766 2

Forty Years On. Play. Alan Bennett
M5 F2. Schoolboys (minimum of 6). A public school assembly hall. Fee code M

At a public school, now past its prime, the annual school play is being prepared. The progress of the play is severely impeded by the conflicts between the Headmaster and the play's producer, Franklin, and by the behaviour of the boys. *Forty Years On* is original, witty, erudite, moving and frequently hilariously funny.

The Fosdyke Saga. Play. Adapted by Alan Plater from the saga by Bill Tidy, music by Bill Wrigley
Variable cast but at least M10 F6. Extras. Simple staging. Fee code K plus fee for use of music.
Music on hire

Anyone familiar with the cartoon characters of Bill Tidy's 'Fosdyke Saga' from the *Daily Mirror* will know these lovable characters. The time is 1902 and the Fosdyke tripe business is failing so they decide to move to greener pastures in Manchester — the land of meat pies and perhaps fortune? We follow their progress through to the First World War.
ISBN 0 573 11135 9

Francis. Play. Julian Mitchell
M18 F2. Extras. Various simple settings. Fee code M

Saint Francis was born in Assisi in 1181 and in his early life was the playboy son of a rich merchant. Today the whole city is a memorial to him, but even during his lifetime there was conflict in his Order as to how far simplicity and poverty were to be taken. The play pictures him as 'a man whose inspiration could never come to terms with the real world'. Period 1205-1226

Frankenstein. Tim Kelly, adapted from Mary Shelley's novel
M4 F4. 1 set. Fee code L

Perhaps the truest adaptation of Mary Shelley's novel, this play opens on Victor's, a young scientist, and Elizabeth's wedding night. Previously Victor has created a 'Creature' out of bits and pieces of the dead. The creature tracks Victor to his sanctuary to demand a bride to share its loneliness. Against his better judgement Victor agrees and soon the household is invaded by murder, despair and terror! However there is enough macabre humour to relieve the mounting tension.
ISBN 0 573 60917 9

The Freedom of the City. Play. Brian Friel
M16 (20s, 60s, elderly) F1 (43). Extras. A parlour in the Town Hall. Fee code M

Set in Derry in 1970, in the aftermath of of a Civil Rights meeting, this play conjures the events of Bloody Sunday. Three unarmed marchers find themselves in the mayor's parlour in the Guildhall. Reports and rumours exaggerate their 'occupation' to forty armed rebels and they are shot by British soldiers as they surrender. The play documents the victims' final hours and a subsequent tribunal of inquiry into their deaths.

French Without Tears. Comedy. Terence Rattigan
M7 (15, 20, 30, 60) F3 (20s). A living-room. Fee code H

At the Villa Miramar, in the south of France, a group of young men are being coached in French by M. Maingot and his daughter, Jacqueline. They do not find French easy, but their progress is bedevilled by Diana Lake who has a gift for making men fall in love with her. Diana resists them, awaiting the arrival of Lord Heybrook, who turns out to be a fifteen-year-old schoolboy. She decamps to pursue a former victim, leaving another to be consoled by Jacqueline.
ISBN 0 573 01144 3

Fringe Benefits. Comedy. Peter Yeldham and Donald Churchill
M3 (21, 40s) F4 (20s-40s). A maisonette. Fee code M

Two couples take their annual holidays together in Torremolinos, but this year the men and women
have decided (separately) they don't want to go: the women because they are sick of it and the
men because there are two very attractive girls in East Croydon who would appreciate their
company. All suggest that plans are changed but as no-one wants to divulge the true reason,
complications inevitably ensue in this fast and furious comedy!
ISBN 0 573 11146 4

The Front Page. Play. Ben Hecht and Charles MacArthur
M17 F5. A press room. Fee code M

This extraordinary play was premièred in New York in 1928 and revived by Michael Blakemore
for the National Theatre in 1972 to great acclaim. One of the most exciting, amusing and intelligent
dramas of its period, it centres on a prisoner's escape on the eve of his execution, his concealment
and final discovery in the press room, and a remarkable reporter who, sick of his profession, tries
to get away from it, only to be pulled back by its irresistible lure.
ISBN 0 573 60912 8

Fuente Ovejuna. Play. Lope de Vega. Adapted by Adrian Mitchell
M17 (young, 40s, middle-age) F4 (young). 1 boy. Extras. Simple settings. Fee code M

De Vega's seventeenth-century play takes its name from an Andalusian hill town whose oppressed
inhabitants bravely rebelled in 1476, resulting in the killing of the tyrannical military overlord.
Adrian Mitchell's adaptation, commissioned by the Royal National Theatre, was produced at the
Cottesloe Theatre in 1989. 'It is hard to imagine a more gripping tale than the one that emerges in
Adrian Mitchell's translation.' *Time Out*

Funeral Games. Play. Joe Orton
M4 F1. Fee code F

Pringle has called in Caulfield to investigate his wife, who is having an affair with McCorquodale,
although Tessa insists she is only giving him blanket baths. According to his religion it would be
best if Pringle murders Tessa, although she will in fact live with her patient, who has already killed
his wife, Tessa's friend. This is true black comedy in best Orton style, with bogus religion, a
severed hand, and a corpse in the cellar.

♦ **Funny Money**. Comedy. Ray Cooney
M6 F2. A living-room. Fee code M

Good friends Betty and Vic arrive for Henry's birthday dinner and Jean is frantic because Henry
is late. When he eventually arrives he wants to emigrate immediately, and with good reason: the
briefcase he accidentally picked up on the Underground is stuffed with £735,000! When two
police inspectors call, Henry, Vic, Betty and a bemused (and tipsy) Jean are forced into a frantic
game of cat and mouse. Hilarious innuendo and cruelly funny turns of fate ensue as the two
couples assume various identities in their battle to keep the money.
ISBN 0 573 01762 X

Fur Coat and No Knickers. Comedy. Mike Harding
M9 (20s, middle-age, elderly) F5 (20s, middle-age), with doubling. Various simple settings. Fee code M

This hilarious play concerns the wedding of Deirdre and Mark. The fun begins on the stag night when an inebriated Mark is chained to a lamppost with a blow-up rubber doll. The wedding itself is quite high spirited too with half the guests, including the priest, suffering blinding hangovers. The play ends in comic chaos when Father Molloy, paralytically drunk, stumbles into the reception clad only in his ecclesiastical underwear, brandishing the blow-up doll!
ISBN 0 573 11145 6

Games. Play. James Saunders
Any number of players. Fee code F. (Published with *After Liverpool*.) Playing time one to one and a half hours according to use made of the material

A note on *Games* by the author: 'The script is not the final version, but the raw material from which the actors, the director and I worked out a more or less finished production. *Games* is about freedom, responsibility and choice, treated not as theoretical concepts, but as aspects of an actual event which takes place during rehearsals and during performance.'
ISBN 0 573 02501 0

Gaslight. Victorian thriller. Patrick Hamilton
M2 (45, 60s) F3 (19, 34, 50). A living-room. Fee code M

This classic Victorian thriller was first produced in 1935. Jack Manningham is slowly, deliberately driving his wife, Bella, insane. He has almost succeeded when help arrives in the form of a former detective, Rough, who believes Manningham to be a thief and murderer. Aided by Bella, Rough proves Manningham's true identity and finally Bella achieves a few moments of sweet revenge for the suffering inflicted on her.

♦ **Gasping**. Comedy. Ben Elton
M3 (young, middle-age) F2 (young) with doubling, or M3 F2, 3 other roles M or F. Various simple settings. Fee code M

Lockheart Industries are making serious money, but Sir Chiffley Lockheart is looking for the buzz given by a new way to make money where no money existed before. Philip, his pushy workaholic exec., suggests selling designer air as a privatized alternative to polluted urban fug. Eventually, oxygen runs low and new supplies have to be found. The third world is plundered for its resources, the world starts gasping and only the biggest suckers survive ... Period 1990
ISBN 0 573 01773 5

The Gentle Hook. Play. Francis Durbridge
M6 (30s, 40s, 60) F2 (30s, 50s). A living-room. Fee code M

Stacey Harrison is a charming, intelligent, sophisticated and highly successful career woman. Shortly after her return from a questionable trip abroad she is attacked by a stranger and, in the ensuing struggle, kills him. A second killing, and an attempt at a third occur before the mysteries — which also involve dealings in forged paintings — are finally resolved in this gripping thriller.
ISBN 0 573 11153 7

Gentle Island. Play. Brian Friel
M11 (10, young, 20s, 30s, middle age, 60s) F3. Composite set: a kitchen, a street. Fee code M

A morning in June. The inhabitants of Inishkeen, the Gentle Island, off the west coast of Co. Donegal, are leaving for good — all except Manus Sweeney and his family. In this parable of Ireland one of the characters remarks, 'There's ways and ways of telling every story. Every story has seven faces', and the title of Friel's brave work belies a set of violent sexual and homosexual tensions. The island's story and history unfold towards a shattering climax.

Germinal. Play. William Gaminara, adapted from the novel by Emile Zola
M10 F3. Interior and exterior settings. Fee code M

William Gaminara's memorably atmospheric adaptation of Emile Zola's novel of 1885, *Germinal*, deals with exploitation and oppression, both financial and sexual. The setting is a town in northern France, tragically divided by the effects of a miners' strike. The play was produced by Paines Plough in Plymouth in 1988 for an eleven-week tour culminating in London at The Place.

Getting On. Play. Alan Bennett
M4 (17, 19, middle-age) F3 (30s, 50s, 60). A basement flat. Fee code K

George Oliver is a middle-aged Labour MP who lives in his middle-class home with his children and his second wife, the bustling, attractive Polly. Disillusioned by the passing years and the changing world George is out of touch with his family, his friends and neighbours, with the world he has tried to improve. 'He's a socialist,' says Polly, 'but he doesn't like people' — the disenchanted reformer.
ISBN 0 573 01133 8

Ghetto. Play. Joshua Sobol, in a version by David Lan, with lyrics translated and music arranged by Jeremy Sams
M14 (young, 30s, 40s, 50s) F5 (20s, 30s). Extras. Various simple settings. Fee code M

Set in the Jewish ghetto of Vilna, Lithuania, in 1942, and based on diaries written during the darkest days of the holocaust, *Ghetto* tells of the unlikely flourishing of a theatre at the very time the Nazis began their policy of mass extermination. Premièred in Britain in 1989 at the Royal National Theatre.

The Ghost Train. Drama. Arnold Ridley
M8 (young, 20s, 60, elderly) F4 (20s, elderly). A station waiting-room. Fee code M

Arnold Ridley's classic drama was first produced in 1925 and filmed no less than three times. A very silly young man accidentally strands six passengers at a small Cornish wayside station. Despite the pyschic stationmaster's weird stories of a ghost train, they decide to stay the night in the waiting-room. Soon they regret this decision as ghostly and not so ghostly apparitions materialize before the young man reveals the true reason behind the night's events.
ISBN 0 573 01155 9

Gigi. Comedy. Colette and Anita Loos
M2 (30, elderly) F5 (16, young, 32, 60, 70). Two interiors. Fee code H. Period 1900
ISBN 0 573 01158 3

The Gin Game. A tragi-comedy. D. L. Coburn
M1 F1. A sunporch. Fee code M

In a seedy nursing home, the destitute Weller sits playing a lonely, unsuccessful game of solitaire. Prim, self-righteous Fonsia Dorsey joins him and they begin to play gin rummy while revealing intimate details of their lives. Fonsia wins every time and finally Weller leaves, a broken man, while she realizes her rigidity in life has left her an embittered, lonely old age. '... a vibrant study on loneliness, disillusion, old age and death yet fiercely funny.' *Boston Globe*
ISBN 0 573 60976 4

The Gingerbread Lady. Play. Neil Simon
M3 (20s-40s) F3 (17, 40s). A flat. Fee code M

Evy, a popular singer and an alcoholic, completes a ten-week drying-out period. Her friend, her daughter and an actor try to help her adjust to sobriety. But all have the opposite effect: the birthday party washes out, the gingerbread lady falls off the wagon and careers onward to her own tragic end. 'His characteristic wit and humor are at their brilliant best, and his serious story of lost misfits can often be genuinely and deeply touching.' *New York Post*
ISBN 0 573 60935 7

The Gioconda Smile. Play. Aldous Huxley
M5 (45, 55, elderly) F5 (22, 35, 45). Interiors. Fee code H
ISBN 0 573 01159 1

♦ **Give Me Your Answer, Do!** Play. Brian Friel
M4 (30s, 50s-60s) F5 (20s, 40s-60s). Composite set: a living-room, a lawn/garden. Fee code M

David Knight is staying in Donegal with novelist Tom Connolly and his wife, Daisy. He has been assessing Tom's papers, which he may purchase. Also visiting are novelist Garret Fitzmaurice and his wife whose marriage may break up, and Daisy's father and arthritic mother who may be soon in a wheelchair. Absent but casting a dark shadow is the Connolly daughter, institutionalized since she was a child. Everybody is waiting for an answer which may — or may not — come.

The Glass Menagerie. Play. Tennessee Williams
M2 (young) F2 (young, middle-age). A living-room. Fee code M

In a St Louis slum apartment lives Amanda Wingfield who clings frantically to another time and place when she was a southern belle with a myriad of 'gentlemen callers'. With her live her son Tom and crippled daughter Laura. Tom spends every spare moment losing himself at the movies while Laura's separation from reality increases until she is like one of her glass collection, too fragile to move from the shelf. Period 1945

Glengarry Glen Ross. Play. David Mamet
M7 (40s, 50s). A restaurant, an office. Fee code M

The scene is a real estate office in America — a fly-by-night operation selling tracts of underdeveloped land in Arizona to gullible Chicagoans. A sales contest is near its end; the winner will get a Cadillac, the second a set of knives, the bottom two get fired. This is the background to Mamet's seedy morality play filled with the spiralling obscenity and comic bluster of the salesmen. 'The dialogue becomes mesmerizing ... rich seam of humour and pathos ... ' *New Statesman*

A

God's Favorite. Comedy. Neil Simon
M5 F2. Interior. Fee code M

Neil Simon's actually made a funny play from the Book of Job — transferring the scene to a Long Island mansion where resides a tycoon, his wife, a prodigal son and a pair of zany twins. Then a messenger from God enters (wearing a big 'G' on his sweatshirt) and everything becomes a test of the tycoon's faith, including his family. 'Awesomely funny ... The work of a man of vision. It'll make you laugh out loud.' *New York Daily News*
ISBN 0 573 60972 1

The Golden Pathway Annual. Play. John Harding and John Burrows
M13 F7 but can be played by as little as M3 F1. A bare stage. Fee code M

The structure of this play is a loosely connected sequence of sketches, some deliberately written for great comic effect, and others pitched in a much lower key. It is about a boy growing up in the period from the end of the Second World War to the late 1960s. '*The Golden Pathway Annual* has things to say, says them well, looks you in the eye.' *Plays and Players*
ISBN 0 573 01666 6

♦ **Goldhawk Road**. Play. Simon Bent
M5 F3. A back room. Fee code M

Paul, a retired coach-driver, will soon be dead (or so he thinks) and the battle is on for his money. Paul's two illegitimate sons (of different mothers) are summoned to the scene. The dodgy, dealing Ralph is working for his financial stake, whilst John, a philandering coach driver, is equally keen to benefit from the will. Mary the cleaner has her own problems when her daughter Julia arrives having run away from her husband. This biting, funny look at contemporary living is easily staged.

Gone Up in Smoke. Thriller. Georgina Reid
M3 (35, 45, middle-age) F3 (17, 35). A drawing-room. Fee code L

Set on Guy Fawkes' night, this thriller has all the ingredients for a spectacular evening, full of surprises for everyone. Rod, a master at an exclusive girls' boarding school, and his wife Marian prepare the firework display. They are visited by a man who attempts to kill Rod but gets shot himself. In the ensuing panic Marian substitutes the body for the guy and it is now the twists and turns begin. ' ... good evening's entertainment.' *The Stage*
ISBN 0 573 11210 X

The Good and Faithful Servant. Play. Joe Orton
M3 F3. Fee code F

This is a savage study of the disintegration of an old man when he retires after fifty sterile years in the service of a factory. More badgered than solaced by the attentions of the personnel officer and the works club for retired employees, George Buchanan's belated search for happiness lurches breathtakingly from moments of hilarity to moments of extreme pathos.

The Good Doctor. Comedy. Neil Simon. Music by Peter Link
M2 F3, much doubling and trebling. Various interior and exterior settings. Fee code M. Fee for music available on application to Samuel French Ltd

This comedy, a composite of Neil Simon and Anton Chekhov, from whose short stories Simon adapted the twelve vignettes of this collection, was first seen at the Eugene O'Neill Theatre in New York in 1973 with Christopher Plummer playing a variety of leading roles. **NB: certain Musical Material must be used in all productions, a tape of which is available on hire from Samuel French Ltd.** 'As smoothly polished a piece of work as we're likely to see.' *New York Daily News* 'A great deal of warmth and humour — vaudevillian humour — in his retelling of the Chekhovian tales.' *Newhouse Newspapers*
ISBN 0 573 60971 3

♦ **Good Grief.** Play. Keith Waterhouse
M2 (35, 50s) F2 (32, middle-age). A living-room, hall and landing, a pub

A sensitive, wryly humorous study of a middle-aged widow who finds the courage to break with the past. June keeps a diary in the form of private conversations with her late husband Sam, a national newspaper editor. Her stepdaughter, Pauline, determines to keep an eye on June. Likewise, Eric Grant, an ex-colleague of Sam's. But June strikes out on her own and befriends Duggie, who, like June, is lonely. June, however, discovers that Pauline, Eric and Duggie have their own hidden agenda.
ISBN 0 573 01777 8

The Good Person of Sichuan. Play. Bertolt Brecht, translated by Michael Hofmann
M14 F8. 1 child. Extras. Various interior and exterior settings. Fee code M

This translation for the National Theatre production in 1989 starring Fiona Shaw, is based on Brecht's 'Santa Monica' version of the play first staged in 1943. Vibrant and hard-hitting, Brecht's famous theatrical parable begins when the gods award money to the prostitute Shen Te but greedy neighbours instantly take advantage of her good nature. 'Michael Hofmann's translation is engagingly free ...' *Daily Telegraph* '... a beautifully natural-sounding translation.' *Sunday Correspondent*

The Good Person of Szechwan (The Good Woman of Setzuan). Parable play. Bertolt Brecht
Translations: John Willett, music by Freda Dowie and Stephen Oliver
                Eric Bentley, music by Dessau
M17 F9. Interior and exterior settings. Fee code M for play, code C for music

Three gods appear on a mission — to find one really 'good' person. A kindly prostitute, Shen Teh, offers them lodging and is rewarded. To protect herself from spongers she masquerades as her male cousin, Shui Ta. Later she falls in love with an unemployed airman, finds he also is a sponger, reverts to the cousin impersonation, and is accused of murdering the missing Shen Teh. The gods appear as her judges and accept her plea that everything she did was with good intentions.

Goodnight Mrs Puffin. Play. Arthur Lovegrove
M5 (19, 20s, 50) F5 (20s, 45, 50). A drawing-room. Fee code J

The Fordyces are preparing for the wedding of their daughter, Jacky, to Victor, son of Stephen Parker, with whom Henry Fordyce is planning a business merger. Then in walks Mrs Puffin from Clapham who announces that she saw in a vision that Jacky would not marry Victor, and that she will in fact marry the young business associate, Roger Vincent, a friend of the Parker family. She also announces that Victor is in love with Jacky's younger sister, Pamela. The oracle proves accurate but no wonder as Mrs Puffin has been carefully primed for her role as suburban seer.
ISBN 0 573 01163 X

Goose-Pimples. Devised by Mike Leigh
M3 (30, one Arabic) F2 (20s). A flat. Fee code M

Vernon, Irving and Frankie have gone out to dinner. Meanwhile, Jackie, Vernon's lodger, returns to the flat with Muhammed, a non-English-speaking Arab who thinks he has been brought to a brothel. When the others return Muhammed assumes Vernon is the barman and produces wads of cash. The others make Muhammed the hapless butt of their tawdry humour, mocking, abusing and feeding him alcohol until he collapses sick, in tears and most of all bewildered at this strange display of English hospitality.
ISBN 0 573 11160 X

♦ **Grace Note**. Play. Samuel Adamson
M3 (20s, 34) F3 (30s, 67). A living/dining-room. Fee code M

When Grace decides to leave her sheltered accommodation and return to her old home, her children start to worry. Only Ellie, her daughter-in-law, seems to understand her need to dwell on the past and her passion for the Australian soprano Joan Sutherland. The family gather round to protect their inheritance, but behind the mask of genteel senility is cunning: Grace has plans of her own.

The Grace of Mary Traverse. Play. Timberlake Wertenbaker
M5 F3, with doubling. Extras. Various simple interior and exterior settings. Fee code M

The play, presented at the Royal Court Theatre in 1985, starts with Mary Traverse, the enclosed daughter of a rich city merchant breaking out to explore rakish life of eighteenth-century, male-dominated London. After many experiences Mary finally returns to her father, diseased, with her daughter and disillusioned in the realization that the injustices of this world remain. She is aware of the agonizing price which must be paid for knowledge but her optimism for a better world to come is not entirely quenched.

Grand Magic. Play. Eduardo de Filippo. Translated by Carlo Ardito
M11 (30-60) F8 (17, 20, 30, middle-age). A large hotel garden and two simple interiors. Fee code M

In this masterly black comedy the illusionist Otto gives his best performance ever. When Marta offers herself as victim in his disappearing act and takes the opportunity of running off with her lover, Otto convinces her husband, Calogero, that if he truly believes in his wife's fidelity she will reappear when he opens a certain Japanese box; if he does not truly believe and opens the box, she will be lost forever. Calogero suffers four years of indecision and his denial of reality is so complete that when Marta returns of her own accord he does not recognize her. He is condemned to the solitude of his illusory world.

♦ **Great Expectations**. Play. Hugh Leonard, adapted from the novel by Charles Dickens
M9 F5. Doubling possible. Various interior and exterior settings. Fee code M

Bringing to life all the vivid characters of the original and conveying the story with great clarity, atmosphere and theatrical flair, Hugh Leonard's adaptation of Charles Dickens's most popular novel is both exciting and haunting. Period early 19th century
ISBN 0 573 01778 6

Green Fingers. Play. Michael Wilcox
M10 F1. Various simple settings. Fee code **M**

When a young gardener and his lover are accused of burglary, the ensuing trial exposes the fear, prejudice and blackmail so often faced by homosexuals in this play from the author of *Rents* and *Massage*. Premièred at the Northern Stage Company with Live Theatre, Newcastle-upon-Tyne, in 1990, it was subsequently revived at the King's Head Theatre, Islington, in December 1990.

♦ **Greetings!** Comedy.Tom Dudzick
M3 (30s, mid 60s) F2 (29, mid 60s) A sitting-room and dining-room, with insert. Fee code **M**

Andy Gorski has a sweet Catholic mother, a sour Catholic father and a severely retarded younger brother who live in a working-class neighbourhood of Pittsburgh, Pennsylvania. When Andy reluctantly brings home his Jewish atheist fiancée to meet the folks on Christmas Eve, his worst fears about family blow-ups are realized. Brother Mickey, whose vocabulary thus far has been limited, suddenly says "Greetings!" and sends us on a wild, improbable and hilarious exploration into the nature of earthly reality.
ISBN 0 573 69257 2

Groping for Words. Comedy. Sue Townsend
M2 (young, 50) F2 (young, middle-age). Various simple settings. Fee code **K**

Joyce begins an Adult Literacy class. Her pupils are Thelma, a nanny, and George who is living in a hostel. Their classes, held in a nursery classroom, are interrupted by Kevin, the caretaker, who is illiterate himself. Act II sees the class three months later. George is making good progress and now living in the Wendy House while Thelma is concerned over her inability to read 'Janet and John'. Things come to a head on Joyce's birthday and culminate in Kevin's heartrending plea: 'Teach me to read'.

The Gut Girls. Play. Sarah Daniels
M6 F11, may be played by M2 F6. Various simple interior and exterior settings. Fee code **M**

Premièred at London's Albany Empire in 1988 and set in Deptford at the turn of the century this play traces the lives of the girls who work in the gutting sheds of the Cattle Market and how their lives are changed when the sheds are closed down. Although the girls are unwilling participants in a club founded by Lady Helena to find alternative employment the results are not without tragic consequences.

The Gypsy's Revenge. Comedy melodrama. Michael Lambe
M3 F6. 1 child. A wood, a cottage, a hall. Fee code **G**

Edward seduces and murders Xenia the werewolf who bites him. He then seduces Victoria. When Victoria is about to go into labour with child, he casts her out, and she gives birth to a werewolf. Xenia's father tries to exact retribution for the murder of his daughter and after much thunder and lightning, hooting and howling, this uproarious 'Victorian' melodrama closes with Edward getting his just deserts. This is a play written in the best tradition of look-behind-you melodrama.
ISBN 0 573 11151 0

Habeas Corpus. Play. Alan Bennett
M6 F5. A bare stage. Fee code M

Simply staged, this play introduces the Wicksteeds, a family for whom the determination to put sex and the satisfaction of the body before everything else is the ruling passion of their lives. Permissive society is taken to task in this farcical comedy in which the characters move in and out through a maze of mistaken identities and sexual encounters. As Wicksteed says, 'He whose lust lasts, lasts longest'.
ISBN 0 573 0 1325 X

Hadrian the Seventh. Play. Peter Luke
M9 (29, 40) F2 (40, elderly). Extras M. Various very simple settings. Fee code J

In his shabby bedsitter, Rolfe is writing his book, 'Hadrian the Seventh'. He reads of the Pope's death, and from now on the story of Rolfe's book becomes the action of the play — the events which befall Rolfe's autobiographical hero, George Rose, now seem to happen to Rolfe himself. He is summoned to Holy Orders, taken to Rome, elected Pope and assassinated. The play ends with a return to Rolfe's lodging where two bailiffs arrive with a Warrant of Execution.
ISBN 0 573 01168 0

Hamp. Play. John Wilson
M13. A barn/court-martial room. Fee code H

Hamp crawls out of a shell-hole at Passchendale and walks away from the battle. He is court-martialled for desertion in the face of the enemy. Many people try to make him realize that the court could insist on the maximum penalty. Obtusely, Hamp has utter faith in his counsel's power of words and believes that everybody is too busy with the war to trouble about his insignificant crime. But it is decreed: Hamp has to meet a death as unceremonious as the Army can make it. Period 1917
ISBN 0 573 04018 4

Hand Over Fist. Play. Richard Everett
M5 (20s, late 40s, 50s) F2 (40s). A patio and living-room. Fee code M

Angus, returning home to convalesce after a serious heart attack brought on by City job stress, finds a less than peaceful household. Sid and Gary, archetypal British workmen, are endeavouring to finish a kitchen extension; son Philip conducts a 24-hour shares dealership, and inept brother Roger and his long-suffering wife, Gwen, bring their never-ending financial problems round.
ISBN 0 573 01783 2

♦ **The Handyman**. Play. Ronald Harwood
M5 (30s, 42, 78, 82) F3 (30s, 75). A garden terrace. An interview room. Fee code M

Cressida and Julian live comfortably in the English countryside with their elderly Ukrainian odd-job man and friend of the family, Romka. Suddenly the police arrive. What has Romka done? Is he guilty? Is there a time limit on revenge and punishment? *The Handyman* looks at questions surrounding culpability, retribution, universal responsibility and the possibility of evil. 'Harwood's best and finest play. Its questions hurt because they are never theoretical: they are wrung from the flesh and mind of his characters.' *Sunday Times*

Hapgood. Play. Tom Stoppard
M7 (11, 20s-40s (1 Black), 50s) F1 (38). 1 boy (11). Various simple interior and exterior settings. Fee code M

Duality is the name of the game in Tom Stoppard's intricate spy thriller, seen at the Aldwych Theatre in 1988, where double agents, duplicity, twins and quantum physics are inextricably bound together. Hapgood runs a British counter-espionage agency in Mayfair and someone is leaking information to Moscow ...
ISBN 0 573 01781 6

The Happiest Days of Your Life. Farce. John Dighton
M7 (12, 20-50s) F6 (14, 20-50s). A masters' common-room. Fee code M

The masters of Hilary Hall School for Boys are told that St Swithin's, a girls' school, will be billeted upon them. The staff try desperately to conceal the fact that boys and girls are housed together, but in vain, for the parents find out. They are about to remove their offspring when a message arrives: a third school is to share Hilary Hall. Against this common enemy, both staff and parents unite to barricade the gates. Period 1940s
ISBN 0 573 0 1169 9

Happy Birthday. Comedy. Marc Camoletti, adapted by Beverley Cross
M2 (30s) F3 (20, 36). A living-room. Fee code M

Bernard invites his mistress, Brigit, to his home on her birthday despite the fact that his wife Jacqueline is present. To lull Jacqueline's suspicions he has also invited his oldest friend, Robert, and asks him to complete the cover-up by pretending that Brigit is his own mistress. Thus are laid the foundations for a shaky edifice of frantic complications, in which identities, plots and bedrooms are changed around with ever-increasing confusion.
ISBN 0 573 11172 3

Happy Event. Comedy. Richard Everett
M3 (30) F3 (20, 30). A living-room. Fee code L
ISBN 0 573 01614 3

Happy Families. Play. John Godber
M3 (young-70s) F6 (young-70s), may be played by M3 F5. Various simple settings. Fee code M

Full of warmth, understanding and humour, this is an affectionate and appealing portrait of an ordinary family struggling with change, bereavement and the generation gap. On his graduation day in 1978, John looks back over his teenage years, from 1967-1973, recalling all the embarrassments, tensions, joys and sorrows of family life in West Yorkshire. Older and better educated, he finds himself alienated from his working-class family who cannot understand his growing intellect and theatrical aspirations.
ISBN 0 573 01782 4

Happy Family. Play. Giles Cooper
M2 (39, 40) F2 (35, 40). A living-room. Fee code M
ISBN 0 573 11278 9

Happy Jack. Play. John Godber
M1 F1. A bare stage. Fee code M

Written a year after *September in the Rain*, we here encounter the same two characters, Liz and Jack, addressing the audience about the biographical details of the characters they play, and then slipping into those characters. Small, lovingly detailed extracts from the couple's lives are shown from their early courtship days, through to their retirement, but not in chronological order, so we constanty weave a path through their long life together. The *Financial Times* described the play as 'Neat, touching and joyously celebratory'.

The Happy Wizard. Satirical Fairy Tale. Kathleen Edleston
M7 F5. Extras. Composite setting. Fee code L. Music printed in the copy

A fairy story with a difference. The hero breaks with tradition in that he has the failings of an ordinary young man; the heroine is a radical; the 'baddie' is a not-unlikeable villain; the fairy is a graduate of a most unusual university. The adventures of these and other characters are slyly manipulated by a wizard whose absentminded magic produces unexpected results. Needless to say, there is a happy ending, but this too has an unforeseen twist.

Hard Feelings. Play. Doug Lucie
M3 F3. A living-room/ kitchen area. Fee code M

Viv, an unemployed university graduate is looking after the house for her parents and has surrounded herself with Oxford graduate friends/lodgers. As the Brixton riots begin to break out on the streets, four of the inmates are too taken up with their own domestic feuds to notice what is happening in the world outside. Eventually Viv succeeds in getting rid of them but not before the situation has shown the empty lives of these style-crazed people and their lack of human sympathy.

Hard Times. Play. Stephen Jeffreys, adapted from the novel by Charles Dickens
M2 F2 (minimum). Various interior and exterior settings. Fee code M

The wide expanse of Dickens's novel on the riches and hardships of the Industrial Revolution is triumphantly brought to life in this skilful adaptation. The nineteen or so main speaking parts are portrayed by two actors and two actresses, although it can be produced on a larger scale with each role cast individually. 'The strength of this version ... is its preservation of the satiric vitality of Dickens's original, and a real feel for the superb rhetoric of his prose.' *Time Out*
ISBN 0 573 01659 3

Harvest. Play. Ellen Dryden
M2 (35, 40) F5 (18, 30, 60). A chapel, a living-room. Fee code M
ISBN 0 573 11171 5

Haunted. Play. Eric Chappell
M4 (30s, 40s, middle age) F2 (30s). A study. Fee code M

Nigel Burke, aspiring playwright, is neurotic and agoraphobic and hasn't written a word for three months, to the chagrin of his wife, agent and friends. He is visited by the mysterious Potter, who knows of Nigel's interest in Byron and gives him a goblet used by the poet. Drinking from the goblet brings about subtle changes in Nigel's confidence and manner — and then, out of nowhere, Byron himself appears! *Haunted* is a flippant and exciting play from the author of *Natural Causes*.
ISBN 0 573 01794 8

The Haunted Through Lounge and Recessed Dining Nook at Farndale Castle. Comedy. David McGillivray and Walter Zerlin Jnr
M1(20) F5 (20-50). A through lounge, car, bedroom. Fee code K

The ladies of the Farndale Avenue Housing Estate Townswomen's Guild Dramatic Society make yet another spectacle of themselves, complete with their harassed producer and some extremely vigorous sound effects, in this sinister, spine-chilling mystery of murder and mayhem that is guaranteed to bring the house down, or at least a substantial part of the set.
ISBN 0 573 01615 1

Hay Fever. Comedy. Noël Coward
M4 (young, middle-age) F5 (young, middle-age, elderly). A hall. Fee code M

The Bliss family are ultra-Bohemian. One Saturday, they all casually announce that they have invited guests for the weekend, and each Bliss is furious. When the guests arrive, they suffer an uncomfortable tea and then, after dinner, have to play a word game which only the family understand. The evening is capped by a histrionic display by the whole family which succeeds in sending their terrified guests scuttling away by the first train the following morning. Period 1925
ISBN 0 573 01174 5

◆ **Haywire**. Comedy. Eric Chappell
M2 (20s, 50s) F4 (20s, 30s, 50s, 70s). A living-room. Fee code M

Alec Firth is having an affair with his assistant, Liz, and has organized his domestic life so that they can go to Spain on holiday without making Alec's wife Maggie remotely suspicious. What could possibly go wrong? The answer: plenty. On the doorstep, in dizzyingly rapid succession, are: Phoebe, Alec's mother, who has discharged herself from her old people's home; Alec's son Jamie, with a broken ankle; and his daughter Mandy, heavily pregnant and not planning to marry the child's father ...
ISBN 0 573 01798 0

◆ **Heatstroke**. Comedy. Eric Chappell
M4 (30s, 50) F2 (20s, late 30s), 1F voice. 2M extras. A living-room/terrace. Fee code M

Assumed identities, breakneck pace and hilarious mishaps of farce mix with the tension and startling plot reversals of a thriller in this clever, amusing play. The Spencers arrive for a peaceful holiday in a luxurious Spanish villa, closely followed by actor Howard Booth and his girlfriend. Unfortunately, Sam and Howard have matching holdalls which have become mixed up. Yet a third, identical holdall, full of money, brings the sinister Raynor to the villa ...
ISBN 0 573 01800 6

Hedda Gabler. Play. Henrik Ibsen. A new version by Christopher Hampton
M3 (29, 33) F4 (33, 45, 65). A drawing-room. Fee code M

The Ibsen classic, in a new version by Christopher Hampton, was seen at the Royal National Theatre in 1989 starring Juliet Stevenson as Hedda '... Hampton's was, above all, language made to be spoken not quoted. As such it is the key to the production's success in establishing the sense of the, at times, appallingly comic spectacle of a claustrophobic and fragile world coming apart at the seams.' *What's On*
ISBN 0 573 01693 3

Hedda Gabler. Play. Henrik Ibsen, adapted by John Osborne
M3 F4. Fee code M

Hedda's father seems to have been the only person Hedda loved. He left her his duelling pistols and in her hands they play an important part in the life of more than one person. Thea is loving, talented, and doomed, it seems, to be one of Hedda's victims. Yet at the end Thea saves herself through her own unselfish love of another victim of Hedda's cruelty. John Osborne's adaptation ofIbsen's drama was first seen at the Royal Court Theatre in 1972 with Jill Bennett in the role of Hedda.

Heil, Caesar! Play. John Bowen
M17 F5, doubling possible. Extras. An open stage. Fee code L

Although not a modern-dress version of Shakespeare's play it does show how closely its situation of democracy versus dictatorship is applicable to all times. At the opening Caesar and his entourage are playing cards at an exclusive club, while Antony and others are at the craps table. The Senate House becomes a present-day Committee Room, with a secretary serving coffee and Caesar assassinated by the use of flick-knives; the forum speeches become television appearances — and so on throughout the action.
ISBN 0 573 01705 0

The Heiress. Play. Ruth and Augustus Goetz. Based on the novel *Washington Square* by Henry James
M3 (young, middle-age) F6 (late 20s-40). A sitting-room. Fee code M

Compared to her mother, the heiress Catherine Sloper seems dull and lifeless, or at least that's what her father believes. With her lack of confidence Catherine becomes easy prey for fortune hunter Morris Townsend who deserts her on finding out she has been disinherited. Two years later, we see Catherine, her father dead, having matured considerably after her experiences and prepared to take revenge on Morris Townsend. Period 1850
ISBN 0 573 01176 1

Henceforward ... Play. Alan Ayckbourn
M2 (40s) F3 (teenage, 30s, 40s). Extras 1M 1 girl. A studio. Fee code M

In a fortified, steel-shuttered flat in North London, lonely composer Jerome sits surrounded by sophisticated, high-tech audio-visual equipment with only a robot nanny for company. Jerome desperately wants to get his teenage daughter back from his estranged wife, and enlists the services of Zoë, an unemployed actress, in his cunning plan. When his plan doesn't work, Jerome has to improvise and it's amazing what can be done with some new microchips and a screwdriver ...
ISBN 0 573 01691 7

♦ **Heritage**. Play. Stephen Churchett
M3 (19, early 50s, mid 70s) F2 (mid 30s, 50). A public garden. Fee code M

Three generations of a family come to terms with change over the course of a year. Stephen Churchett's elegiac new play considers how we deal with what's handed down to us, both the tangible and the not-so-tangible. How do we confront our mortality, and if we do live on in some way, what is the nature of our immortality? ' ... infinitely touching in its weary acceptance of the personal and environmental destruction wrought in the name of progress.' *Spectator*

Hiawatha. Play. Michael Bogdanov
M8 F3. Extras if required. A giant tepee. Fee code M. Certain music must be used with this text. Please enquire for details

This adaptation of Longfellow's poem into a fast-moving spectacle of dance and rhyme had a very successful run at the National Theatre. All actors are called upon to perform the fast, athletic dancing, mime and percussion that makes this play an exciting and vivid visual experience.
ISBN 0 573 01786 7

Hidden Laughter. Play. Simon Gray
M5 (teenage, middle-age, elderly) F3 (teenage, 30s). Composite setting: garden, kitchen and sitting-room. Fee code M

Harry and Louise, a London couple, decide they have found the perfect weekend retreat in a Devon cottage: they can escape London's trials and traumas, their two children can grow up with nature and without television, and Harry's widowed father can relax. But the wiles of the outside world obtrude into this rural idyll and the cottage is soon for sale, leaving a trail of failure and disillusionment in its wake.
ISBN 0 573 01784 0

High Profiles. Comedy. Woodrow Wyatt
M4 (17, middle-age) F4 (15, 20s, 40s, 50s). A luxury flat in Westminster, the Garrick Club. Fee code M

Conservative MP Philip Grantly has a loving wife, loving mistress, two teenage children and a good chance of a seat in the Cabinet. One by one his wife discovers his affair, his daughter is suspended from school for snorting cocaine and his socialist son is involved in a public brawl. Finally a newspaper discovers his affair and threatens to publish, resulting in a comedy which combines romance and wit with fun and suspense.
ISBN 0 573 01785 9

Hobson's Choice. Lancashire comedy. Harold Brighouse
M7 (26, 30, 50s, elderly) F5 (20s, elderly). Three interiors. Fee code M

Henry Hobson, widower and boot-shop proprietor, twits his daughter Maggie on her being past the marrying age. Maggie retaliates by marrying Hobson's best boot-hand, Will Mossup, and turning this retiring youth into a sturdy fellow whose new confidence makes him a real business rival to Hobson. Bowing to the circumstances, Hobson has no choice but to accept Will as partner in the new firm of 'Mossup and Hobson'. Period 1880
ISBN 0 573 01181 8

Holiday Snap. Comedy. Michael Pertwee and John Chapman
M4 (40, 50) F3 (20, 30, 70). Extra 1F. The living-room of a villa. Fee code M

A time-share villa has been double booked unbeknown to the company rep, myopic tippler 'Chitto' Chittenden. When Mary and Henry arrive shortly after Eve and Leslie, Chitto manages to remain unaware that there is more than one couple on the scene. The confusion is compounded when each couple mistakes the other for the servants and what follows is a tale of comic predicament and mistaken identity which unfolds with real wit and style.
ISBN 0 573 11284 3

Holidays. Play. John Harrison
M2 (30s, 40s) F1 (40s). A stone cottage. Fee code M

Rose, faced with a further spread of cancer, has come, on her counsellor's advice, to a lonely Yorkshire cottage. For a week she will live alone, without the aid of her smothering husband, and make some decisions about where she is going. Embracing her solitude avidly, she nevertheless reckons without Ralph, a very unusual odd-job man, who proves to be not the solution she seeks but the catalyst to her ultimate decision.
ISBN 0 573 01780 8

The Hollow. Play. Agatha Christie
M6 (38, 40, elderly) F6 (30s, 60). A sitting-room. Fee code M

Gathered at the home of Sir Henry and Lucy Angkatell are various guests amongst whom is Dr John Cristow, his mistress Veronica, his ex-mistress and his wife. Veronica ardently desires to marry Cristow but he refuses to divorce, and Veronica unwisely declares that if she can't have him no-one else will. Within five minutes he is dead. Nearly everyone had a motive and opportunity to murder Cristow, but who actually committed the deed has to be discovered by Inspector Colquhoun and Sergeant Penny.
ISBN 0 573 01182 6

The Hollow Crown. Anthology. Devised by John Barton
M3 F1, 4 Musicians. Fee code H

A unique entertainment composed of the letters, speeches, poems, songs and music by and about Kings and Queens of England. Against a background of the simplest design four readers, three singers and a pianist can perform this work, which sparkles with the wit of several centuries and demonstrates the vulnerable humanity of those who have worn the crown.
ISBN 0 573 01183 4

The Holy Terror: Melon Revised. Play. Simon Gray
M7 (17, young, middle-age, elderly) F3 (young, 30s-40s), may be played by M4 F3. A platform, the mind. Fee code M

The original version of this hilarious, coruscatingly witty play was produced as *Melon* in 1988 with Alan Bates in the lead. The revised version, entitled *The Holy Terror*, had its stage première in the USA in 1991. Mark Melon addresses the Cheltenham W.I. on his career as a successful, ruthless publisher who has suffered a breakdown. The events that he describes then come to life.

Home. Play. David Storey
M3 (middle-age, elderly) F2 (middle-age). A terrace. Fee code J

Two elderly gentlemen stroll on to an almost bare terrace. They discuss various subjects — the past, schooldays, climate, the sea, moustaches, the war, families, etc., etc. It is not until the following scene when we meet two women that we realize we are actually in the grounds of a mental hospital, and that these people are patients. Although with no plot at all in the conventional sense and sparse dialogue, by the end of the afternoon we have been moved to compassion and respect.
ISBN 0 573 01220 2

Home Before Dark, or the Saga of Miss Edie Hill. Play. Jimmie Chinn
M12 (teenage-40s, 2 black) F9 (teenage-middle-age). Extras. Various simple settings. Fee code M

In this portrait of a small cotton mill town in Lancashire, Edie Hill is essentially portrayed as a tragic heroine: she works hard; raises an illegitimate son, and loses her family one by one as they fall victim to the cotton dust from years spent at the mill. However, Edie is a very funny character, and the tragic points in her story are interspersed with moments of great warmth and humour. Period 1946-1964
ISBN 0 573 01787 5

Home Is Where Your Clothes Are. Comedy. Anthony Marriott and Bob Grant
M4 (20s-50s) F4 (20s, 40s). A garden flat. Fee code M

When his wife runs off with another man, the Major solves his debt problem by letting the basement of his wife's house — to two different tenants simultaneously! Jill only uses the flat at weekends, while Philip lives there during the week, and the Major swaps their belongings at the beginning and end of each week. But then Jill unexpectedly gets a week off work and a whole set of complications, wild confusion and awkward confrontations follows!
ISBN 0 573 01789 1

The Homecoming. Play. Harold Pinter
M5 (30, 63, 70) F1(30). One interior. Fee code M

Teddy arrives home to pay his family a visit with his wife Ruth, who settles into the household as if into a well-known niche. Teddy's brothers and his father all take it for granted that she is anyone's for the asking — and she is. It is then suggested that they should set her up in trade, in a little flat in Soho. Calmly Ruth lists the conditions she requires before accepting, barely batting an eyelid as Teddy returns to America.
ISBN 0 573 01555 4

The Hostage. Play. Brendan Behan
M8 (18, middle-age, elderly) F5 (18, 35, black youth). A lodging-house. Fee code M

The play is about a young Cockney soldier who is taken as a hostage for an IRA man who is due to be hanged in Belfast. His captors are obsessed with memories of 1916 and dreams of Irish freedom. His companions in the disreputable lodging house where he is held prisoner are a cross-section of Dublin derelicts. As well as being a profound comment on Anglo-Irish relations and the Irish themselves, it is also full of comedy.

The Hotel in Amsterdam. Play. John Osborne
M5 F4. An hotel room. Fee code L

Gus, Laurie and Amy with their respective husbands and wives are all planning a weekend away in Amsterdam to escape the influence of the producer, 'the biggest, most poisonous, voracious, Machiavellian dinosaur in movies'. Although they agreed to keep their arrangement secret, word does get out. Finally a telephone call announces that the producer is dead — suicide. In the period which culminates in this climax we have also learnt a good deal about the three couples themselves.

A

Hotel Paradiso. Farce. Georges Feydeau and Maurice Desvallieres. English adaptation by Peter Glenville
M9 F8. Extras. Two interiors. Fee code M

Boniface arrives at the Hotel Paradiso to meet Marcelle; Maxime has been enticed there by an enterprising and amorous maidservant; Cot goes there to investigate the strange noises which he is convinced emanate from the drains. In order to avoid extremely compromising confrontations, everyone spends the entire night dashing up and down the stairs and in and out of beds in a crescendo of hilarious chaos which is made even worse by a sudden police raid on the unsavoury hotel. Period 1910

The Hothouse. Play. Harold Pinter
M6 F1. Composite set: 2 offices, a stairway, a sitting-room, a soundproof room. Fee code M

It is Christmas Day and a mysterious death and an unexpected birth are troubling Roote, the director of a Government 'rest home'. Who the patients are and what they might be suffering from, we never discover, but as the unstable, megalomaniacal and terminally insecure Roote begins to investigate, we find that the other members of staff are, in various ways, as mad and as dangerous as the people they are supposed to be helping.

The Hound of the Baskervilles. Mystery play. Tim Kelly, from the thriller by Sir Arthur Conan Doyle
M5 (young, 40s, 50s) F5 (young, 50s). A sitting-room. Fee code L

In this modernization of the classic spine-chiller, Sir Henry is heir to the Baskerville fortune as well as the family curse: death at the fangs of a living horror prowling the moors. Only Sherlock Homes can stop the beast from striking again. Is the supernatural at work? Audiences will have a terrific time attempting to discover the true killer — and reacting to the surprise twist.
ISBN 0 573 61041 X

House Guest. Thriller. Francis Durbridge
M4 (young, middle-age) F4 (young, middle-age). A living-room. Fee code M

Robert and Stella learn that their son has been kidnapped — not for ransom, but to force them to allow one of the kidnappers to remain in their house. Two other men, supposedly police officers, arrive and reveal that one of the kidnappers has been murdered. Soon, however, it is clear that these two are far from what they seem. A highly exciting thriller, first seen at the Savoy Theatre in 1982 with Gerald Harper and Susan Hampshire.
ISBN 0 573 11178 2

The House of Bernarda Alba. Tragedy. Federico García Lorca. Translated by Richard L. O'Connell and James Graham-Luján
F11. Extras. A living-room. Fee code J

Although fully grown, with the older ones approaching middle-age, the five daughters of Bernarda are kept under strict subjection, prevented from marrying because no suitors appear who are of the right class. Accused by her old servant of blindness towards her children, Bernarda refuses to relent. All the daughters suffer from her repression, and the youngest, Adela, suddenly rebels against it. Her attitude, however, leads to dissension among them and eventually to tragedy.

The House of Blue Leaves. Play. John Guare, music and lyrics by John Guare
M3 (45) F6 (20s-40s). Extras 2M. A shabby apartment. Fee code M

Artie, a New York zookeeper, dreams of becoming a successful songwriter but is thwarted by his insane wife and an unfortunate lack of songwriting talent. Egged on by his mistress Bunny, Artie attempts to remedy his situation on October 4th, 1965 — the day the Pope visits New York — but the arrival of his army-deserter son (who wants to assassinate the Pope), three nuns, a Hollywood producer and a deaf starlet only ensures catastrophic results.
ISBN 0 573 61028 2

The House of Dracula. Comedy-horror. Martin Downing
M7 F5, extra 1M; or M6 F5, extra 1M, with doubling. A castle hall. Fee code L

Hailed as 'A Monster Hit' by the Yorkshire Evening Post, this clever spin-off from *The House of Frankenstein!* sees the Baron, Baroness and their repulsive retainers, Ygor and Frau Lurker, going to stay at a macabre Transylvanian fortress. Excitement turns to terror, however, when they are greeted by more than a few of their mortal (and immortal) enemies. A wickedly funny, fast-moving horror farce.
ISBN 0 573 01790 5

The House of Frankenstein! Comedy-horror. Martin Downing
M6 (30s, 40s) F4 (20s-40s). A castle hall. Fee code L

Baron Von Frankenstein, bored with his attempts to give life to the lifeless, has turned his attention to curing the supposedly incurable. He plays host to various mysterious and menacing denizens of the night (invited or otherwise) who visit the Baron to beg him to rid them of their vices. But his challenge, although a welcome diversion for the headstrong young scientist, proves to be no picnic ... more of a living nightmare!
ISBN 0 573 11356 4

Edith Wharton's **The House of Mirth**. Adapted by Dawn Keeler
M5 (20s, 30s, 40s, 50s) F5 (20s, 30s, 40s). Grand Central Station. Fee code M

Set in New York in the early part of the twentieth century the play charts the disastrous career of socialite Lily Bart. Educated to be nothing more than a highly decorative ornament, she is forced by her father's financial ruin into the invidious status of impoverished house guest of rich friends while in pursuit of a wealthy husband. But Lily's ultimate tragedy is her inability to forsake her free spirit and independence to achieve that goal.
ISBN 0 573 69573 3

House of Secrets. Play. Peter McKelvey
M3 (late 20s, early 30s, late 50s) F3 (20, late 20s, early 30s). A sitting-room/kitchen alcove. Fee code L

Richard and Sarah Higgs' house is thrown into utter turmoil when Julie, one of their lodgers, is attacked and a phone call confirms that a neighbour saw Julie's attacker, and that he was someone from the lodging house. Suspicion rises and falls in turn upon each man in the household until the police are able to arrest the culprit ... but have they actually found the guilty party? A wryly funny, well-observed and agonizingly suspenseful drama.
ISBN 0 573 01788 3

The House on the Cliff. Mystery Comedy. George Batson
M2 (25, middle-age) F4 (23, 35, 50, middle-age). A living-room. Fee code L
ISBN 0 573 01190 7

How the Other Half Loves. Comedy. Alan Ayckbourn
M3 (30s, middle-age) F3 (30s, 40s). Two merged living-rooms. Fee code M

In this suburban trio of married couples, one couple is at the top of the social ladder. One of the other couples is attractive and upcoming, despite the fact that she is an utter slob and he is a boor; and the third pair is socially hopeless but earnest. The action takes place at two dinner parties given on consecutive nights. The single set, representing two living-rooms, is almost a character in itself.
ISBN 0 573 11166 9

◆ **Hysteria**. Play. Terry Johnson
M3 (60s, old) F1 (20s-30s). A room. Fee code M

First produced at the Royal Court Theatre, London, in 1993, *Hysteria* was staged in this revised version at the Duke of York's Theatre, London, in 1995. 'One of the most brilliantly entertaining new plays I have seen in years: wild, weird and funny, serious, compassionate and shocking, blasphemous and reverential, intellectual and frivolous, a factual fantasy, a demented farce, a black nightmare.' *Sunday Times* 'A brilliant play ... sheer theatrical audacity incorporates authentic pain into a farcical framework.' *Guardian* Period 1938

I Have Been Here Before. Play. J. B. Priestley
M4 (28, 40s, 60s) F2 (28, 35). An inn sitting-room. Fee code H

Dr Görtler believes that a future dimension of time can be entered in dreams, and is drawn to a Yorkshire inn in search of proof. He had dreamed of an unhappy couple coming to this inn, the wife meeting a lover, and the discovery driving her husband to suicide. To his horror, Dr Görtler sees the dream in danger of becoming reality. He warns them of the potential unhappiness and fortunately, they heed him. Written in 1938
ISBN 0 573 01194 X

I Have Five Daughters. Comedy. Adapted from Jane Austen's novel *Pride and Prejudice* by Margaret Macnamara
M4 (20s, 40) F10 (teenage, 20s, 40, 50). A morning-room. Fee code K

The author has adapted Jane Austen's great novel with the particular problems and needs of the amateur stage in view. The actual course of events has been, in the author's words , 'pretty drastically simplified', but the essential spirit of the novel has been delightfully retained. Period early nineteenth century
ISBN 0 573 01195 8

I Love My Love. Play. Fay Weldon
M2 (30s) F3 (30s). Various simple settings. Fee code L

Trendy magazine *Femina* offers two contrasting wives — country-bumpkin Anne and sophisticate Cat — £1000 to swap places for a week to compare lifestyles. Anne goes to London to run the chic apartment of Cat's advertising executive husband, while Cat journeys to deepest Devon to cook, clean and care for gentle, sexually-repressed, shopkeeper Derek. Violent snowstorms mean that Cat and Derek are cut off, and when the snow ploughs eventually arrive the life-swap has become a wife-swap. A witty, finely observed study of middle-class contrasts.
ISBN 0 573 11253 3

I Remember Mama. Play. John van Druten
M11 (teenage, young, 40s, 50s, elderly) F15 (young, 20s, 40s, 50s) 2 boys. Three interiors and insets. Fee code M

The play opens with Katrin Hanson, a young Norwegian girl living in San Francisco, reading from the manuscript of her autobiography. Then follow scenes from an important period of her life giving us glimpses of the career of this delightful, affectionate, impecunious family of Hansons. Mama, the real heroine, is responsible ultimately for Katrin's literary career, in which *I Remember Mama* is her first success. Period 1910
ISBN 0 573 01197 4

I Thought I Heard a Rustling. Play. Alan Plater
M3 (20s-40s) F2 (50s). A library backroom; Civic Centre room. Fee code M

An ex-miner turned poet is appointed writer-in-residence at Eastwood branch library. Ellen, senior librarian, soon realizes the feckless but charming Geordie is no poet. Despite this she finds him highly entertaining, much to the disgust of Nutley, an earnest young man who covets the writer-in-residence role. These three find themselves an unlikely but united strike group when the Libraries sub-committee proposes demolishing the library. '... warmth, affection and humour ... ' *Sunday Telegraph*
ISBN 0 573 01791 3

Icecream. Play. Caryl Churchill
M7 F6, may be played by M3 F3. Various simple settings. Fee code H

Produced to acclaim at the Royal Court Theatre, this eighty-minute play was subsequently produced in New York as a double bill with *Hot Fudge*. A middle-class American couple travel to England on a genealogical search and find third cousins who are decidely low-life and whom they aid following a violent event. Who is the worse: the doer of evil deeds or he who enables him to continue? 'Highly comic ... works like a short, sharp shock: an acidly entertaining statement about mutual cultural incomprehension.' *Guardian*

If We Are Women. Play. Joanna McClelland Glass
F4 (18, 40s, 60s). A beach-house veranda, a kitchen and dining area. Fee code M

Jessica, a writer approaching middle-age, her mother Ruth (who is unable to read or write) and her Jewish mother-in-law, Rachel, find themselves emotionally stranded in Jessica's Connecticut beach home. Weighing the choices each have made as women, as daughters, as mothers, their recollections of guilt and regret are punctuated by wry observations on sex, history, ideas and their relationships with the men in their lives.
ISBN 0 573 13009 4

I'll Be Back Before Midnight! Thriller. Peter Colley
M2 (30s, 50s) F2 (20s). A farmhouse living-room. Fee code M

Following a nervous breakdown, Jan is brought to an isolated farmhouse by her husband Greg, ostensibly to complete her recovery. But unsettling things start to happen as soon as they arrive. First, Greg's sister Laura, with whom he seems to have an unnaturally close relationship, arrives. There is also George, the slightly demented old farmer who lives nearby. A nightmare of frightening occurrences results in a thrilling and heart-stopping ending!
ISBN 0 573 01652 6

I'll Get My Man. Farce. Philip King
M4 (20s, 40s, 60s) F5 (20s, 40s). A lounge-hall. Fee code L

Peter, a famous television series hero, seeks refuge at a country rectory with his mild Uncle Humphrey from all the females who continually chase after him. Humphrey, horrified by the dismissal of his housekeeper by his formidable sister, advertises for a wife, but absent-mindedly omits the important word 'marriage'. Answers to the advertisement arrive by the sack-load and the arrival of the dignified Bishop of Lax adds to the hectic confusion.
ISBN 0 573 01533 3

I'll Leave it to You. Comedy. Noël Coward
M4 (20s, 40s) F6 (young, middle-age). 1 girl. A hall. Fee code M

A poor widow with five grown-up children, Mrs Dermott turns to her rich brother Dan for help. When Dan arrives, he finds the charming, lazy family all ready to live on his supposed wealth. He announces that he will leave his fortune to the member of the family who has accomplished the most in three years; after three years he then informs them he has no money at all. Period 1920
ISBN 0 573 61060 6

I'm Not Rappaport. Comedy. Herb Gardner
M5 (16, 35, 40s, 80 (one Black)) F2 (25, 40s). Central Park. Fee code M

This warm comedy concerns two octogenarians determined to fight off all attempts to put them out to pasture. Nat is a lifelong radical determined to fight injustice (real or imagined) and has a delightful repertoire of eccentric personas, which makes the role an actor's dream. The other half of this unlikely partnership is Midge, a black apartment janitor who spends his time hiding out from tenants who want him to retire.

The Imaginary Invalid. Play. Molière. Adapted by Miles Malleson
M8 (25, middle-age, 50s-70s) F4 (15, 20s, 30s). A sitting-room. Fee code H

To reduce his medical fees, hypochondriac M. Argan decides to marry off his daughter Angelica to a physician's son. Unfortunately, Angelica loves Cléante. Argan's brother Béralde and Toinette, an inventive maid, save the situation for the lovers and expose Mme Argan's schemes to bleed her husband of his fortune. Then they persuade the hypochondriac to turn physician so that he can quack himself free of charge. Period 1674
ISBN 0 573 01200 8

Imaginary Lines. Comedy. Reggie Oliver
M2 (30s, 60s) F3 (20s, 30s, 60s). A flat and a bookshop. Fee code L

Wanda takes things Very Seriously Indeed. Matchmaker, idealist dreamer, she is the despair of the men — gentle, serious bookshop owner Howard and successful MP and publisher Sir Michael Thurston — who love her and who try vainly to beat paths, imaginary or otherwise, to her door. This delightful new comedy was first seen at the Stephen Joseph Theatre in the Round in a production directed by Alan Ayckbourn.
ISBN 0 573 11241 X

The Importance of Being Earnest. Comedy. Oscar Wilde
M5 (young, middle-age) F4 (young, middle-age). Two morning-rooms, one garden. No fee

Jack Worthing is 'Ernest' in town. He wins Gwendolyn's hand, but Gwendolyn declares that she chiefly loves him for his name — Ernest — the name Jack has allotted his non-existent brother whose peccadilloes explain his frequent absences from his country home where lives his pretty ward, Cecily. Meanwhile, Cecily has decided to marry rake-hell 'Ernest' and when Algernon presents himself in this guise, she immediately accepts his smitten proposal. However, through some highly improbable coincidences, all is happily resolved. Period 1890s
ISBN 0 573 01202 4

The Importance of Being Earnest. Oscar Wilde. Four-act version reconstructed by Vyvyan Holland
M7 (young, middle-age) F4 (young, middle-age). Two morning rooms, one garden. Fee code J

Wilde originally wrote this play in four acts, but it was thought too long and he was asked to reduce it to three. In 1954 the BBC broadcast the 'lost scene' with Mr Gribsby, an amusing character with a short scene in the second act. Dramatic critic James Agate commented, 'The fun in the scene Wilde deleted is better than any living playwright can do.'
ISBN 0 573 11198 7

In for the Kill. Thriller. Derek Benfield
M3 (25, 40s) F2 (19, 30s). A living-room. Fee code L

Paula has arranged to receive a young admirer, Mark, one evening when her husband, James, is away, but before he arrives an old friend of James's turns up and seems to suggest a plot to kill him. Mark appears, as does James, unexpectedly. Mark then dies in an apparent car accident which soon proves to be deliberate murder. The suspicions, accusations and unexpected revelations among the four characters culminate at last in a surprising and dramatic climax.
ISBN 0 573 11180 4

In Praise of Love. Play. Terence Rattigan
M3 (young, 40s, 50s) F1 (50s). A living-room, hall and kitchen. Fee code J

Lydia has an incurable disease, a fact she conceals from her husband Sebastian, a man apparently totally bound up in himself. They are visited by Mark, who discovers that in reality Sebastian has known about Lydia's illness but thinks she does not know of it herself, and puts on a false front to protect her. Mark contrives that Lydia should discover the truth, knowledge which she decides to keep to herself.
ISBN 0 573 11170 7

In the Bar of a Tokyo Hotel. Play. Tennessee Williams
M3 (young, middle-age) F2 (middle-age, Hawaiian). An hotel bar. Fee code M

An artist, Mark, is worn to a nervous ruin by a breakthrough in his painting technique and is abandoned and destroyed by his witch of a wife. The intensity of the work, the unremitting challenges and demands it makes of him leave so little of him after the working hours that simple comfortable *being* is impossible for him ...

In the Jungle of the Cities (In the Cities' Jungle). Play. Bertolt Brecht
Translations: Gerhard Nellhaus
Ronald Hayman
Anselm Hollo
Eric Bentley
M12 F5. Extras. Interior and exterior settings. Fee code M

Shlink, a Chinese timber dealer, and his underworld friends turn his lover and sister into prostitutes. Garga, Shlink's business competitor, demolishes Shlink's business at the cost of himself going to gaol. There he denounces Shlink for enticement of the two girls, and arranges that he should be lynched at the time of his own release. They escape the lynchers together. Shlink dies as the mob arrives; Garga sets fire to the timber business and leaves for New York. Set in Chicago, August 1912 - November 1915

Inadmissible Evidence. Play. John Osborne
M3 (young, 30s, middle-age) F5 (young, middle-age). A solicitor's office. Fee code J

This is a partly impressionistic portrait of Bill Maitland, a seedy middle-aged solicitor, head of a small firm. Everything around him is crumbling away: his business, his marriage, his love affairs. In an opening sequence he dreams of his own trial, with his colleagues as judge and clerk of the court. The scenes that follow represent both actual events — his relationships with colleagues, staff and clients and the deepening turmoil in his own mind.

The Inconstant Couple. Play. John Bowen, translated and adapted from *L'Heureux Stratagème* of Monsieur de Marivaux
M5 (20s-middle-age) F3 (early 20s, early 30s). A terrace and garden. Fee code M

Marivaux wrote with a pointed wit and cunningly affected style, and this translation preserves the light, satirical flavour of the original. This play tells of the involved amorous relationships between the country gentleman, the Chevalier, the Countess and the Marquise, which are reflected in and influenced by corresponding situations between their servants. After many complications and conspiracies the gentlefolk are paired off — with a six months' trial of constancy.

The Increased Difficulty of Concentration. Comedy. Václav Havel. Translated by Vera Blackwell.
M4 F4. A living-room and hall. Fee code M

First performed just four months before the Russians invaded Czechslovakia in 1968, the play was presented in London at the Old Red Lion in 1989. Here we see a doctor with his mistress and his wife and a female social worker with a special computer that interrogates and interviews. The gaps in our lives cause the gaps in concentration. Very deftly the author elides one scene with another, one situation with another.
ISBN 0 573 61082 7

◆ **Indian Ink**. Play. Tom Stoppard
M11 (20s, 30s, (2 Indian) middle-age (1 Indian)) F4 (young, 30s, elderly) Male extras. Various simple settings. Fee code M

Flora Crewe, a liberated English poet, travels to India for health reasons in 1930 and meets Nirad Das, an Indian artist. Their developing friendship mirrors the shifting relationship between the Indians and English in the latter stages of the Raj. Five and a half decades later her sister Eleanor helps an earnest American academic, Eldon Pike, research Flora's life. As he travels to India, Nirad's son, Anish arrives in Shepperton ... Period 1930 and 1985
ISBN 0 573 01796 4

Inner Voices. Play. Eduardo de Filippo. English version by N. F. Simpson
M14 (20, 40s, 50, middle-age) F5. A kitchen, a sitting-room. Fee code M

This English version, commissioned by the Royal National Theatre, was presented at the Lyttelton Theatre in 1983. Alberto accuses the Cimmarutas of murdering Aniello. The police arrest the whole Cimmaruta family, but Alberto begins to think he dreamt the murder. The Cimmarutas are freed but, one after another, each member of the family denounces another. Solemn farce and knockabout tragedy become indistinguishable and fear makes a fool of everyone.

Inside Job. Thriller. Brian Clemens
M2 (30s, 40s) F1 (30s). A living-room. Fee code M

Spain is a well-known haven for criminals who skip abroad. On the Costa del Sol, professional safe-cracker Larry has struck it lucky. Gorgeous Suzy asks him to steal the diamonds from her husband Alex's safe and run away with her to Rio. At the same time Alex also employs Larry to murder Suzy for her £100,000 life insurance policy. Larry decides to tell Suzy about her husband's plans, and they together plot to steal the diamonds, murder Alex, and make off with the dividend from Alex's similar insurance policy. Several twists add to the suspense in this exciting thriller. ISBN 0 573 01792 1

◆ **Inside Trading**. Comedy. Malcolm Bradbury. Heavily adapted from the play *Jugend Voran or Ho-Ruck* by Paul Vulpius
M12 F2, M10 F2 with doubling. An executive suite. Fee code M

Based on a 1933 German satire by Paul Vulpius, Malcolm Bradbury has written a satirical comedy for the nineties, moving the play to an age of the dream-filled, scheme-filled millennium and the big deal. Set in Battenberg's, an ancient London merchant bank with a proud tradition and suspect past, the play centres on a rogue trader whose ambitions for his own survival draw in government, European funding and our millennial dreams.

Insignificance. Play. Terry Johnson
M3 (40s, middle-age, 70) F1 (30s). An hotel room. Fee code M

It is New York, 1953. High above the city, in a luxury hotel bedroom, on a hot summer's night, four of America's most famous legends — a beautiful film star, a Nobel Prize-winning scientist, a renowned baseball player and an infamous senator — meet for an extraordinary confrontation. '... a young writer of peculiar promise ... Mr Johnson is that rare creature; a moralist with wit. He writes with responsible gaiety.' *Guardian* '... tremendously powerful and moving ...' *Time Out*

Inspecting Carol. Comedy. Daniel Sullivan and The Seattle Repertory Co.
M7 (African-American 30, 40s, 60s) F4 (40s, 60s). 1 boy (11). A bare stage. Fee code M

Dickens's *A Christmas Carol* meets Gogol's *Government Inspector* meets *Noises Off* in this hilarious American hit which satirizes theatre management and the rehearsal process. An amateur actor decides to turn professional and auditions for a small American Midwest theatre. He is so naïve that he is suspected of being an informer for the government and soon everyone is obsequiously trying to cater to the bewildered wannabe actor. ISBN 0 573 69368 2

An Inspector Calls. Play. J. B. Priestley
M4 (25, 30, 50s) F3 (20s, 50). A dining-room. Fee code M

Priestley's classic play of the believable middle-class Yorkshire family called to account for its moral crimes by the enigmatic Inspector Goole stands as a metaphor for our own failure to accept our responsibility to others. Stunningly revived by the Royal National Theatre in 1992, the production transferred to the West End the following year. Period 1912 ISBN 0 573 01205 9

Inspector Drake and the Perfekt Crime. Comedy. David Tristram
M3 F2. A living-room. Fee code K

When a genius commits a murder, the plan is perfect. But is it foolproof? Inspector Drake is back to face his greatest-ever challenge. Who is the mysterious Doctor Short, and why did he marry a warthog? Has he murdered his fourth wife — or did she murder him first? These are just some of the questions facing the indomitable Drake in this hilarious sequel to *Inspector Drake and the Time Machine*.

Inspector Drake and the Time Machine. Comedy whodunit. David Tristram
Nine characters, may be played by a cast of five with doubling. Interior of an old house, a spaceship. Fee code K

The professor's dead body is found floating weightlessly in the study, his daughter has vanished, and everything points to the mysterious Time Machine. Can the intrepid Inspector Drake, ably hampered by Sergeant Plod, solve the crime of the century? — the thirtieth century that is. Fasten your seat belts for a comedy that's way ahead of its time!

Inspector Drake's Last Case. Comedy. David Tristram
M7 F4 or 5. A room. Fee code K

No-one could have foreseen the strange events that took place one dark evening at the home of Mrs Gagarin. We see her taking a stroll. Next she screams, 'Who is it? Oh, it's you!' Next a gunshot! It's up to the world's greatest detective to solve the crime. But, in the words of Sergeant Plod, 'don't believe everything you see ...' After all, is it safe to say that Mrs Gagarin is actually dead?

Interpreters. Play. Ronald Harwood
M4 (40s, 50s) F2 (40s, 93). A small conference room, a living-room. Fee code M

This ingenious ironical comedy of betrayed love was produced at the Queen's Theatre, London, in 1985-86. Nadia is an interpreter at the Foreign Office in London involved in negotiations with a Russian delegation. Her Russian counterpart turns out to be Victor, with whom she had a tempestuous affair some ten years previously. Moving and comic complications ensue in this tale of love across the Iron Curtain.

Intimate Exchanges. A related series of plays. Alan Ayckbourn
M1 F1 (minimum). A garden. Any one of several places. A churchyard. Fee code M for each play

Intimate Exchanges is a related series of plays totalling eight scripts which can be performed by just two actors, although more could be used if desired. As each scene ends, a character faces a decision, the result of which determines the course of the rest of the play.

VOLUME I: **Affairs in a Tent, Events on a Garden Terrace, A Garden Fête, A Pageant**
ISBN 0 573 016127

VOLUME II: **A Cricket Match, A Game of Golf, A One Man Protest, Love in the Mist**
ISBN 0 573 016135

◆ The Invention of Love. Play. Tom Stoppard
M12 (18, 20s-77) F1 (19, and 35) with doubling. Various simple settings. Fee code M

'From the bare bones of the dry life of A. E. Housman ... Tom Stoppard has been inspired to write the most emotionally powerful and enthralling play of his career. Never before has he written with such exciting eloquence ... It's a tremendous, scaring vision of a sacrificed life.' *Evening Standard*. Period 1877-1936. **Available 1st March 2000**

The Invisible Man. Play. Ken Hill, from the novel by H. G. Wells
M17+ F5+. A stage. Fee code M (play) Fee code A (music). Optional illusions available under licence

Ken Hill has turned H.G. Wells's gripping novel into a music-hall romp, combining tongue-in-cheek humour with tragedy and magic. The sinister Griffin arrives in the village of Iping with a bandaged face and an unsociable manner. Was it really an accident that destroyed his face, or is he a criminal on the run? He takes off his gloves to reveal no hands and his bandages to reveal no head! Then the pranks — comic and malevolent — truly begin ...
ISBN 0 573 01793 X

◆ Ion. Play. Euripides, in a new version by David Lan
M6 F2, or M5 F3. F chorus. The Temple of Apollo. Fee code M

In Euripides' enchanting play, the young hero, Ion — a foundling engaged to keep the Temple of Apollo tidy — meets the Queen of Athens. The two strike up an instant rapport. She tells him of a 'friend' who was seduced by Apollo and gave birth to a child whom she abandoned ... After a series of surprising and disturbing twists, mother and son are reunited and the story is resolved in a manner which foreshadows a new genre of European drama: the family romance.

The Island. A male chauvinist comedy. James Saunders
M2 F5. A clearing on a semi-tropical island. Fee code H

It is sometime in the future, in the new age of woman, which began when women, sick of the destruction and futility of war, turned on their men and killed them. On a semi-tropical island, five sisters live in idyllic paradise, until one day two brothers are washed up on the beach. The two sexes try to come to terms with each other despite the handicap of being unable to communicate verbally.

It Can Damage Your Health. Comedy. Eric Chappell
M5 (1 Indian) (20s, 30s, 40, 50s) F1 (20s). A hospital ward. Fee code M

Based on Eric Chappell's hit TV series *Only When I Laugh*, this traces the fortunes of a disparate trio who share a Men's Surgical ward: the cynical, defensive Higgins; the young, nervous Gary; and the weary hypochondriac Palmer. Together, they form an uneasy alliance against the confusions and insecurities of hospital life.
ISBN 0 573 01795 6

A

◆ **It Could Be Any One of Us**. Comedy. Alan Ayckbourn
M3 (early 40s, mid 50s) F3 (16, late 40s, mid 50s). A living-room. Fee code M

A thunderstorm. A windswept country house. A family of failures — a detective who has never solved a case; a writer, an artist and a composer whose work has never been aired publicly; a dysfunctional teenager — wrangling over a bequest ... All the prime ingredients for a murder-mystery thriller in the traditional mould. But this thriller is by Alan Ayckbourn and has within it a number of surprises.
ISBN 0 573 01797 2

It Runs in the Family. Comedy. Ray Cooney
M7 (20s, middle-age, 50s, old) F5 (18, 40s, old). A doctors' common room. Fee code M

Dr David Mortimore is about to address a neurologists' convention, which will probably earn him a knighthood. While putting the final touches to his speech an old flame arrives and announces that their liaison years ago resulted in a son who is downstairs desperate to meet his dad. Frantic to hide this catastrophic news from his wife and the hospital authorities, David is forced to invent not one but two non-existent husbands!
ISBN 0 573 01799 9

It Was a Dark and Stormy Night. Mystery-comedy spoof. Tim Kelly
M6 F8, or M5 F9. An isolated house. Fee code L

A shameless spoof that's loaded with laughs and thrills. The creepy, haunted *Ye Olde Wayside Inn* oozes New England Gothic atmosphere and never has guests. Ebenezer, one of the residents, is dangerous when there's a storm — and there's a storm! Several intruders from the outside world are forced to seek shelter, but who's the skeleton in the wheelchair and why is it wearing a bridal veil? When the wind howls and the lights flicker the chilling time begins!

It's Ralph. Play. Hugh Whitemore
M3 (young, 40s, 50s) F1 (40s). The ground floor of a converted farmhouse. Fee code M

Andrew and his wearily frustrated wife Clare are spending the weekend in their Gloucestershire cottage, which, like their marriage, is well in need of repair. Ralph, an old friend of Andrew's, visits and remembers their shared radical youth. Ralph brings Andrew face to face with his own spiritual bankruptcy and the latter finally unburdens himself to his visitor. Clare leaves, the house decays rapidly and Ralph helps Andrew to regain his integrity, but at a price ... **NB**. Contains explicit language

◆ **Ivanov.** Play. Anton Chekhov, adapted by David Hare
M7 (wide range of ages) F5 (wide range of ages). Extras. Various interior and exterior settings. Fee code M

Perhaps the least performed of Chekhov's plays, *Ivanov* is the fierce and funny portrait of a man whose life is plummeting fast into domestic and philosophical chaos. Ivanov is an impoverished, anti-Semitic landowner who has rejected his Jewish wife who is dying of tuberculosis, and is now infatuated with the daughter of a rich neighbour. Period nineteenth century

Jack the Lad. A musical celebration. Book and lyrics by David Wood and Dave and Toni Arthur. Music by Dave and Toni Arthur
M6 (20s, 50s, 80) F4 (20s-40s). 3 children, 1 dog. A gypsy encampment. Fee code M

In a gypsy encampment, a series of Jack tales and songs (from Little Jack Horner, through Jack and the Beanstalk to Spring Heeled Jack) is performed by the gypsies, with singing and dancing, a mumming play, a shadow-mime and puppetry, to celebrate the eightieth birthday of their senior member, Jack the Lad. Vocal score sold separately.
ISBN 0 573 01801 4

Jack the Ripper. Musical reconstruction. Ron Pember and Denis de Marne
M8 (young, middle-age) F8 (young). Extras. Equally suitable for small drama societies as well as musical societies. Composite standing set: a music hall, a pub, London streets. Fee by arrangement

The play is a musical reconstruction of the East End murders which took place in 1888, an atmospheric commentary rather than an historical re-enactment, shifting between reality and artificiality, with characters representing 'real' people as well as members of the music hall audience and players. Period late Victorian
ISBN 0 573 08042 9

Jane Eyre. Play. Willis Hall, adapted from the novel by Charlotte Brontë
M4 F8, with doubling. Various simple settings. Fee code M

Whilst retaining all the familiar passionate qualities of Charlotte Brontë's novel, Willis Hall successfully transposes the nineteenth-century world of *Jane Eyre* to the stage with simply staged short interconnected scenes and intimate locations. With the passages of direct narration broken up and shared out amongst the Company, a fictional tale of a penniless, plain girl becomes a work of great emotional force in the most complete stage adaptation of the classic novel.
ISBN 0 573 01802 2

Jane Eyre. Drama. Helen Jerome. Dramatized from Charlotte Brontë's novel
M7 (20s, 30s, elderly) F9 (18, 20s, 30s, middle-age, elderly). 1 girl (7). A library, a living-room. Fee code M

Literature has not duplicated such a love story as follows between the embittered, tragically lonely Rochester, landed proprietor and Jane's employer, and Jane 'untouched and innocent but intellectually his equal'. We meet Rochester's mad wife; follow Jane through her frustrated marriage and flight; her happy association with Diana and St John Rivers; her coming into her fortune; and the happy ending.
ISBN 0 573 01207 5

Jane Eyre. Play. Charlotte Brontë. Adapted by Charles Vance
M4 (30s) F6 (young, 18, 20s, middle age, elderly) (F5 with doubling), 1 child. A library and passageway. Fee code M

Focusing on the love story between Jane and Rochester, the play begins as Jane arrives in 1846 to take up the post of governess to Rochester's ward, Adèle, at Thornfield Hall. Jane and Rochester fall in love but their happiness is jeopardized by the discovery of the terrible secret from Rochester's past, resolved by the dramatic fire which maims Rochester. The action, contained in a single setting with one small inset scene, makes for exciting theatre.
ISBN 0 573 01803 0

Jeffrey Bernard Is Unwell. Play by Keith Waterhouse, based on the life and writings of Jeffrey Bernard
M1. M2 F2 playing at least 22 parts. A pub. Fee code M

Gambler, journalist, fervent alcoholic and four-times married Jeffrey Bernard writes the weekly 'Low Life' column for the *Spectator* magazine, chronicling Soho life as well as offering a very personal philosophy on vodka, women and race-courses. From this, Keith Waterhouse has brilliantly constructed a play which is set in the saloon bar of Bernard's favourite Soho pub, the *Coach and Horses*.
ISBN 0 573 01804 9

Jekyll and Hyde. Play. Leonard H. Caddy, based on the novel *Dr Jekyll and Mr Hyde* by Robert Louis Stevenson
M4 (40, middle-age, 60) F4 (young, 20s, 30). Extra 1 child. A parlour and part of the adjoining laboratory. Fee code K. Period 1851
ISBN 0 573 11186 3

♦ **John Gabriel Borkman**. Play. Henrik Ibsen, in a new version by Nicholas Wright
M3 (young, 60s) F5 (15, young, middle-age). A drawing-room, a ballroom, a courtyard. Fee code M

In Ibsen's penultimate play, written in his late sixties, a former 'pillar of the community' has been in voluntary seclusion in an upstairs room since enduring a prison sentence for embezzlement. His wife, her twin sister, his son and even Borkman himself are all entrapped in the suffocating atmosphere of his claustrophobic household ... Period 1890s

Joking Apart. Play. Alan Ayckbourn
M4 (20s, 30) F4 (20s). A garden. Fee code M

Charming, naturally successful in everything, Anthea and Richard almost unconsciously but ruthlessly dominate the lives of those with whom they are associated. Over twelve years Sven, Richard's partner, is virtually nudged out of the firm. Brian, who works for Richard, is ineffectual; Hugh, the local vicar, whose wife is on drugs, falls hopelessly in love with Anthea. The play ends with Anthea's daughter awaiting her eighteenth birthday; perhaps a new reign may be beginning ...
ISBN 0 573 11204 5

Joseph Andrews. Comedy. P. M. Clepper, from the novel by Henry Fielding
M7 (20s, 50, middle-age) F10 (18, 20, 45, middle-age). Extras. Various simple settings. Fee code K

Fielding's novel recounting the adventures and misadventures of the handsome footman and the simple parson is dramatized for an easy-to-stage production, requiring a minimum of props and settings. Robbers, grasping innkeepers, love, jealousy, rivalry, personal misunderstandings, revelations of unexpected relationships — all find their places in the exuberant story. Period about 1740
ISBN 0 573 11209 6

Journey's End. Drama. R. C. Sherriff
M11 (young, 40s, middle-age). A dug-out. Fee code M

Second Lieutenant Raleigh, the new officer assigned to C Company, is welcomed by everyone except, apparently, Captain Stanhope, who reveals, later, that Raleigh was at school with him and hero-worshipped him. What neither of them knows is that if 'Stanhope went up those steps into the front line without being doped with whisky, he'd go mad with fright.' The drama of the personal relationships between the men is played out against the larger tragedy raging around them. Period 1918
ISBN 0 573 04003 6

Jumpers. Play. Tom Stoppard
M12-17 (40-50s, old) F2 (young). Multiple interior set. Fee code M

The hero is a professor of moral philosophy, and the play is a serious attempt to debate the existence of a moral absolute, of metaphysical reality, of God. Unfortunately, George's trained hare disappears and an Inspector Bones arrives to investigate the rumour that one of George's team of gymnasts has been shot dead while performing in his sitting-room. Intelligent, surreal and zany, this is Stoppard at his best.

June Moon. Comedy with music. George S. Kaufman and Ring Lardner
M7 (20s-40s) F5 (20s-40s). Simple interior settings. Fee code M (for play), separate fee code for music

A gauche, naïve, but talented young lyricist, Fred, arrives in New York to make a bit of money on Tin Pan Alley in 1929. There he falls into the clutches of Eileen — a money-grabbing vamp — before he returns to his faithful true love, Edna. The play enjoyed a successful London revival at the Hampstead and Strand Theatres in 1992. '... wise-cracking comedy.' *Evening Standard*

Juno and the Paycock. Play. Sean O'Casey
M12 (young, 20s, 50s, 60, elderly) F6 (22, 45, very old). A tenement room. Fee code M

A stark, uncompromising tragedy which unsparingly shows that Irish gaiety and song are the despairing camouflage for a dirge. It is the waste that is tragic — Juno's staunchness has to suffer a shiftless strutting husband, 'Captain' Jack Boyle, the 'Paycock' of the title. True, there are moments of raucous comedy, but they are satire, O'Casey's revelations by antithesis. Period 1922
ISBN 0 573 01214 8

Just Between Ourselves. Play. Alan Ayckbourn
M2 (30s, 40s) F3 (30s, 40s, 60s). A garage, pathway and yard. Fee code M

Dennis spends his spare time messing about in his untidy garage, indifferent to the fact that his wife is being driven to distraction by his possessive and jealous mother who is slowly undermining her, both physically and mentally. Each scene occurs on the birthday of one of the characters, but the comedy becomes increasingly sharp and ironic as the action proceeds and darkens.
ISBN 0 573 11212 6

◆ **Just the Three of Us**. Play. Simon Gray
M1 (50s) F2 (20s, 50s). A studio. Fee code M

Whenever Enid writes one of her best-selling novels, she adopts a domestic pet as a companion, sends her husband away and retreats to her converted lighthouse. This time there is a difference — her adopted "pet" is Terri, her husband's PA. Chained up, but with plenty of home comforts, Terri is desperate to escape initally. Then she settles into the odd ménage consisting of herself, Enid and the eccentric vicar, Ronnie. Dependence, obsession, redemption and retribution are all themes of this unusual and observant comedy.

Just the Ticket! Comedy. John Waterhouse
M3 (20, middle-age) F3 (19, middle-age, elderly). A living-room. Fee code J

Harry is a zealous traffic warden. One of his hobbies is collecting stuffed birds and this is a cause of great friction between him and his wife. Harry's daughter, Ruby, is engaged to weedy Gerald who has an allergy to the birds. However, Harry's hobby seemingly pays off when he returns home with an owl stuffed with money. Enthusiastic plans are made but when Inspector Travers arrives Harry discovers he has been spending stolen money and he is led off to the police station!
ISBN 0 573 11281 9

Kafka's Dick. Comedy. Alan Bennett
M5 F1. A living-room, heaven. Fee code M

It is 1919 and the tubercular Kafka adjures Max to burn his writings after his death. Max doesn't and goes on to publish all Kafka's work. Moving to the 1980s, in an English suburban living-room sit Sydney, a Kafka-besotted insurance agent, his frustrated wife and his elderly father. Into their midst descends the dead but lively Max, closely followed by a cadaverous Kafka and Kafka's larger-than-life father. It seems everyone wants to get in on the act ... This text is the revised 1992 edition.
ISBN 0 573 01663 1

◆ **Katherine Howard**. Play. William Nicholson
M7 (50s-60s) F4 (18, 20s, 40s). Extras. Various simple settings. Fee code M

Opening on the wedding night of Henry VIII and his fourth wife, Anne of Cleves, and closing with the execution of his fifth wife, Katherine Howard, found guilty of adultery, Nicholson's play takes a slice of Tudor history and turns it into pure theatrical magic. A touching May-to-September romance; political intrigue, plots and betrayals; a pointed and sometimes comic portrayal of women's lives in Tudor times: all these, and more, are elements of this entertaining, thoughtful, intelligent play from the author of *Shadowlands*. Period 1540-1542
ISBN 0 573 01811 1

Keep an Eye on Amélie. Farce. Georges Feydeau. Translated and adapted by Robert Cogo-Fawcett and Braham Murray
M13 F5. Extras. A salon, the Town Hall, two bedrooms. Fee code M

Feydeau's hilarious farce *Occupe-toi d'Amélie* is here translated in a lively new version — seen at the Royal Exchange, Manchester, under the title *She's in Your Hands!* Marcel will inherit one million francs — on his wedding day. Unwilling to relinquish his bachelorhood, but in dire need of cash, he persuades Amélie, a cocotte, to act as his fiancée for benefit of his godfather. But events don't go according to plan!
ISBN 0 573 01813 8

Keeping Down With the Joneses. Comedy. John Chapman and Jeremy Lloyd
M5 (1 Asian-Indian) F4. An underground atomic shelter. Fee code M

Convinced the Russians are about to launch a nuclear strike, Geoffrey Jones builds a shelter in his garden which the family decide to try out. Inadvertently they are trapped inside with the telephone engineer and their Indian milkman. Trying to make the best of the situation they are surprised by the arrival, through the side hatch, of their next door neighbours. Ever striving to keep *up* with the Joneses they are now keeping *down* with them by building their own shelter ...!
ISBN 0 573 61115 7

Kennedy's Children. Play. Robert Patrick
M2 (young) F3 (young). Extra 1M. A bar. Fee code L

'The theme of the play is the death of the ideas of heroes as guides for our lives. I think the sad thing about Kennedy's children is that they have so very much to offer one another and are held away from one another by fear and despair ... the play stands as my tribute to their valour and suffering.' Robert Patrick.
ISBN 0 573 61126 2

Key for Two. Comedy. John Chapman and Dave Freeman
M3 (30-50) F4 (30-middle-age). Composite setting. Fee code M

In this wickedly amusing play Harriet solves her financial problems by entertaining two married gentlemen on different days of the week. The scheme faces collapse when her friend, Anne, arrives, hotly pursued by her husband; one of Harriet's lovers is confined to bed with a sprained ankle and the second lover turns up unexpectedly, closely followed by two irate wives in search of their itinerant husbands! The long-running London production starred Moira Lister, Patrick Cargill, Barbara Murray and Glyn Houston.
ISBN 0 573 11258 4

The Kidnap Game. Play. Tudor Gates
M3 (20s, middle-age, 50s) F2 (late teens, 30s). Composite setting: an office and a street area. Fee code M

Paul Kendon is a highly-successful international businessman whose world is turned upside down when a man claims to have kidnapped his daughter. Although Kendon is prepared to quietly pay the ransom, his security officer calls in the police in the form of the cool, intelligent Inspector Joy Hart. Kendon must take a back seat as Hart engages the kidnapper in a battle of wits, leading to the exciting climax with unexpected twists.
ISBN 0 573 11217 7

Killers. Play. Adam Pernak
M6 (20s-elderly) F4 (20s, middle-age). Simple interior and exterior settings. Fee code M

Winner of the Royal Court Young Writers' Festival this brilliant début play shows two brothers and their working-class parents. Jonathan, the high-flier, causes the death of his errant girlfriend's older lover, whilst David, a fighter pilot, is sent to the Gulf War. Both are killers, but one is revered as a patriotic hero whilst the other is imprisoned for his *crime passionel*. '... a beautifully simple play that wafts over the audience with the warmth of reality.' *City Limits*
ISBN 0 573 01815 4

The Killing of Sister George. Comedy. Frank Marcus
F4. A living-room. Fee code M

Sister George is a fictional character in a popular radio serial about English village life. To boost ratings, this character is to be killed off and Mrs Mercy of the BBC comforts June Buckridge who has played the part for some 2000 performances. June has a lesbian relationship with 'Childie' McNaught, a babyish 'girl-woman' who shares her home, and the impending catastrophe of June's lost job tips the insecure relationship over. Beryl Reid triumphed in both the stage and screen versions of this comedy.
ISBN 0 573 03017 0

◆ **Killing Time.** Play. Richard Stockwell
M1 (30s) F1 (30s). A living-room/kitchen area. Fee code M

A chance meeting brings Rick and Jane together. Gradually the clues to the truth assemble: he engineered their meeting; he knows all about Jane's marriage to the violent, unsavoury Michael — and he wants Michael dead, for reasons of his own. Surprisingly, Jane is happy to collude with Rick in this plan, but then she isn't all she originally appears to be either. By degrees, the two reveal increasingly more of their true identities and the crimes and violence that have linked them in the past.
ISBN 0 573 01818 9

◆ **Kindly Keep It Covered**. Farce. Dave Freeman
M3 (early middle-age) F4 (20s, middle-age). A reception area. Fee code M

Roland Dickerby runs a health farm with his wife Julia, bought with the proceeds of a hefty insurance payout on the demise of Julia's first husband, Sidney. Life isn't easy for Roland and today Fate has something extra special in store for him: Sidney has decided to resurrect himself and turns up at the farm, just as Vanessa, the wife of Roland's ex-boss from the Kindly Mutual, checks in for a health-giving visit. A fast, furious and frantic farce.
ISBN 0 573 01817 0

Kindly Leave the Stage. Comedy. John Chapman
M3 (40s, old) F5 (young, 30s-60s). A sitting-room. Fee code M

To the embarrassment of their dinner guests Rupert and Sarah announce that they are to divorce. Moments later, the actor playing Rupert stumbles on a line and we realize that the previous action is a play within a play. As the prompter tries to get the show moving again the cast begin to argue, out of character, and the result is complete chaos. Laughs abound in this fast-paced comedy of theatrical disasters.

Kingdom of Earth. Play. Tennessee Williams
M2 (one black) F1. Composite setting. Fee code M

Lot, a seriously ill young man, still unhealthily weighed down by the memory of his dead mother, has married — on a TV show — a young woman, Myrtle. Goodheartedly she hopes to nurse him back to health. Lot takes her back to the family home, inhabited by his half-brother, Chicken, and Myrtle discovers that Lot intends she should steal the deeds of the place from Chicken to whom he has weakly given them. But Chicken has other ideas for Myrtle as he waits for Lot to die.
Period 1960

The Kingfisher. Comedy. William Douglas Home
M2 (70, old) F1 (60). A garden. Fee code M

Cedric is a best-selling novelist living comfortably with his butler, Hawkins, who has served him for fifty years. There have been many women in Cedric's richly disordered life but now he is contemplating marriage to the only one he has loved. The object of his proposal, Evelyn, has just been to her husband's funeral, whom she married on the rebound from Cedric. Now she is confronted by Cedric's charming and candid proposal and must make a decision.
ISBN 0 573 61130 0

A Kiss on the Bottom. Comedy. Frank Vickery
F7 (20s, middle-age, 60s). May be played by F5. 2F extras. A hospital ward. Fee code L

Three women are in East Glamorgan hospital for cancer treament. Each woman must cope not only with the uncertainties of her health, but with the inevitable secrets and half-truths which are maintained by relations and nursing staff. It's up to Marlene, the strongest and most outspoken of them all, to keep the atmosphere in the ward cheery. Her activities make her bedfellows' time in hospital somewhat more interesting than it would otherwise have been!
ISBN 0 573 13004 3

The Knack. Comedy. Ann Jellicoe
M3 (young) F1 (17). A room. Fee code M

Jellicoe's best play, written in 1961 and later filmed with Rita Tushingham, is an exuberant, liberating youthful comedy. Three young men share a flat. Into their midst wanders Nancy, a gawky seventeen-year-old Northerner looking for the YWCA, who will give the tough Tolen a chance to demonstrate his knack with women. The staccato dialogue skims along in this study of the shifting relationships and power balances among the four young people. An undercurrent is Tolen's Nazi characteristics and whether negotiation is possible with such people.

Knuckle. Play. David Hare
M4, including doubling, F2. Simple settings. Fee code K

Curly, a young arms merchant, determines to discover the secret behind the disappearance of his sister, Sarah, from the deserted stretch of beach between Pevensey and Eastbourne. Also involved is the Shadow of the Moon Club in Guildford. Curly's investigations lead him to uncover corrution and rottenness under the placid surface of Guildford, where his father, a City man, lives in circumstances of some intimacy with his housekeeper.
ISBN 0 573 01570 8

Laburnum Grove. Comedy. J. B. Priestley
M6 (young, 40, middle-age, 50) F3 (20, 40s). A living-room. Fee code H

George is apparently a respectable businessman with quiet domestic hobbies. His daughter is bemoaning the monotony of their suburban round at Sunday supper but to refute this George makes the startling revelation that he has for years belonged to a gang of counterfeiters. His wife pooh-poohs the story but a different aspect is thrown upon it by the arrival of Inspector Stack, whose investigations of a gang have led him to George! Written in 1933
ISBN 0 573 01221 0

A

Ladies of Spirit. Comedy. Georgina Reid
F9 (20s, 40s, elderly). A school staffroom. Fee code H

Gibraltar School was founded as a private school for young ladies by the two dear old Misses Pye, now deceased. The long-suffering teachers have their lives made miserable not only by their pupils but also by the present headmistress, Miss Rowe, known universally as 'Hard Rowe'. They resign themselves to the fact that there is very little they can do about it, but they find help coming from a very unexpected quarter indeed.
ISBN 0 573 13002 7

♦ **Ladies Who Lunch**. Comedy. Tudor Gates
M3 (middle-age, 50s) F7 (21, 30s, 40s, middle-age), with doubling. 1 male voice. A drawing-room, a duplex apartment, an apartment. Fee code M

In *Ladies Who Lunch,* commissioned for the BT Biennial 1998, Amelia, Rachel and Joane, wives of three of the world's richest men, meet regularly to do charity work. In order to increase the charity's turnover Amelia thinks up a scheme to play the stock market, exploiting the information gained secretly from their spouses' business dealings. When the husbands find out, the resulting showdown is not the walk-over they think it will be ...
ISBN 0 573 01853 7

Lady Audley's Secret, or **Death in Lime Tree Walk**. Melodrama. Brian J. Burton, based on the novel by Mary Braddon
M4 (20s, 60s) F4 (20s) Various settings. Fee code L

Lady Audley has recently married a rich old man and is secure in wealth at last. A visitor from Australia is distraught to find his wife died during his absence. But lo! yet she lives! This same Lady Audley is the wife reported dead. Fearing her ex-husband might upset the applecart she cracks him on the head and drops his body in the well. Period 1850s

The Lady's Not for Burning. Play. Christopher Fry
M8 F3. A room. Fee code M

Mendip, an embittered discharged soldier, demands to be hanged, claiming to have killed the rag-and-bone man and another, but no bodies are to found and the Mayor refuses — 'the gallows are not a charitable institution'. Jennet enters to seek the Mayor's protection, having been accused of witchcraft and of changing the rag-and-bone man into a dog. The Mayor, however, treats the absurd accusation seriously and arrests her. Eventually the 'victim' turns up, alive and tipsy. Jennet is allowed to escape and Mendip goes with her. Period around 1400

Largo Desolato. Play. Václav Havel. English version by Tom Stoppard
M9 (middle-age) F3 or M7 F3. A living-room. Fee code M

Professor Nettles lives in constant fear because of his refusal to denounce his work. The play's sense of the sinister gives a chilling edge to this account of life in totalitarian state by the once-banned writer and president of Czecoslovakia. Stoppard's English version was premièred at the Bristol Old Vic in 1986 and seen subsequently at the Orange Tree, Richmond, in 1989. 'It is unlikely that we shall see a better play this year. Inconceivable that we shall see one more important.' *Daily Telegraph*

The Lark. Play. Jean Anouilh. Translated by Christopher Fry
M16 F5. A permanent setting. Fee code M

To the great lords of her time as well as the politicians of the Church expediency was God. So the Maid had to die. So to Warwick and Cauchon, her life has the somewhat artificial, and certainly impersonal, quality of a play. Short scenes from it are played out during the trial as they struggle to turn her simplicity into heresy. But it is the glory of her life rather than the tragedy that is the triumphant climax of the play. Period 1429-31
ISBN 0 573 01225 3

Lark Rise. Play. Keith Dewhurst, from the book by Flora Thompson
M12 F7, with doubling. An open stage. Fee code M. (In a volume with *Candleford*)

A literary sampler of English village life in late Victorian Oxfordshire, *Lark Rise* re-enacts the first day of harvest. The play is written to be peformed as a promenade production with no distinction between stage and auditorium. The interest lies in the lively picture of typical country life of the period, with music and songs, with a brief flash forward to the 1914 war. Period 1880s
ISBN 0 573 10011 X

The Last Gamble. Play. Bill MacIlwraith
M2 (36, 64, 72) F2 (27, 64). A living-room and a kitchen. Fee code M

From the author of *The Anniversary* comes an exciting thriller. The Colonel has never got over the loss of his elder son, killed in action in Cyprus. Peter, his younger son, a corrupt solicitor, feels his father's resentment and hates him for it. When Peter becomes involved in another unethical scheme that goes badly wrong, he is forced to turn to his father for help, with unexpected and tragic results.
ISBN 0 573 01821 9

Last of the Red Hot Lovers. Comedy. Neil Simon
M1 (46) F3 (20, 30s). An apartment. Fee code M

Barney, who has been married to an irreproachable wife for twenty-three years, feels the urge to join the sexual revolution before it is too late. Taking advantage of the fact that his mother's flat is unoccupied two days a week he invites three women to his lair in succession. With no experience of adultery he fails on each occasion. As the play ends he is telephoning his wife — to meet him that afternoon in his mother's apartment.
ISBN 0 573 61143 2

Last Tango in Whitby. Play. Mike Harding
15 speaking, 6 plus non-speaking can be played by M4 (middle-age) F8 (young, middle-age), with doubling. Extras M and F. Various simple settings. Fee code M

For Pat, recently widowed, this year's charabanc trip to Whitby is tinged with sadness, but she is determined to enjoy herself. Phil and Edna provide entertainment with old-time dancing. Phil, too, is trying to enjoy himself, despite being trapped in a dead marriage, and during their first dance together he and Pat feel the unexpected spark of mutual attraction. Despite disapproval from others, they decide to seize this second chance and start a new life together.
ISBN 0 573 01822 7

A

The Late Christopher Bean. Comedy. An adaptation of Réné Fauchois's *Prenez Garde à la Peinture* by Emlyn Williams
M5 (20, young-elderly) F4 (young, 20s, 50). A living-room. Fee code M

The Haggetts extended asylum to a tubercular stranger, Christopher Bean, fifteen years ago. The many paintings he left were used to patch up leaks in the roof, etc. Only one portrait has been treasured — that of Gwenny, their servant. Suddenly strangers call, announcing the paintings are worth a fortune. These innocent folk become eaten up with comical cupidity and do their best to get hold of Gwenny's portrait. But Gwenny is Bean's widow, owner of the portrait, and seventeen other pieces she rescued from the fire!
ISBN 0 573 01227 X

The Late Edwina Black. Please see the entry for *Edwina Black*.

The Late Mrs Early. Comedy. Norman Robbins
M4 (14, 40, 60) F4 (17, 40s). A living-room. Fee code K

Terry Early's announcement that he and Susan intend to marry rouses the fury of his overbearing mother Alice. Alice's sudden demise, following her handling of a faulty electric kettle, promises a peaceful solution. But Alice as a vengeful ghost is even more formidable than as a live wife and mother. Much drama ensues in which both families are involved before Alice's ashes can be persuaded to lie quiet in her urn.
ISBN 0 573 01586 4

Laugh? I Nearly Went To Miami! Comedy. Miles Tredinnick
M4 (30, 40) F3 (20, 30, 60). A sitting-room. Fee code L

A zany, fast-moving comedy of confusion. When Tom, an Elvis fanatic, and Alice his fiancée are unable, due to fog, to fly to Miami for an Elvis Convention, they arrive back at Tom's flat to find they have inadvertently picked up the wrong suitcase at the airport and are now in possession of half a million dollars. Confusions arise when Auntie arrives with a bag containing $20,000 as does Frankie, a thug working for the owner of the suitcase dollars, and it takes Inspector Hendy to sort everything out.
ISBN 0 573 01633 X

Laughing Wild. Comedy. Christopher Durang
M1 F1. A supermarket. Fee code M

A provocative, brilliantly inventive and very funny study of the perils of modern life in urban America from the author of *Beyond Therapy* and *Sister Mary Ignatius Explains It All For You*. It was first presented with great success in New York and subsequently seen at London's Boulevard Theatre in 1988. The play consists of two monologues plus an hilarious playlet which brings the two together and explores more fully the converging dreams and themes set forth in their solo expeditions.

Laughter in the Dark. Comedy. Victor Lucas
M6 (20s, 50s) F5 (20s, 50, 70s). Extras. A manorial hall. Fee code K

Strange but very funny happenings are occurring at the faded manor of Creeching Cheyney in Hampshire where a nicely assorted group of people are assembled on Christmas Eve to hear the reading of a will which makes it a condition that they live in the place a year before they get their legacies. There are also some unforeseen guests including a skeleton rattling chains and a ghost or two!
ISBN 0 573 11218 5

Leaving Home. Play. Julia Kearsley
M2 (22, 50) F4 (20s, 36, 49). A living-room. Fee code K

A touching, yet humorous play which wryly examines the effects of loss and dependency on the family. When Dad walks out, his family must try to come to terms with his mysterious disappearance: his grief-stricken wife, his pregnant, widowed daughter, his slightly eccentric son, and his career-girl step-daughter. But the arrival of down-at-heel Malcolm brings about an amazing transformation. 'Not least of the author's qualities is a sparky, unpredictable humour ...' *New Statesman*
ISBN 0 573 01647 X

Lend Me A Tenor. Comedy. Ken Ludwig
M4 (young, 30s, 50s) F4 (20s, 30s, 50s). An hotel suite. Fee code M for play, fee code A for music

A concert in Ohio in 1934 is jeopardized when the lead Italian tenor falls into a drunken stupor. So the impresario's diminutive assistant blacks up and goes on as Otello. The tenor awakens, dons his costume, and thence follows an hilarious comedy involving two Otellos, a volatile Italian wife, an outrageous bellhop and a cynical impresario. 'A furiously paced comedy with more than a touch of the Marx brothers ... wonderful farcical moments and funny lines ...' *Time Out*
ISBN 0 573 01640 2

◆ **Lent**. Play. Michael Wilcox
M2 F2, 1 boy. Various simple interior and exterior settings. Fee code L

Orphan Paul Blake's prep school is also his home. So, when the other boys leave for the 1956 Easter vacation, Paul is thrown upon the company of the despised headmaster and his wife and his somewhat eccentric grandmother, Mrs Blake. He is befriended by fellow sufferer Matey, the elderly Latin master also condemned to spend his vacation at the school, who provides an avuncular companionship for the boy on the painful, yet exciting, verge of adolescence.

Lenz. Play. Mike Stott, loosely based on the story by George Büchner
M4 (20s-30s) F2 (20s-30s). Various simple interiors. Fee code M

Jacob Lenz, gifted, highly intelligent but seriously unbalanced, is invited to stay at the house of Oberlin, a philanthropic parson. The play examines the effects on the household of Lenz's erratic, sometimes dangerous, behaviour, which gradually makes him the centre of all attention and activity, and ultimately, madness is powerfully depicted as the height of selfishness. Oberlin's compassionate, Christian attempt to give Lenz love and shelter fails, and he is returned to Strasburg. Period 1778

Léocadia. Play. Jean Anouilh, translated by Timberlake Wertenbaker
M8 F3. Extras. The drawing-room, the Château grounds. Fee code M

This is a new translation, broadcast on BBC Radio, of the Anouilh play which first appeared in 1939. Léocadia was an opera singer who died after three blissful days of love with Prince Albert who has mourned her eversince. His aunt, the Duchess, does everything she can to help him and finds Amanda, who bears a striking resemblance to Léocadia, and encourages her to lay Léocadia's ghost which she does with honesty and gentle perseverance.

A

Lessons and Lovers: D. H. Lawrence in New Mexico. Play. Olwen Wymark
M4 F5. Various interior and exterior settings. Fee code L

This beautifully written play is set chiefly on Lawrence's New Mexico ranch between the years 1922-45, and also in the present. It centres on the extraordinary personality of Lawrence who inspires fierce loyalty in the women around him and the love between Freida and Lawrence which survives the conflict of their two strong characters and the pain of Lawrence's last years. This is observed and commented on by a professor and his four students, involved both inside and outside the action.
ISBN 0 573 01644 5

♦ **A Letter of Resignation**. Play. Hugh Whitemore
M3 (35, middle-age, 60s) F2 (50s, 60s). A castle library. Fee code M

1963 was an amazing year and life was changing. Britain was becoming a different place and to many people, Harold Macmillan, the Prime Minister, seemed outdated and irrelevant — an Edwardian grandee lingering uncomfortably in the world of E-type Jaguars, Carnaby Street and Beatlemania. But few were aware that his life was scarred by domestic unhappiness and sexual betrayal. Hugh Whitemore explores the events that lay hidden behind the headlines and examines a complex web of personal and political morality.

Lettice and Lovage. Comedy. Peter Shaffer
M2 (middle-age) F3 (middle-age). Extras. A grand hall, an office, a basement flat. Fee code M

Daughter of an actress who toured with an all-female company playing Shakespeare's plays, Lettice has inherited both theatricality and eccentricity. Now employed as a tourist guide in a shabby stately home, she enlivens its dull history with her own over-imaginative fantasies, until she is caught in the act and promptly sacked. She is later visited by the starchy Preservation Trust official who fired her, and an unlikely friendship develops between the two.
ISBN 0 573 01823 5

Les Liaisons Dangereuses. Play. Christopher Hampton
M3 (20s, 30) F6 (15, 20s, late 30s, elderly). Extras. Various interior and exterior settings. Fee code M

Le Vicomte de Valmont begins the play as an unworthy, cynical pleasure-seeker, proud of his reputation as a seducer. He is encouraged in his enterprises by his former mistress, La Marquise de Merteuil, who would seem to share his cynicism, but who has an ulterior motive. Set in France among aristocrats before the Revolution, this is nevertheless a play for all time about sexual manners and manipulation, ending in tragedy.
ISBN 0 573 01639 9

A Life. Play. Hugh Leonard
M4 (20s, 60s) F4 (20s, 60s). Triple set: a kitchen, living-room, bandstand. Fee code M

Drumm visits his neighbour Mary for the first time in six years. She describes her new kitchen — but when she takes him into it, it is as it was forty years ago, and seated at the table is her young self. From then on, the lives of four people, their intermingled relationships, whims of chance and clashes of personality which affected their destinies, are recounted by a method which mingles past and present.
ISBN 0 573 11244 4

The Life and Death of Almost Everybody. Play. David Campton
M12 F5. An empty stage. Fee code H

A sweeper tidying an empty stage experiments with the magic power of theatre — creating life through the exercise of the imagination. He creates a Young Man and Young Woman then, as ever more characters are called for, events go beyond his bewildered control. The potent forces of love, hate, politics and religion emerge and dominate, along wit the dissension and decadence they can engender. Eventually a universal Aunt Harriet comes to marshall the forces into a hedonistic and fatefully doomed communal order.
ISBN 0 573 11223 1

◆ **Life Goes On**. Comedy. Adrian Hodges
M2 (30s, 42) F3 (20s-40). 1 female voice. A living-room, a bedroom. Fee code M

A thoughtful and engaging comedy which opens in the hours following the funeral of George Marlowe who left this life unexpectedly. George's younger brother, Michael, attempts to seduce Debbie, youngest sister of his partner Helen and of George's widow, Joyce. During the evening Michael leaps from one sisterly assignation to another until the arrival of George's ghost, back to tie up the loose ends of his life, including Michael's philandering ways. The play ends with the right balance having been struck for all concerned.
ISBN 0 573 01809 X

A Life in the Theatre. Play. David Mamet
M2. Various spots around a theatre. Fee code L

In twenty-six scenes the play presents 'two actors — a seasoned professional and a novice — backstage and onstage, going through a cycle of roles and an entire wardrobe of costumes'. In some scenes they are seen portraying characters in various plays from the repertory theatre in which they work. Though there are many scenes — some very brief — staging is simple.
ISBN 0 573 64024 6

The Life of Galileo. Play. Bertolt Brecht
Translations: Charles Laughton, music by Hanns Eisler
                Desmond Vesey
                Howard Brenton
                John Willett
                Ralph Manheim and Wolfgang Sauerlander
M35 F11, with doubling possible. Extras, children. Interior and exterior settings. Fee code M for play, code C for music

Brecht charts the progress of Galileo's life, from his first demonstration (to his housekeeper's son, Andrea Sarti) of his theory that the earth revolves round the sun, to his final years in a house near Florence, old, half blind, a prisoner of the Inquisition. Galileo secretly writes a book which Andrea shamefacedly declares will 'found a new physics', and Andrea manages to smuggle the book across the Italian border. Period 1609-1637

The Light of Heart. Play. Emlyn Williams
M4 (young-50s) F4 (20s-elderly). A room in furnished lodgings. Fee code M

Crippled Cattrin looks after her father Maddoc, once a famous actor who has not worked for years. During the eleven months this touching, poignant play covers, their impoverished existence is turned upside down by the arrival of a young musician who encourages Maddoc to resume his career and secretly asks Cattrin to marry him and go to America. Maddoc is set to perform Lear at Covent Garden, but when he discovers their plans his new-found confidence is shattered.

Light Shining in Buckinghamshire. Play. Caryl Churchill
M21 F4 originally played by M4 F2. Various simple settings. Fee code M

First staged in 1976 by the Joint Stock Company at the Royal Court Theatre Upstairs. Set in England in the Civil War, twenty short scenes depict the life of a struggling nation: the Putney Debates, the war in Ireland, poverty, preaching and hypocrisy. The Millennium approaches and with it the Parousia; how do the beggar, the butcher, and the soldier approach this belief? Period 1640s

The Lights are Warm and Coloured. Play. William Norfolk
M2 (30s) F6 (20s-50s). A living-room. Fee code L

Several years after Lizzie Borden's trial and acquittal following the murder of her father and stepmother, she lives with her sister in another house in the same district. One evening she invites some actors from a visiting touring company who re-enact the crime. Later, the Bordens receive an unexpected visit from Bridget Sullivan, the servant at the time of the crime and a crucial witness. It transpires that Lizzie gave her a sum of money. Why? To conceal her own guilt or was Bridget the murderess? Period 1905
ISBN 0 573 11230 4

The Lion in Winter. Play. James Goldman
M5 (teenage, 20s, 50) F2 (young, middle-age). Henry's castle at Chinon. Fee code M

Although the outcome of the relationships depicted in this play is historical fact, the quality and content of these relationships are here imagined to be as vitriolic, lacerating, witty, disillusioned and self-destructive as anything created by Strindberg or Albee. Henry II and his Queen, Eleanor, whose mutual passion has long since been destroyed by their obsession with intrigue and power, barter, cajole and threaten to win for their favourite sons the Aquitaine, Alais Capet, or the throne of England. Period 1183
ISBN 0 573 01234 2

Little Boxes. Two plays. John Bowen
M4 F5. Composite setting. Fee code J

The Coffee Lace
Six old theatre folk share a shabby flat in Kennington. They plan an anniversary celebration intending to raise funds by selling Lily's prized coffee lace dress. Unfortunately, the money raised is not enough and it is only Lily's death which provides the money in a very unusual, macabre way.

Trevor
Jane and Sarah live in a smart Kensington flat. To conceal their relationship from their parents they have invented mythical fiancés called Trevor. As Jane's parents are to visit, the girls hire the services of an unemployed actor to play Trevor but when Sarah's parents unexpectedly arrive, Trevor has to put on a double-act.
ISBN 0 573 01238 5

A Little Hotel on the Side. Translation by John Mortimer of *L'Hôtel du Libre Échange* by Georges Feydeau and Maurice Desvallieres
M9 F4. 4 girls. Extras. An apartment, an hotel. Fee code M

Seen at the Royal National Theatre in 1984, this witty, stylish translation remains true to the Feydeau spirit of backfiring and naughty wordplay, containing all the classic ingredients: thwarted lust, spiralling panic and a seedy hotel where the corridors see more action than the beds. 'Mr Mortimer's translation never sounds like one. Can one pay a higher compliment.' *Daily Telegraph*
ISBN 0 573 01616 X

A Little Like Drowning. Play. Anthony Minghella
M6 F7. Most characters age throughout the play. Various simple settings on a bare stage. Fee code M

Seen at Hampstead Theatre in 1984, the play suggests the visions of her whole life that pass through old Leonora's mind as she chats with her little granddaughter. Spanning nearly sixty years Leonora recalls in short, beautifully observed scenes, the peaks and troughs — marriage, children, her husband's desertion of her and her final triumph over his mistress. '... it is piercingly authentic and distressingly all-pervasive in its emotional onslaught.' *City Limits*

The Little Photographer. Play. Derek Hoddinott, based on a short story by Daphne du Maurier
M3 (young, 22, 45) F4 (21-40s). 1 or 2 girls (9-14). An hotel room. Fee code L

Marie finds life with her conservative, passionless husband suffocatingly repressive and starts an affair with a handsome young photographer, undeterred that he has a club-foot. The infatuation brings tragedy and horror, leading to his death; a threat of blackmail from his sister (similarly deformed) and, finally, an even more fearful dread that such deformities are sometimes inherited, latent in an unborn child. Period 1900
ISBN 0 573 11237 1

Little Women. Play. Peter Clapham, adapted from the novel by Louisa M. Alcott
M4 (young, 40s, elderly) F7 (20, 40, 70). A parlour. Fee code L

This revised version of Clapham's earlier play is now shorter in running time and has one fewer male character. It still faithfully keeps to the novel, interweaving the lives of the March girls and the boy next door as they grow happily together, yet the action is contained neatly in one set. A full introduction and helpful production notes complete the text.
ISBN 0 573 11232 0

Living Quarters. Play. Brian Friel
M5 (24, 30s, middle age, 50s, 64) F4 (18, 20s) Composite set: a living-room, a garden. Fee code M

Living Quarters reconstructs a day in the life of the Butler family in the village of Ballybeg. Frank Butler, who has served all his life in the Irish army, returns from United Nations service a hero, to learn of his young wife's affair with his son from a previous marriage. Parallels with Greek tragedy are marked in Friel's absorbing study of family relationships and the absence of a refuge from destiny.

The Living Room. Play. Grahame Greene
M2 (40, 65) F5 (20, 45, middle-age, 70). A living-room. Fee code M

After her mother's death young Rose comes to live with her two elderly, religious aunts and their brother James, a crippled priest. Every room where someone has died has been shut up, leaving only one open. Rose, who has been the mistress of an elderly psychologist, wants to go away with him. She begs the help of the priest but when he can offer her no comfort she commits suicide in the one remaining room — the 'living room'.

Living Together. Play. Alan Ayckbourn
M3 F3. A sitting-room. Fee code L. See the entry under *The Norman Conquests*
ISBN 0 573 01574 0

Lloyd George Knew My Father. Comedy. William Douglas Home
M5 (20, 40s) F3 (20-40, 60). A living-room. Fee code M
ISBN 0 573 01233 4

A

Local Affairs. Play. Richard Harris
M4 (20, 40s) F5 (20-40, 60). A living-room, a bedroom, a kitchen. Fee code M

An earlier version of *Party Piece*, this play ingeniously uses the same set to represent three different homes. We see Charles, preoccupied with finding a fancy dress costume, and Norma, obsessed with her garden and kitchen; Hilary, returned from a health farm to find her mother-in-law in residence; and Susan and Keith, unable to enjoy a weekend without their children. Add a suicidal Katy and an incorrect party date and we are set for a confusing evening!
ISBN 0 573 11236 3

The Local Authority. Play. Eduardo de Filippo. Translated by Carlo Ardito
M15 (20, 60, middle-age, 75) F5 (20, 45, middle-age, 65). A living-room and a dining-room. Fee code M

Antonio Barancano acts as the arbitrator in local disputes, but interference in a certain quarrel is resented and he is fatally wounded. His last hours are spent covering up the cause of his death so that his sons will not seek to avenge him. However, his assisant, Dr Fabio, feels that for once he must tell the truth, even if a blood-feud which will last for generations is the result.

Local Murder. Thriller. Peter Whalley
M4 (18, 30) F2 (30). A through lounge. Fee code M

Alan is accused of murdering a young woman of dubious morals and this has a devastating effect on his family. His father, convinced the police are framing Alan, does some detective work of his own. He discovers a friend, Ron, visits the road regularly and the real reason for this, coupled with Alan's eventual confession, makes him take matters into this own hands with tragic results. A domestic thriller with more than one surprising twist.
ISBN 0 573 01655 0

The London Cuckolds. Play. Edward Ravenscroft adapted by John Byrne
M9 (young, middle-age) F4 (young). Various simple interior and exterior settings. Fee code M

Originally written in 1681, this adaptation by John Byrne, seen in Leicester and at the Lyric Theatre, Hammersmith, in 1985, allows Ravenscroft's Rabelaisian wit to be sophisticated and polished rather than crudely vulgar. Two aldermen with young wives argue about the qualities in a woman that make for the secure marriage. But before long both husbands find themselves cuckolded, not once, but several times! Period 1600s
ISBN 0 573 01630 5

The Long and the Short and the Tall. Play. Willis Hall
M8 (young, 30s). A store hut. Fee code M

Set in the Malayan jungle, this critically acclaimed play is tough, realistic and full of comedy. Its characters are British soldiers who look upon their duty in the jungle with a marked lack of enthusiasm until they discover that soldiering is something more than the game they thought it was at first. Before the play comes to its unexpected climax, the men have faced up to unforeseen issues of loyalty and danger. Period 1942
ISBN 0 573 04016 8

Look Back in Anger. Play. John Osborne
M3 (25, 60) F2 (25). A one-room flat. Fee code M

Jimmy Porter, frustrated and bitter in his drab flat, lives with middle-class wife Alison. Also sharing the flat is Cliff who keeps things tenuously together. Alison's friend Helen arrives and persuades her to leave Jimmy only to fall for him herself. When Alison becomes pregnant Helen leaves them together. This play originally opened at the Royal Court Theatre in 1956 and has since proved to be a milestone in the history of theatre.
ISBN 0 573 11255 X

Look, No Hans! Comedy. John Chapman and Michael Pertwee
M2 (30s, middle-age) F4 (20, 30). Extras 1M (voice only) 1M (optional). An office/living-room. Fee code M

This play enjoyed a successful run at the Strand Theatre starring David Jason as the hapless Fisher, manager of the West Berlin office of a British car company. When his wife Monica returns from the airport because her flight has been delayed, what follows is a fast-paced fun-filled farce by the masters of the genre involving Heidi, Fisher's mistress, Mitzi, a voluptuous singing telegram girl and Cadwallader, from British Security of Industry, amongst others.
ISBN 0 573 01606 2

Look Who's Talking! Comedy. Derek Benfield
M2 (40, 50) F3 (26, 40). A drawing-room. Fee code L

When two unexpected guests, Jane and Brian, drop in on Sheila and Andrew, a devoted middle-age couple, what ensues is a complicated and hilarious series of misunderstandings and mistaken identities as Sheila and Andrew begin to weave an elaborate web of lies and half-truths to hide their own possible infidelities.
ISBN 0 573 11250 9

Loose Ends. Comedy. Frank Vickery
M2 (20s, middle-age) F3 (20s, middle-age). A caravan site. Fee code L

Marlene is an interfering mother who has an almost unbearable influence on her children Darren and Louise. Louise is married and now Marlene decides it's time to get Darren hitched. On a weekend break at a caravan park Marlene sees her opportunity: Bev, who owns the caravan, would be the perfect match for Darren! But there is a reason for Marlene's sometimes infuriating behaviour — she is due to have chemotherapy. This entertaining comedy is the sequel to *A Kiss on the Bottom*.
ISBN 0 573 01824 3

Loot. Play. Joe Orton
M5 (middle-age, young) F1 (young). A living-room. Fee code M

When Hal robs a bank and hides the money in Mrs McLeavy, his late mother's, coffin, Fay, who is trying to marry Mr McLeavy for his money, becomes suspicious and demands a share. From then on, outrageous development follows outrageous development. Truscott the police inspector accuses Fay, rightly, of having poisoned Mrs McLeavy, but the evidence is destroyed. Finally McLeavy finds himself arrested for the robbery and Truscott shares in the proceeds.

A

Lord Arthur Savile's Crime. Improbable Comedy. Constance Cox. Based on the short story by Oscar Wilde
M5 (20, 40, 50, elderly) F5 (20, 40, middle-age, 60). A drawing-room. Fee code L

After Lord Arthur has had his palm read by Podgers who tells him he will commit a murder, he feels duty bound to get it over with before his marriage to Sybil. But, aided by the anarchist Winkelkopf, his attempts prove futile. It emerges Podgers is a charlatan and so Lord Arthur is free but on the way to the wedding rehearsal he finds the carriage contains Winkelkopf's newest bomb. Period 1890
ISBN 0 573 01245 8

Lorna Doone. Play. Dramatized by Jill Hyem from the novel by R. D. Blackmore
M18 F8 (much doubling possible) 2 boys, 2 girls. Extras. Composite setting. Fee code M

Exmoor's haunting beauty dominates this irresistible blend of romance and adventure that is R.D. Blackmore's famous novel, here superbly adapted for the stage. Spanning thirteen years, all the characters are present from the ruthless Doones to the peace-loving Ridds; from the highwayman Tom Faggus to Hanging Judge Jeffreys. But the love of John Ridd for Lorna Doone remains firmly at the heart of the play. Period seventeenth century
ISBN 0 573 01827 8

Lost in Yonkers. Comic drama. Neil Simon
M2 (30s, 40s) F3 (30s, 70s).2 boys. An apartment. Fee code M

New York, 1942. When Eddie Kurnitz's wife dies he deposits his two teenage sons with their formidable Grandma Kurnitz who runs a candy store in Yonkers. But Grandma Kurnitz is not all the boys have to contend with. There is also Bella, and Louie her brother, who may have mob connections. Gradually the mood deepens and darkens, as we become aware that this is a family full of emotionally crippled people. (*Available with restrictions*)

Love Forty. Play. Frank Vickery
M2 (20s ageing to 60s) F2 (20s ageing to 60s). A bedroom. Fee code M

As Marcia and Ralph prepare to celebrate their Ruby Wedding Anniversary, Marcia reflects on lonely years spent in an empty, loveless marriage. Conjuring up memories, Marcia watches her young self and Boy Ralph re-enact the pledges they made and the subsequent self-deception, lies and infidelities. Finally she decides to leave but with the help of Girl Marcia and Boy Ralph, the anniversary will be celebrated; the lie is buried again — and will continue.
ISBN 0 573 01826 X

Love of the Nightingale. Play. Timberlake Wertenbaker
M12 F8, with doubling. A bare stage. Fee code M

In this treatment of the Philomele myth, war hero Tereus takes his Athenian wife Procne to live in Thrace. She becomes lonely and begs him to fetch her younger sister, Philomele, from Athens to be her companion. During the arduous return journey Tereus rapes Philomele and then cuts out her tongue. Despite Tereus's claim that Philomele died at sea, the two sisters are finally reunited, whereby, through a disturbing puppet show, Philomele reveals her horrific ordeal. The sisters wreak their revenge in true tragic style.

Loved. Play. Olwen Wymark
M3 (30, 40s) F3 (19, 38). Various settings. Fee code L

Amy and Lawrence, whose marriage is on the brink of collapse, invite Cissy to live with them. Gabriel, a friend of Lawrence's arrives, on the verge of a nervous breakdown. Amy's attempts to provoke an emotive reaction from those around her are ineffective. The breakdown in communication is half-resolved and the play ends with Cissy personifying Lawrence's idea of hope as '... a rather plain but really very nice woman of indeterminate age sidling into a room dressed in a pink tutu ...'
ISBN 0 573 11247 9

Lovers. Double-bill. Brian Friel
M3 or 2 (17, 50) F5 or 4 (17, 40, 60). Adaptable setting. Fee code L

The first play, *Winners*, tells the story of Mag and Joe. Young and in love, they spend a glorious summer's day laughing and talking together and planning their future. But for Mag and Joe there is to be no future. The second play, *Losers*, tells of Hanna and Andy, a couple to whom love has come late, and for whom courting is made almost impossible by the upstairs presence of Hanna's demanding invalid mother. They do eventually get married, but gradually Andy realizes that Hanna is bidding fair to becoming a replica of her mother.

Lovers Dancing. Play. Charles Dyer
M2 (middle-age) F2 (middle-age). A sitting-room/hall. Fee code M

Presented at London's Albery Theatre with Paul Eddington, Colin Blakely, Jane Carr and Georgina Hale, this play tells the story of George, Alicia, Albert and Cheryl who nineteen years previously drunkenly shared the same bed and where Cheryl conceived a son whose paternity was decided by the toss of a coin. Here they are now for the annual celebration of the Night of the Dreadful Bed anniversary and as ever the bitter recriminations and resentments begin.
ISBN 0 573 11265 7

The Loves of Cass McGuire. Play. Brian Friel
M4 (17, 60s, elderly, 70) F6 (18, 50, 70s, 89). A spacious room. Fee code M

For more than fifty years Cass McGuire has worked a block from Skid Row, among deadbeats and washouts — people who live in the past. This bawdy, vital, compassionate play deals with her return to Ireland and her genteel family's rejection of her. It follows her lonely struggle to rediscover the home she's dreamt of all her life and her eventual surrender to the make-believe of Eden House, rest home for elderly people.

Low Level Panic. Play. Clare McIntyre
F3 (20s). Fee code H

Presented by the Women's Playhouse Trust at the Royal Court Theatre Upstairs in 1988 and the Lyric Studio, Hammersmith in 1989, this is a careful examination of the role of pornography in our society and the way it affects three young women in particular, using short scenes to show how popular images of women influence the way they are seen by others and the way they see themselves.

Lucky Sods. Play. John Godber
M4 (30s, 40s) F4 (30s, 40s, 70s) can be played by M2 F2. Various simple interiors and exteriors. Fee code M

When Morris and Jean win the National Lottery — to the tune of two million pounds — they can't believe their luck. But the cracks in their marriage widen, their past catches up with them and their relatives become increasingly resentful. Jean keeps winning and Morris takes off to Amsterdam with an old flame, but will his prophecy that bad luck always follows good turn out to be true? ISBN 0 573 01825 1

The Lunatic View. Four Comedies of Menace. David Campton
These four plays can be performed as a whole, when the fee will be code H, or separately as under, with the stated fees

A Smell of Burning
M2 F1. A living-room. Fee code D
An insight into the vulnerability of the 'little man' to officialdom and its impersonal dictates personified by a bickering married couple and a man from the City Surveyor's epartment.

Memento Mori
M2. A room in an empty house. Fee code D
An elderly estate agent is trying to sell a young man an old house in a bad state of repair. Or is he?

Getting and Spending
M2 F2. A room. Fee code D
Newly-weds Bobby and Evelyn enter their new house full of ideas for the future but life passes without their plans coming to fruition.

Then ...
M1 F1. Fee code D
Touching and illuminating, this plays deals with the last two survivors of a nuclear holocaust who fall in love.

Luther. Play. John Osborne
M12 F1. Extras. Various interior and exterior settings. Fee code J

A brilliant study of a rebel. Luther, perhaps the first real Protestant, outspoken, fearless critic of High Church hypocrisy is, nevertheless, a very ordinary monk. We see his acceptance into the brotherhood, his subsequent doubts and his preoccupation with health, his uncompromising attack on the abuse of Indulgences and his refusal to capitulate before the Diet of Worms. The play provides a wide variety of challenging, rewarding parts but the production itself demands nothing lavish. Period 1506-27

Mad Forest. Play from Romania. Caryl Churchill
40 characters, may be played by a cast of 11. Various interior and exterior settings. Fee code M

Focussing on two families, life before the 1989 Romanian revolution is portrayed. The play, with a large cast, was performed by eleven actors and was seen at the Royal Court Theatre in 1990. 'The work is speedy, poetic, urgent and electrifying ... The trial and execution of the Ceausescus is done as a sickening revue sketch, an indicator of the double-edged, sceptical tone throughout. A triumph! The future of our theatre, if not that of Romania, is secure.' *Observer*

Made in Bangkok. Play. Anthony Minghella
M7 (20s, 30s, 50s) F5 (30s), with doubling. Various interior settings. Fee code M

The setting is Bangkok — market place of the world where everything is for sale; the message is a bleak indictment of commercial sex and the condemnation of human exploitation. The main characters are a bunch of British tourists who arrive in Thailand armed with good intentions but are soon unzipping their sexual frustrations of a lifetime. 'Minghella handles his powerful, complex theme with great accomplishment, building to a scarifying climax.' *Time Out*

A Madhouse in Goa. A double bill by Martin Sherman
M4 (Part One: 18, 20s, 30s; Part Two: 19, 20s, 40s) F2 (Part One: 60s; Part Two: 20s, 40s). Two verandas. Fee code M

Part One, *A Table for A King*, chronicles the experiences of a young writer, David, who takes part in a plan to blackmail another guest into giving up her favourite table for the King of Greece. Part Two, *Keeps Rainin' All the Time*, moves to the volcanic island of Santorini, where the existence of several disparate expatriates is ruptured by nuclear rain, terrorism and the impending eruption of the volcano.

The Madness of George III. Play. Alan Bennett
M22 F5, with doubling. Various simple interior and exterior settings. Fee code M

What, what? Is the King mad? The Whigs think so, and begin campaigning for the Bill of Regency to allow the power-hungry Prince of Wales to ascend the throne. Meanwhile the King endures humiliating, torturous treatment at the hands of incapable doctors. Bennett's clever, funny and ultimately compassionate play sheds new light on a monarch often dismissed as inconsequential. It was first performed to great acclaim by the Royal National Theatre with Nigel Hawthorne in the title role.

The Magistrate. Farce. A. W. Pinero
M11 F5 or M12 F4. A sitting-room, an hotel room, a magistrate's room. Fee code M

Pinero's classic farce follows the misadventures of Mr Posket, the mild magistrate of Meek Street, who gets disgracefully involved in the reprehensible junketings of his stepson. The hideous complications that ensue result in Mr Posket unwittingly sentencing his wife to a prison term: but needless to say all is happily resolved before the final curtain falls. Period 1880s
ISBN 0 573 01264 9

The Maiden Stone. Play. Rona Munro
M2 (30s-50s) F4 (14, 16, 30s, 40s). A boy. Children. Various simple settings. Fee code M

Set in the North-east of Scotland in the early nineteenth century, this tells a story of women struggling against their circumstances, desires and ambitions in the persons of Harriet, an educated English actress leading her touring troupe in search of work, and Bidie, the Scottish traveller she engages as a wet nurse.

Mail Order Bride. Play. James Robson
M2 (30, 50) F3 (26, 35, 55). 2M 4F, voices only. A large kitchen. Fee code M

Martin, a craggy, hard-working Yorkshire landowner and bachelor, lives with his punctilious spinster sister Ivy on the farm they inherited from their parents. Desperate for companionship, Martin pays for a Filipino woman, Maria — whom he has discovered through a video-dating agency — to come and live with them. But Ivy resents the intrusion, and, on the day of Maria and Martin's wedding, she digs up information about Maria's past, with shocking consequences for them all.
ISBN 0 573 01847 2

The Maintenance Man. Play. Richard Harris
M1 (40) F2 (40). Two living-rooms represented by the same set. Fee code M

A bitter-sweet, witty and perceptive look at the collapse of a marriage and the development and decay of an affair. Bob is a do-it-yourself enthusiast with a longing to be needed. Even after he is divorced from Chris he constantly returns to his former home, until Diana, his new love, begins to resent having to face competition for his time from his children and his Black and Decker.
ISBN 0 573 01651 8

Make and Break. Play. Michael Frayn
M11 (20s-50s) F2 (young, 40). An exhibition stand in an hotel bedroom. Fee code M

John Garrard is a compulsive businessman, and his self-absorption is complete. During one climactic night amid the hectic activities of a trade fair in Germany, it looks as if the shell of his self-concern might at least be pierced; an unexpected relationship with an attractive secretary, a lesson in Buddhism, a sudden apparent heart attack and confrontation with death. But death when it comes strikes unexpectedly elsewhere — and Garrard's character seems unchanged, unless for the worse ...
ISBN 0 573 11257 6

♦ **Make Way for Lucia**. Comedy. John van Druten from the novels of E. F. Benson
M5 (38-45, 45, 50, old) F6 (35, 40s, 50, old). A drawing-room. Fee code M

E. F. Benson's hilarious novels, written in the 1920s and 30s, of the war for social supremacy between Lucia and Miss Mapp in Tilling are brought to the stage with all the wit, irony and humour of the originals. Hitherto, Tilling's doyenne has been Miss Mapp; Lucia is the supreme poseuse who peppers her speech with Italian phrases she doesn't understand. When Lucia rents Miss Mapp's house for the summer the battle lines are drawn ...
ISBN 0 573 01820 0

Making History. Play. Brian Friel
M4 (20s, 40s) F2 (20s). A living-room, a thicket, a palace apartment. Fee code M

The central character of this play is Hugh O'Neill, Earl of Tyrone, who led an alliance of Irish and Spanish against the armies of Elizabeth I in an attempt to drive the English out of Ireland. The action takes place before and after the Battle of Kinsale, at which the alliance was defeated: with O'Neill at home in Dungannon, as a fugitive in the mountains, and finally exiled in Rome. Period Elizabethan

Making It Better. Play. James Saunders
M3 (20s, 40s, 50s) F1 (40s). Various simple interior and exterior settings. Fee code M

It is 1989; Czechoslovakia is struggling with its new-found freedom. In London, Pavlicek and Tomas, two Czechoslovakian émigrés, become involved in the tangled relationship between Diana and Adrian Harrington, who purvey British culture across the globe via the World Service. Betrayals — of friends, loves, countries and ideals — abound in this emotionally exacting and politically stringent comedy.
ISBN 0 573 01834 0

Man Alive! Unlikely story. John Dighton
M7 (20s-60s) F7 (20s-middle-age). A shop window. Fee code H

In preparation for the January Sale, a window-dresser has the idea of utilizing a very special sun-lamp in the window which contains two blasé female dummies and Waldorf, a male dummy. But the lamp's rays have fantastic properties: they turn the waxen dummy into a beguiling young man and the store's unpopular owner, Hathaway, into a dummy. Waldorf's human life is short but exceedingly merry and he revolutionizes life in the store while Hathaway learns some valuable lessons.
ISBN 0 573 01259 8

Man and Boy. Drama. Terence Rattigan
M5 (young, 30s, 50s) F2 (young). A basement apartment. Fee code M

A tense drama of the business world which requires a comparatively simple set. Gregor, a tycoon of Hungarian origin, arrives at the apartment of his illegitimate son, Basil, for a business meeting to discuss a highly-profitable merger. After achieving apparent success he finds everything collapsing aound him and learns from Basil that a warrant is out for his arrest. Basil offers help, but Gregor acquires a conscience for the first time in his life and determines his own way out.
ISBN 0 573 61214 5

A Man for All Seasons. Play. Robert Bolt
M11 (30s, 40s, 60s) F3 (24, 47, 55). Composite setting. Fee code M

Paul Schofield starred in both play and film as Sir Thomas More, the sixteenth-century Chancellor unwillingly in conflict with Henry VIII. More loves God, but he loves the world also. He has a subtle intellect, a scrupulous conscience and a very human fear of death, knowing full well the penalty of even silently opposing the king. All the while the chorus figure of the Common Man evades all personal responsibility for orders carried out, even to being More's executioner.
ISBN 0 573 01260 1

Man Is Man. (Man Equals Man) Play. Bertolt Brecht
Translations: Steve Gooch
                Carl Mueller, music by Dessau
                Gerhard Nellhaus, music by Dessau
M8 F2. Soldiers. Various interior and exterior settings. Fee code M for play, code C for music

Four soldiers loot an Indian temple, but one is left behind. Terrified of their fierce Sergeant, they get Galy Gay, an Irish docker, to pose as the fourth man. Galy Gay witnesses his own supposed execution and funeral; in the last two scenes he takes part in a war against Tibet and has become the perfect soldier. The missing man tries to rejoin his comrades, but is turned away with Galy Gay's old identity papers. The story is vaguely set in British India, but both time and geography are largely nonsensical.

Man of the Moment. Play. Alan Ayckbourn
M6 (30s-50s) F4 (19-50s). Extras 3M 3F, 1 child (7). Male voices. A patio/pool area of a Mediterranean villa. Fee code M

This joint winner of the *Evening Standard* Best Comedy Award starred Peter Bowles as the ex-robber turned successful media personality and Michael Gambon as the timid clerk who once heroically foiled his bank raid. ' ... one of the best things he has ever done ... It is, in fact, a masterpiece ... Ayckbourn at the peak of his powers using comedy to say harsh, true things about our society ...' *Guardian*
ISBN 0 573 01833 2

A Man with Connections. Play. Alexander Gelman. Translated by Stephen Mulrine
M1 (40s) F1 (40s), voice (1M). A bedroom. Fee code M

Andrei Golubev realizes that his desire to further his career has led him to ignore his wife's affair with his superior; he is also partly responsible for his son's horrific injuries in an industrial accident. Andrei eventually declares that he will quit his job, and his wife remains with him on this understanding. She is then horrified when Andrei reveals that he has been promoted and cannot leave his job for some time, and she walks out on him.

Mansfield Park. Play. Adapted by Willis Hall from the novel by Jane Austen
M11 (young-elderly). F9 (young-elderly). Various interior and exterior settings. Fee code M

As a timid nine-year-old, Fanny Price is taken to live with her affluent cousins, the Bertrams, at Mansfield Park. Despite suffering many hardships as the poor relation in her early years, Fanny, by her gentle good-natured disposition, becomes an indispensible member of the household and finally marries her true love Edmund. This skilful dramatization preserves all the plot and characterization of the classic novel. (*Restricted availability*)
ISBN 0 573 01839 1

Map of the Heart. Play. William Nicholson
M4 (20s-40s) F4 (17, 30s, 40s). Extras. Various interior and exterior settings. Fee code M

Albie, dissatisfied with his life, decides to perform charitable work in The Sudan with his doctor lover, Mary, but his decision has damaging repercussions on those around him, especially his wife, Ruth. Whilst in The Sudan, Albie is held hostage leaving Ruth and Mary to poignantly take stock of their emotions. ' ... the most profoundly moving play in the West End since *Shadowlands,* which isn't surprising as William Nicholson wrote them both.' *Daily Express*
ISBN 0 573 01832 4

The March on Russia. Play. David Storey
M2 (30s, 80) F3 (30s, 70). A living-room. Fee code M

The sixtieth wedding anniversary of Tommy Pasmore and his wife is little cause for celebration. The elderly couple live together despite each other — their bickering banter revealing deep disappointment — but only by incanting memories can they come to terms with their barren present and terrifying future. Seen at the Royal National Theatre in 1989 this is a worthy successor to the author's earlier *In Celebration.* '... deeply moving ... a play of delicate half-tones and pastel shades ... impressive ...' *Guardian*
ISBN 0 573 01698 4

♦ **Mariana Pineda**. Play. Federico García Lorca. Translated by Gwynne Edwards
M8 F10, 1 boy, 1 girl. Extras. Various settings. Fee code M

Lorca's second play, and his only historical play which is based on a traditional tale, tells the story of a liberal heroine of Granada, her opposition to King Ferdinand VII in the late 1820s, her love for another liberal, Don Pedro de Sotomayor, and her final execution.

♦ **Marking Time**. Comedy. Michael Snelgrove
M3 (20s-50s) F2 (30s-40s). A room. Fee code L

In a tiny, tatty room in a residential teachers' centre, Team B are up to their eyebrows in A level English Literature marking. Elsewhere in the building, the dreaded Team A are coping far better with their marking band guidelines, matrix grids and marked pilot samples and managing to spend plenty of time in the bar; Team B, led by the far-from-perfect Howard, lurch from disaster to disaster. Doors slam, tempers are lost and personalities crumble as the situation becomes ever more chaotic.
ISBN 0 573 01828 6

Marvellous Party. Play. John Wynne-Tyson
M6 F4 or M5 F3, with doubling. An hotel suite. Fee code L

This sophisticated, revealing comedy supposes a middle-age reunion in Las Vegas between Noël Coward and Esmé Wynne-Tyson, his real-life, oldest, closest and most exacting female friend. Although entirely imaginary, it is based on special knowledge and offers a character assessment of two very real, remarkable people. Period 1950s. 'I enjoyed [it] hugely. You have caught Noël completely — the whole man.' Richard Briers. 'Terribly clever ... so convincing ... a brilliant play, extremely amusing and often touching.' Dodie Smith

♦ Terry Pratchett's **Maskerade**. Play. Adapted by Stephen Briggs
M16 F9. Extras. Various simple interior and exterior settings. Fee code M

All is not well in the Ankh-Morpork Opera House. A ghost stalks the dark corridors, leaving strange letters for the management and ... killing people. Granny Weatherwax and Nanny Ogg, two Lancre witches, investigate, and are soon involved in all kinds of skulduggery, mayhem and ear-splittingly loud singing. Quirky and original characters, a labyrinthine plot and numerous witty one-liners make this a treat for Discworld fans and 'uninitiated' theatregoers alike.
ISBN 0 573 01829 4

♦ **Massage**. Play. Michael Wilcox
M2 F1. A living-room. Fee code L

Tony Dodge hires Rikki from a massage agency to help him celebrate a child's birthday tea. The absent child in question — for whom Dodge has more than a tender affection — is Simon, twelve-year-old son of Dodge's former girlfriend Jane. Rikki, though a rent boy, is heterosexual with his own childhood memories of sexual abuse. Gradually, under his sharp questioning, the complex nature of Dodge's dilemma is revealed: what began as innocent paternal friendship for a child has developed into a great deal more.

The Matchmaker. Farce. Thornton Wilder
M8 F7. Four interiors. Fee code M

An rich old merchant in Yonkers decides to take a wife and employs a matchmaker. She subsequently becomes involved with two of his menial clerks, assorted young, lovely ladies, and the headwaiter at an expensive restaurant where this swift farce runs headlong into a hilarious climax of complication. After everyone gets straightened out romantically, and everyone has his heart's desire, the merchant of Yonkers finds himself affianced to the astute matchmaker herself. Period 1880s. 'Loud, slapdash and uproarious ... Something extraordinarily original and funny.' *New York Times*.

Me and Mamie O'Rourke. Play. Mary Agnes Donoghue
M2 (20s, 30s) F2 (30s). A converted basement. Fee code M

Louise's Los Angeles house is rapidly turning into rubble as her architect husband David takes a sledgehammer to it as effectively as he has to their marriage. Louise escapes her unhappiness through fantasies of a former lover and through her close, but often stormy, friendship with Bibi, a cook who dreams of becoming an animal behaviourist.
ISBN 0 573 01844 8

Me and My Friend. Play. Gillian Plowman
M2 (30s-40s) F2 (20s-30s). Two flats. Fee code M

(Please note that the first two acts of this play may be presented as one-act plays, but that the third act may not.)

A black comedy, the play explores the relationships between two 'odd' couples thrown prematurely out of hospital care. Firstly, we see two men conduct fantasy interviews for jobs they will never get, then two women trying to 'make plans' as urged to do by the hospital. They all meet when Oz throws a disastrous party with the four desperately attempting the niceties of social intercourse.
ISBN 0 573 01831 6

Medea. A play by Euripides, translated by Alistair Elliot
M5 (50s, middle-age, old). F2 (middle-age, old). Greek chorus, 2 children. Various exterior settings. Fee code M

Medea finds herself wronged by her husband Jason when he marries the King's daughter. She is banished by the King, Creon, but, fatally, he gives her one day to prepare for her departure; 'one day,' he says, 'is too short a time to do us harm.' Racked with grief and anger and hatred, Medea undertakes horrendous acts of revenge that see the death of Jason's new wife, and, most brutally, of her own children.

The Memorandum. Play. Václav Havel. Translated by Vera Blackwell
M12 F3. Three offices. Fee code M

Written and performed during Czechoslovakia's era of relative political freedom in the 1960s, this is a provocative and witty assault on the madness of 'efficiency' peculiar to total bureaucracy. The action takes place in a model political bureaucracy where a harassed manager introduces a new jargon designed to supplant the popular language and expedite regimentation, but which proves to be unworkable.

Men Should Weep. Play. Ena Lamont Stewart
M4 F9. 1 girl (11), 1 boy (8), babies (voices only). A kitchen. Fee code M

Written for Glasgow Unity in 1947, this extraordinarily moving play of women surviving in the east end of Glasgow of the 1930s was revived by 7:84 Company to tremendous critical acclaim. It finds in the lives of Maggie, her family and her neighbours not only all the tragedy that appalling housing, massive unemployment and grinding poverty can produce, but alo a rich vein of comedy — the sense of the ridiculous, the need for a good laugh.

Messiah. Play. Martin Sherman
M2 (24, 50s) F4 (28, late 40s, middle-age). Extras. Musicians. Various simple interior and exterior settings. Fee code M

Messiah is set in Poland in 1665 following the Cossack uprising in which over a third of the once thriving Jewish community has been slaughtered, the rest impoverished. Now everyone is obsessed with the certainty that the Messiah will come. So, with the news that the Messiah is preaching in the Middle East, Rachel and her family journey to Gallipoli with tragic results. ' ... handles the Jewish dilemma with humanity and humour.' *Standard*

Mick and Mick. Play. Hugh Leonard
M6 (20s, 30s, 60s, 80s) F4 (20s, 30s, 60). Extras. A hall/living-room, a garden, a pub. Fee code M

Fran returns home to Ireland for her brother's ordination and is confronted by her mother and sister, who are concerned with the neighbours' reactions to Fran's bleached hair and low-cut dress. Fran finds a soul-mate in her brother-in-law who is trapped in a web of stifling domesticity and meets up again with the fiancé who jilted her eight years previously. But a cruel misunderstanding forces her to leave home once more.
ISBN 0 573 11272 X

Midsummer Mink. Comedy. Peter Coke
M4 (20s, young, middle-age, elderly) F7 (20s, middle-age). A living-room. Fee code H

The amiable aristocratic crooks of *Breath of Spring* are at it again. Brigadier Rayne deploys his charity campaigns with little monetary success until Nan is passed a mink coat by a crook on the run, and soon they are running a meticulously organized receiving system for stolen furs, giving all their profits to charity. Finally, with the house full of furs and a police inspector making inquiries, they decide to retire — temporarily.
ISBN 0 573 01277 6

The Milk Train Doesn't Stop Here Any More. Play. Tennessee Williams
M5 (young, 17) F4 (young, elderly). Composite setting. Fee code M

A stranger arrives at Mrs Goforth's Italian villa, a young poet known as the Angel of Death because he has been present at the decease of a number of elderly ladies. She thinks that he will afford her a final fling before she dies, but it turns out that he is there as a spiritual rather than fleshly guide and merely wishes to comfort her during her declining years. The author describes his play as 'a comedy about death'.

A

The Miracle Worker. Play. William Gibson
M6 (9 (Black), 20s, 40s, 60s, elderly) F7 (6, 8 (Black), 17, 20s, 35 (Black), middle-age). Composite setting. Fee code M

Helen Keller is world-famous for her work with those born blind, deaf and dumb. The play tells the story of Annie Sullivan's efforts to teach Helen to communicate, fighting against the thoughtless indulgence of Helen's family and her doting possessive mother until, at last, Annie achieves the miracle of teaching Helen language. Here, Helen's life can truly be said to have begun. Period 1880
ISBN 0 573 61238 2

The Misanthrope. Comedy. Molière. English version by Tony Harrison
M8 F2. A room. Fee code M

Commissioned by the National Theatre for the 1973 production starring Diana Rigg and Alec McCowen, Harrison's transposition of the action to the 'reign' of Charles de Gaulle helps to clarify the truly human dilemmas in the play so often obscured behind the frills and stiffness of traditional productions. This comedy of manners centres on the high-principled Alceste who cannot bring himself to temper the truth with tact and has the comic misfortune to be in love with the frivolous wayward Célimène. Period 1966

The Miser. Comedy. Molière. Adapted by Miles Malleson
M11 (20s, middle-age, elderly) F3 (young, 20s, middle-age). A room in Paris. Fee code H

Harpagon, the miser, loves his gold but decides to take for his second wife Mariane, the beloved of his son Cléante. Meanwhile, Valère and Elise are in love. Harpagon threatens to marry Elise to a certain Seigneur Anselm, so the four lovers urgently plot to save themselves. It transpires that Valère and Mariane are the lost children of wealthy Seigneur Anselm. As Anselm is a benevolent fellow, the lovers' happiness is assured. Period 1668
ISBN 0 573 01279 2

Misha's Party. Play by Richard Nelson and Alexander Gelman
M7 (30s-60s) F7 (16, 20s-50s). Various interiors. Fee code M

In 1991, Mikhail celebrates his sixtieth birthday in a Moscow hotel; outside, communist reactionaries are attempting a coup. Mikhail has gathered together an uneasy group: his two ex-wives, and their new husbands, his disgruntled daughter Masha, and his young fiancée Lydia, Masha's flatmate. Meanwhile, an American, Mary, frantically searches for her lost granddaughter. Using a recent event in Russia's volatile political history as its backdrop, this poignantly explores many themes pertinent to Russia and the West, from historical determinism to the conflict between generations.

◆ **Miss Roach's War**. Play. Richard Kane. Adapted from *The Slaves of Solitude* by Patrick Hamilton
M3 (35, 59, 70s) F5 (20, 39, 60s) or M3 F4 with doubling. Five acting areas. Fee code M

1943. The Rosamund Tea Rooms houses several women and elderly men, all of them single and lonely, who nurse resentments and wage minor wars with each other. Enid Roach makes two unfortunate friendships which heighten the tension to breaking point: one with Pike, an American lieutenant, the other with Vicki Kugelmann, a German who steals Pike from Enid and then sets about humiliating her former friend.
ISBN 0 573 01919 3

Mistress of Novices. Play. John Kerr
M3 (middle-age, elderly) F12 (young, middle-age, elderly). Extra 1F. Standing set. Fee code K

The play recounts the story of Bernadette and the miraculous vision she claims to have been granted, and also the conflict that this assertion causes in her relationship with the sceptical and strong-willed Mistress of Novices. Set mainly in the Convent of St Gildard, Nevrs, it follows the life of Bernadette until its agonized end, and closes with the announcement of Bernadette's canonization. Period mid-nineteenth to early twentieth century.
ISBN 0 573 06012 6

Mixed Doubles. An entertainment on marriage by George Melly, Alan Ayckbourn, James Saunders, Harold Pinter, Alun Owen, Fay Weldon, David Campton, Lyndon Brook and John Bowen. M1 F1 for each sketch. M1 for linking scenes. Fee code M

If individual scenes are presented separately fee codes vary. Please enquire for further details to Samuel French Ltd.
ISBN 0 573 01584 8

Mixed Feelings. Comedy. Donald Churchill
M4 (young, middle-age) F2 (middle-age). A basement flat. Fee code M

Arthur is extremely satisfied with his Friday evening interludes with Sonia, but trouble starts when his ex-wife persuades him to help her get rid of her own lover, and Sonia becomes so jealous that she fakes a confession to her husband, Dennis. Norma and Arthur invite Dennis round to give their side of the story. However, when he arrives they discover that Dennis has been perfectly happy to condone Sonia's affair with Arthur as long as she tells him all about it — and now he wants to join in.

Moment of Weakness. Comedy. Donald Churchill
M1 (40s) F2 (18, 40s). A cottage living-room. Fee code M

When Audrey and Tony meet some while after their divorce, they share memories, rekindle arguments and re-open wounds. Audrey, uncertain about her new boyfriend's offer of marriage, finally makes up her mind and accepts. Lucy, Audrey and Tony's daughter, reveals that Tony had been hoping to start again with Audrey, but had been too nervous to ask. Audrey marries her boyfriend, immediately regrets it and is partially reconciled with Tony.
ISBN 0 573 69280 7

A Month in the Country. Play. Brian Friel, after Turgenev
M7 (21, 30s, 40s, 57) F5 (17, 20s, 37, 58). A drawing-room, a garden. Fee code M

In the introduction, Brian Friel identifies the novelty of Turgenev's drama 'where psychological and poetic elements create a theatre of moods and where the action resides in internal emotion and secret turmoil'. His lively, comic play describes the course of a passionately eventful summer month in which Natalya, luminous, anguished and possessed by love, is left to recover a measure of happiness after her turbulent disquiet. Period early 1840s

A Month in the Country. Comedy. Ivan Turgenev. Adapted into English by Emlyn Williams
For cast and settings see above. Fee code M

This play, originally censored on the ground of immorality, is the story of Turgenev's own disappointed romance with the wife of a friend. The young tutor who arrives on the Yslaev estate stays a month, during which both the land-owner's wife and her ward fall in love with him. He has to leave as does his wife's platonic lover. A sub-plot interwoven into the play reveals a world of sexual and mercenary intrigue. Period early 1840s Russia

A Month of Sundays. Play. Bob Larbey*
M3 (40s, 60s) F3 (24, 40s). A room in a rest home for the elderly. Fee code M

Set in a rest home, this play revolves around two residents: Cooper, who has voluntarily left his family to avoid the indignity of depending on them, and his friend Aylott, both on the verge of some geriatric embarrassment. To the painful ritual of family visits and empty condescension the two inmates reply with humour and wit, aware that life can only be endured if treated as a comedy. *(Please specify author when ordering this title.)

A Month of Sundays. Comedy. Gerald Savory*
M3 (25, 50s, elderly) F4 (15, 20s, 45). A farm kitchen. Fee code H. *(Please specify author when ordering this title.)
ISBN 0 573 01283 0

Moonlight. Play. Harold Pinter
M4 (20s, 50s) F3 (16, 50s). Simple settings depicting 2 bedrooms and an undefined space. Fee code M

Andy is a civil servant who lies dying in his bed. Desperate for consolation from his family, he spends his time railing against his long-suffering wife Bel. They remember their past, in particular their friendship with Maria, with whom they both had affairs. Alongside them, Andy's unemployed sons act out a series of fiercely high-powered mind-games, while daughter Bridget hovers over the action, subtly suggesting that she was the victim of some terrible childhood wrong.

The Morning Star. Play. Emlyn Williams
M4 (30s, 50s, 60s, 70s) F4 (20s, 30s, middle-age). A drawing-room. Fee code M. Copies available on hire.

Set in the London of 1940, this poignant and touchingly sentimental play tells the story of how one family comes to terms with the harsh realities of war. Yet they rise above it all: as one character says, buildings can burn and 'our lives can crash before our eyes, there'll be that we can be sure of, for ever — our love and trust, and courage — as long as we stick together and fight'.

Moscow Stations. Play. Stephen Mulrine, adapted from the novel *Moscow to Petushki* by Venedikt Yerofeev
M1, plus offstage voices. An empty stage. Fee code M

On a Moscow railway platform, Venya, an alcoholic wanderer, regales us with details — funny, shocking and sad — about his fascinating, complicated and ultimately hopeless life. Painting a darkly comic but despairing picture of Russia under Brezhnev, this rambling and random memoir is lyrical and moving, and provides a bravura role for a versatile actor.

The Mother. Play. Bertolt Brecht. Translated by Steve Gooch, music by Hanns Eisler
M15 F3. Extras. Various simple exterior and interior settings. Fee code M for play, code C for music

Pelagea Vlassova is drawn by her son Pavel into the revolutionary movement. Though hostile to it at first, she refuses to let him distribute leaflets, preferring to run the risk herself. She takes part in a peaceful demonstration, where Pavel is arrested; she learns to read, helps striking peasants, and works an illegal press. Pavel escapes from Siberia, but is caught and shot. Pelagea is beaten up for protesting against the 1914 war and finishes by carrying the red flag in a huge anti-war demonstration in the winter of 1916.

Mother Courage and her Children. Chronicle play. Bertolt Brecht
Translations: John Willett
                Eric Bentley, music by Dessau
                Ralph Manheim
                Hanif Kureishi
                ◆ David Hare
M19 F6. Extras. Twelve simple exterior settings. Fee code M for play, code C for music

For years through the terrible Thirty Years War Mother Courage has followed the Swedish armies with her mobile canteen, and her three children (each by a different man). Life during war is reduced simply to a series of business transactions: soldiers rob peasants and steal from their own stores, peasants sell their last cherished possessions. Mother Courage's business and motherly instincts constantly betray her. Finally, alone, she hitches herself to her wagon and continues to follow the army. Period 1624-1636

The Mother Tongue. Play. Alan Franks
M3 (18, 50s) F4 (40s, 60s). A living-room. Fee code M

Premièred at the Greenwich Theatre in 1992 starring Prunella Scales and Gwen Taylor. Dorothy, a snob in the grand colonial manner, goes to stay with her daughter Harriet when Dorothy's Kensington home is destroyed by fire. In the course of the next three weeks, Dorothy works her way deep into the fabric of Harriet's life and family skeletons come clattering out of cupboards on both sides. 'This is an absorbing, entertaining, ingeniously-written play — apparently light, actually dark.' *Observer*
ISBN 0 573 01836 7

Moving. Play. Hugh Leonard
M5 (any age, 18, 40s) F4 (17, 18, 40s, 60s). A living-room. Fee code M

It is 1957 and the Noone family is moving into a new house in Dublin. Presiding over the event is the Removals Man, who steps in and out of the action to explain the characters and their stories. The second half of the play is set in 1987 and the same family, no older than before, is moving into an even better house, their new relationships reflecting the revolutions that have taken place in family life in the intervening years.
ISBN 0 573 01837 5

Mr Puntila and his Man Matti. Play. Bertolt Brecht
Translations: John Willett, music by Dessau
                Paul Kriwaczek
                Gerhard Nellhaus
                ◆ Lee Hall, music by Chris Larner (for details of the music please apply to Samuel
                French Ltd)
M14 F7 (children). Extras. Interior and exterior settings. Fee code M for play, code C for music

Mr Puntila suffers from a dual personality. When drunk he is human and humane; when sober he is surly and self-centred. In the former condition he proposes to Eva to marry his own loyal and sardonic friend, his chauffeur Matti. When he sobers up he throws Eva out and abuses Matti. However, after putting Eva's suitability to the test, and having had enough of Puntila's instability, Matti leaves him, saying 'water and oil can never blend.'

Mr Quigley's Revenge. Play. Simon Brett
M14 F20 (speaking parts). A village hall. Fee code M

Frinsley Village Hall is the hub of community life, lovingly tended by the amiable Mr Quigley, whose little blue book ensures the aerobics class never clashes with the wedding bookings. But plans are afoot to change this cosy existence ... the invidious Keith has plans to sell the site. Feeling sure of success, Keith launches his attack on Mr Quigley — a big mistake, for Mr Quigley is wilier than he looks. Offers acting opportunities for all and great fun for the audience!
ISBN 0 573 01845 6

Mr Whatnot. Comedy. Alan Ayckbourn
M7 F4, doubling possible. Various settings. Fee code M

Mr Whatnot is Mint, a piano tuner, summoned to the stately home of Lord and Lady Slingsby-Craddock. Once there he falls in love with their daughter, Amanda, elopes with her, fails to save her from marriage to Cecil but wins through in the end. With plenty of mime and sound effects *Mr Whatnot* offers great opportunities to an imaginative director for a highly entertaining and unusual production.
ISBN 0 573 11287 8

Mrs Klein. Play. Nicholas Wright
F3 (30s, 52). A living-room. Fee code M

Seen in London at the National and Globe theatres in 1988 starring Gillian Barge, Francesca Annis and Zoë Wanamaker, this powerful drama centres on an episode in the life of controversial child-psychoanalyst Melanie Klein. Because of the death of her son, Hans, Melanie is confronted with the irony of being a successful child analyst but a failed mother. She attacks her own daughter Melitta who leaves for good and whose role as daughter is replaced by Melitta's friend, Paula. Period 1934

The Mummy's Tomb. Play. Ken Hill. Songs by Alan Klein and Ken Hill
M7 (young, middle-age) F2 (young, middle-age), with doubling. Interior and exterior settings. Fee code L

In ancient Egypt, Pharaoh's wife Ashayet kills her lover's mistress. Pharaoh banishes Ashayet and entombs and mummifies her lover. But Ashayet also is immortal, having bathed in the River of Life. AD 1922 — Professor Niven sets out for Egypt with his daughter, Nancy, and rather unwisely, both her present and past fiancés. Almost at once strange things happen. Period 1380BC; AD 1922
ISBN 0 573 11288 6

Murder Assured. Thriller. Tony Clayton
M4 (middle-age) F2 (20s, middle-age). A living-room. Fee code L
ISBN 0 573 01611 9

Murder at the Vicarage. Drama. Dramatized by Moie Charles and Barbara Toy from the novel by Agatha Christie
M7 (young, 16, 30, 40, elderly) F6 (young, 17, 35, middle-age). A living-room. Fee code M

Everyone has a motive for wishing Colonel Protheroe dead. Amidst the heightening tension fostered by anonymous letters and bogus telephone calls moves the gentle figure of Miss Marple, whose old-maidish exterior conceals a very shrewd brain. She has the uncanny knack of knowing most people's secrets and it is she who is ultimately responsible for solving the mystery.
ISBN 0 573 01291 1

Murder by Appointment. Play. Frank Williams
M4 (young, 17, middle-age) F2 (young, middle-age). A drawing-room. Fee code L

This play cleverly manipulates modern trends and conceptions of behaviour to the murderer's advantage. Building on present psychological ideas of heredity and sexual tendencies the author has designed such a plot that not only is the murderer's identity concealed right to the end but the audience is lured into condemning the wrong man, not once, but twice. Red herrings abound to make this into an exciting and devious thriller for ambitious societies and adult audiences.
ISBN 0 573 01621 6

Murder by Misadventure. Play. Edward Taylor
M3 (30s-40s) F1 (30s). A penthouse flat. Fee code M

Laughs, thrills and mind-boggling twists abound in this ingenious thriller which played at the Vaudeville Theatre in 1992 with a cast including Gerald Harper and William Gaunt. Despite their success as authors of TV thrillers, Harold Kent has become dissatisfied with his writing partner, and wants to dissolve their association. So he takes inspiration from one of their scripts ... 'It has a last-scene denouement which turns every available table, until you are left giddy with bewilderment ... ' *Evening Standard*
ISBN 0 573 01835 9

Murder by the Book. Thriller. Duncan Greenwood and Robert King
M3 (late 20s, middle-age) F2 (early 20s, mid-30s). A drawing-room. Fee code L

Crisp, witty exchanges of dialogue pepper this light-hearted and inventive thriller. A thriller writer indulges in vitriolic verbal duels with his estranged wife, until she turns a gun on him and fires. An amateur detective from the next flat attempts to solve the murder puzzle — then the 'corpse' rises, full of life, and the tables are turned, more than once, for victim and killers alike ...
ISBN 0 573 11300 9

The Murder Game. Play. Constance Cox
M2 (28, 40) F2 (26, 35). A living-room. Fee code L

Brian and Sheila Hamilton live in apparently affluent comfort; but in reality their marriage is breaking up. In fact, it would be considerably to Brian's advantage if Sheila were to die. His friend Gerry suggests a fool-proof method of bringing this about. The murder is carried out — and successfully — but it is not long before Brian realizes that, by putting himself in Gerry's power, he has indeed exchanged the frying-pan for the fire.
ISBN 0 573 01222 9

A Murder Has Been Arranged. Ghost Story. Emlyn Williams
M4 (young, 40s) F6 (young, 20s, middle-age, 45). A stage. Fee code H

There is a legend concerning a murder once committed at the St James' Theatre, that a dumb woman will appear on stage to reveal the murderer. Sir Charles Jasper holds a dinner-party in the theatre. Tonight he will come into a vast fortune. Should he die before eleven, his nephew Maurice will inherit it. Maurice arrives and engineers his uncle's murder. Then the dumb woman of the legend appears ...
ISBN 0 573 01294 6

Murder in Company. Play. Philip King and John Boland
M4 (21, 40s) F4 (20s-40). An empty stage. Fee code L

A dramatic society is assembling on the stage of a church hall to rehearse a production of a mystery-thriller. The rehearsal proceeds under difficulties until the mysterious death of the caretaker brings the situation of the whodunit even more closely into real life. It transpires that almost everyone might, and could have, murdered the dead man — eventually the identity of both killer and prowler is revealed.
ISBN 0 573 01289 X

Murder in Mind. Play. Terence Feely
M5 (young, middle-age) F2 (young, slightly older). Extras 1M. A hall/sitting-room. Fee code M

Mary, an international art dealer, arrives home to find her house occupied by three 'strangers' claiming to be her husband, cousin and sister. Even more mysterious is the fact that they seem aware of details of her family life which could only have been known to her most intimate circle. The nightmare situation becomes more and more complicated, including the sudden appearance of a murdered man ...
ISBN 0 573 11303 3

Murder in Neighbourhood Watch. Thriller. Stewart Burke
M4 (30s-50s) F3 (teenage, 30s, 40s). A living-room. Fee code L

Panic grips West Lynstead when a famous dress designer is raped and strangled. Andrew Wingate, headmaster of the local school, sets up his own 'neighbourhood watch' and, disguised as a woman, walks the woods at night, laying himself open as bait for the killer. Suspense builds in this exciting play as Andrew is accused by an anonymous caller of attempted rape and a schoolgirl is lured into the hands of the killer ...
ISBN 0 573 11290 8

Murder in Play. Play. Simon Brett
M3 (30s, 40s, 60s) F5 (20s, middle-age). A living-room box set. Fee code M

Boris Smolensky's budget repertory production of 'Murder at Priorswell Manor' is looking decidedly shaky. The cast are more interested in their egos than the play and life imitates art when Boris's wife, Renee, is murdered on stage. Simon Brett's hilarious text, a worthy companion to his Charles Paris theatrical thriller novels, ruthlessly satirizes the politics of the inept company and the numerous red herrings keep the audience guessing until the final moments of the play.
ISBN 0 573 01840 5

A Murder is Announced. Play. Agatha Christie. Adapted by Leslie Darbon
M5 (young, 20s, 50s) F7 (20s, middle-age, 50s, elderly). A drawing-room. Fee code M

The 'announcement' is in the local paper, stating time and place of a murder to occur in Miss Blacklock's early Victorian house. However, the victim is not one of several occupants, temporary and permanent, but an unexpected and unknown visitor. What follows is a classic Christie puzzle, with Miss Marple on hand to provide the final solution in a dramatic confrontation scene just before the final curtain.
ISBN 0 573 11295 9

The Murder of Maria Marten or The Red Barn. Melodrama. Brian J. Burton
M5 F8. Various simple interior and exterior settings. Fee code L

In 1827, Willam Corder murdered Maria Marten, the mother of his illegitimate child, and buried her body in the Red Barn. Because of his wife's recurring dream, Thomas Marten searched the barn and discovered the body of his daughter. The fact that this production gets unsullied, hearty fun from these macabre ingredients is proof of its sureness — of its energy that pushes aside any attempt to think seriously about the horrors. Period 1820s

Murder on the Nile. Play. Agatha Christie
M8 (young, 28, middle-age) F5 (young, 24, 60). A ship's saloon. Fee code M

Simon and Kay Mostyn are honeymooning aboard a Nile steamer. With them, apparently by accident, are Canon Pennefather, Kay's guardian and Jacqueline, Simon's ex-girlfriend. During the course of the voyage Jacqueline works herself into a state of hysteria and shoots at Simon, but only wounds him in the knee. A few minutes later Kay is found shot. Canon Pennefather lays bare an audacious conspiracy and ensures that the criminals shall not go free.
ISBN 0 573 01298 9

The Murder Room. Mystery Farce. Jack Sharkey
M3 (young, 40s, 50s) F3 (young, 30s, 60s). A living-room. Fee code M

Two days after their marriage Edgar catches Mavis, a villainess if ever there was one, telling obvious lies about where she has spent the evening. After a first attempt to kill him by poisoning his cocoa fails — the cat dies instead — she fires three shots into him and phones her lover. Later it transpires that the pistol contained only blanks, and Edgar's body vanishes. From then on complication follows complication until chaos reigns supreme.
ISBN 0 573 61283 8

Murder with Love. Play. Francis Durbridge
M6 (28, 40s) F3 (young, 30s, middle-age). Split set: two living-rooms. Fee code M

Many people dislike Larry Campbell but none feel more embittered than David Ryder. Ryder pursues his vendetta by nefariously obtaining a key to Campbell's flat to kill him. Deceit, suspicion, blackmail and incrimination are woven into the web of crime which is completed by a second killing and a tantalizing twist at the climax.
ISBN 0 573 11302 5

Murderer. Play. Anthony Shaffer
M2 (35, 40s) F2 (25, 30s). A living-room, bathroom and sauna. Fee code M

An unusual and macabre beginning to this play sets the audience's nerves twitching well before any dialogue confuses their minds! Norman apparently murders his girlfriend, Millie, and is in the process of disposing of her body when he is interrupted by a Sergeant Stenning. The ensuing hunt for the victim and the ghoulish discovery of a head burning in the stove is fiendishly climaxed by the revelation that it is only a dummy. Yet is Millie really dead or not? For connoisseurs of murders only. (NB *This play contains violent scenes*)
ISBN 0 573 01590 2

A

Murmuring Judges. Play. David Hare
M19 F6. Extras. Various simple interior and exterior settings. Fee code M

When Irina Platt embarks on her first case as a lawyer, she finds that all sections of the criminal justice system — police, courts and prisons — are running far from smoothly. With its large multicultural cast and contemporary settings ranging from prison interiors to the Inns of Court, *Murmuring Judges* presents a broad yet finely detailed picture not only of the judicial system but of British society in the 1990s.

My Cousin Rachel. Play. Diana Morgan. From the novel by Daphne du Maurier
M5 (young, 40s, 50s, elderly) F2 (18, 30s). A hall. Fee code L

Philip Ashley travels to Italy to find his cousin Ambrose has died suddenly and Rachel, Ambrose's wife, has gone. Philip returns to England convinced Rachel was responsible for Ambrose's death, hoping to inherit his possessions. When Rachel arrives in England Philip falls in love with her. One small event after another causes a kind of see-saw of belief and disbelief. Is Rachel a scheming murderess or a grossly maligned woman? Period mid-1800s
ISBN 0 573 11305 X

My Fat Friend. Comedy. Charles Laurence
M3 (18, 30s, 40s) F1 (29). A flat in Hampstead. Fee code K

Vicky, a Hampstead bookseller, is a heavyweight. When a handsome customer seems attracted to her she resolves that while he is abroad she will slim. Aided by the two male 'characters' who share the flat above her shop, hard exercise, diet and a graph, she manages to reduce to a streamlined version of her former self — only to find that it was her rotundity that attracted the book buyer in the first place.
ISBN 0 573 01545 7

My Friend Miss Flint. Comedy. Donald Churchill and Peter Yeldham
M3 (20s, 50s, middle-age) F3 (30s, 40s). A studio/apartment. Fee code L

When Tom Lambert receives a telephone call one morning from the Inland Revenue enquiring about his public relations consultant, a Miss Joanna Flint, he can honestly say he has never heard of her. By lunchtime, however, he knows all about Miss Flint and rather wishes he didn't, for Sarah, his accountant and ex-wife, confesses that she invented Joanna Flint as a tax dodge and that unfortunately the Revenue have rumbled her. A highly entertaining comedy.
ISBN 0 573 11271 7

My Heart's a Suitcase. Play. Clare McIntyre
M2 (18, early 50s) F4 (early 20s, 30, indeterminate age). A room. Fee code M

Chris is an impoverished waitress, paranoid and angry at her lot in life. Hannah, a ceramics teacher with the beginnings of multiple sclerosis, is calm and genuinely unmaterialistic. Their weekend in Brighton is interrupted by visits from Tunis, shopaholic wife of the flat-owner, and Elliott, a drunken down-and-out. Chris also has spectral visits in the shape of Pest, a bad memory, and Luggage, the Patron Saint of Heavy Burdens. It seems Chris can never escape her lot.

My Mother Said I Never Should. Play. Charlotte Keatley
F4. Various simple interior and exterior settings. Fee code M

Charlotte Keatley's first play was premièred at the Contact Theatre, Manchester in 1987 and produced at the Royal Court, London. 'Totally engrossing, warm, funny, human look at four generations of women, Ms Keatley refuses to preach about a woman's nature and her place in the world, letting action and characters speak for themselves.' *Manchester Evening News*
ISBN 0 573 01700 X

My Sister in this House. Play. Wendy Kesselman
F4. 3 male voices. Composite setting. Fee code M

Set in Le Mans in the early 1930s, this extraordinary, award-winning drama is based on a celebrated historical murder case in which two maids, sisters, were convicted of murdering their employer and her daughter. Wendy Kesselman's very cinematically structured work explores the motivations which lead the two emotionally repressed sisters to commit the most gruesome of murders. The play was presented by Monstrous Regiment at the Hampstead Theatre Club in 1987.
ISBN 0 573 61872 0

My Three Angels. Comedy. Sam and Bella Spewack. From the French play *Cuisine des Anges* by Albert Husson
M7 (20s, 40s, middle-age) F3 (20s, middle-age). A living-room. Fee code M

It is Christmas Eve in the tropical prison colony of Cayenne. Felix Dulay, a hopeless storekeeper, is fearfully awaiting the owner, Gaston. Providence has given the Dulays three guardian angels — three convicts! In no time they have cooked Christmas lunch — and Felix's books — and will loose their own executioner on Gaston for his cruel behaviour!
ISBN 0 573 01304 7

The Mysteries. Trilogy of plays. Tony Harrison
M17 F3. A bare stage. Fee code M for each play

Revived at the Royal National Theatre in 1999, these three plays — *The Nativity*, *The Passion* and *Doomsday* — are moving and theatrically exciting reworkings of the traditional York, Wakefield, Chester and Coventry cycles of Mystery plays.

♦ **The Mysterious Mr Love**. Play. Karoline Leach
M1 (early middle-age) F1 (39). Various simple settings. Fee code M

Mr George Love is a gentlemanly diplomat, polite and charming, or so he would have you believe; in fact, he is a fortune-hunter, marrying vulnerable young women and stealing their nest-eggs. At first, Adelaide Pinchin, an overweight milliner lacking in confidence, seems like just another of his victims, but then the unexpected happens: Mr Love begins to feel emotionally involved with her. From this point, the plot twists and turns in many surprising ways until it reaches a chilling conclusion ... Period 1910 (**Available in the British Isles only**)
ISBN 0 573 01830 8

Mystery at Greenfingers. Comedy of detection. J. B. Priestley
M4 (28-50) F6 (20s, 35). An hotel staff-room. Fee code H

In a big hotel in Derbyshire before opening for the season the staff are coping as best they can, trying feverishly to get things ready. The whole company, marooned in the snowbound hotel, is bullied by Crowther, the stupid house detective, after the mysterious disappearance of an unexpected guest. Miss Tracey, another guest, holds the key to the mystery and the denouement is sufficiently unexpected.
ISBN 0 573 01307 1

The Mystery of Irma Vep. A penny dreadful. Charles Ludlam
M2 playing various male and female roles. A library drawing-room, various simple sets. Fee code M

The definitive Gothic melodrama written to be performed as a quick-change act in which two actors perform all the roles. A sympathetic werewolf, a vampire and an Egyptian princess brought to life when they open her tomb make this the play that has everything. This American award-winning romp was cited by *Time* magazine and the *New York Times* as one of the best plays of its year. ISBN 0 573 64046 7

Nana. Play. Olwen Wymark. Adapted from the novel by Emile Zola
40 characters, may be played by M5 F5. Various simple interior and exterior settings. Fee code M

Olwen Wymark's splendid dramatization of Zola's *Nana* is a story of sexual and financial greed in nineteenth-century Parisian society, depicting the rise and tragic downfall of a young courtesan. The play was commissioned by Shared Experience and had a highly acclaimed run at the Almeida Theatre, London, in 1988. 'Olwen Wymark has filleted the flesh from Zola's novel to produce a work which reeks of sex and pleasure.' *Time Out*

Napoli Milionaria. Play. Eduardo de Filippo. Adapted by Peter Tinniswood
M14 F11. A large room. Fee code M

Life is hard in Naples during World War II but Donna Amalia does her best to keep the family afloat by dealing on the black market. Amalia prospers while Gennaro, her law-abiding husband, goes missing and is presumed dead. He returns unexpectedly to find his wife unfaithful, his son a car thief, his daughter pregnant and his other daughter critically ill. Shocked by the effects of corruption on his family, Gennaro prepares to resume his role as head of the household. Tinniswood's adaptation for the National Theatre moves the play to Liverpool.

The National Health or Nurse Norton's Affair. Play. Peter Nichols
M12 (18, 30s-60s, 82, very old) F8 (young West Indian, young, 30, old). A hospital ward (with insets). Fee code M

The scene is a men's hospital ward. Against a beautifully detailed documentary background the author juxtaposes scenes of rich satire, in which the hospital staff become the highly romanticized characters of a television hospital series. The author's comments on the joys and pains of living and his observations on society are juggled with breath-taking dexterity.

Natural Causes. Comedy thriller. Eric Chappell
M3 (40s), F2 (20s, 40s). A study/library. Fee code M

Vincent is a professional suicide merchant. Contracted by Walter Bryce, he arrives at his country house and mistakenly assumes that the potion was intended for Walter's consumption. It then becomes clear that Walter's wife Celia is the client — or is she? Why are her suicide letters all typed and unsigned? After several thwarted attempts to poison various characters (resulting in multiple poisonings of a rubber plant), will anyone actually manage to drink the potion? This is black comedy at its blackest and best. ISBN 0 573 01841 3

The Neighbour. Play. Meredith Oakes
M4 (young, middle-age) F4 (young, middle-age). Various simple settings. Fee code M

Two young men living on a London council estate suddenly become enemies, invoking destructive forces beyond their control. NB: this play contains explicit language.

The Nerd. Comedy. Larry Shue
M5 (10, 30s, 40s) F2 (30s, 40s). A living-room. Fee code **M**

A Nerd — for which there is no British equivalent — is a mixture of twit, wimp, wally and creep. Staid Willum is having a birthday party. Rick, the Nerd, arrives in full Hallowe'en dress — four days late — and within minutes manages to insult, sicken and bore the guests. Willum endures this because Rick saved his life in Vietnam. Willum discovers that Rick is not what he seems and his reappearance stuns us all.
ISBN 0 573 01635 6

◆ **Never the Sinner**. Play. John Logan
M6 (late teens, 20s, middle-age, 67) F1. Various interior and exterior settings on an open stage. Fee code **M**

Seduction. Deception. Murder. This stunning Broadway hit (also seen at the Playhouse Theatre, London, in 1990) takes the audience back to 1924, to Chicago, where the Leopold and Loeb murder stunned and fascinated the nation. '... sweeps the audience into the boys' friendship without ever losing sight of the brutal murder. They lay out the furore and the legal manoeuvring surrounding this "Trial of the Century" particularly well, suggesting that nothing much has changed.' *New Yorker*
ISBN 0 573 62671 5

Neville's Island. Comedy. Tim Firth
M4 (40s) The shore of a wooded island. Fee code **M**

Four out-of-condition, middle-aged businessmen sent off on a team-building exercise in the Lake District succeed in being the first people ever to get shipwrecked on an island on Derwentwater. Bound in by fog, menaced by the wildlife and cut off from the world, this perfunctory middle-class exercise turns into a carnival of recrimination, French cricket and sausages. What should have been a bonding process for Gordon, Angus, Roy and Neville turns into a muddy, bloody fight for survival.
ISBN 0 573 14005 7

New Anatomies. Play. Timberlake Wertenbaker
F5, 1 musician, play 15 characters. Various interior and exterior settings. Fee code **H**

Timberlake Wertenbaker's second play for the Women's Theatre Group, first seen at the Edinburgh Festival, considers women trapped in the 'golden cage' of normality. It portrays the eccentric Isabelle Eberhardt, an explorer who lived from 1877 to 1904, who travels through Algeria dressed as an Arab boy before going to Paris, where she encounters other women adopting male dress as a basis for greater freedom. ' ... an ambitious drama. Ms Wertenbaker's writing shows remarkable range ... ' *Time Out*

New England. Play. Richard Nelson
M4 (may be played by M3 with doubling) (30, 40s, 60s) F4 (30s, 41, 54). A study, part of a kitchen. Fee code **M**

Harry Baker, an English music professor, lives with his English girlfriend in a farmhouse in Connecticut. When he commits suicide, his children, his brother and his daughter-in-law, all expatriates, descend on the house and find comfort in attacking their adopted country, sneering at its apparent lack of culture. But cracking jokes at the expense of the natives is merely a mask for their own insecurities, disappointments and rivalries.

Next Time I'll Sing to You. Play. James Saunders
M4 F1. A bare stage with platform. Fee code M

In 1942 a man, who had lived as a hermit for the last thirty-six years of his life, died. Taking this fact, the author of this play re-examines why the man chose to live alone for so long. Rudge reconstructs and examines the facts, their implications and inferences, with the help of four actors, Meff, Dust, Lizzie and an unnamed actor to play the Hermit.

Night and Day. Play. Tom Stoppard
M7 (8, 20s (Black), 40s, 50s (Black)) F1 (30s). A living-room, hall and stairs. Fee code M

The action takes place in the imaginary African state of Kambawe, which is undergoing a civil war against a dictatorial President. The main subject of the play, however, is British journalism — the relationships and competitiveness between rival journalists. Underlying both themes is that of the freedom of the press and, more widely, freedom itself. Presented at the Royal National Theatre starring Diana Rigg.
ISBN 0 573 11308 4

Night Must Fall. Play. Emlyn Williams
M4 (young, 50s, old) F5 (28, 35, 50s). Interior setting. Fee code M

Danny has already murdered one woman, and there is little doubt that he will soon murder another — the aged owner of the house. He gradually insinuates himself into her affections in a skilful manner, for Dan is a dashing young assassin, a completely self-centred psychopath with no feelings and a vast imagination, who is perpetually acting, for his own edification, the part of the murderer.
Period 1935
ISBN 0 573 01843 X

The Night of the Iguana. Play. Tennessee Williams
M8 (1 Black) F6. A roofed veranda. Fee code M

Shannon, a minister defrocked for blasphemy and seduction, is now a travel guide in Mexico. Coping with a group of Baptist women furious because he has taken them off the advertised route and slept with a girl in the party, he arrives at a ramshackle inn run by a brash and 'rapaciously lusty' proprietress. The confrontations among these ill-assorted characters lead to Shannon's final degradation, and to a general acceptance that personal fates must be accepted, and life endured.
Period 1940

A Night on the Tiles. Play. Frank Vickery
M4 (20s, middle-age, old) F3 (20s, middle-age). A backyard. Fee code L

A perceptive, entertaining and highly comical play from the author of *One O'Clock from the House*. Gareth and Shirley's wedding day does not get off to an auspicious start. Gareth, egged on by his cocky, good-looking brother Kenneth, has a post-stag-night hangover so bad that he can barely speak, the bride is three months' pregnant and Grandad, confused after getting stuck in the outside loo, is unsure whether Shirley is marrying Gareth or Kenneth!
ISBN 0 573 11350 5

Night Watch. A play of suspense. Lucille Fletcher
M5 F4. Interior set. Fee code L

Unable to sleep, Elaine restlessly paces the living-room of her Manhattan townhouse. Seeing the body of a man in the window of an abandoned tenement opposite, she calls the police, but they find nothing. Elaine's terror grows as shortly thereafter she sees another body — this time a woman — but by now the police are sceptical and pay no heed to her frantic pleas. Suspense and mystery infuse the play as it draws inexorably towards its riveting and chilling climax.

Nightmare. Play. Norman Robbins
M3 (20, 35, 40) F4 (24, 36, 71). A living-room. Fee code L

Marion Bishop, an elderly writer, is dying. Katherine looks after her in a most caring way, while coping with her mentally retarded brother. When Katherine takes some leave, Laura, an experienced nurse, comes to take care of Marion. A series of mysterious phone calls and the appearance of Raymond, Marion's rapacious nephew, set off a nightmare situation. Deceit, suspicion, blackmail and incriminations are subtly woven into a web of crime which is completed by a dramatic confrontation scene with an ingenious twist.
ISBN 0 573 11306 8

Nightmare: the Fright of Your Life. Horror thriller. Roger S. Moss
M2 (20s, 50s-elderly) F2 (20s, 40s-elderly). A converted chapel. Fee code L

Frank and Jenny Gilman think they have found their dream house: a converted chapel in a quiet country village. The dream soon turns into a nightmare, however, as they are attacked by intruders who seem, for some reason, to be interested only in the contents of the deep freeze. Frank and Jenny investigate and the true horror of their situation soon emerges in this taut and exciting, yet often blackly hilarious, horror thriller.
ISBN 0 573 01842 1

◆ **No Love Lost**. Play. Rony Robinson
M4 (young, 40-50s, old) F5 (20s, 40-50s, old) 2 sitting-rooms. Fee code M

This wry romantic comedy was commissioned for the 1998 BT Biennial. Max narrates, in Act I, in reverse from his surprise birthday party in June back to the previous Christmas. In Act II Kate tells her story from Christmas to June. Kate feels under-appreciated by Max and leaves to start a theatre studies course. Her father Daniel moves in with his son-in-law because he cannot bear his wife Jenny any longer, whilst Jenny moves in with Kate, considering herself to be a widow. It's mayhem all round ...
ISBN 0 573 01810 3

No More Sitting on the Old School Bench. Play. Alan Bleasdale
M5 (20s-middle-age) F3 (30s, middle-age), 1 boy (14-16). Extras: class of multi-racial schoolchildren. A staffroom. Fee code L

A serious comedy vividly portraying the staff of a multi-racial comprehensive school regrouping for the autumn term and facing two problems: the redeployment of two members and the arrival of an earnest middle-aged novice teacher who tries hard to ingratiate himself with staff and pupils alike. ' ... tart, painfully astringent drama that dares us not to laugh.' *Plays and Players*

No One Sees the Video. Play. Martin Crimp
M3 (20s-40s) F3 (teenage, 20s, 30s), with some doubling. Various simple interior and exterior settings. Fee code M

Premièred at the Royal Court Theatre Upstairs in 1990, Martin Crimp's examination of the world of market research starred Celia Imrie. Liz, recently deserted by her writer husband, is accosted in the street and quizzed about frozen pizzas. Reluctant at first and then resentful, Liz finds herself persuaded to take part in an intensive video-recorded interview with market-research executive Colin, and it isn't long before he offers Liz a job herself.

No Sex Please — We're British! Comedy. Anthony Marriott and Alistair Foot
M6 (young, 30s, 50s) F4 (young, 50). A living-room and kitchen. Fee code M

This riotous comic farce notched up a staggeringly successful sixteen-year run in the West End! Peter and Frances could reasonably expect to look forward to a calm, happy start to their married life together. Owing to an unfortunate mistake, however, they find themselves inundated with pornographic material from the 'Scandinavian Import Company'. Senior bank officials, Peter's snobbish mother, and a prim, respectable bank cashier become inextricably entangled in the rumbustious events that follow.
ISBN 0 573 01309 8

No Time for Fig Leaves. Comedy. Duncan Greenwood and Robert King
M2 F7. A room in a country house. Fee code K

The women are running the world. An atomic accident has resulted in the disappearance of all men. All, that is, but two who were protected in an underground shelter. The women keep these potential supermates under close guard but, spurred on by the thought of a whole world of desirable women at their disposal, the men try to escape.
ISBN 0 573 01523 6

Noises Off. Comedy. Michael Frayn
M6 F4. A living-room stage set, backstage behind the set. Fee code M

This clever, smash-hit farce won numerous awards. 'The play opens with a touring company dress-rehearsing *Nothing On*, a conventional farce. Mixing mockery and homage, Frayn heaps into this play-within-a-play a hilarious mêlée of stock characters and situations. Caricatures — cheeky char, outraged wife and squeaky blonde — stampede in and out of doors. Voices rise and trousers fall ... a farce that makes you think as well as laugh.' *Times Literary Supplement*
ISBN 0 573 11312 2

The Normal Heart. Play. Larry Kramer
M14 (or M10) F1. Various interior settings. Fee code M

Set in New York in the early 1980s, this powerful, passionate and controversial play was the first to treat seriously the poignant and awesome subject of AIDS, following a writer's struggle to break through indifference and hypocrisy surrounding the killer disease and his attempt to draw attention to the plight of the gay community in contemporary America. After a successful New York run, the play was acclaimed in London at the Royal Court Theatre with Martin Sheen in the central role.

The Norman Conquests. Three plays. Alan Ayckbourn

> **Table Manners**. M3 F3. A dining-room. Fee code M.
> ISBN 0 573 01573 2
> **Living Together**. M3 F3. A sitting-room. Fee code L
> ISBN 0 573 01574 0
> **Round and Round the Garden**. M3 F3. A garden. Fee code M
> ISBN 0 573 01575 9

These three plays form a trilogy. They are not consecutive, but all occur during a single weekend, and each takes place in the same house, with the same cast of characters, set individually in two of the rooms and the garden. Thus we are watching, at times, but not all the time, events which are taking place simultaneously with those we have seen (or about to see) in another set. Each play is complete in itself and can be played as a separate entity. However each benefits if all can be produced as one threefold whole.
ISBN 0 573 01576 7 (complete volume)

♦ Jane Austen's **Northanger Abbey**. Play. Adapted by Matthew Francis
M9 (wide range of ages) F7 (wide range of ages). Extras. Children. Can be played by M5 F4. Various interior and exterior settings. Fee code M

Matthew Francis's adaptation of Jane Austen's first novel wryly dramatizes Catherine Morland's romantic fantasy world alongside the real one, and captures all Austen's irony and acerbic comment in witty dialogue and narration. Period early 1800s
ISBN 0 573 01849 9

Not About Heroes. Play. Stephen MacDonald
M2 (24, 30s). Several simple sets on an open stage. Fee code M

The play 'shows the strangely fruitful encounter between Siegfried Sassoon, war hero and aristocrat, now obsessed with exposing every sham ideal used to justify war, and Wilfred Owen, recovering from the effects of neurasthenia attributable to shell-shock, looking desperately for a hero who was not immune to the pity of war.' *Times Literary Supplement*. Period 1917-18

♦ **Not About Nightingales**. Play. Tennessee Williams
M14 F3. Male extras. A prison. Fee code M

Written in 1938 and based on fact, the play follows the events of a prison scandal which shocked America when convicts leading a hunger strike were locked in a steam-heated cell and roasted to death. Its sympathetic treatment of a black character and of a transvestite may have kept the play suppressed and unproduced during its own time. But its flashes of lyricism and compelling dialogue presage the great later plays of Williams and shows young Williams as a political writer, passionate about social injustice. **Available in the UK only.**

Not Quite Jerusalem. Play. Paul Kember
M4 F2 (20s). Four settings. Fee code M

This traces the effect of kibbutz life on four disillusioned volunteers who arrive for a working holiday and find the work more like hard labour. Two of the English, Pete and Dave, soon alienate themselves by their foul-mouthed, high-spirited behaviour. The third, Carrie, nervous and lonely, desperately tries but cannot relate to either her compatriots or the Israelis and it is left to Cambridge drop-out Mike to convey something of the frustration and impotence felt by many of the young of modern England. Winner of the *New Standard* Most Promising Playwright Award in 1980.
ISBN 0 573 11311 4

Not with a Bang. Play. Mike Harding
M3 F4. A living-room; outside an army barracks. Fee code M

When their wives join the Women's Peace Movement, Nobby, Tommy and Ken, pals in the Territorial Army, treat it as a joke. But as the women become more involved in demonstrations the men become the laughing stock of their TA battalion. Finally, the women, attempting to make their husbands give up the army, go on sexual strike with the slogan 'No Nooky Against the Nukes'. A wry, amusing look at the nuclear disarmament issue set in the author's North of England.
ISBN 0 573 11299 1

Now You Know. Play. Adapted from his novel by Michael Frayn
M4 (19 (Black), 30s, 50s) F4 (20s (Asian), 30-40s). A small office. Fee code M

Terry runs an organization campaigning for freedom of information which is funded by his girlfriend who also organizes the close-knit staff. When Hilary, a civil servant, arrives with a highly-confidential file detailing a cover-up Terry is given a not-to-be-missed opportunity. But his increasingly intimate involvement with Hilary presents him with a personal and professional dilemma, exposing the ultimate irony that everyone has something to hide.
ISBN 0 573 01848 0

Nude with Violin. Light comedy. Noël Coward
M8 (1 West Indian) F6. A Paris studio. Fee code M

Paul Sarodin the great painter is dead: his family and Jacob Friedland, the art-dealer who discovered him, are aghast. For Paul has left a letter stating the valuable 'Masterpieces' hanging in the great galleries of the world are not his work. They were painted by a Russian tart, an ex-chorus girl, a Negro revivalist, and a fourteen-year-old. This was the uproarious spoof perpetrated on the art world by a man who loathed the commercializing of creative talent.
ISBN 0 573 61318 4

Number One. Play. Jean Anouilh. Translated by Michael Frayn
M5 F5. An attic studio and bedroom. Fee code M
ISBN 0 573 01619 4

Observe the Sons of Ulster Marching Towards the Somme. Play. Frank McGuinness
M9 (20s, 30s, old). Various simple interior and exterior settings. Fee code M

Eight men volunteer to serve in the 36th Ulster Division at the outbreak of the First World War. Seven are from working-class backgrounds, fervent Protestants united in hatred against the Fenian. The eighth is from a wealthy family, a widely-travelled sculptor who has lost faith and enlists in the sole hope of dying. 'A play of extraordinary depth of feeling and understanding.' *Sunday Telegraph*

The Odd Couple. Comedy. Neil Simon
M6 F2. A living-room. Fee code M

Divorced from his wife, Oscar lives in the cheerful chaos his carefree nature thrives on. Into the midst of his smoke-laden, beer-sodden weekly poker session, comes Felix, newly separated from his wife and, so he says, suicidal. At Oscar's invitation Felix moves in, and is soon finding comfort in performing, with the same thoroughness which lost him his wife, the cooking, cleaning, polishing and laundry until Oscar is almost reduced, by continuous nagging, to a nervous wreck.
ISBN 0 573 61331 1

The Odd Couple (Female Version). Comedy. Neil Simon
M2 F6. An apartment. Fee code M

In this hilarious female version of *The Odd Couple*, Olive Madison, like her original male counterpart, is divorced and living in cheerful chaos in her New York apartment. At Olive's invitation, the suicidal Florence Ungar, newly separated from her husband, moves in and is soon finding comfort in cooking, cleaning, and fussing until Olive is almost reduced to a nervous wreck. It becomes clear that the patterns of their disastrous marriages are already re-occurring. **NB. Please state Female Version when ordering.**
ISBN 0 573 61828 3

The Odd Women. Play. Michael Meyer. After the novel by George Gissing
M4 (20s-40s) F6 (20s, 30s). Simple settings. Fee code M

Michael Meyer's play, based on Gissing's feminist Victorian novel, was presented at the Royal Exchange, Manchester in 1992. Genteel but impoverished Monica escapes her life of drudgery by marrying, with disastrous results, a rich man twice her age. In contrast, the emancipated Rhoda rejects marriage to secure her own freedom. Period 1880s. 'It was a remarkably prescient book when it first appeared in 1893, and in spite of its period flavour still seems topical.' *Financial Times*
ISBN 0 573 01852 9

Oedipus at Colonus. Play. Sophocles. Translated by Christopher Stace
M6 F3. Chorus. Simple settings. Fee code H

The blind Oedipus, close to death, accompanied by his faithful daughter Antigone, arrives at his final resting place near Athens, only to become involved in a power-struggle with his sons and his brother-in-law, Creon. In death, Oedipus' sins are expiated and he becomes a hero. This translation of *Oedipus at Colonus* was first performed at the Royal Exchange Theatre, Manchester with *Oedipus the King*, under the collective title *Oedipus*. 'Christopher Stace's new translation ... bright, brisk and accessible ...' *Guardian*

Oedipus the King. Sophocles. Translated by Christopher Stace
M7 F3, Chorus. Simple settings. Fee code H

Oedipus, King of Thebes, discovers that he is the cause of a curse that has fallen upon the city. As revelation falls upon revelation — he has, unwittingly, fulfilled a prophecy that he would kill his father and marry his mother — his very sense of identity is shattered, leading to a tragic act of self-mutilation. Commissioned as the 100th production of the Manchester Royal Exchange Theatre Company, this new translation renders Sophocles' tragedy into clear modern English, making the play accessible, thrilling, taut and powerful.

Off the Hook. Farce. Derek Benfield
M5 (30s-50s, elderly) F5 (20s, 40s). An hotel bar. Fee code K

Harold Spooks is sprung from prison to tell the gang where in the hotel he stashed the loot. Unfortunately, he's the wrong Harold Spooks and he hasn't a clue where the money is hidden. Worse still, this Harold is a twit and likely to give the gang away any minute. More hazards include Norah, the man-eating manageress, Edna, continually interrupting the gang's frenzied plottings, and the redoubtable Mrs Fletcher-Brewer who is suspicious of all men.
ISBN 0 573 11332 7

Office Suite. Double-bill. Alan Bennett

Green Forms
M2 (1 Black) F3 (30s, 40s). An office. Fee code F

Doris and Doreen are comfortably installed in an obscure department of a large organization. It is a cushy number: on a normal day work is nowhere. However, this is not a normal day. A shadow falls across their tranquil lives. Is it redundancy?
ISBN 0 573 12087 0

A Visit from Miss Protheroe
M1 (60s) F1 (middle-age). A living-room. Fee code E

Retired and sitting at home, Mr Dodsworth contemplates his life and achievements with quiet satisfaction when there is sharp ring at the door: his former secretary has come to ruin it all.
ISBN 0 573 12286 5

The Old Country. Play. Alan Bennett
M3 (20s, 50s, 60s) F3 (30s, middle-age, 60s). A veranda. Fee code M

Hilary and Bron await the arrival of Hilary's sister and brother-in-law in a very English setting: Bron potters about the garden and Hilary sits asleep on the veranda, Elgar's music drifts from the house. The visitors arrive, bringing an assortment of particularly English things, and as the conversation proceeds, it becomes apparent they are not in England. In fact Hilary fled into exile some years previously after betraying his country, but now it seems he must return.
ISBN 0 573 11317 3

Old Times. Play. Harold Pinter
M1 (40s) F2 (40s). A sitting-room, a bedroom. Fee code M

Kate and Deeley are married and live in a large country house. Into their calm, composed world comes Anna, Kate's best friend — her only friend — whom she has not seen for twenty years. '*Old Times* is a tone poem — an ironic elegy to lost youth and hopes, set at the crossroads where memory meets fantasy and cut through with the searing recognition of the power games people play.' *City Limits*

Old-World. Play. Aleksei Arbuzov. Translated by Ariadne Nicolaeff
M1 (65) F1 (60). Simple settings. Fee code M

Peggy Ashcroft and Anthony Quayle starred in the original RSC production of this tender, gentle play. Rodion is medical head of a sanatorium where Lidya is a patient, suffering from arteriosclerosis. They first meet following complaints from other patients of her habit of reciting poetry in the middle of the night and singing at dawn. She is clearly no ordinary patient and the play follows, with warmth and gentle humour, the mutual growth of interest and liking, to lasting affection.
ISBN 0 573 01708 5

Oliver Twist. Play. Jeremy Brock. Adapted from the novel by Charles Dickens
34 characters. Extras. May be played by a cast of eleven. Various interior and exterior settings.
Fee code M

Jeremy Brock's splendidly theatrical stage version of *Oliver Twist* combines all the richness of Dickens's story — the sinister antics of Fagin, the comic pomposity of Mr Bumble the Beadle, and the horror of Nancy's murder at the hands of Sykes. Originally devised for eleven actors playing multiple roles, the play is easy to stage, makes good use of sound effects for atmosphere and makes more than a nod to the contemporary world.
ISBN 0 573 01851 0

On Approval. Comedy. Frederick Lonsdale
M2 (middle-age) F2 (young, middle-age). A drawing-room, a living-room. Fee code M

Richard adores the widow Mrs Wislack, who has a friend in Helen, herself in love with the Duke of Bristol. The Duke urges Richard to press his suit, but the widow proposes a test. They are to spend one month in her house in Scotland. However Mrs Wislack proves a tyrant: Richard's life becomes a burden, and Helen finds the Duke impecunious. Richard and Helen slip away from the house, leaving the selfish couple possibly snowbound for weeks together.
ISBN 0 573 01855 3

On Monday Next. Comedy. Philip King
M9 F5. A stage. Fee code M

The Drossmouth Repertory Company are holding the second rehearsal of the play they are hoping to perform the following week. The proceedings are complicated by the strong-willed producer's rows with his equally strong-willed actors; by the stage carpenter who insists on sawing up the stage during rehearsals; by the author who also wants to direct. Finally, the leading man and lady start to squabble furiously and there seems little chance the play will open. But these are old troupers, and the show goes on.
ISBN 0 573 01318 7

On the Razzle. Farce. Tom Stoppard. Adapted from *Einen Jux Will Er Sich Machen* by Johann Nestroy
M13 F9. 1 boy. Extras. Six settings. Fee code M

Deciding to wine and dine his intended in town, Zangler, a prosperous merchant grocer, leaves his shop in the charge of two assistants who decide they, too, will have a day out. As they pursue wine, women and song through 1850s Vienna the precise intricate machinery of plot and sub-plot is soon whirring at full speed to deploy all the elements of classic farce. 'A dazzle of verbal wit.'
Daily Telegraph

On the Verge. Farcical comedy. Peter Horsler
M4 F6 (young, middle-age). A country cottage ground floor, with bedroom (optional). Fee code L

Gerald, an archaeological lecturer, rents a remote country cottage for the weekend — ostensibly to work, in reality hoping for a little middle-age philandering with his attractive college librarian, Ruth. He introduces her as his secretary but their privacy is soon invaded by various locals, a menacing bull and finally by Gerald's wife, Alison. After increasingly hilarious complications Ruth and Alison ally themselves against Gerald, but Hamish the bull has the last word.
ISBN 0 573 11326 2

On the Verge, or the Geography of Yearning. Play. Eric Overmyer
M1 (playing various parts) F3. Various simple settings. Fee code M

In 1888, three experienced American lady adventurers — armed with umbrellas, a picnic and pith helmets — set out to explore 'terra incognito' eagerly embracing cultures and replicas of distant civiliztions. Caught in a time warp, they find themselves in Eisenhower's 1950s America. The trio split when two decide to remain in 1955 and it is left to Mary to continue the journey of exploration. This witty, surreal play was seen in London in 1989 starring Paola Dionisotti and Juliet Stevenson. ISBN 0 573 01712 3

Once a Catholic. Comedy. Mary O'Malley
M4 F10. Various interior and exterior settings. Fee code M

In choosing the title, the author would seem to imply 'always a Catholic', but this extremely funny, irreverent comedy based on her own school days in a London convent certainly belies the Church's claim, as far as the author is concerned. For what emerges rather is the resilience of children to survive — in spite of, not because of, their upbringing and indoctrination. Period 1956-57

Once in a Lifetime. Play. Moss Hart and George S. Kaufman
M24 F14, much doubling possible. A living-room, an hotel room, a reception room, a film set, a Pullman car. Fee code M

Three down-and-out troupers go to Hollywood and try their luck with the newly invented 'talkies'. Owing to a series of blunders the most stupid of the three is carried to pinnacles of fame and fortune and becomes a god of the industry. The whole mad world of early sound film is treated with dazzling satire as one wild event follows crazily on another. Period 1920s
ISBN 0 573 61388 9

One Fine Day. Play. Dennis Lumborg
M1. A kitchen, a bedsit, a prison holding cell. Fee code M

Eddie, a young metal worker, lives contentedly on a suburban housing estate with his wife, Jeanie, and two adored small children, Katie and Billy. He and Jeanie have always believed in being frank with their children about matters of sex, but when his little daughter stumbles into their bedroom during her parents' lovemaking and then cheerfully recounts the details next day at school, Eddie finds himself investigated by social services, suspected of child abuse. This is his story.
ISBN 0 573 04021 4

One Flew Over the Cuckoo's Nest. Play. Dale Wasserman. From the novel by Ken Kesey
M17 F5. A ward in a mental hospital. Fee code M

The story of the devil-may-care rogue who has committed himself temporarily to a mental home rather than work in a prison. He transforms the home, charming everyone, except the fierce martinet of a head nurse, and works wonders with a presumed deaf-and-dumb Indian. However, he is condemned by the nurse to a frontal lobotomy, which will leave him a vegetable, and to save him his fellow inmates smother him.
ISBN 0 573 61343 5

One for the Road. Comedy. Willy Russell
M2 (35) F2 (30s). A lounge. Fee code M

This wickedly observant comedy by the author of *Educating Rita* finds Dennis on the eve of his thirty-fifth birthday, making a last-ditch attempt to break away from the confines of his middle-class, housing-estate existence. Reaching breaking point at his birthday party he packs a rucksack to make his escape but everyone wants to accompany him and he sinks down in front of the television, defeated. But there's always next year ... and the year after ...
ISBN 0 573 11320 3

One O'Clock from the House. Comedy. Frank Vickery
M5 (30s-50s) F8 (30s-40s). 1 boy (9). Extras. A living-room. Fee code L

The funeral of an elderly father is not usually an occasion for hilarity, but when the family concerned numbers among its members a wellington-clad cook who bakes almondless almond cakes, another who's convinced his shopping trolley is a dog, and a sister who's a happy inmate of a psychiatric home, the proceedings are bound to be lively! A scorching comedy of personalities and situations!
ISBN 0 573 01628 3

One Way Pendulum. A farce in a new dimension. N. F. Simpson
M10 (20s-50) F4 (18, 45, 50). A living-room (containing a court room in Act II). Fee code M

Each of the Groomkirbys has an *idée fixe*. Kirby is teaching his speak-your-weight machines the 'Hallelujah Chorus'; his mother pays the neighbour to eat their left-overs; his aunt in her wheelchair is convinced she's touring the Hebrides; his father is building the Old Bailey in the living-room. When this is complete the judge and jury move in with some bizarre results ...
ISBN 0 573 01321 7

The Opposite Sex. Comedy. David Tristram
M2 F2. A living-room. Fee code L

David Tristram, author of *What's for Pudding?*, turns his attention to marital infidelity and its warring consequences in this adult-humoured comedy. Mark and Vicky and Judith and Eric have something in common and a chance meeting could have made for a pleasant social evening. Unfortunately, as they all come face to face, the common denominator turns out to be that they each had an affair with their opposite partner and it isn't long before the air is thick with insults, black eyes and broken china!

Orphans. Play. Lyle Kessler
M3 (20s, middle-age). A living-room. Fee code M

Two adult but somehow childlike brothers live in an old row house in North Philadelphia. Treat, the elder brother, supports himself and his slightly retarded younger brother by petty thievery. He brings home a rich man, Harold, intending to get him drunk and swindle him. Harold moves in and establishes the house as a hideout and base of operations and, in a strange, hilarious, moving, tender way, becomes the father figure the boys have never had and always longed for.
ISBN 0573 61978 6

Orpheus Descending. Play. Tennessee Williams
M10 F9. Extras. Split set: a dry goods store, a confectionery. Fee code M

A vague reworking of the Orpheus and Eurydice legend in modern America, with a Southern township presumably representing Hell. Thirty-year-old Val Xavier arrives in the gossipy, prejudice-ridden township with his guitar, and meets 'Lady' Torrence, whose elderly husband is dying of cancer. His attempts to bring some happiness into her sex-starved life, together with other developments, lead to tragedy for both of them. Period 1940

Other People's Money. Play. Jerry Sterner
M3 (40s, 68) F2 (35, 60s). Composite setting: three offices. Fee code M

This award-winning off-Broadway play was seen at London's Lyric Theatre starring Martin Shaw and Maria Aitkin. Doughnut connoisseur and Wall Street takeover artist Lawrence Garfinkle goes after a vulnerable company. Set against the charmingly rapacious financier are genial company chairman Jorgensen, and his chief executive. They bring in Kate who specializes in fending off takeovers ... 'It is something to find a modern American comedy that openly criticizes the moral bankruptcy of our times.' *Guardian*
ISBN 0 573 69101 0

Otherwise Engaged. Play. Simon Gray
M5 (young, 39, middle-age) F2 (young). A living-room. Fee code M

Simon lives surrounded by all the comforts of the day and strives to keep himself 'otherwise engaged' from the demands of friends, relatives and associates. However, the world keeps intruding: his attempts to play his new *Parsifal* recording are continually thwarted; his answerphone recounts the tragic results of a casual, thoughtless liaison with a girl; and there is a final shock from his wife. Eventually he finds himself listening to *Parsifal*, but perhaps with a little less than his usual self-absorption.
ISBN 0 573 01261 X

Our Boys. Play. Jonathan Lewis
M6 (20s). A hospital ward. Fee code M

1984. Five soldiers, among them veterans of the Falklands War and the Hyde Park bombing, are convalescing in a military hospital, with pornography, bragging one-upmanship and cynical humour as their only means of mental escape. Tensions arise when an officer is billeted with them, and a bitter, savage war of words, only just disguised as humour, is waged against him. After an hilarious birthday party, the six find themselves facing charges of misconduct — and then the fighting really starts.
ISBN 0 573 14009 X

Our Country's Good. Play. Timberlake Wertenbaker. Based on the novel *The Playmaker* by Thomas Keneally
M17 F5 or M7 F4. Various interior and exterior settings. Fee code M

This adaptation was performed at The Royal Court Theatre in 1988 and 1989 to critical acclaim. Set in Botany Bay in 1789 it tells of the rehearsals for the first play to be performed in Australia. Surrounded by forbidding conditions Lieutenant Clark attempts, under the authority of the first Governor General, to bring culture to the penal colony through a production of Farquhar's *The Recruiting Officer,* with a motley bunch of villains, murderers and prostitutes.

Our Song. Play. Keith Waterhouse, adapted from his own novel
M4 (middle-age, 50s) F3 (late 20s, middle-age). Various simple settings. Fee code M

Pulling himself out of the rut of his middle-aged executive lifestyle, Roger Piper stumbles into a sixteen-month tempestuous affair with the effervescent Angela Caxton, and is thrown into a whirlwind of romances and champagne. He discovers that Angie does not share his obsession with their relationship and after multiple crises the affair ends in tragedy.
ISBN 0 573 01856 1

Our Town. Play. Thornton Wilder
M17 F7. Extras. A bare stage. Fee code M

With compelling simplicity Wilder depicts New Hampshire village life through the story of two families. George and Emily grow up together as children, they fall in love and marry. All too soon Emily dies and goes into the village cemetery where the former inhabitants of Grover's Corner welcome her to the peace that can never be understood by the living. When first produced, *Our Town* was considered a remarkable theatrical innovation and it still has a universality that does not date. Period 1901-11
ISBN 0 573 61349 4

Out of Order. Comedy. Ray Cooney
M6 (young, middle-age) F4 (young, 40s, 50s). An hotel suite. Fee code M

When Richard Willey, a Government Junior Minister, plans to spend the evening with Jane Worthington, one of the Opposition's typists, things go disastrously wrong, and he sends for his PPS, George Pigden who, through Richard's lies, sinks further and further into trouble and ends up going through an identity crisis! A hugely successful sequel to Ray Cooney's *Two Into One*, *Out of Order* received the 1990 Olivier Award for Comedy of the Year.
ISBN 0 573 01858 8

Out of Sight ... Out of Murder. Mystery comedy. Fred Carmichael
M4 (young, 30s, middle-age, 60s) F5 (young, 40s, middle-age, 60). A living-room. Fee code L

Peter has come to a lonely old house to finish a play — a thriller featuring all the old stock characters such as butler and maid, but with new twists. Amazingly the characters manifest themselves and take over the situation, one of them trying to kill Peter. Events follow a typical thriller to a hair-raising climax until Peter manages to type 'The End' — but an even more surprising twist is in store.
ISBN 0 573 61360 5

Outside Edge. Play. Richard Harris
M5 (20s-40s) F4 (19, 28, 30s). A cricket pavilion. Fee code M

Roger has enough trouble assembling his cricket team to play against the British Railways Maintenance Division Reading East, but these complications pall before those occurring among their various wives and girlfriends. As a final catastrophe, rain starts to fall. The play, from the author of *Stepping Out*, was first seen at the Queen's Theatre, London, starring Julia McKenzie and Maureen Lipman.
ISBN 0 573 11314 9

A

Outward Bound. Play. Sutton Vane
M6 (young-elderly) F3 (young, middle-age). The lounge of a small liner. Fee code L

A collection of people embark for the fateful journey across the Styx to meet the Examiner who has surprises in store for the passengers.
ISBN 0 573 01328 4

The Owl and the Pussycat. Comedy. Bill Manhoff
M1 (35) F1 (26). An apartment in San Francisco. Fee code M

Doris storms into the apartment of F. Sherman, would-be writer, and states that because his report to the landlord got her evicted for taking paying gentlemen callers, she is now going to camp in his apartment. She says she is a prostitute but not promiscuous, and is hurt when Sherman questions her respectability. He is a self-advertising intellectual whose counterfeit emotions are reflected in his unsuccessful writing. Their exchanges are turbulent and very funny.
ISBN 0 573 61354 0

Pack of Lies. Play. Hugh Whitemore
M3 (40s, 50s) F5 (16, 20s-40s). A living-room, kitchen, hall. Fee code M

Based on the true story of the Krogers, convicted in 1961 of spying for the Russians, Whitemore has written a fictional account of the quiet, totally unsuspecting Jackson family who live opposite the Krogers and consider them their closest friends. When an MI5 official arrives suddenly to use the Jacksons' house as a surveillance post their decent, happy life is shattered as they are plunged into a sordid, alien world of deceit and intrigue.
ISBN 0 573 11343 2

Paddywack. Drama. Daniel Magee
M4 (20s, 30s, 50s) F2 (20s, 60s). A living-room. Fee code M

Damien, a young Irishman, moves into lodgings in London where he is befriended by a student and his girlfriend. When the IRA mounts a bombing campaign, it seems the enigmatic Damien may be involved. He is drawn into an affair with the girlfriend who is attracted by the IRA spectre, but when he confesses he's a dispatch clerk with no IRA ties, she shuns him and Damien returns to the lodgings where misconceptions and resentments explode into sudden violence.
ISBN 0 573 69578 4

Page 3 Murder. Comedy-Thriller. Larry Beghel
M5 (23, 40s, 50s) F2 (25, 35). The living-room of a flat. Fee code L

In this stylish comedy-thriller, attractive glamour model Jenni Brandon and her ex-live-in boyfriend Len Carrington have concocted what appears to be the perfect plot to acquire a very large amount of money. The would-be murder plan involves Jenni's current boyfriend Tom and his parents — lustful MP Geoffrey Holden and stepmother Marion. But these two characters are not the only ones plotting — everyone, it seems, is double-crossing another.
ISBN 0 573 01697 6

Pains of Youth. Play. Ferdinand Bruckner, translated by Daphne Moore
M3 F4. A room in a boarding house. Fee code M

Written in 1926, this was the play that established Ferdinand Bruckner. It depicts with unprecedented candour the moral corruption and cynicism of a group of medical students. For these young people, youth itself is a fatal disease and the idea of death by suicide is always present in their minds.

Painting Churches. Play. Tina Howe
M1 (70s) F2 (30s, 60s). A living-room. Fee code M

Gardner Church, once a famous poet, slips in and out of senility as his wife Fanny valiantly tries to keep them both afloat. Their daughter Mags, an artistic celebrity, comes home hoping to finally paint their portrait and, in this way, to come to terms with them — and they with her. Mags triumphs in the end as Fanny and Gardner actually step through the frame and become a work of art, ineffable and timeless.
ISBN 0 573 61939 5

Panic Stations. Farce. Derek Benfield
M4 (35, middle-age, 60s) F5 (20s-60). A cottage interior. Fee code L

Chester Dreadnought has bought a lovely country cottage, dreaming of idyllic peace, but is he able to enjoy it? Not with Abel Bounty, the local unhandyman, always around, and not with Carol, an attractive girl who seems to have mysteriously moved in. Those who have met Chester already in *Wild Goose Chase* and *Post Horn Gallop* know his aptitude for social and anti-social blunders, and Lord and Lady Elrood and scatty Miss Partridge also make a reappearance.
ISBN 0 573 11352 1

♦ **The Parasol**. Play. Anton Chekhov. Adapted from the novel *Three Years* by Frank Dunai
M8 (20s, 30s, 50s, 60, 80) F2 (21, 30). 2 drawing-rooms, an office. Fee code M

'*The Parasol* has an authentic Chekhovian feel — the bourgeois boredom and guilt, the aching, aimless loneliness — without the musty archaism we get in some translations. It's crisp and sharply witty and has the emotional directness of the real thing ... It's a richly intricate, carefully crafted fusion of sociology and psychology and the private pains of a pre-revolutionary world ... It's like discovering an old master in the attic.' Robin Thornber, *Guardian*

Pardon Me, Prime Minister. Farce. Edward Taylor and John Graham
M4 (30s, 50s) F5 (20s-40s). A study. Fee code L

The Prime Minister and Chancellor are preparing a puritanical budget taxing amusements such as bingo, gambling and night-clubs out of existence. On the afternoon before its presentation, however, each in turn appears to be the father of the pretty Shirley, the result of a post-party conference night many years ago. In an even less expected family bombshell, it transpires that the Prime Minister's deferential Parliamentary Private Secretary, Campbell, is, in fact, his son ...
ISBN 0 573 11334 3

Partners. Comedy. Richard Harris
M3 (20s, 30s) F4 (20s). A sitting-room. Fee code K

Paul, a script-writer, and Graham, a novelist, have to produce a film 'treatment' of Graham's novel. The film producer has lent them his luxurious penthouse. They make a stab at their 'treatment' but it's impossible — who can work in these fabulous surroundings? Their train of thought is continually interrupted by strings of girls telephoning to speak to the producer. What a good life the man must have! They see no reason why they shouldn't enjoy a bit of it too.

Party Piece. Comedy. Richard Harris, suggested by the author's earlier play, *Local Affairs*
M3 F4. The gardens of a pair of Victorian terraced houses. Fee code M

This is a fast-paced and very funny play set in the back gardens of feuding neighbours. It is the night of Michael's and Roma's fancy dress house-warming party. The evening looks set to be a lively one until a string of hilarious disasters strike, including a distinct lack of guests, a burning garden shed, a marauding Zimmer frame and the prospect of an irate husband on the prowl.
ISBN 0 573 01862 6

♦ A Party to Murder. Play. Marcia Kash and Douglas E. Hughes
M3 (40s, 50s) F3 (late 20s, 40s). A living-room. Fee code M

Writer Charles Prince has invited six people to play a murder mystery game at a rustic cottage on an island somewhere in North America. They appear set for a fun weekend until past ghosts begin to haunt the proceedings and all is not as it seems. The game takes on a sinister dimension when guests begin to die and the remaining players realize that they are playing for their lives.

Passion Killers. Play. John Godber
M4 (20s, 30s) F5 (20s, 30s). Can be played by M4 F3. Composite set. Fee code M

Despite misgivings at leaving his wife Gail, Tom joins his friend Andy on a holiday in Spain. Andy enthusiastically joins the lager-louts and takes every opportunity available for illicit sex; Tom embarks on a wistful, platonic friendship with Trish. Back home, Andy keeps his infidelity secret and his marriage continues as before; Tom tells Gail of his innocent holiday friendship and the seeds of suspicion are instantly sown ...
ISBN 0 573 01868 5

A Passionate Woman. Play. Kay Mellor
M3 (early 30s, 50s) F1 (50s). F1 extra, offstage voices. A loft and rooftop. Fee code M

Betty, a passionate, doting mum from Leeds finds it hard to accept that her son, Mark, is leaving the fold to get married. On the wedding morning she retreats to the loft where she re-lives her long-lost youth and the affair with the man she might have married, and gradually reconciles herself to the imminent departure of Mark. A heartfelt, provocative, masterful play.
ISBN 0 573 01866 9

♦ Pastimes. Comedy. Brian Jeffries
M2 (late 50s/early 60s) F3 (17, late 50s/early 60s). A living-room, a café kitchen. Fee code M

Sam and Bill, two middle-aged brothers, own and run 'Cobblers', a café in a seaside town. Their peace is shattered by the arrivals of a runaway, Linda, who is after a job, and her grandmother, Connie, who is after Linda. A terrible coincidence is revealed as Connie is brought face-to-face with George, the husband who left her forty years ago and who is now Sam; likewise, Connie's friend Win finds, in Bill, her errant Arthur.
ISBN 0 573 01870 7

The Patrick Pearse Motel. Comedy. Hugh Leonard
M4 (30s, elderly) F3 (20s, 30s). A living-room, two hotel bedrooms and corridor. Fee code J

When her husband plans to be away with his business partner, Gráinne seizes the opportunity of spending the night with an ex-flame, now a TV personality. She also involves the partner's wife, Niamh, in the plot. Things go wrong when Niamh's furiously jealous husband returns unexpectedly, and matters are further complicated by the manageress of the motel turning out to be the spurned love of the TV personality.
ISBN 0 573 01333 0

◆ **Peer Gynt**. Play. Henrik Ibsen. Translated by Christopher Fry and Johan Fillinger
Large cast. Various interior and exterior settings. Fee code M

Written in 1867, *Peer Gynt* was Ibsen's last work to use verse as a medium of dramatic expression but it carries the marks of his later, prose plays in the kind of spare, dramatically eloquent dialogue which has become characteristic of twentieth-century drama. At the same time the poetry is brilliantly appropriate to the imaginative swings between Scandinavian oral folk traditions, the Moroccan coast, the Sahara Desert, and the absurdist images of the Cairo madhouse. Period: early to mid nineteenth century

The Perfect Party. Comedy. A. R. Gurney
M2 (middle-age) F3 (middle-age). A study. Fee code M

Tony, a professor of American literature and quintessential WASP, concentrates on staging a party to end all parties. His aim appears to be, as a member of the WASP former ruling class, to teach America how to entertain properly. He has also invited a critic from a 'major New York newspaper' in the hope of getting a perfect review for the perfect party, but the critic announces that the evening lacks 'the essential element of danger'.

Period of Adjustment. Comedy. Tennessee Williams
M4 (30s, middle-age) F4 (young (Black), middle-age). A living-room, with dining alcove and bedroom visible. Fee code M

Ralph Bates and his wife are on the verge of breaking up after five years together, partly through trouble with in-laws. George Haverstock, a wartime friend of Bates is a newly-wed concealing beneath his ebullient exterior a secret fear, which seems to be that he may be impotent. By the end of the day, however, all ends well — with each pair correctly together.

The Petition. Play. Brian Clark
M1 (80) F1 (72). A living-room. Fee code M

Sir Edmund Milne is aghast to learn that his wife of more than fifty years is a long-standing, covert Labour voter. In the acrimonious argument that follows, she reveals that she is dying from cancer with only three months to live. The truth, spoken on both sides for the first time in a marriage which has survived by compromises, humour and genuine mutual fondness, serves to unite the couple for the impending ordeal. Sir John Mills and Rosemary Harris starred in the National Theatre's 1986 production.

Philadelphia, Here I Come! Play. Brian Friel
M10 (young, 40s, 60s) F3 (young, 50s, 60s). Composite setting. Fee code M

Gar O'Donnell has accepted his aunt's invitation to come to Philadelphia, as he is fed up with the dreary round of life in Ballybeg with his uncommunicative father, his humiliating job, his frustrated love for Kathy Doogan, and the total absence of prospect and opportunity in his life at home. Now, on the eve of his departure, he is not very happy to be leaving Ballybeg, despite his fantasies of success, wealth and endless love that he will attain in America.

The Philanthropist. Comedy. Christopher Hampton
M4 (young, middle-age) F3 (young). A living-room. Fee code J

Philip gives a small party for his fiancée Celia and a few friends. Afterwards Celia leaves with the others, while another young lady offers to help wash up, later revealing more intimate intentions. Celia discovers what happened and breaks things off, revealing that she spent the night of the party with another man. Philip then joins another couple for dinner, apparently deciding to re-enact the end of his deceased friend John's original play, which had been responsible for John's suicide.
ISBN 0 573 01336 5

The Physicists. Play. Friedrich Dürrenmatt. Translated by James Kirkup
M16 (teenage, 40s, middle-age) F4 (30s-50s). A drawing-room. Fee code M

Because in a mad world the only defence of the sane is to assume madness, the genius who has invented a nuclear weapon of world-consuming force decides he can only protect the world from destructive ambition by pretending to be mad. He is pursued by two agents of the super-powers who also pretend to be madmen. In the end, all three find themselves totally in the power of a truly mad megalomaniac.
ISBN 0 573 01340 3

◆ **Picasso at the Lapin Agile**. Comedy. Steve Martin
M7 (20s, older) F2 (19, older). A Parisian bar. Fee code M

This long-running Off-Broadway absurdist comedy places Albert Einstein and Pablo Picasso in a Parisian café in 1904, just before the renowned scientist transformed physics with his theory of relativity and the celebrated painter set the art world afire with Cubism. Bystanders, including Picasso's agent, the bartender and his mistress, Picasso's date, an elderly philosopher, Charles Dabernow Schmendimen, and an idiot inventor introduce additional flourishes of humour. Period 1904
ISBN 0 573 69564 4

◆ **Pickwick Papers**. Play. Lynn Brittney, adapted from *The Posthumous Papers of the Pickwick Club* by Charles Dickens
28 characters may be played by M12 F10. Extras. Various simple interior and exterior settings.
Fee code L

Mr Pickwick and his companions journey round the country, to report on the character of its populace. Their high notions and even higher ambitions are tested by con-men, deaf old matrons, servants, landladies, jailers and many others that complete the picture of Britannia the way Hogarth might have painted it: raucous and cheeky, but ultimately bound together by a sense of fair play.
Period 1830s
ISBN 0 573 01860 X

The Picture of Dorian Gray. Moral entertainment. John Osborne. Adapted from the novel by Oscar Wilde
M11 F4. Extras. A studio. Fee code M

A brilliant dramatization of Wilde's classic novel about a young man who, magically, retains his youth and beauty while the decay of advancing years and moral corruption appears on a portrait painted by one of his lovers. 'Osborne has done much more than a scissors-and-paste job on Wilde's famous story ... he has highlighted the topical concept of youth as a commodity for which one would sell one's soul ... *Guardian*
ISBN 0 573 69231 9

A Piece of My Mind. Play. Peter Nichols
M3 (40s, 50s) F2 (20s, 40s). A study, also serving as various other simple locations. Fee code M
ISBN 0 573 01673 9

The Pied Piper. Play with music. Based on Robert Browning's poem. Book and lyrics by Peter Terson. Music by Jeff Parton
M12 F3, doubling possible. Extras. Various settings on an open stage. Fee code M for play, fee code D for music

Browning's famous poem is here transformed and developed into a play with music. Originally written for in-the-round performance at the Victoria Theatre, Stoke-on-Trent, the play can equally be performed in a proscenium setting. The edition includes detailed production notes.
ISBN 0 573 05060 0

Pinocchio. Family Entertainment. John Morley
9 to 14 principals, adult and/or juvenile chorus. One permanent set with three or four frontcloths. Fee code L

This delightful dramatization of Collodi's story of Pinocchio has all the charm of the original. The story is simple to stage with many music and production suggestions, and the cast is flexible for both large and small companies.
ISBN 0 573 11345 9

Pizzazz. Three plays. Hugh Leonard
Fee code M (for trilogy). ISBN 0 573 01641 0

These three plays, intended solely as entertainment, share the common theme of travelling — near Dublin, in Rome and on the Shannon river.

A View from the Obelisk.
M2 F1. A hilltop. Fee code D

Convalescing fom heart surgery, Owen returns to his native Ireland with Rosemary and insists on showing her the view from a hilltop near Dublin. But the climb takes rather a lot out of him and Rosemary goes off to summon a car. While she is gone, a young man appears, sketching the view. Owen strikes up a conversation with him, talking as though he'd known him for years. The boy goes, and it is only when Rosemary returns that Owen realizes why the boy seemed so familiar to him ...

Roman Fever. From the story by Edith Wharton
M1 F2. A terrace. Fee code E

On a restaurant terrace in Rome, Mrs Slade and Mrs Ansley are reminiscing about a Roman holiday they had together many years before. Mrs Slade, envious of Mrs Ansley's daughter's engagement to a young and rich *marchese* cannot resist a spiteful jibe at Mrs Ansley, thereby destroying a cherished memory. But in the end it is Mrs Slade herself whose illusions are shattered. Period 1930

Pizzazz.
M2 F3. A reception area. Fee code F

Whilst waiting to hire out cabin cruisers on the River Shannon, two apparent strangers play an elaborate game, which involves re-enacting a marriage on the rocks, with the other people in the reception area as supporting cast. But this is a Chinese Box of a play, and all is not what it seems ...

Play it Again, Sam. Comedy. Woody Allen
M3 (young, 28) F8 (young). A living-room with platform area. Fee code M

Allan has this thing about Humphrey Bogart. His wife has left him and his friends have been trying to fix him up with beautiful dates, but he is so gauche they always end abysmally. His day-dreams of Bogart and the beautiful people are always rudely shattered by real life. And when he falls for his best friend's wife things really seem black. But the homely hero is saved and is left to dream of being greater things.
ISBN 0 573 61404 0

Play On! Comedy. Rick Abbot
M3 (20, 25) F7 (17, 22, 35, 42, middle-age); or M6 F4 if preferred. A stage in a community theatre. Fee code M

A theatre group try desperately to put on a play, amid all kinds of maddening interference from its authoress, Phyllis, who keeps revising the script until almost opening night and during the actual performance anything that can go wrong does. At the curtain call Phyllis decides to give a speech on the state of the modern theatre and what befalls her is the madcap climax to this hilarious romp.
ISBN 0 573 61361 3

Playhouse Creatures. Play. April De Angelis
F5 (16, 20s, 50, 60). Simple settings. Fee code M

Of vital importance to the development of English drama was the entrance of the first actresses upon the English stage. April De Angelis has taken five actresses — Nell Gwyn, Elizabeth Farley, Rebecca Marshall, Doll Common and Mary Betterton — and given us a fascinating look at the precarious lot of actresses in the Restoration period. A moving and often comic account of a true story, with some earthy language! Period 1669
ISBN 0 573 13007 8

Playing Sinatra. Play. Bernard Kops
M2 F1. A living-room. Fee code M

A powerful psychological drama set in an oppressive old house in London, where grown-up siblings Norman and Sandra resist their lonely future by living out their fantasies in the music of their idol, Frank Sinatra. Norman, an agoraphobic bookbinder, works at home and heats microwave meals to perfection; Sandra, with outside job and interests, longs to break free of her existence. But the option of leaving her mentally-disturbed brother and running off with the 'mystic' Phillip proves less than straightforward ... This tense play's clammy grip never slackens.
ISBN 0 573 01863 4

Playing the Wife. Play. Ronald Hayman
M2 (20s, 52) F2 (20s, 40s). A stage. Fee code **M**

August Strindberg directs two actors in an autobiographical play detailing his difficult, stormy relationship with his first wife Siri von Essen. Siri is played by Harriet Bosse, with whom Strindberg falls in love and marries; Strindberg himself is played by Bengt Anders, an earnest, ardent young actor who is also in love with Harriet. This impressive drama about a sensitive, driven, turbulent and mystical playwright uses a fictional play-within-a-play device to brilliantly approximate the environment in which Strindberg lived and worked.
ISBN 0 573 01867 7

Plaza Suite. Comedy. Neil Simon
M3/2/2 F1/2. An hotel suite. Fee code **M**

The comedy consists of three separate plays all occurring in the same hotel suite, and all parts can be played by separate artists. In the first play, *Visitor from Mamaroneck*, a middle-aged couple re-visit the hotel room of their honeymoon — but the arrangement does not end as romantically as might have been expected. *Visitor from Hollywood* recounts the meeting of two old flames and what can happen under the influence of repeating magic Hollywood names. The last play, *Visitor from Forest Hills*, tells of a mother and father and their daughter who has locked herself in the bathrooom and refuses to come out for her wedding.
ISBN 0 573 61407 5

The Plough and the Stars. Tragedy. Sean O' Casey
M9 (25, 40, middle-age) F6 (15, 20, 23, 40). Three interiors. One exterior. Fee code **M**

To the Irish Citizen Army 'The Plough and the Stars' symbolizes their futile patriotism. To all the slum dwellers the Easter rebellion brings the realization that there is no help against the strength of the English forces. This tragic satire ends amid a scene of final desolation where two Irishmen sit playing cards until they are rounded up by the King's soldiers. Period 1915-16
ISBN 0 573 01344 4

The Pocket Dream. Comedy. Elly Brewer and Sandi Toksvig
M4 F2. Extras. A stage. Fee code **M**

The Henry Irving Strolling Players (HISP) Memorial Theatre are to present a production of *A Midsommer Night's Dream* but when the majority of the cast walk out and the house manager can't refund the audience's money (because it's riding on a dog) desperate measures need to be taken by the stage manager and anyone else she can find to step into the breach! ' ... the audience laughed like mad ... and were happy to help in the gags impressed on them from the stage. It's like a springtime pantomime.' *Financial Times*
ISBN 0 573 01864 2

◆ **Popcorn**. Play. Ben Elton
M4 (young, late 30s, middle-age) F5 (teenage, young, late 30s). A lounge-room. Fee code **M**

Set in the Beverly Hills home of Tarantino-style, Oscar-winning, movie director Bruce Delamitri, *Popcorn* is a satirical comedy thriller that took the West End by storm. Notorious killers Wayne and Scout interrupt Bruce and Brooke Daniels (nude model and actress) intending to use Bruce's 'art' as justification for murder. Events are disrupted with the arrival of Karl (Bruce's producer) and Farrah Delamitri (Bruce's soon-to-be-ex-wife) with spoilt daughter, Velvet. But Wayne means to succeed — whatever the cost. **Available 1st September 2000**
ISBN 0 573 01869 3

The Pope and the Witch. Play. Dario Fo. Edited by Franca Rame. Translated by Ed Emery
M8 F3. Doubling. Extras. A corridor and room in the Vatican, a room. Fee code M

The Vatican is the target of this fast and furious satire. The Pope is to give his first world televized press conference but is suffering from acute paranoia and nervous paralysis. Enter Elisa, the 'witch' of the title, who alone seems to have the power to cure the Pope. Visiting her drug clinic he is so impressed that he issues a papal encyclical with startling global results.

Portrait of Murder. Drama. Robert Bloomfield
M3 (35, 40, middle-age) F3 (25, 30s). A living-room. Fee code H

Eliot and his mistress tried to kill Eliot's wife Paula but suceeded only in giving her amnesia. Paula's personality seems changed; now she is charming and considerate. Paula is once again involved in another accident and reverts back to being as unpleasant as she used to be. Are there two Paulas? Gradually a cunning masquerade unfolds.
ISBN 0 573 01351 9

Portraits. Play. William Douglas Home
M6 or M4 (20, 50s, 60s, 80s) F1 (60s). Two artists' studios. Fee code M

Augustus John's ability as a portrait artist won him the admiration of fellow artists, public recognition and the Order of Merit. This play presents various points in this Bohemian artist's turbulent life from 1944-1961 through a reconstruction of sittings with three of his subjects. 'This charming, literate ... and often touching study of the man who invented Bohemianism ... splendid dialogue from William Douglas Home ... one of the best plays to hit the West End in some time.' *Time Out*
ISBN 0 573 01672 0

◆ **The Positive Hour**. Play. April de Angelis
M2 (30s-40s, 51) F4 (30s, 46), 1 girl. Various simple settings. Fee code M

Miranda is a social worker, with no shortage of problems herself. Her best friend, Emma, is a failed artist having a mid-life crisis; her partner, Roger, is a frustrated academic, desperately trying to finish his book on Hegel. Personal problems are exacerbated by work and, especially, Miranda's relationship with Paula, an unemployed single mother who takes up prostitution to survive. Funny and disturbing, *The Positive Hour* brings issues of gender and sexuality into a new, modern context.

Post Horn Gallop. Farce. Derek Benfield
M6 (30, middle-age) F6 (20s, 40s, middle-age). A baronial hall. Fee code K

A sequel to *Wild Goose Chase*. In the ancestral home the nerve-shattered Chester is again menaced by his old enemies Capone and Wedgwood. In the flowerbeds Lord Elrood lurks with his shotgun ready to repel attacks by the butcher's boy, the postman and other desperate characters. Through the ancestral living-room wander Maggie and Bert, come for two-and-sixpence-worth of gawp and suitably awestruck by the goings-on of the country-house set.
ISBN 0 573 11341 6

The Potting Shed. Play. Graham Greene
M6 (40s, 58, 60) F5 (13, 36, 70s). A living-room, a lodgings room, a presbytery. Fee code M

James Callifer, long estranged from his family, returns home to his dying father. He learns there that as a boy he had hanged himself in the potting shed, but had been cut down and 'resurrected'. It transpires his father had lost his agnosticism and as a result James's mother had disowned her son — who was a living proof that a 'miracle' had occurred in his past.

The Power of the Dog. Play. Ellen Dryden
M2 (young, 30s) F4 (17, 40s, 60s, 70s) A cottage interior, an office. Fee code M

Vivien, an English teacher, is about to become headmistress of another school, thus leaving Lisa, her difficult but bright protégée, stranded without her inspiration. When Lisa takes violent action to express her unhappiness, Vivien is shocked out of her usual detached emotional state into an understanding of the consequences of her actions, which have affected all her relationships, including that with her crippled mother.

Present from the Past. Play. Richard Everett
M3 (40s, 69). F2 (40s). A living-room, a hallway. Fee code M

Frances, Howard and Rachel have always believed that their father, David, died in a boating accident when they were children ... but he didn't. When the three siblings, along with Rachel's husband Colin, gather to clear out the house of their recently-deceased mother, several long-hidden secrets are revealed, but none of the skeletons to fall from their collective closets is more tangible or more shocking than David, who arrives with the news that the house is, in fact, his.
ISBN 0 573 11361 0

Present Laughter. Light comedy. Noël Coward
M5 (30-40) F6 (23-40). A studio. Fee code M

Popular actor Garry Essendine revels in being a temperamental prima donna. Now separated from wife Liz he still remains under her control. When he becomes more deeply involved with Joanna, his manager's wife, and it becomes clear that it will be difficult to extricate himself, Liz returns and takes him once again under her control.
ISBN 0 573 01354 3

The Prime of Miss Jean Brodie. Play. Jay Presson Allen
M4 (young, middle-age) F8 (young, middle-age). 4 girls non-speaking (11-12); 7 girls non-speaking (8-11). Fee code M

Jean Brodie, teacher at the Marcia Blaine Academy, incurs the disapproval of her colleagues by her unconventional teaching methods, her favouritism among her pupils, and also by her admiration for Mussolini and Italy. Scandals increase, chiefly involving the art teacher and the music teacher. One member of her group of favourites is killed while running off to fight for Franco. Her chief protégée, Sandy, denounces her as a murderer. Period 1930s
ISBN 0 573 61427 X

Prin. Play. Andrew Davies
M3 (30s, 40s) F3 (20s, 30s, 50s). An academic office. Fee code M

Prin, the principal of a teachers' training college, has spent thirty years in the pursuit of excellence; however, she seems more concerned with the 'prima donnas' than with nurturing the 'job lots'. When it appears that she may be losing her job, she shuts out reality with the same myopic view that she takes of life outside herself. Her inability to compromise leaves her contemplating the ruins of her personal and professional lives.
ISBN 0 573 01861 8

Princess Ascending. Play. Norman Holland
F12 (16, 20, 37, middle-age). An open stage. Fee code J

The play follows the course of English royal history from Lady Jane Grey, through the reign of Queen Mary, to the accession of Elizabeth I. The framework of the chronicle is provided by four Ladies-in-Waiting, who serve as a combination of chorus, commentators and other participants in the events. The audience are taken to represent the Commons of England. Against the simplest of scenic backgrounds, the story is unfolded, through Elizabeth's darkest years to her accession to the throne. Period sixteenth century
ISBN 0 573 03011 1

The Prisoner of Second Avenue. Comedy. Neil Simon
M2 (40s, 50s) F4 (40s, 50s). A 14th floor apartment. Fee code M

When Mel is made redundant he starts to fight a battle with the environs of New York: the pollution, the paper-thin walls of the high rise apartment. When his apartment is burgled and his psychiatrist dies with $23,000 of his money Mel has a nervous breakdown. It is on recovery that we come to esteem him all the more. For Mel and his wife and people like them have the resilience, the grit to survive.
ISBN 0 573 61429 6

The Prisoner of Zenda. Play. Matthew Francis, adapted from the novel by Anthony Hope
M17 (can be played by M9) F2, 1 child. Various interior and exterior settings. Fee code M

Anthony Hope's fine imperialist adventure is brought vividly to life in Matthew Francis's stirring adaptation which plunges straight into the heart of the Ruritanian dynastic conflict. Rudolph Rassendyll, young English gallant, is distantly related on the wrong side of the blanket to the Ruritanian royal family. When the Crown Prince is drugged by Black Michael, Rudolph steps in and takes the Prince's place at his coronation. Period early twentieth century
ISBN 0 573 01865 0

Private Lives. Intimate comedy. Noël Coward
M2 (30) F3 (young, 30). A balcony, a living-room. Fee code M

Sybil and Elyot arrive at a hotel in France for their honeymoon. Amanda, Elyot's first wife, happens to take the adjoining suite with her new husband Victor. When Amanda and Elyot meet they elope but together they veer between happiness and bickering which turns into physical fighting. Victor and Sybil discover them rolling on the floor and a four-handed quarrel begins during which Elyot and Amanda steal away. Period 1930
ISBN 0 573 01357 8

Privates on Parade. Play with songs. Peter Nichols. Music by Denis King
M10 (20s, 35, 45, 50s) F1 (28). Several simple settings on an open stage. Fee code M

Designed in the form of a variety show, the production of an Army Concert Party show in Malaya is intermingled with the story of their adventures, comic and tragic, as they tour the jungle-type countryside, menaced by Communist guerrillas. Among the varied company are an aggressive, dishonest Sergeant-Major, a raw newcomer, an earnestly religious major, and a colourful homosexual. Finally, bruised, battered but still ebullient, the survivors board ship for England and home. Period 1948
ISBN 0 573 11347 5

The Prodigious Snob. Comedy. Molière. Adapted from *Le Bourgeois Gentilhomme* by Miles Malleson. Music by John Hotchkis
M16 (young, middle-age) F6 (young, middle-age). A room in Paris. Fee code H. Period 1670
ISBN 0 573 01359 4

Progress. Play. Doug Lucie
M6 (21-30s) F2 (20, 33). A living-room. Fee code M

Progress exposes the hard underbelly of a slightly older generation of trendy lefties and sexual liberationists living appalling lives in London NW6, where Will, a Channel 4 researcher, and his wife Ronee, breakfast to the accompaniment of the taped sob-outs from his men's therapy group, plus the occasional phone call from Ronee's German girlfriend. '... brutally satiric eye for modern manners and speech ...' *Guardian*. '... vicious satirical comedy ... appallingly funny ...' *The Times*

The Promise. Play. Alexei Arbuzov. Translated by Ariadne Nicolaeff
M2 (17) F1(15). A living-room. Fee code M

During the siege of Leningrad in 1942, three young people — a girl and two boys — find shelter in a semi-derelict house. The play follows the intricacies of their triangular relationship over the next seventeen years, as their hopes and feelings for themselves and each other rise and fall, and offers a moving and fascinating glimpse of life in the Soviet Union after the Second World War. *The Promise* was originally performed at the Oxford Playhouse in 1966, in a production starring Judi Dench, Ian McKellen and Ian McShane.

Pull the Other One. Farce. Norman Robbins
M4 (35, 65, elderly) F3 (18, 35, 60). A living-room. Fee code L

When Albert's mother-in-law Boadicea discovers a letter written to Albert from his friend Hilary she refuses to believe it is perfectly innocent or that Hilary is a man. Along comes Hilary in blonde wig and evening dress straight from his drag act at the local pub. Further disasters ensue as Hilary attempts to make amends for the trouble he has caused and tries to help Albert.
ISBN 0 573 11358 0

The Quare Fellow. Play. Brendan Behan
M22 or M18 with doubling. Various simple settings. Fee code M

The emotional atmosphere of a prison on the eve of an execution is sustained with subtle and humorous control throughout.The central theme is the paradox of man's urge towards love and fellowship on the one hand and his persistent practice of inhumanity on the other.

Quartermaine's Terms. Play. Simon Gray
M5 F2. A staffroom. Fee code M

Set in the 1960s in a school of English for foreigners in Cambridge, *Quartermaine's Terms* is an often humorous but ultimately moving account of several years in the lives of seven teachers. The play was first presented at the Queen's Theatre, London, in 1981 and won the 1982 Cheltenham Prize for Literature, the first time a play has won this award. '... thoroughly crafted, sharp-witted piece of drama.' *Guardian* '... a refreshingly sensitive, observant piece ...' *New Statesman*
ISBN 0 573 11364 5

Racing Demon. Play. David Hare
M8 (20s, 40s-60s). F3 (20s, 30, 50s). Extras. Various simple interior and exterior settings. Fee code M

Racing Demon focuses on the Church of England. A disparate body, the Church now finds itself attracting unwanted publicity, wracked by the dissension of its members on matters of doctrine and practice and at odds with the government. In this climate the Reverend Lionel Espy and his team of clergymen struggle to make sense of their mission in South London, as the arrival of a zealous young curate intensifies their personal and professional problems.
ISBN 0 573 11369 6

Rain. Play. John Colton and Clemence Randolph. From the story *Miss Thompson* by W. Somerset Maugham
M7 (young, 35, 40, elderly) F4 (young, 30s, Kanaka). Extras. An hotel living-room. Fee code M

Torrential rains have trapped a party of Europeans in a small hotel in the South Seas. To the missionary Davidson and his wife, the presence of the prostitute Sadie Thompson is an insult. Davidson provokes a trial of strength between Sadie's love of life and his own suppressed desires. On the point of succeeding, he finds that the strength of his own self-denial is insufficient. Period 1925
ISBN 0 573 01368 3

The Rape of the Belt. Comedy. Benn W. Levy
M3 (young) F7 (young, middle-age, elderly). Two exteriors. Fee code M

The Amazons have a perfect kingdom full of peacefully creative women who have, through propaganda, created such a fearsome reputation that no-one dares attack. Heracles, who has to steal the belt of the Amazon Queen for his ninth labour, would undoubtedly have fallen victim to their charms had divine Hera not intervened, turning the Amazons into warriors. Heracles easily wins the belt, but he knows he has lost a paradise. Period Ancient Greece
ISBN 0 573 01371 3

Rattle of a Simple Man. Play. Charles Dyer
M2 (28, 52) F1 (26). A basement flatlet. Fee code M

A friend bets Percy fifty pounds that he will not spend the night with a prostitute and do his duty like a man, so he goes home with Cyrenne. When her brash jokes and open suggestiveness fail to bring Percy up to scratch, the two start chatting and, gradually, a bond grows up between them. A gentle blend of humour, sentiment and emotion, the play depicts with charm and perception how loneliness can drive people to opposite extremes.
ISBN 0 573 01372 1

Real Estate. Play. Louise Page
M2 (30s, 50s) F2 (38, 60). Various simple interior and exterior settings. Fee code M

First performed at the Tricycle Theatre, London, in 1984, this is a touching, sensitive play which stirs deep emotions. Jenny, single and pregnant, returns to visit her mother after twenty years, hoping to find some kind of assistance and support, and possibly a home in which to raise her child. As the play unfolds, the characters are visibly fighting to penetrate each other's defences and ultimately Jenny realizes that her mother is not prepared to give up her happiness for her daughter's sake.

♦ **The Real Story of Puss in Boots.** Play. David Foxton
M6 F3, or M7 F4. Various interior and exterior settings. Fee code K

The story of *Puss in Boots* is ingeniously combined with that of *Cinderella* in this hilarious new show. Puss in Boots transforms humble Colin Miller into Prince Charming. Cinderella's Fairy Godmother helps her to become Princess Priscilla, despite the meddlings of her stepsisters. Prince Charming and Princess Priscilla marry, thus providing happy endings for both their stories. This hugely likeable show, which can be performed by a small cast without songs, is suitable for any scale of production.
ISBN 0 573 06497 0

The Real Thing. Play. Tom Stoppard
M4 (20s, 40s) F3 (17, 30s). Various interior settings. Fee code M

Tom Stoppard's brilliant, award-winning play of surprise and deftly witty comparison was premièred at London's Strand Theatre in 1982 starring Roger Rees and Felicity Kendal and revived in 1999. Henry is a successful playwright married to Charlotte who has the lead role in his latest play about adultery. Her co-star, Max, is married to another actress, Annie, and Annie and Henry are madly in love but is it any more real than the subjects of Henry's play?
ISBN 0 573 01637 2

Rebecca. Play. Daphne du Maurier
M8 (young, 30s, middle-age) F3 (young, middle-age). Extras. A lounge-hall. Fee code M. Period 1940
ISBN 0 573 01373 X

Rebecca. Play. Daphne du Maurier. Adapted by Clifford Williams
M8 (young, 30s, middle-age) F3 (young, middle-age). Extras. A lounge-hall. Fee code M

Max de Winter brings his shy young bride to Manderley, his great house in Cornwall. Everywhere, she senses the overpowering presence of Rebecca, Max's drowned wife. Mrs Danvers, the grim housekeeper, will not allow her to forget her shortcomings. She doubts Max's love until Rebecca's body is found. Max confesses that he murdered Rebecca, hating her depravity. The husband and wife now face the exciting fight to save Max from the gallows. Period 1940
ISBN 0 573 11365 3

The Red Devil Battery Sign. Play. Tennessee Williams
M14 F4, doubling possible. Extras. Various interior settings. Fee code M

One of Williams' later plays, this is his indictment of the military-industrial complex and all the dehumanizing trends it represents, from mindless cocktail party chatter to bribery of officials, to assassination plots directed against those who will not play the game, to attempted coups by right-wing zealots.

Red in the Morning. Thriller. Glyn Jones
M4 (23, 40s) F3 (30s, 70s). Extras. A conservatory and part of the hall. Fee code L

A truly Grand Guignol play, with rapacious servants, venomous dobermans, meat-hooks and mutilations. Two men abduct a boy for ransom, and his grandmother, in order to keep hidden certain family skeletons, readily pays. But then the bloody machinations begin, and before the grisly ending there are multiple disclosures, including the discovery of a Nazi death camp commandant.
ISBN 0 573 69094 9

Redevelopment. Play. Václav Havel. English version by James Saunders. From a literal translation by Marie Winn
M7 F3, with doubling. A spacious hall in a medieval castle. Fee code M

This English version of Václav Havel's play received its British première at the Orange Tree Theatre, Richmond. 'On a realistic level, the play is about a universal architectural dilemma ... But it also works as a political metaphor about the whimsical arbitrariness of autocracy ... This is vintage Havel: creating a work that is both specific and universal, tragic and comic.' Michael Billington, *Guardian*

The Rehearsal, or Love Punished. Play. Jean Anouilh. Translated by Jeremy Sams
M5 F3. An elegant room, an attic room. Fee code M

A hedonistic Count and his friends rehearse Marivaux's *The Double Inconstancy* in the rural splendour of a provincial castle. Most of the 'actors' keep to the amorous rules and restrict their dalliances to their own class. Yet when the Count himself threatens to step beyond theatrical boundaries by falling in love with a young governess, stage romance suddenly becomes the drama of life. This sparkling translation was presented in the West End to critical acclaim.

Relative Strangers. Play. Trevor Cowper
M2 (middle-age) F4 (teenage, 20s). A living-room. Fee code L
ISBN 0 573 11353 X

Relative Values. Light comedy. Noël Coward
M5 (30-middle-age, 60) F5 (18, 35-50s). A library living-room. Fee code M

Moxie is maid to Felicity, Countess of Marshwood. When Felicity's son Nigel announces his engagement to Miranda Frayle, the film star, Moxie is distressed as Miranda is really her sister, who ignored her family after becoming famous. Miranda starts describing the home from which she ran away, saying her sister drank and she had to care for her mother. Outraged, Moxie blurts out the truth — and the engagement becomes rather strained.
ISBN 0 573 01375 6

Relatively Speaking. Comedy. Alan Ayckbourn
M2 (young, middle-age) F2 (young, middle-age). A bedsitting-room, a garden patio. Fee code M

Greg and Ginny are living together, but Greg is becoming somewhat suspicious that he is not the only man in her life. He wonders about Ginny's plan 'to visit her parents' and decides to follow her. Ginny is really going to see a considerably older lover, but only in order to break with him. Greg mistakes the ex-lover and his wife for Ginny's parents. Ginny's arrival further compounds an already wildly hilarious situation.
ISBN 0 573 11355 6

The Reluctant Debutante. Comedy. William Douglas Home
M3 (20s, middle-age) F5 (young, middle-age). A sitting-room. Fee code M

Jane is totally uninterested in her mother's valiant efforts to give her a successful 'season', and much prefers the company of horses to that of the chinless drips who are assigned to her as escorts. When she does fall in love with a man, it is with one who seems to her parents to be most unsuitable. However, he turns out to be much more acceptable than they had thought — he even has a title — so everybody is happy.
ISBN 0 573 11348 3

Remembrance. Play. Graham Reid
M2 (30s-40s, 68) F4 (30s-40s, 63). A cemetery, two living-rooms, a garden. Fee code M

Bert and Theresa, both mourning sons, meet in the cemetery and fall in love. Their blossoming relationship is complicated by the fact that he is a Protestant and she a Catholic ... and this is Belfast. Bert's son, who believes his father would rather have lost him than his adored brother, and Theresa's daughters, one of whom is married to an imprisoned IRA gunman, oppose the romance from the start, but Bert's daughter-in-law, herself trapped in an unhappy marriage, supports the elderly lovers.
ISBN 0 573 69321 8

♦ **Rents**. A play by Michael Wilcox
M10 (can be played by M5). Various simple interior and exterior settings. Fee code L

Through an episodic style which mirrors the fragmentary nature of the characters' lives, the play describes the fleeting sexual encounters of the homosexual rent boys in 1970s' Edinburgh. Phil, a droll drama student, shares a flat with Robert, an 18-year-old shop assistant who has had many years on the game. Both become involved with Richard, a mature lecturer from Newcastle desperately in need of sexual humiliation.

The Resistible Rise of Arturo Ui. Play. Bertolt Brecht
Translations: Ralph Manheim
                George Tabori
          ♦ Ranjit Bolt, music by Dominic Muldowney
M28 F2. Extras. Numerous simple interior and exterior settings. Fee code M for play, code C for music

A grimly humorous 'parable play' in blank verse, in which Hitler's rise to power is illustrated in the story of a small-time gangster's take-over of the greengrocery trade in Chicago. A brief six-line Epilogue points out how nearly Hitler ruled the world.

The Restless Evil. Play. Charlotte Hastings
M3 (24, 38) F7 (20s West Indian, 40s, 50s, 60, 70s). A café. Fee code L

After a prison break, convict Jubilee, with two companions, takes over a small roadside café. The owners are temporarily absent; however, a speial party of their friends is expected to lunch. After serving the visitors lunch, the gang tells them they are prisoners. The mutual reactions of 'respectables' and 'villains', the mounting tension of the situation, and instinctive groping towards some sort of understanding, form the basis of the events that follow.
ISBN 0 573 11370 X

The Restoration of Arnold Middleton. Play. David Storey
M2 (30s, 40) F4 (young, 20s, 30s, 50s). A living-room. Fee code H
ISBN 0 573 01376 4

Retreat. Play. James Saunders
M1 (middle-age) F1 (young). A living-room. Fee code M

Harold Hopper has retreated to a cottage in Wales following a car accident in which his wife died and his daughter was disabled. But his 'retreat' is disturbed by the arrival of Hannah, daughter of his closest friends who have died in a plane crash. Hannah forces him to confront the facts, unleashing the repressed bitterness within him. At the end the doorbell rings again — did Hannah truly arrive or has Harold conjured her to catharize his guilt?

Retreat from Moscow. Play. Don Taylor
M2 (50s) F2 (16, 22). A living-room. Fee code M

Cocooned in their suburban home are Tom, idealistic socialist and unemployed classics lecturer, and Phillipa, his disillusioned daughter. Into their lives unexpectedly comes Boris, a bellowing bear-like Muscovite who only wants to enjoy the fruits of the capitalist good life. But beneath Boris's laughing exuberance lies a bitter, dreadful secret past which, when revealed, shakes the beliefs Tom holds firm. The play was presented at the New End Theatre, Hampstead, in 1993 in a production directed by the author.

The Return of A. J. Raffles. Edwardian comedy. Graham Greene
M8 (young, 30s, middle-age, elderly) F2 (young, 30). An apartment in Albany, a bedroom. Fee code M

In this light-hearted pastiche E.W.Hornung's famous 'amateur cracksman' is persuaded by Lord Alfred Douglas to break into and rob the house of the latter's hated father, the Marquess of Queensberry, accompanied by the ever-faithful Bunny. Douglas intends to send part of the proceeds to Oscar Wilde, now living in poverty. They then become involved in a plot to secure certain compromising letters written by no less a personage than King Edward VII!

The Revengers' Comedies. Play in two parts by Alan Ayckbourn
M11 F10, M1 F1 voices only, some doubling possible. Various interior and exterior settings. Fee code M for each part

Hapless Henry Bell, depressed at being ousted from his firm, is distracted from committing suicide by another would-be suicide. He rescues her, and after hearing her tale of abandonment by her married lover, agrees that revenge is sweeter than suicide. Karen persuades Henry that they should swap revenges — she will see to the man who took Henry's job, while he will take care of her ex-lover's wife, Imogen.
ISBN 0 573 01881 2

Richard of Bordeaux. Drama. Gordon Daviot
M23 F6. Nine interiors. Fee code H

This is a sympathetic study of Richard II, laying special stress on Richard's desire to foster the arts and crafts, and to promote the cause of peace, both in Ireland and France. How the young and gradually spoilt and embittered, as well as favourite-ridden King was impeded by the inveterate prejudices of his uncles, especially Gloucester, is shown vividly in the course of twelve scenes, ending with the penultimate stage of Richard II's life. Period 1385-97
ISBN 0 573 01379 9

Ring Round the Moon. Play. Jean Anouilh. Adapted by Christopher Fry
M8 (young, middle-age, old) F6 (young, 30, middle-age, elderly). A winter garden. Fee code M

Christopher Fry calls this play 'A Charade with Music'. The same actor plays the twins Hugo and Frederic. Hugo, fascinating and heartless, sets the charade in motion. He has invited Isabelle, a ballet dancer, to the ball that evening, intending that she should make diffident Frederic love her and leave the beautiful Diana. The would-be puppetmaster is overruled by his aunt, who arranges for the four young people to be happy.
ISBN 0 573 11380 7

◆ **The Ring Sisters**. Comedy. Charles Laurence
M4 (30-50s) F3 (50s, 70s). A living-room. Fee code M

Silva Ring is a world-famous singer with a severe hangup about her age so when an interviewer reveals it she resorts to increasingly desperate measures to prove him wrong. Aided by her housekeeper she pretends to be her own sister Iris, who is tough. Lola Wales, an old singer, is brought in to be her aunt and Fred, a petty forger, is persuaded to attempt to destroy her files at the Family Record Centre. But Silva wins through and emerges stronger than ever.
ISBN 0 573 62677 4

The Rise and Fall of Little Voice. Play. Jim Cartwright
M3 (young, 40s, 50s) or 4 F3 (young, 40s). A living-room and club. Fee code M

Little Voice (LV) lives alone with her mother Mari whose sole purpose is to find another man. Mari's imposing presence drives the shy LV into spending her time in her bedroom listening to her beloved father's records. When small-time impresario Ray Say hears LV's faultless impersonation of famous singers, he recognizes the gold in her voice and determines to exploit it, but the whirlwind rush for success breaks LV. Later, however, she learns to sing in her own voice ...
ISBN 0 573 01883 9

◆ **A Rise in the Market**. Comedy. Edward Taylor
M4 (40s, elderly) F3 (20s, late 30s). A lounge area. Fee code L

Sir Clive Partridge hopes to be president of European Community, but he needs the support of puritanical elder statesman Jacques Berri. So it's bad news for Partridge when Berri calls on a day that he is trapped in a luxurious Paris flat where he is beset by glamorous young women he can't account for, plus an angry wife and an exploding boiler. Wild mishaps and comic confusion abound right up to the hilarious climax in this sharp satire.

The Rivals. Comedy. R. Brinsley Sheridan
M8 (young, middle-age) F4 (young, middle-age). Four interiors, three exteriors. No fee

Captain Absolute, heir to a tidy fortune, has disguised himself as penniless Ensign Beverley, all because his lady-love, Lydia Languish, is determined to marry a man who despises wealth and who will marry her despite the fact that the disapproval of her tough old aunt, Mrs Malaprop, will cost Miss Languish her immense fortune. Another pair of lovers, Julia and Falkland, have their own peculiar difficulties ...
ISBN 0 573 01382 9

Road. Play. Jim Cartwright
M17 F13, can be played by M4 F3 with doubling. In and around a road in a small Lancashire town. Fee code M

Under the guidance of the rum-soaked wideboy Scullery, we are taken on an evening's tour of a scruffy, depressed road in a small Lancashire town. Moving from street corner to living-room, from bedroom to kitchen, we meet the inhabitants, glimpsing their socially and emotionally wretched lives in this sharp, sad, funny and angry play. ' ... the most significant and original new English play to appear in London for a long time ...' *Observer*
ISBN 0 573 01664 X

Robin Hood. Comedy drama. Larry Blamire
M14 F7, doubling possible. Extras. Various simple settings. Fee code M

Larry Blamire has accomplished the enviable task of synthesizing the conflicting legends and ballads about the outlaw folk hero into a sometimes hysterical, sprawling action-packed drama. Besides ably retelling the legend, he indulges in and makes fun of the stilted dialogue found in tiresome historical novels and adventure films. He has created roles that challenge and reinvent the myth, including a wise-cracking Maid Marion who is arguably a better swords*person* than any of Robin's merry men.

Robin Hood. Musical celebration. David Wood and Dave and Toni Arthur
M14 or F14 (minimum). An open space. Fee code M

This is a series of playlets which tell the various well-known tales of Robin Hood. The possibilities for presenting the play are numerous — open stage, promenade, open air as well as on a proscenium stage. There is a basic cast of fourteen, but the authors envisage productions 'in which large numbers of local people take part', emphasizing the basic concept of the play which is that of a musical celebration by a whole community.
ISBN 0 573 05063 5

Robin Hood — the Truth Behind the Green Tights. Play. David Neilson
M7 F2, with doubling. Various interior and exterior settings. Fee code L

'Feared by the bad, loved by the good' goes the song about Robin Hood, but in the case of Albert Ross, the distinction is not quite so clear-cut. For Albert is a coward, transferring his allegiance from Merry Men to Sheriff and back again at the drop of a hat — or rather, at the point of a sword. All of which lands Albert, his wife, Robin and Maid Marian in some very awkward situations ...
ISBN 0 573 11381 5

Robin Redbreast. Play. John Bowen
M5 (young, 30s, middle-age) F3 (30s, elderly). A cottage and adjoining lane. Fee code L

Norah decides to live alone in a remote country cottage. She is soon attracted to Rob but there is something very strange about their brief affair — the local villagers are odd and when Norah becomes pregnant and wishes to leave the place and have an abortion she finds increasingly sinister forces arrayed against her. The tension mounts to a horrifying climax of witchcraft ritual, in which Rob — or Robin — is hideously sacrificed.

Romantic Comedy. Comedy. Bernard Slade
M2 (30s) F4 (young, 20s, 30s, 54). A study. Fee code M

Jason Carmichael, successful co-author of Broadway romantic comedies, is about to marry a society belle and his collaborator is retiring from the fray. Enter Phoebe Craddock, a mousy Vermont schoolteacher and budding playwright and Jason acquires a talented, adoring collaborator. Fame and success are theirs for ten years and then Jason's world falls apart — his wife divorces him and Phoebe marries a journalist and moves to Paris. Jason goes into decline but re-enter a chic, successful Phoebe — and guess the ending!
ISBN 0 573 61504 7

La Ronde. Ten Dialogues. Arthur Schnitzler. English version by Eric Bentley
M5 F5. Simple settings. Fee code M

This is Schnitzler's popular roundelay of love, as practised in Old Vienna, and as told in ten interlocking scenes. Each scene is made for two persons, and each person plays two consecutive scenes, serving alternately as the link between them. Thus the soldier of the first scene leaves his lady of the evening to appear in the next scene with a parlour maid. An amusing *tour de force*, popular throughout the world.
ISBN 0 573 61192 0

Rookery Nook. Farce. Ben Travers
M5 F6. A lounge-hall. Fee code M

Gerald rents Rookery Nook where his wife, Clara, will join him later. He is agreeably surprised by a pretty stranger called Rhoda who comes running to him for protection against her irascible German stepfather. Gerald allows her to stay in one of the bedrooms but as she is clad only in pyjamas, it is vital to conceal her presence from nosy neighbours. Rhoda gets herself some clothes just in time before Clara arrives but Gerald has some difficulty in convincing Clara of his innocence. Period 1920s
ISBN 0 573 01389 6

Roots. Play. Arnold Wesker
M5 (young, 50s, 65) F4 (young, 50). Three cottage living-rooms. Fee code M

This is the second play of the trilogy which opens with *Chicken Soup with Barley*. Beatie returns for a holiday to her fenland farm home trying to impose on her stolid family the ideas of a young Jewish intellectual, Ronnie, whom she believes will marry her. But, awaiting his arrival, slowly Beatie realizes he will never come and her famous final speech exults that Ronnie has taught her independence and how to free herself from him. Period 1950s
ISBN 0 573 11377 7

◆ **Roots and Wings**. Play. Frank Vickery
M3 (20s, 40s, 50s) F3 (youngish, 40s, 50s). A hospital corridor and room. Fee code M

Griff has discovered that his son Nigel is not only a drag queen but gay; hours later, Nigel is in hospital having been hurt in a car crash in which his lover, Kevin, has incurred much worse injuries. Robust, sensible Ruby, Griff's wife, has much to deal with — Nigel's fears, Griff's prejudices, her own confused emotions, Kevin's parents — and has to use every resource at her disposal to keep the peace.
ISBN 0 573 01885 5

Rope. Drama. Patrick Hamilton
M6 (young, 20s, old) F2 (young, 50). A study. Fee code M

Brandon wants excitement at any price. He persuades his weak-minded friend, Granillo, to assist him in the murder of a fellow undergraduate, Ronald Raglan. They place the body in a wooden chest and invite some acquaintances, including the dead man's father, to a party, the chest and its gruesome contents serving as a supper table. The horror and tension are worked up gradually and we see the reactions of the two murderers, closely watched by the suspecting Rupert Cadell, until finally they break.

Rose. Play. Andrew Davies
M3 (young, middle-age) F5 (young, 30s, middle-age). Various simple settings on an open stage.
Fee code M

Rose, a disenchanted teacher, feels frustrated in all walks of life: at her tough Midlands school, in her relations with her mother, the school staff, her dullish husband. Her professional efforts to introduce new ideas are blocked; her husband threatens suicide and a possible affair dwindles to a few brief moments in a car. Finally she faces her class as so often before — 'What are we going to do today?' The original production starred Glenda Jackson.
ISBN 0 573 11392 0

The Rose Tattoo. Play. Tennessee Williams
M7 (25, middle-age) F13 (young-old). 1 small girl, 2 small boys. Exterior of a cottage, living-room interior. Fee code M

The Rose Tattoo, says the author, is 'the Dionysian element in human life, its mystery, its beauty, its significance'. Serafina boasts of her husband's prowess as a lover and nephew of a Baron. On hearing he had not been at all what she supposed she takes up life again with a flourish. In addition she now gives consent to her daughter's marriage to a young sailor.

Rosencrantz and Guildenstern Are Dead. Comedy. Tom Stoppard
M14 F2, flexible casting. Unit setting. Fee code M

Rosencrantz and Guildenstern sit in the Court of Elsinore endlessly spinning a coin, waiting for their stage entry — which may never come. Unsure who they are and why they are there they even have difficulty remembering which goes by which name. Against the action of *Hamlet* they seek their identities and their purpose and reflect the feelings of all those who question existence. While this play deals with themes already familiar from Beckett, its style is that of brilliant, literate comedy.
ISBN 0 573 01338 1

The Roses of Eyam. Play. Don Taylor
Large flexible cast including children (young-80). A village: open stage. Fee code L

A remarkable and true story of a village stricken with plague through the arrival from London of a box of clothing; of the villagers' determination, under the persuasions of the present and former Rectors, to prevent its spread by remaining within the village and containing the disease at the certain risk of their own lives; of the human tragedies and even comedies that ensued; of the idealism and the courage required to live with that idealism. Period 1666
ISBN 0 573 11386 6

Ross. Play. Terence Rattigan
M22 (20s, 30s, middle-age, 6 Turks) Extras. An R.A.F. depot, various locations in the Middle East. Fee code H

The story starts at the end, with T. E. Lawrence as Aircraftsman Ross seeking anonymity. A prey to fever contracted in the East, he relives his past in a night of delirium: his early enthusiasm and triumphs; living with the Arabs; the capture of Akaba; meeting with Allenby; engendering of Turkish hatred and final betrayal into Turkish hands. The refinements of destruction which he underwent as prisoner of the Turkish Governor are made to account for the complete change in character. Period First World War
ISBN 0 573 04006 0

Rough Crossing. Comedy. Tom Stoppard, from an original play by Ferenc Molnar
M5 (25, middle-age) F1 (35-40). Extras. A pre-war, ocean liner. Fee code M

This hilarious play, freely adapted from Molnar's classic farce *Játék a Kastélyban*, was seen at the National Theatre in 1984 starring Michael Kitchen, John Standing and Sheila Gish. Two playwrights and collaborators, the composer and most of the cast of a musical comedy destined for Broadway are trying to finish and rehearse the play while crossing from Southampton via Cherbourg, to New York. With music by Andre Previn, Tom Stoppard wittily parodies thirties' musicals.

Rough Justice. Play. Terence Frisby
M5 F3. Number One Court at the Central Criminal Court, a cell. Fee code M

James Highwood is on the stand for the murder of his severely handicapped child. He refuses his solicitor's plea to obtain legal representation, and conducts his own defence, admitting responsibility but pleading manslaughter. The battle to have his intentions understood brings him into conflict with the Prosecutor, Margaret Casely, QC, a well-known Catholic and pro-lifer. Then there's the question of whether Highwood killed his child after all ...
ISBN 0 573 01882 0

Round and Round the Garden. Play. Alan Ayckbourn
M3 F3. A garden. Fee code M. See the entry for *The Norman Conquests*
ISBN 0 573 01575 9

Roundheads and Peakheads (Rich and Rich). Play. Bertolt Brecht
Translations: N. Goold-Verschoyle, music by Hanns Eisler
                 Alan Brown and Kyra Dietz
M12 F6. Children. Extras. Interior and exterior settings. Fee code M for play, code C for music

This play is described by the author as a 'horror tale' in blank verse. Though the basic plot loosely follows that of Shakespeare's *Measure for Measure*, the play in fact is an allegory of the rise of Hitler (Angelo Iberin), a Roundhead who is appointed temporary ruler when the Regent leaves the country. Towards the end of the play the Regent returns and tells Angelo to prepare for war against a threatening distant country; the people are subdued and the revolutionaries executed. Period 1930s

The Royal Baccarat Scandal. Play. Royce Ryton
M9 (20s-elderly) F4 (20s-50). Extras. Composite setting. Fee code M

Based on the book by Michael Havers and Edward Grayson, and first seen at Chichester and subsequently at the Theatre Royal, Haymarket, London, in 1989, the play dramatizes the Victorian scandal of 1890 in which Sir William Gordon Cumming, a baronet and personal friend of the Prince of Wales, was accused by his mistress's husband of cheating at baccarat.
ISBN 0 573 11374 2

The Royal Hunt of the Sun. Play. Peter Shaffer
M21 F2. Fee code M

This is the story of the conquest of Peru, the defeat by 167 men of a highly organized, communistic empire of over ten million people. It is also the story of two men, Francisco Pizarro, the embittered, defiant commander of the invading Spanish forces, and Atahuallpa, the young king, Sun god-upon-earth, ruler of a vast empire. Between the two, both illegitimate usurpers, there grows a deep and understanding friendship.
ISBN 0 573 01388 8

The Ruffian on the Stair. Play. Joe Orton
M2 (young) F1 (young). A kitchen/living-room. Fee code F

One day a strange man appears asking for a room. He begins taunting the woman and comes close to viciousness. The next day he returns, but this time Mike is there too. We can now piece things together — Mike has killed the homosexual lover and brother of Wilson. So Wilson pretends to ravish Joyce and forces Mike to shoot him — 'The heart is situated just below this badge on my pullover. Don't miss, will you?'

◆ **Rumours** (The British Version). Farce. Neil Simon
M4 (40, 50) F5 (30s, 40s). A living-room. Fee code M

Ken and Chris have found their host Charley, a prominent Government official, in his bedroom, too dazed to speak, with a bullet wound in his ear lobe! Len and Claire arrive, themselves injured in a car crash, and are soon joined by Ernest and Cookie, Glenn and Cassie, each with their own problems. A second, accidental, gunshot leaves Ken temporarily deaf, the police arrive and Len has to pretend he is Charley, concocting a touching and fantastic explanation ... **Available with restrictions.**
ISBN 0 573 01884 7

Rumpelstiltzkin. Play. Norman Robbins
M9 or 10 F2 or 3. Extras. Various simple settings. Fee code L

In this adaptation of the Grimms' story some children are discovered playing 'Ladder-words', a word game to change one word to another. Grettle says she can change 'flax' into 'gold'. The King hears this, mistakes it for an actual boast and orders Grettle to work the change. The gnome, Rumpelstiltzkin, offers to help her — at a price. The play then follows the story of the gnome's defeat by the guessing of his secret name.
ISBN 0 573 06459 8

Run for Your Wife. Comedy. Ray Cooney
M6 (young, middle-age) F2 (20s). Composite setting: two living-rooms. Fee code M

John Smith is a London cabbie with his own taxi, a wife in Streatham, a wife in Wimbledon — and a knife-edge schedule! He has been a successful, if tired, bigamist for three years, but one day he is taken to hospital with mild concussion. In the ensuing complications, aided by an unwilling Stanley, John tries bravely to cope with a succession of well-meaning but prying policemen, two increasingly irate wives, and others, until he manfully confesses the truth.
ISBN 0 573 11383 1

Running Riot. Farce. Derek Benfield
M5 (30s, 40s) F4 (young,19, 30s, 40s). A small hotel. Fee code K
ISBN 0 573 11393 9

Rutherford and Son. Play. Githa Sowerby
M4 (20s, 40s, 60) F4 (26, 36, middle age, 60). A living-room. Fee code M

Written in 1912 during the upsurge of the British feminist movement, this powerful play deals with the oppressive patriarchal system of the industrial North at that time. Rutherford is the hard tyrannical master of both his glassworks and his family who attacks, degrades and rejects each of his children in turn. To his daughter Janet, her banishment is a release, and she forcefully condemns her father and his values.

The Sacred Flame. Play. W. Somerset Maugham
M4 (young, 30s, middle-age) F4 (20s, elderly). A drawing-room. Fee code H
ISBN 0 573 01394 2

◆ **Sad Hotel**. Play. David Foley
M3 (40s, 50s) F3 (40s). A kitchen and sitting-area. Fee code M

Set in a house on the Florida coast in the early sixties, *Sad Hotel* is a fictionalized account of a famous playwright's relationship with his male lover. The play traces the dissolution of a fifteen-year relationship under pressures of fame, failure and addiction. Trapped between a choice of love or loneliness, and the extremes of desire and betrayal, the characters in *Sad Hotel* test the limitations of human contact. Yet in the face of final loss, they struggle towards reconciliation, forgiveness and a kind of peace. Period 1961-1963

Sailor Beware! Comedy. Philip King and Falkland Cary
M4 (20s, 40s, 50s) F5 (20s, 40s). A living-room. Fee code M

Beware of mothers-in-law, especially of one like Emma Hornett. Albert Tufnell, A.B., is anxious that his fiancée, Shirley, should not take after her mother, Emma. Albert is also disturbed to find that Shirley has weakly acquiesced to living only three doors away from her mother. Albert's only defence is not to turn up at the church. Later he makes peace with Shirley and the wedding is 'on' again.
ISBN 0 573 01395 0

Salt of the Earth. Play. John Godber
M5 F6 or M3 F3. Various simple settings. Fee code M

Hull Truck Company's production of this richly humorous, affectionate and touching portrait of life in the West Yorkshire coalfields won a Fringe First at the Edinburgh Festival and was presented in London at the Donmar Warehouse Theatre. Spanning three generations, from 1947 to the present, this compelling saga vividly captures the dreams, ambitions, joys, fears, heartaches and disappointments of the Parker sisters, Annie and May, whose hopes centre on May's son, Paul, and his academic success.
ISBN 0 573 01689 5

Same Old Moon. Play. Geraldine Aron
M10 F11, may be played by M3 F5 (minimum). Various simple settings. Fee code M

Chosen to reopen the Oxford Playhouse in 1991, and then seen in London's West End, *Same Old Moon* shows us scenes in the life of Brenda Barnes, the aspiring writer. We follow her from age nine to fortyish, and see through her eyes her eccentric and sometimes fiery Irish family: her wilful and self-destructive Dad, her put-upon, sometimes hot-tempered Mum and many others. A charming, but not uncritical, look at family life with some wonderful acting roles.
ISBN 0 573 01892 8

Same Time, Next Year. Comedy. Bernard Slade
M1 F1. A bedsitting-room. Fee code M

This long-running Broadway hit is about an adulterous love affair taking place only once a year — and also a reflection of twenty-five years of American attitudes. George picks up Doris in a California inn in 1951 and they agree to meet there once a year. Before each scene, tapes portray America of the time in speeches, sports and news broadcasts. *The New York Times* described it as the 'funniest comedy about love and adultery to come Broadway's way in years'.
ISBN 0 573 61604 3

A

Sarcophagus. Play. Vladimir Gubaryev. Translated by Michael Glenny
M12 (20s, 50s) F6 (20s, 40s, 70s). Extras. A clinic ward. Fee code M

In this moving play by the science editor of *Pravda*, victims of the explosion at the Chernobyl nuclear power station embark on a non-return journey in a terminal radiation clinic. The arrival of nine survivors from the disaster starts a string of confessions and recriminations which ends in a powerful condemnation of the bureaucratic muddle and official cover-up.

Saturday, Sunday, Monday. Play. Eduardo de Filippo, adapted by Keith Waterhouse and Willis Hall
M11 F6. An apartment in Naples. Fee code M

At first sight a typical picture of Italian family life with characteristic displays of Mediterranean temper, the play concerns the essence of any relationship between a man and a woman after years of married life. A monumental family row begins to brew on Saturday night while the Sunday *ragu* is being prepared in the kitchen. The row breaks on Sunday, the traditional day for family quarrels, and is finally and touchingly resolved on Monday.

Savages. Play. Christopher Hampton
M10 (3 Brazilian Indians) F1. Extras M. Multiple set. Fee code M

In a passionately angry, bitterly cynical and yet wholly workable play which veers from the soapbox to high comedy we are shown the contrasting publicity surrounding the murder of one diplomat and the anonymity surrounding the slaughter of a hundred Brazilian Indians. Period 1963 to 1970

Say Who You Are. Comedy. Keith Waterhouse and Willis Hall
M2 (30s) F2 (30s). Various settings. Fee code J

A telephone booth is an important cast member in this comedy! Every Friday evening David Lord's wife, Sarah, lends their flat to her unmarried friend, Valerie, so that the latter can entertain her married lover, Stuart. David does not know of this arrangement and Stuart believes that Valerie is married to David! When David rebels one Friday at being dragged to yet another foreign film and Stuart has a fit of masochistic jealousy the resulting embroilments defy further description.

Scapino! Play. Frank Dunlop and Jim Dale, a long way off from Molière
M10 F4. A café bar. Fee code K

Inspired, at some distance, by Molière's *Les Fourberies de Scapin*, this 'comic madness' is set in present-day Naples. Ottavio's and Leandro's fathers are away, leaving their sons in the care of guardians — Scapino and Sylvestro. Ottavio marries Giacinta and when he learns that his father plans to 'marry him off' he seeks Scapino's help. The spirit of the play is evident at the outset, when a slapstick sequence is accompanied by a crazy song made up from the menu at an Italian restaurant.

The Scarlet Letter. Play. Phyllis Nagy, adapted from the novel by Nathaniel Hawthorne
M4 (20s, 50s) F3 (20s, 30). Various simple settings. Fee code M

The setting is Boston, Massachusetts, 300 years ago, a puritanical world dominated by religious obsession, superstition and secrecy. Hester Prynne, a convicted adultress, will not reveal the identity of the father of her curious, illegitimate daughter, Pearl. Her bitter husband, Chillingworth, plots a wicked revenge which leads him to the guilt-ridden minister, Dimmesdale. A symbolic and tragic depiction of the human response to love, sin, betrayal and repression.
ISBN 0 573 69529 6

The Scarlet Pimpernel. Play. Baroness Orczy adapted by Beverley Cross
M17 F3, doubling possible. Various interior and exterior settings. Fee code M

This swashbuckling tale of English aristocrats rescuing their French brethren from the jaws of Madame la Guillotine in revolution-torn, eighteenth-century France has something for everyone — humour, adventure and just a dash of romance! Beverley Cross's spectacular adaptation was seen at Chichester and subsequently at the Theatre Royal, London, starring Donald Sinden. 'It is a long time since the theatre saw an adventure so joyous ... a stunning adaptation ... an evening of simple but unalloyed theatre magic.' *Daily Telegraph*
ISBN 0 573 01650 X

A Scent of Flowers. Play. James Saunders
M7 F2. A room. Fee code M

A girl has died in deep distress, and as the priest and the undertaker's men proceed with burial, she is present on stage. Imagine Zoe's first real brush with life, perplexed, afraid, alone. To whom should she turn? Her family, her friends, her priest? They offer the help they deem necessary, not that which her need demands. None of them realize that interest, concern, even love, are not the same as compassion and charity. Although it is a poignant story, the dialogue is unsentimental, often grimly comic.

The School for Wives. Comedy. Molière. Freely adapted by Miles Malleson from *L'École des Femmes*
M6 F2. Inside and outside a house. Fee code M

Arnolphe has selected as his wife the charming, innocent Agnes, his ward, whom he trusts will not succumb to the prevailing vice of infidelity. But Agnes falls in love with Horace, whose father, Oronte, is Arnolphe's friend. Oronte, delighted at the romance, confides to Arnolphe that the young lady is bedevilled by a tyrannical guardian. Furious, Arnolphe plans to remove Agnes to a safer place but the lovers are united in the end. Period 1660
ISBN 0 573 01399 3

Schweyk in the Second World War. Play. Bertolt Brecht
Translations: William Rowlinson, music by Hanns Eisler
                 Susan Davies
M12 F3. Numerous simple sets. Fee code M for play, code C for music

Brecht transposes Jaroslav Hasek's satirical 'hero' from World War I to the Prague of Hitler and Heydrich. Schweyk gets out of awkward situations in his farcical adventures by a combination of cheek and guile. Eventually he is sent to fight the Russians at Stalingrad, and on the way he meets an equally lost Hitler who asks him if he knows the way back. Interludes show Goering, Goebbels and others assuring Hitler of the loyalty and devotion of the Little Man.

The Scottish Play. Play. Graham Holliday
M6 F7. Various simple interiors. Fee code L

Michael has always harboured an ambition to direct *Macbeth*, so when he is offered the autumn production by the Shellsfoot Thespians he seizes his opportunity. He encounters problems, of course, from finding enough men, to telling *grande dame* Geraldine that he doesn't want her as Lady Macbeth, despite being offered a bribe that would pay production costs. The theatrical jinx surrounding the play extends to amateur productions and Michael's life, too. A witty, humorous play, totally true to life, which was first broadcast on BBC Radio.
ISBN 0 573 01679 8

The Sea. Comedy. Edward Bond
M7 F7. Extras M and F. Composite setting: a beach, a shop, a house, a cliff. Fee code M

The Sea is a comedy set in an East Coast village in 1907. The action centres around the drowning of a young man and the repercussions, emotional and political, it has on the tight, inward-looking village community.

The Seagull. Comedy. Anton Chekhov, translated by David Iliffe
M7 F6. Two interiors, two exteriors. Fee code H. Period 1894
ISBN 0 573 01400 0

◆ **The Seagull.** Play. Anton Chekhov. A new version by Tom Stoppard
M7 F5. Various interior and exterior settings. Fee code M

Tom Stoppard made this English version for the Peter Hall Company at the Old Vic. Here, amid 'the weariness of life in the country', the famous actress Arkadina presides over a household riven with desperate love, with dreams of success and dread of failure. Her son, Konstantin, shoots a seagull; the novelist, Trigorin, will one day write the seagull's story; but it is Nina, 'the seagull' herself, whose life to come will rewrite the story. Period early 1900s

Season's Greetings. Play. Alan Ayckbourn
M5 (20, 30, 40, 60) F4 (30s). Composite setting: a hall, a dining-room, a sitting-room. Fee code M

Half a dozen relatives and friends are celebrating Christmas with Neville and Belinda. Petty, and not so petty, squabbles break out. Christmas presents are rifled, mechanical toys are set off. Hilarious highlights include a chaotically incompetent puppet show and a midnight love scene that goes wrong. A final climax leads to what momentarily appears to be a tragedy as Clive, mistaken for a looter, is shot by the trigger-happy Harvey.
ISBN 0 573 11401 3

Second from Last in the Sack Race. Play. Michael Birch, from the novel by David Nobbs
M20 F12, 2M or F. Can be played by M3 F2. Various simple interior and exterior settings. Fee code M

This play traces the ups and downs in he life of Henry Pratt. Born in 1935 Henry's childhood is disrupted first by war, then by the death of his mother and father. Henry is packed off to prep school and then public school and then lives with grown-up cousin Hilda. The play ends in 1953, as he begins his National Service. David Nobbs is well known as a TV writer of quality and this play was screened under the title *Life and Times of Henry Pratt.*
ISBN 0 573 01900 2

The Second Mrs Tanqueray. Drama. Arthur W. Pinero
M7 F4. A sitting-room, a morning-room, a drawing-room. Fee code M

Aubrey Tanqueray willingly withdraws from London society to marry his second wife, for Paula Ray has had a notorious past. She has all the warmth that Aubrey's first wife lacked. But in the country, ostracized by the respectable, their relationship becomes intolerably strained. Paula realizes that her past will always harm those she loves. Even before Aubrey is told of Paula's suicide he curses men of his class who wreak such incalculable harm merely by leading a 'man's life'. Period 1893
ISBN 0 573 01402 7

The Secret Diary of Adrian Mole Aged 13¾. Play with music. Sue Townsend. Songs by Ken Howard and Alan Blaikley
M7 F6, doubling possible. 1 boy 2 girls. Extras. Various interior settings. Fee code M

Adapted by Sue Townsend from her bestseller, this satirical comedy of adolescent manners follows the efforts of a spotty teenager to make sense of the erratic behaviour of the adults around him. The disintegration of his parents' marriage, threats from the local bully, first love pains and spots are a series of minor tragedies he must cope with in the transition from puberty to manhood.

The Secret Rapture. Play. David Hare
M2 (30s, 40s) F4 (20s, 30s). Various simple settings. Fee code M

In David Hare's 'greatest play' (*City Limits*) two sisters, Isobel, a serene and good person, and Marion, an ambitious Tory Junior Minister, gather at the home of their late father for his funeral. Katherine, the sisters' young, alcoholic, stepmother announces her intention of joining Isobel's design company. Reluctantly Isobel agrees and this act paves the way for tragedy and disaster involving Isobel's lover Irwin, and Marion's evangelical, earnest husband Tom.
ISBN 0 573 11408 0

The Secretary Bird. Comedy. William Douglas Home
M2 (middle-age) F3 (young, middle-age). A living-room. Fee code J

After over twelve years of seemingly happy marriage to her somewhat older husband, Liz suddenly announces she has fallen for John and wants a divorce. Apparently acquiescing, Hugh says he will provide the grounds. Everything seems set for a calm passage until it turns out that the plan includes Hugh's pretty secretary as co-respondent and that the action is to take place in their own home! A long-running West End hit.
ISBN 0 573 01387 X

See How They Run! Farce. Philip King
M6 (20-40, middle-age) F3 (18, 20, 30). A lounge-hall. Fee code M

The Rev. Lionel Toop's wife, Penelope, is an ex-actress. While Lionel is away Clive, an actor, calls. He invites Penelope to dine in town which is out of bounds to servicemen. He dresses in Lionel's blacks. Miss Skillon, a parishioner, sees the couple repeating one of their theatrical scenes and draws the wrong conclusion. Matters become highly complicated when Lionel arrives, followed by the Bishop of Lax and a German POW disguised as a vicar! Period 1947
ISBN 0 573 01403 5

Semi-Detached. Play. David Turner
M5 F4. Split set. Fee code J

The characters are not naturalistic portraits but rather caricatures of contemporary types. As in the older comedies their names suggest their identities (Midway, Makepiece, Freeman, etc). The model Midland householder, Fred Midway, sedulously climbing the business and social ladders, self-educated by correspondence courses, with his material yardstick, his oratory, self-knowledge and pathetic faith in himself, provides a brilliant centre to a highly entertaining and satiricial play.
ISBN 0 573 11456 0

A

Separate Tables. Two plays. Terence Rattigan
M3 F8. A dining-room, a lounge. Fee code M. Each play fee code F when performed separately

The typical South Coast Hotel Beauregarde is peopled by the old, the lonely and the indigent. The manageress, Miss Cooper, is unable to remain aloof from their troubles. In *Table No. 1* she attempts to help John Malcolm and his ex-wife Ann, who have ruined each other, find salvation together. In *Table No. 2* Major Pollock and Miss Railton-Bell are misfits and their despair draws them together. Miss Cooper gives them the courage to face life.
ISBN 0 573 01404 3

Separation. Play. Tom Kempinski
M1(40) F1 (20). Split set. Fee code M

Joe Green is a fat, unsociable, unproductive, phobia-ridden writer whose one hit play is the subject of a transatlantic phone call from a New York actress, suffering from a paralysing disease, who wants to perform it. They become friends over the phone but when she arrives in London Joe's neurotic terrors almost, but not quite, kill the love affair completely. Funny, tender and completely captivating, the play was seen at Hampstead and the Comedy Theatres with David Suchet and Saskia Reeves.
ISBN 0 573 01677 1

September in the Rain. Play. John Godber
M1 F1. A bare stage. Fee code M

This play, together with its companion, *Happy Jack*, is described by the author as 'autobiographical, but not in the strict sense. Both plays are about my grandparents and chronicle their lives. All the incidents are based on fact — they were the myths of my childhood.' Their marriage is explored with great pathos and humour and '... transmitted with a directness that touches the heart ...' *Guardian*

September Tide. Play. Daphne du Maurier. Revised version by Mark Rayment
M3 (20s, middle-age) F3 (20s, middle-age). A living-room. Fee code M

In a Cornish house lives the widowed Stella, a woman of considerable gifts and beauty who regularly rejects proposals of marriage from her neighbour Robert Hanson. Cherry, Stella's daughter, brings home her artist husband Evan for the first time and Stella is shocked by the bohemian incompleteness of their marriage. She finds herself attracted to Evan and soon they are passionately in love: although much is left unspoken, Evan eventually compels Stella to admit her feelings. Period 1950s
0 573 01905 3

Serious Money. City comedy. Caryl Churchill. Songs by Ian Dury, Micky Gallacher and Chas Jankel
M14 F6, may be played by M5 F3. Extras. Various simple interior and exterior settings. Fee code M

Set post-Big Bang 1980s in the Square Mile, the action centres on a takeover bid led by the ruthless Billy Corman. When cartel member Jake Todd dies amidst the amassing of a fortune, his sister, Scilla, investigates his murder, initially from curiosity but later from greed. Churchill's witty dialogue is complemented by two songs with bawdily-satiric lyrics by Ian Dury. NB. This play contains explicit language.
ISBN 0 573 01711 5

The Servant of Two Masters. Comedy. Adapted by David Turner and Paul Lapworth from the original by Carlo Goldoni
M8 F3. Extras. A room. Fee code M

Goldoni skilfully adapted the *commedia dell'arte* pattern to his own very funny plots, and the most famous is this play wherein the story concerns the terrible complications wrought by Truffaldino when he gets himself engaged as a servant by two different people at the same time. The plot sparkles with invention and this adaptation in the modern idiom brilliantly matches the spirit of the play.
ISBN 0 573 11412 9

Shadowlands. Play. William Nicholson
M11 F2, may be played by M7 F2. 1 boy. Various simple settings. Fee code M

Nicholson's stage adaptation of his award-winning TV play relates the story of shy Oxford don and children's author C. S. Lewis and poet Joy Davidman in academic Oxford in the 1950s. Their relationship starts as an exchange of literary correspondence. When Joy arrives in Oxford her intellectual assertiveness delights Lewis but appalls his condescending fellow academics, who are further shocked when Lewis goes through a marriage of convenience with her for immigration purposes.
ISBN 0 573 01894 4

She Stoops to Conquer. Comedy. Oliver Goldsmith
M8 (young, 20s, 60s) F3 (young, 20s, 50s). Extras. Two interiors, one exterior. No fee

Mr Hardcastle and Sir Charles Marlow have arranged a match between Miss Kate Hardcastle and young Marlow. The fun arises when Marlow is directed to the Hardcastles' house rather than a neighbouring inn, and mistakes Hardcastle for the landlord and Kate for one of the servants. Period 1700s.
ISBN 0 573 01413 2

She Was Only an Admiral's Daughter ... Comedy. Harold Brooke and Kay Bannerman
M4 (young) F2 (young, middle-age). An apartment. Fee code K
ISBN 0 573 01560 0

Shirley Valentine. Play. Willy Russell
F1. A kitchen, a beach. Fee code M

Underneath Mrs Joe Bradshaw — 42-year-old mother of two grown-up children — there is the former Shirley Valentine longing to get out. Her feminist friend offers her a free holiday in Greece and she seizes the opportunity. Shirley, breaking out of the mould cast for her by society, is brilliantly shown with humour, warm sympathy and human insight. 'In this play [Mr Russell] touches English audiences directly in a way that no other playwright has done since the early John Osborne ... brilliantly funny ...' *The Times*.
ISBN 0 573 03102 9

Shock! Thriller. Brian Clemens
M4 (20s-40s) F3 (young, 30s). A converted windmill. Fee code L

Maggie lives in a converted windmill, to which her lover, Terry, and Maggie's friend Ann are coming to celebrate her birthday. Maggie has some peculiar tastes, including tape-recording the most private intimacies between herself and her lovers. This indulgence soon causes consternation among the visitors, culminating in the death of Ann's fiancé. A second horror is the discovery that Maggie has been murdered. A final twist proves the relevance of the play's title.
ISBN 0 573 11410 2

Shock Tactics. Farce. John Dole
M6 (20s, middle-age, 50s) F5 (10, 20s, 40s, 50s). A living-room. Fee code K

Fred is a home-built computer given to uttering loud and embarrassing remarks at inopportune moments. He all but ruins the courtship of his owner's daughter, but does have his uses: he is able to forecast the weather with complete accuracy. News of this reaches the Met. Office, who send a spy posing as a believer in the occult to infiltrate the Shaw household, while Uncle Ben finds out if Fred can predict the winner of the 3.30.

Shut Your Eyes and Think of England. Comedy. John Chapman and Anthony Marriott
M6 (40s-50s) F3 (young, early middle-age). A penthouse apartment. Fee code M

This hilarious, smash-hit West End comedy starred Frank Thornton and Donald Sinden. When Mr Pullen comes into the office on Saturday to finish the books for the audit he is astonished to find his employer, Sir Justin Holbrook, in the penthouse flat with a call-girl. As the day progresses and new arrivals include Lady Holbrook, Mrs Pullen and a very influential Arab sheik events lead to an impenetrable maze of confused identities.
ISBN 0 573 11411 0

♦ **Silas Marner**. Play. Adapted by Geoffrey Beevers from the novel by George Eliot
M14 F6. Extras. May be played by M4 F3. Various simple settings. Fee code M

The story of Silas Marner, reclusive miser transformed by the arrival of a young girl, is one of the most memorable and moving in Victorian literature. This adaptation captures the novel's thirty-year sweep in a series of telling scenes, each displaying Eliot's gifts for humour, insight, narrative and simple beauty. The twenty named parts can be played by a cast of seven with a minimum of costume changes and props. Period: c.1830-1860
ISBN 0 573 01912 6

♦ **Silhouette**. Play. Simon Brett
M5 (30, 35, middle-age) F3 (young, middle-age) or M4 F2. A sitting-room and study. Fee code M

In Act I of this ingeniously-structured thriller, Detective Inspector Bruton questions actress Celia Wallis about the murder of her husband Martin. Celia is quite obviously in the clear, but Neville Smallwood, the drunken journalist sleeping in her bed, argued with Martin shortly before the murder, and the solution to the initial puzzle seems simple. Act II takes place *before* the murder, and all our expectations, of the characters as well as of the plot, are turned on their heads.
ISBN 0 573 01877 4

♦ **Silly Cow**. Play. Ben Elton
M3 (21, middle-age, old) F2 (young, 40s). A living-room. Fee code M

Doris Wallis, tough tabloid columnist, has just won a libel case brought by an actress she insulted. Just as she starts celebrating, things begin to go wrong. Her TV treatment is missing, her pal Sidney is out to get her for her double-crossing him, her accountant is about to grass on her ... To her shock and horror, Doris discovers that the actors she had defamed in her column can indeed act. NB. This play contains explicit language.
ISBN 0 573 01875 8

Sing On! Comedy musical. Rick Abbot
M4 F7. A stage. Fee code M

Here is the long-awaited sequel to Rick Abbot's hilarious *Play On!* in which the same disaster-prone theatre group find themselves in dire straits and need to do yet another show by the redoubtable Phyllis (with songs by her hobbyist-songwriter nephew Monte) to win a theatre-saving $10,000 endowment. The musical numbers have been designed so that your cast need *not* be able to sing, just carry a tune. The music for this show is available separately.
ISBN 0 573 69271 8

Single Spies. Double bill (**An Englishman Abroad** and **A Question of Attribution**). Alan Bennett
Fee code M as a double bill

An Englishman Abroad (originally a television play), is based on a true incident in the life of the actress Coral Browne and tells the witty and touching story of her meeting with Guy Burgess in Moscow in 1958. In *A Question of Attribution*, 'an inquiry in which the circumstances are imaginary but the pictures are real', Anthony Blunt, Surveyor of the Queen's Pictures, tries to solve the riddle of an enigmatic painting and is himself the subject of a more official investigation.
ISBN 0 573 01891 X

An Englishman Abroad.
M4 (20s, 40s, 50s) F1 (40s). A flat. Fee code F if performed separately

A Question of Attribution.
M5 (20s, 40s, 50s) F1 (40s). An office, a corridor. Fee code G if performed separately

Sister Mary Ignatius Explains It All For You and **The Actor's Nightmare.**

A double-bill by Christopher Durang. Fee code M as a double bill. For separate fee codes see below

Sister Mary Ignatius Explains It All For You.
M2 (30s) F3 (30s, 50s). 1 boy (8). A lecture platform. Fee code J

The play opens with a long lecture on Roman Catholicism by Sister Mary, starting conventionally but growing in morbidity and even horror as it proceeds. The lecture is interrupted by four of her ex-students, who present a religious 'pageant', then reveal how far they have strayed from her teaching. A climax is reached in an emotional statement of the truth from Diane, leading to the violence of two deaths by shooting. Playing time approximately 75 minutes

The Actor's Nightmare.
M2 (20s, 30s) F3 (20s, 30s). An empty stage. Fee code E

George wanders on stage and is met by stage manager Meg, who says he is to fill in for an actor who has had an accident. George is confused as Ellen Terry, Sarah Siddons and Henry Irving arrive, all apparently about to perform. But what in? *Private Lives*? *Hamlet*? Or something by Beckett? As each starts playing his or her respective part George tries valiantly to follow them, but is apparently facing the Executioner as Thomas More in *A Man for All Seasons*.

The Sisterhood. Play. Molière, translated and adapted by R. R. Bolt
M5 (young, middle-age) F5 (young, middle-age), doubling possible. A salon in Paris. Fee code L

This audacious adaptation of *Les Femmes Savantes*, Molière's mischievious farce indicting the intellectual ladies of the salons, is full of contemporary allusions. Henriette has had the misfortune to be born into a family of pontificating pseudo-intellectual women. Her only desire is to get married and to live in 'wedded bliss'. The quirks of the cultural snobs are ridiculed while Henriette gets her man.
ISBN 0 573 01681 X

Sisterly Feelings. A related comedy. Alan Ayckbourn
M8 (20s, 30s, 50s, 60s, 70s) F4 (20s, 40s). A small hill. Fee code M

There are four possible versions of this play, each version a complete play in itself. Sisters Dorcas and Abigail are faced with a dilemma and decide to toss for it. The result is that one of them goes with Simon. Later Dorcas has a deliberate choice. One decision leads to a night under the canvas for Abigail, the other to a day at the races for Dorcas. The inevitable end of either choice is a wedding.
ISBN 0 573 11420 X

The Sisters Rosensweig. Play. Wendy Wasserstein
M4 (17,40, 58) F4 (17, 40s, 50s). A sitting-room. Fee code M

The sisters Rosensweig are three extraordinary Brooklyn-born Jewish women. Sara lives an ostensibly happy, man-free life in London with her intelligent daughter, Tess. Pfeni is an eccentric travel writer who pursues an unsatisfactory relationship with Geoffrey, a bisexual theatre director. And Gorgeous has the perfect husband and family in Massachusetts, where she pursues a 'funsy' career as a radio agony aunt. When they meet up at Sara's home in Holland Park reawakened familial bonds cause each woman to confront her past and her future.
ISBN 0 573 01908 8

Situation Comedy. Comedy. Johnnie Mortimer and Brian Cooke
M3 (30s, middle-age) F3 (40s, middle-age). Composite setting: two living-rooms. Fee code M

Charles Summerskill and Arthur Grey are two sit-com writers with writer's block and a looming deadline for a new TV series. When the Summerskills invite the Greys round one evening, Arthur goes armed with his home-made pea wine and as the repellent vino flows, tempers rise and by next morning they have swapped wives. This provides an idea for a sit-com series, or at least it would if they could agree on an ending. Their frantic efforts to find one are moments of hysterical farce.

Ski Whizz. Comedy. Richard Ingham
M3 (20s, 30s) F3 (20s, 30s, middle-age). The hall of an Austrian pension. Fee code L

It is opening day at Ernst Edelbaum's hotel and already things are going wrong. His English niece turns out to be Leslie, a male punk, most of his guests don't arrive and the tour company are about to discover that his required wife doesn't exist. As for the guests, they all have their own problems ... But this hilarious farce, complete with man in drag and indoor tobogganing, ends happily of course.
ISBN 0 573 01895 2

The Skin of Our Teeth. Play. Thornton Wilder
M5 (young, middle-age) F5 (young, middle-age). Small parts and extras. A living-room, one exterior. Fee code M

Down through the ages the Antrobus family have survived. They are indestructible. Antrobus invented the alphabet, the multiplication table, the lever and the wheel, and Mrs Antrobus invented the apron. Their beginnings are to be found in the Garden of Eden, although they speak in the accents of New Jersey. They are humanity, and whatever happens, they survive all catastrophes — by the skin of their teeth.
ISBN 0 573 61548 9

Skirmishes. Play. Catherine Hayes
F3 (30s, old). A bedroom. Fee code L

An old lady is dying. At her bedside sits her eldest daughter, Jean, who has nursed her throughout. When the younger sister, Rita, arrives the daughters angrily bicker and bait each other, gradually revealing the miserable unhappiness of their own lives. Jean gives vent to her feelings with biting, black humour and sarcasm, berating Rita, who has remained deaf to entreaties for help nursing the mother. The ultimate schism comes with the mother's final outburst, denouncing Jean and telling Rita all will be left to her.

◆ **Skylight**. Play. David Hare
M2 (18, 50) F1 (30). A living-room/kitchen area. Fee code M

Kyra Hollis is a dedicated teacher in a run-down east London school. Tom Sergeant is a successful businessman. When young, Kyra worked for Tom and his wife Alice, became part of the family, and then Tom's lover for six passionate years, finally severing all connections with the family when Alice discovered the affair. Now, a year after Alice's death, Tom's son Edward unexpectedly arrives at Kyra's flat seeking help for his father who cannot cope. Tom also visits Kyra but what is it he seeks?
ISBN 0 573 01876 6

Slapstick Tragedy. Tennessee Williams

The Gnädiges Fräulein. Tragicomedy

M3 (old) F3 (middle-age). Porch and exterior of a frame cottage. Fee code M if performed as *Slapstick Tragedy* or G if performed alone

The Fräulein earns her keep in the bunkhouse for 'transient residents' by trying to catch the fish thrown up by hurricanes, but is frustrated by the jealousy of the Cocaloony, a bird of prey rather like a giant pelican. This and other aspects of the interplay between the strange and odd-looking characters form a nightmarish fantasy open to many different forms of interpretation veering between the comic and the tragic.

The Mutilated. Play

M9 (middle-age) F4 (50s). Extras. A bedroom, with several other skeletal sets. Fee code M if performed as *Slapstick Tragedy* or G if performed alone

Together with *The Gnädiges Fräulein* (q.v.) this forms a double-bill known as *Slapstick Tragedy*. It is Christmas Eve and the carollers are singing. In and around a seedy New Orleans hotel two whores, one a shoplifter, the other morbidly sensitive about having had a breast removed, quarrel and make up in their wretched companionship. The implication is that all of us suffer in one way or another.

Slaughterhouse. Play. Norman Robbins
M4 (30s-60s) F6 (30s-60s). A drawing-room. Fee code L

Ageing horror star Romney Marsh has gathered together a group of theatre people in his great
country house. Once the guests realize they are actually trapped, it is revealed that someone has
been blackmailing Romney. Shortly thereafter one of the guests is found with her throat cut, and
afterwards Romney is poisoned by one of his own chocolates. Marooned in the house, the finger
of suspicion is pointed at each guest until the final truth is revealed with fatal consequences.
ISBN 0 573 01896 0

The Sleeping Prince. Occasional fairy tale. Terence Rattigan
M7 (16, 40s, 60s) F5 (15, 20s, 40s, 50s). A reception room. Fee code H

The Regent, the Grand Duke Charles, intends to spend the eve of the coronation with a chorus-
girl, but when Mary Morgan arrives the liaison turns out to be a disastrous failure. Mary realizes
what loveless and lonely lives these aristocrats lead, and the Regent responds to Mary's naïve
philosophy that everything can be solved by adding more love to life. They fall deeply in love —
but even fairy tales must have an end. Period 1911
ISBN 0 573 01421 3

Sleuth. Play. Anthony Shaffer
M2 (30s, 50s). A living-room. Fee code M

Your programme for this play will list five names for five roles, but the actual cast will be two, for
no-one is ever what he seems in this brilliant whodunit, where every event is bizarre. The scene is
set in a beautiful English country house owned by a famous mystery writer. A young guest arrives
and they begin a convivial round of scotch and dialogue. Suddenly the host says 'I understand you
want to marry my wife' and from that moment the two are locked in mortal combat.

Small Change. Play. Peter Gill
M2 (young) F2 (middle-age). An open stage. Fee code M

The play is a study, set mainly on the east side of Cardiff, of the relationships between two boys —
their relationship to each other and to their respective mothers, and how these conflicting attachments
affect them through life. It is non-naturalistic except for the dialogue, and none of the characters
leaves the stage throughout. The 'scenes' are linked by monologues from all four.
ISBN 0 573 01709 3

Small Craft Warnings. Play. Tennessee Williams
M7 (20s, middle-age, 40s) F2 (30s). A bar. Fee code M

This is an expanded version of the author's one-act play *Confessional*. In a seedy bar on the
Californian coast a group of misfits, 'a fairly raffish bunch', grapple with existence and survival,
quarrelling among themselves. Periodically the lights lower, and a spotlit character speaks as if to
him or herself.

A Small Family Business. Play. Alan Ayckbourn
M7 (20s-40s, 70s) F6 (16, 20s-50s). Composite setting. Fee code M

When Jack, honest and upright, takes over as managing director of the family furniture business,
he finds that his managerial skills are no match for the wholesale fraud, deceit and theft which he
uncovers both in the business and amongst his family. He succumbs almost at once to blackmail
because of his daughter, but this is only the first in a series of moral compromises he is forced to
make.
ISBN 0 573 01669 0

The Small Hours. Play. Francis Durbridge
M5 (young, 30s-50s) F3 (30s). An aircraft, a living-room. Fee code M

What do a Koala bear, a devious chef, and an emerald necklace have in common? Carl Houston, Sussex hotelier, nearly loses his life finding out in this thriller of international intrigue which bears all the Durbridge hallmarks of suspense, mystery and murder and which enjoyed a successful national tour in 1991 starring Patrick Mower. '... well-crafted with a proper sense of dramatic climaxes and some very good scenes ... It all adds up to a very good evening's theatre ...' *Birmingham Post*
ISBN 0 573 01897 9

Smelling a Rat. Play. Mike Leigh
M3 (young, 30, middle-age) F2 (young, 30s). A bedroom. Fee code M

Loathsome *nouveau-riche* tycoon Rex Weasel returns unexpectedly from holiday. When he hears his underling, the garrulous Vic and his wife, coming in to check on the flat as arranged, Rex hides in a cupboard to eavesdrop on the pair, who later also hide in another cupboard as Rex's near-catatonic son and lisping girlfriend arrive in search of sex (which is never realized). Various home truths spill out whilst these 'skeletons' are hiding.

The Sneeze. Plays and stories by Anton Chekov, translated and adapted by Michael Frayn
M4 F3, minimum cast. Extras 2M. Various simple settings. Fee code M. (Please apply to Samuel French Ltd for details of the fee codes for individual items)

This is a marvellous collection of four one-act comic 'vaudevilles' together with four adapted short stories, with Michael Frayn's fresh, idiomatic and playable translations staying close to the spirit of the original. 'Frayn's well chosen and smoothly translated *melange* comes from recognizing in some of these characters similarities with characters one encounters in the later masterpieces.' *Daily Telegraph*

So What Do We Do about Henry? Play. Charlotte Hastings
M3 (30s, 60) F5 (25, 30, 50, 60). A cottage living-room. Fee code L

When Henrietta Ellis's companion dies she moves in with her nephew Dino and his girlfriend Elsie. Once Henrietta has settled in at the cottage she starts, in the nicest possible way, to organize the lives of those around her — the old Admiral, the meek new Vicar, Elsie's sister Delia and of course, Dino himself — enabling them all to realize their full potential, and fulfilling her own at the same time.
ISBN 0 573 11407 2

The Soft September Air. Play. Charlotte Hastings
M4 (21, middle-age) F6 (young, late 20s, 30, 58, 60). A living-room, a bar, a casualty department. Fee code L

Lindsey takes in boarding students for the local University. Gradually she gets involved in their problems — the solid, practical Chris gives her little trouble; the febrile, father-hating, guitar-playing Dickon causes more upheaval, but wins her heart with his warmth and sympathy. Just as she thinks she's free from them all, another student appears at the window, and it looks as if she will be starting all over again.
ISBN 0 573 11423 4

Some Sunny Day. Play. Martin Sherman
M4 (20s, 30s, 50s) F2 (40s). A sitting-room and hallway. Fee code M

Cairo, 1942. As war rages in the desert, cultures collide in the city and six individuals struggle to come to terms with love, lust and fate in an alien country. In a *melange* of Mozart, Carmen Miranda, Vera Lynn, Dixieland and cries from the minarets as the muezzins call the men to prayer, this witty and audacious play inhabits a world where everyone has something to hide and anyone may be a spy.

Someone Waiting. Play. Emlyn Williams
M4 (20, 40, 50) F5 (30s, 40, 60). A drawing-room. Fee code M

Martin's best friend Paul has been wrongfully hanged for murdering a girl in his adoptive father's flat. When he fails his law exams Fenn, a private tutor, arrives and confides to Martin that he is Paul's father and together they determine to discover the true murderer. Period 1956

Someone Who'll Watch Over Me. Play. Frank McGuinness
M3 (young, elderly). A bare cell. Fee code M

An Englishman, an Irishman and an American are locked up together in a cell in the Middle East. As victims of political action, powerless to initiate change, what can they do? How do they live and survive? Frank McGuinness explores the daily crises endured by hostages whose strength comes from communication, both subtle and mundane, from humour, wit and faith. (*Available England, Scotland and Wales only*)

Something to Remember You By. Play. Jimmie Chinn
M2 (30s, 40s) F3 (30s, 40s, 50s). Various simple settings. Fee code M

Enter the strange and lonely world of Armstrong Armstrong. Struggling to become a writer, convinced he is ugly and scarred, he can find escape only at the cinema and in his absent father's collection of records. Meeting Venetia, the very image of his favourite female singer, Armstrong begins to believe that happiness is possible for him, but disillusionment soon sets in and he has to find a more intense form of escapism — becoming his icon herself.
ISBN 0 573 01872 3

Son of Man. Play. Dennis Potter
M15 F2. Extras. Various simple settings on an open stage. Fee code L

Here Jesus is portrayed as a man agonized by the feeling of divinity within him, and with all a man's capacity for suffering and pain. The play also examines the historical and political situation in which the events occurred. Very simple to stage and suitable for production on stage or in church. Period New Testament
ISBN 0 573 16004 X

Spanish Lies. Play. Frank Vickery
M3 F4. An hotel terrace. Fee code L

Hoping to revive their flagging marriage — and celebrate twenty-five years together — Dougie takes Lorna back to their honeymoon hotel in Majorca. The hotel is still managed by the same couple and Lorna is reminded of her liaison with Miguel, the hotel owner and local Romeo. Out of the memories of Lorna, Miguel and his 'wife', Regietta, step their younger selves to re-enact the events of twenty-five years ago and we eavesdrop on earlier decisions with the knowledge of what happens later!
ISBN 0 573 01903 7

Speed-the-Plow. Play. David Mamet
M2 (40s) F1 (20). Gould's office, Gould's home. Fee code M

Produced at the National Theatre in 1989 after a successful run in New York, this play is a satirical and sparklingly funny vision of Hollywood back-stabbing. It centres around Charlie Fox, a producer, and Bobby Gould, studio head of production, and a major film deal involving a well-known actor. It is through the language that Mamet depicts the self-doubts and vulnerabilty that lies behind the self-congratulatory back-slapping. Fast-paced, full of witty one-liners and guaranteed to keep the audience mesmerized.

Spider's Web. Play. Agatha Christie
M8(30-50, 60) F2 (30). 1 girl (12). A drawing-room. Fee code M

When a murder occurs in Clarissa's drawing-room she suspects young step-daughter Pippa. Things are not helped by the imminent arrival of husband Henry with a VIP in tow who might take a dim view of bodies in the drawing-room. However, by the time Henry gets home, the murderer has been unmasked and all is normal, so normal that Henry is utterly unable to believe Clarissa when she explains exactly why there are no refreshments ready for their honoured guest.
ISBN 0 573 01427 2

Spokesong. Play with music. Stewart Parker. Music by Jimmy Kennedy
M4 (young, elderly) F2 (young). Composite interior. Fee code M

Set in and around a bicycle shop in Belfast, Northern Ireland, Frank believes that all the world's transportation problems can be solved if people simply switch to the bicycle. Songs are used to comment upon the action. The bicycle and the shop become a metaphor about the problems in Northern Ireland and, indirectly, about the problems of modern civilization. Period 1970s and the eighty years preceding.

Spring, 1600. Comedy. Emlyn Williams
M13 (20-50) F6 (20s, elderly) 1 boy. Extras. Some doubling possible. Part of a dining-hall, a bed-chamber. Fee code M. Copies available on hire

Ann runs off to London disguised as a young man. Once there she joins Burbage's company of actors. However she soon finds herself in love with Burbage and unable to reveal her true identity. By the end of the play Ann comes to terms with her unrequited love and a very influential and important new patron has been found, in the person of Elizabeth of England! Period 1600

Spring and Port Wine. Comedy. Bill Naughton
M4 (18, 23, 30, 50) F4 (19, 25, middle-age, 47). Composite setting. Fee code M

Rafe Crompton is not a stern man but has such unswerving integrity that his family is forced to hide slight peccadilloes from him. His daughter Hilda particularly resents this and her refusal to eat a herring which is placed before her at dinner makes the situation explosive. The family is almost broken up before Rafe is made to see the dangers in his attitudes, and they are reunited in an atmosphere more progressive and tolerant.
ISBN 0 573 01550 3

St Joan of the Stockyards. Play. Bertolt Brecht. Translated by Frank Jones, music by Dessau
M11 F3. Extras. Chorus. Numerous simple interior and exterior settings. Fee code M for play,
code C for music

A

In the stockyards and commercial exchanges of modern Chicago, Salvation Army girl Johanna
Dark imagines that the meat-packer king Pierpont Mauler is going to save the falling market and
prevent unemployment. She helps the workers to organize a general strike, and Mauler is persuaded
to lead the meat ring out of its troubles. Johanna, desperately ill, is canonized by Mauler for her
work among the poor, and she vainly denounces the class system as she dies.

Stage Struck. Play. Simon Gray
M3 (20, 30, middle-age) F1 (30). A living-room. Fee code M

Robert's conniving wife concocts a plot to obtain grounds necessary for divorce involving the use
of a private detective. Robert, recalling his days as a stage manager, works out a bizarre method of
teaching them a lesson and the final moments give several grim twists to events as the 'little game'
becomes stark reality.
ISBN 0 573 11414 5

Stages. Play. David Storey
M1 (57) F4 (20s, 30, 56). A bare stage. Fee code M

Stages was premièred at the Royal National Theatre in 1992 starring Alan Bates. Fenchurch,
successful novelist and artist from a northern working-class background suffers a mental breakdown.
He is visited by four women: his daughter, his ex-wife, his neighbour, and his psychiatrist to
whom he recounts his past life. '... Storey's starkly observed portrait of an artist *in extremis* leaves
us as close to the core of this eternal enigma as almost anything I have hitherto seen on any stage.'
Daily Mail

Stags and Hens. Comedy. Willy Russell
M6 (one non-speaking) F5. The ladies' and gents' toilets in a dance hall. Fee code M

Set in the ladies' and gents' toilets of a tacky Liverpool club where Dave and Linda are holding
their respective stag and hen parties. Dave gets legless while Linda meets up with ex-lover Peter
whose worldly wisdom leaves Linda uncertain whether to pursue an unsuitable marriage. An
exuberantly cynical play which is also a perceptive study of working-class misogyny.
ISBN 0 573 01609 7

Staircase. Play. Charles Dyer
M2 (middle-age), 1M voice. A barber's shop. Fee code M

Charles Dyer and Harry C. Leeds have lived together as a homosexual couple for many years.
Charles is terrified at the prospect of a forthcoming court case and fears exposure to his daughter
Cassy, who is soon to visit them. Harry realizes that all the names mentioned in Charles' stories
are anagrams of Charles' own name. Harry will give Charles the strength to face the future, but is
it possible that the people we know and love are only figments of our imaginations — or we of
theirs?
ISBN 0 573 04011 7

The Star-Spangled Girl. Comedy. Neil Simon
M2 (20s) F1 (young). A duplex studio apartment. Fee code M

This fast-moving, hilarious comedy deals with two earnest, fiercely dedicated young men who endure near-starvation to put out a 'protest' magazine in San Francisco, and the all-American girl, Sophie, who moves in next door. She is convinced they are editing a dangerously subversive magazine, and finds that the wrong man is pressing his attentions on her. Happily this situation is reversed in time, as love and politics blend delightfully in a bubbling series of funny happenings.

A State of Affairs. Quartet of plays. Graham Swannell
Fee code M (for whole play)

This comedy quartet, witty and penetrating, treats its theme of adultery and marriage with a moving and unforgettable compassion. 'Sharp, funny and pleasingly idiomatic.' *Financial Times* '... full of pitiless observation and compassionate hilarity.' *Sunday Times*

Stuttgart
M1(30s) F1(30s). A bedroom. Fee code D

Terence's interest in sex has begun to pall. He just doesn't have the energy any longer to satisfy his wife's needs. But how to tell her? He practises in front of a mirror, remembering a wonderful time they had in Stuttgart. Caroline, however, is not prepared to let Terence ease up and manufactures another Stuttgart — thigh-high black boots, sexy underwear and all ...!

Consequences
M1 (40) F2 (30). An hotel bedroom. Fee code D

Jack and Frances are having an affair, meeting each week in a seedy hotel. Frances wants the affair to blossom and confesses to being in love with Jack. He, wanting it to be just a 'ding-dong', backs off, but Frances has told her husband and he has spilled the beans to Milly, Jack's wife. Milly arrives, to be told the affair is over, but will Milly, strong and firm, allow Jack to forget it ... ?

Day of the Dog
M3 (30s) F2 (30s). A pub courtyard. Fee code D

Allen has confided a momentary infidelity to his wife. Instead of the hoped-for respect he has been thrown out. Two beery mates in a sun-drenched pub back garden console him before picking up a couple of sunbathers and leaving Allen to seek solace in his whisky.

Commitment
M1 (30s) F2 (30s). A kitchen. Fee code D

A bickering couple, sitting in their (permanently) half-finished kitchen, exhausted by the demands of child-rearing, wistfully fantasize about their friends 'having fun' when one of the envied friends arrives, shattered by her husband's departure with the couple's nanny.

State of Revolution. Play. Robert Bolt
M20 F5, some doubling possible. Extras. Multiple scenes on an open stage. Fee code M. Period 1910-20
ISBN 0 573 11430 7

A

Steaming. Play. Nell Dunn
M1 F6. The Turkish rest-room of a public baths. Fee code M

First seen at the Theatre Royal, Stratford, London in 1981, transferring to the Comedy Theatre later in the year. Set in a dilapidated Turkish Bath somewhere in the East End of London where five women of all conditions come to bare their bodies, souls and fantasies, *Steaming* is a warm-hearted, often humorous portrayal of women coming to know the nature of each other's lives. '... full of lively, ribald humour.' *Evening Standard* '... a lovely play suffused with affection.' *The Times*

Steel Magnolias. Play. Robert Harling
F6 (19, 25, 40s-60s). Beauty parlour. Fee code M

Hilarious and touching, this play for six women is set in a beauty parlour in Louisiana. Through four scenes spanning three years the staff and customers engage in small-town gossip but we see a deep strength and purposefulness emerge when Shelby — a diabetic — dies following a kidney transplant operation. '...warm-hearted and sentimental ... ' *Guardian*
ISBN 0 573 13010 8

Stepping Out. Comedy. Richard Harris
M1(40s) F9 (1 Black or Asian) (19, 35-50s). Optional extras. A church hall. Fee code M

Stepping Out, which enjoyed a hugely successful West End run and won *Evening Standard* Best Comedy Award for 1984, is a warm and very funny play about the lives of a group of women (and one man) attending a weekly tap-dance class in a dingy North London church hall. As the play progresses, the class's dancing improves to such an extent that by the climax, a grand charity show performance, they have been transformed into triumphant tappers, worthy of any chorus line.
ISBN 0 573 11415 3

Stevie. Play. Hugh Whitemore, from the works of Stevie Smith
M1(youngish) F2 (middle-age to elderly). A sitting-room. Fee code M

The play follows the life and career of the poetess, Stevie Smith. Stevie's tragicomic life is portrayed by means of 'naturalistic' dialogue scenes, by her own reminiscences and comments, and by numerous examples of her poems, spoken mainly by herself but sometimes by the Man who also plays several parts. The passage of time extends from the 1950s to the 1960s, up to her death at the age of sixty-nine, time changes in the simple set being indicated by lighting cues.
ISBN 0 573 11418 8

◆ **The Steward of Christendom**. Play. Sebastian Barry
M5 (13, 18, 20s-30s, 50, 70s) F4 (17, 20-32, 50s) A bare room. Fee code M

Set in Baltinglass, Co. Dublin, in about 1932, *The Steward of Christendom* sees Lear-like Thomas Dunne, ex-Chief Superintendent of the Dublin Metropolitan Police, trying to break free of history and himself. The play took London by storm when it premièred at the Royal Court Theatre Upstairs in March 1995. Since then it has won Sebastian Barry numerous awards. 'An authentic masterpiece ... I venture to suggest that not even O'Casey or Synge wrote better than this.' *Guardian*. Period c. 1932

A Sting in the Tale. Play. Brian Clemens and Dennis Spooner
M3 (30s, 40s) F2 (30s). A study. Fee code M

Two crime-writing playwrights are endeavouring to complete a block-buster to pay off their mounting debts — or are they? As the plot develops they realize their full potential — who better to accomplish the perfect murder than themselves? Forbes's nagging wife, Ann, is the perfect victim. Forbes's partner mistakenly kills their secretary; from here the play twists and turns so much that it is difficult to know who has been murdered and by whom.
ISBN 0 573 01645 3

Straight and Narrow. Comedy. Jimmie Chinn
M4, F3. 1 female voice. A living-room. Fee code M

Nicholas Lyndhurst and Carmel McSharry starred in the smash-hit West End production of this sharply-observed comedy of family life. The cosy domesticity of lovers Bob and Jeff is threatened. Can Bob's family — Lois and Bill, Nona and Arthur and matriarch Vera — rescue the situation? And will Bob be able to tell seemingly ignorant Vera that the straight and narrow is not for her favourite little boy ... ?
ISBN 0 573 01902 9

The Strange Case of Dr Jekyll and Mr Hyde. Play. David Edgar, based on the story by Robert Louis Stevenson
M8 F3, or M7 F3 with doubling. 6 children. Interior and exterior settings. Fee code M

The famous tale of Dr Jekyll, the outwardly respectable and virtuous man whose darker side is given terrifying life in the form of murderous Mr Hyde, has been vividly and thrillingly adapted for the stage. Jekyll and Hyde are played by two actors; as a result, the divisions in Jekyll's character are presented in a compelling and truly theatrical style.

The Strangeness of Others. Play. Nick Ward
M11 F8 or M5 F3, with doubling. London. Fee code M

The author creates a panorama of contemporary London: a city in which a range of individuals — rich, poor, young, old — are locked in a network of shifting relationships. On a bare stage Ward surveys the whole spectrum of human love — from hetero- and homosexual, to brotherly, motherly, adulterous, incestuous and the rest. The play was seen in the Cottesloe auditorium at the National Theatre in 1988.

A Streetcar Named Desire. Play. Tennessee Williams
M6 (28, 30, 35) F6 (25, 30, 1 Black, 1 Mexican). Composite setting. Fee code M

Blanche DuBois comes to live in the slums of Elysian Fields, New Orleans, with her sister Stella and Stella's husband Stanley Kowalski. Blanche enrages Stanley by her airs and affectations, her perpetual reminiscences about her genteel past and her open distaste for his coarse vitality. When he discovers that all her refinement is a mere façade, he has no compunction in destroying Blanche's only hope of salvation, which is to marry his friend Mitch.

Strike Up the Banns. Comedy. Olwen Wymark
M3 (21, 40s, 60s) F3 (20, 40s, 60s). A suburban living-room. Fee code L

Geraldine and Reg, ageing hippies now trapped in Green Belt respectability by Geraldine's domineering mother, Mrs Carmichael, are giving a dinner-party. Geraldine decides to liven up the evening a bit by impersonating Reg's imaginary brother Rollo, a cad and a bounder. When Reg retaliates by dressing up as Rollo's eccentric wife, Lillian, chaos ensues. Olwen Wymark's suburban comedy is a rebel's fantasy, a hostess's nightmare, and a hijinks treat for its audiences.
ISBN 0 573 01898 7

Strippers. Play. Peter Terson
M4 (20s, 30s, middle-age) F6 (20s, 30s, 50s). Various simple settings. Fee code M

Inspired by a television documentary, Peter Terson's play looks at the world of the North-East England strippers, centring on Wendy and Bernard, a young couple whose lives are up-ended when Wendy turns, reluctantly, to stripping to support the family after Bernard is made redundant. Although Bernard quite happily watches the 'exotic dancers' over a couple of pints at the club, when it comes to his wife it's a different matter. '... a play full of humour, concern and affection ...' *The Listener*
ISBN 0 573 01632 1

Suburb of Babylon. Three inter-linked plays. Hugh Leonard
Cast as below. Composite setting: a hall and a living-room. (The basic set remains the same in each play with perhaps a few modifications in the third.) Fee code M (for complete play)

A Time of Wolves and Tigers
M1(40s). M1 or F1 voice only

Jumbo, an alcoholic civil servant, returns home half-drunk. His wife has left him and Jumbo is afraid of the empty house. Seeking reassurance he starts phoning friends, only to discover that he is in trouble at work. Feeling isolated, he manages to contact his wife and persuades her to return home, promising to mend his ways. But Jumbo knows he can never change and the play ends with him trying to come to grips with his fear of his empty house and life.

Nothing Personal
M2 (30s, 40) F1 (30s)

Garrulous suburbanite Phil is taken by Pat, whom he has just met in a pub, to No. 19, the home of Betty, whose husband is interned in the North. Initially, the atmosphere is jovial as they await a fourth member of the party, but it becomes increasingly sinister and Phil realizes he has been kidnapped. He must await the fourth member — and execution.

The Last of the Last of the Mohicans
M3 (40, middle-age) F2 (30s, middle-age). M1 or F1 voice only

In the final play the mood changes to one of hilarious comedy as Dominick, having packed his wife off on retreat to an obscure saint's shrine, is poised to enjoy an adulterous affair with sexy Grace. Grace arrives, followed by Dominick's wife, followed by Grace's husband — a formidable Aer Lingus pilot. Eventually the evening is resolved amicably although not quite how Dominick intended!
ISBN 0 573 11426 9

Successful Strategies. A translation of Marivaux's *L'Heureux Stratagème* by Timberlake Wertenbaker
M5 F3. Exterior settings. Fee code H

A rich, rose-decked Comtesse, turning infidelity into a style, whimsically abandons her lover, Dorante. Instead she takes up with the posturing Chevalier. And, in order to get her revenge, the latter's lover, the Marquise, forms an amorous alliance with Dorante. The surface of wit, elegance and good manners never ceases to shimmer but, beneath it, we are aware of genuine passion, suffering and bewilderment. Running time approximately 90 minutes. Period 1733

Suddenly at Home. Play. Francis Durbridge
M4 (30s-50s) F4 (20s, 30s). A living-room. Fee code M

When Glenn Howard decided to get rid of his wealthy wife he worked out a complicated but seemingly foolproof plan which would not only keep him in the clear but involve his wife's former lover, detective-story writer Sam Blaine. The plan, however, depends on the co-operation of another person, Sheila Wallis, and with the unexpected arrival on the scene of the formidable Remick, things begin to fall apart.
ISBN 0 573 01452 3

Sufficient Carbohydrate. Play. Dennis Potter
M3 (16, 30s, 40s) F2 (30s). A living-room and terrace of a Greek villa. Fee code M

From the start the holiday seems doomed to failure: two senior executives, at daggers drawn over company policy, are holidaying together in a Greek villa with their families ... This play is a masterpiece of stage-craft and human perception. The crisis in the play rests on a bitter conflict of wills between two men, and yet there are episodes of humour, when the play is jolted from its expected track.

The Suicide. Satirical comedy. Nikolai Erdman, translated by Peter Tegel
M11 F5. Extras. Various interior and exterior settings. Fee code M

A brilliant and penetrating satirical comedy about an unemployed 'little man' who contemplates suicide and is besieged by spokespeople of discontented groups, from butchers to intellectuals, who want him to turn his suicide into a gesture on their behalf. As one of the characters says, 'Nowadays only the dead may say what the living think.'

Summer. Play. Hugh Leonard
M4 (18-24, middle-age) F4 (17-23, middle-age). A hillside. Fee code M

Three married couples, accompanied by the son of one and daughter of another, assemble on a hill near Dublin to picnic. During the afternoon the various relationships between them, on the surface and beneath it, become apparent, while the young people regard their elders somewhat sardonically across the generation gap. Six years pass, and the group come together again — but the place has changed, as they have. In their various ways all show the passage of the years.
ISBN 0 573 11431 5

Summer and Smoke. Play. Tennessee Williams
M8 (young, 30, middle-age) F7 (young, 20s, middle-age). 1 girl 1 boy. A park with fountain, a rectory parlour, an office, an arbour. All sets are skeletal on an open stage. Fee code M

Alma, a nervous, ardent spinster, falls in love with John, a dissolute medical student. Though they attempt mutually to bridge the gap in their different natures this proves impossible, even though each in a sense converts the other. John marries a different, more earthy, girl; in the final scene Alma returns to the fountain and picks up a travelling salesman.

A

Summit Conference. Play. Robert David MacDonald
M1 (19) F2. A room. Fee code M

Theatrical invention brings together the mistresses of Hitler and Mussolini in 1941 and, in daringly controversial repartee, they assume the roles of their dictator lovers. An intense atmosphere of political and sexual oppression parallels seemingly innocent worship of movie stars, but reveals the evils of twentieth century idolatry, charting the perverse, cold logic of the Nazi party. Glenda Jackson and Georgina Hale starred in the London production. '... wonderful political comedy ... develops the blueprint to say serious and pertinent things about power, lust and nationalistic endeavour.' *Financial Times*

The Sunshine Boys. Comedy. Neil Simon
M5 (30s, 70s) F2. A flat, an office, an hotel room. Fee code M

An ex-vaudeville team, Al Lewis and Willie Clark, in spite of playing together for forty-three years, have a natural antipathy to one another. CBS-TV wants to make a 'History of Comedy' series which will of course include their act. Will has been doing TV commercials and Al has been happily retired, but they get back together for the series, only for Al to start picking on Willie again.
ISBN 0 573 61596 9

Surprise Package. Farcical comedy. Duncan Greenwood and Derek Parkes
M4 (young, middle-age) F7 (young). A patio. Fee code K

The Tinsley family's package holiday in Spain proves to be an even greater change from Blackpool than expected. To start with, it seems young Ron had persuaded his father to book the same hotel as Gloria, the girl Ron loves despite the disapproval of her mother, who also turns up. Everyone becomes involved in general misunderstandings, and a final surprise shatters everyone.
ISBN 0 573 01585 6

Suspects. Play. Giles Cole
M3 (30s, 40s) F2 (20s, 30s), 1 extra M. A flat. Fee code L

Duels of words and power struggles abound in this tense and thoroughly absorbing thriller. Ellen Stacey brings home Fisher, seemingly a genial insurance salesman, but the shadowy figure in the bedroom has more sinister plans for him than a sales pitch. A double-indemnity insurance policy and the contents of a pill box play their part in this exciting play where each new revelation adds to the overall mystery ...
ISBN 0 573 01899 5

Suspicions. Play. N. J. Crisp
M2 (30s, 40s) F2 (30s). A living-room. Fee code M

Bill announces to his friend and lover, Lucy, that he and his wife, Kate, have decided to separate. The future looks rosy until Lucy's husband arrives and begins to plant seeds of suspicion in Lucy's mind concerning Kate's sudden disappearance. Suddenly the large chest freezer and Kate's abandoned car gain significance until the flamboyant entrance of Kate herself destroys the theory of Bill as a murderer. However, as accusations fly and recriminations grow, speculation turns quickly into reality.
ISBN 0 573 01901 0

Sweeney Todd. Melodrama. C. G. Bond
M8 (young, middle-age, elderly) F3 (middle-age, elderly). Extras. Standing set. Fee code M

In this version of the old melodrama Todd has some grounds for his nefarious activities in that his wife was raped by the Judge, and his daughter abandoned, while he himself was deported on a false charge. He returns to avenge his family, accompanied by a sea captain, Anthony, whose life he has saved. Todd sets up with Mrs Lovett and provides her with fillings for her pies. He proceeds with his vengeful plans, but the outcome is bitterly ironic. Period early nineteenth century
ISBN 0 573 01547 3

Sweeney Todd the Barber. Melodrama. Brian J. Burton, from George Dibdin Pitt's Victorian version of the legendary drama
M10 F6. Extras. Composite setting. Fee code L

This version of the classic story of the demon barber of Fleet Street is laced with both song and humour in the best of the old-fashioned melodramatic styles. The play can be performed without the songs, but their inclusion follows the custom of the time. Period 1840
ISBN 0 573 11405 6

Sweeney Todd, the Demon Barber of Fleet Street. Victorian Melodrama. Austin Rosser, based upon the original by George Dibdin Pitt
M6 (10, young, 50s, 60) F3 (young, 20s, 40s). 4 small parts: M3, 1 boy. Composite setting: two rooms and an alley. (Can be performed in separate settings.) Fee code H

Apart from a surprising change of heart and bid for sympathy at the final moments of this version of the classic story, Todd glories in his villainies throughout and gleefully slaughters right and left until the cast is almost eliminated. Commendably, the story is treated seriously and 'guying' is discouraged.
ISBN 0 573 01516 3

Sweet Bird of Youth. Play. Tennessee Williams
M15 (young, 20s, 30s, middle-age) F7 (young, old). A bedroom, a terrace, a cocktail lounge and palm garden. Fee code M

Chance Wayne, an ambitious hustler, has taken up with a fading movie star hoping this might help his own career in films. She accompanies him to his home town to see a girl with whom he had had an affair, and still loves. Unknown to him, he had infected the girl with venereal disease. Learning of his arrival, the girl's malevolent father, Boss, plans to have the young man castrated.

♦ **Sweet Panic**. Play. Stephen Poliakoff
M3 (19, 30s, 40) F3 (22, late 30s). A room, other simple settings. Fee code M

A child psychologist's understanding of contemporary life is brought into question when she finds herself stalked by the mother of one of her young clients. Casting an acute eye over the changing face of urban life, Stephen Poliakoff's vibrant and compelling play pits the two women against each other in a battle for the soul of the city.

Sweet Revenge. Play. Francis Durbridge
M6 (30s-middle-age) F3 (30s-40s). A living-room. Fee code M

Ross is a successful, happily married cardiac consultant — until his wife Fay announces she has fallen in love with the notorious womanizer Julian Kane. Later, Ross's assistant discovers two phials missing of Zarabell Four, a drug potentially lethal to cardiac patients. When Julian dies from a heart attack, all fingers point to Ross. But as the play progresses many enemies of the deceased are revealed and audiences will guess right up to the final moments of this well-wrought thriller.
ISBN 0 573 01904 5

Sylvia's Wedding. Play. Jimmie Chinn
M3 (32, 50s-60s) F4 (30s, 50s-60s). Three rooms in a terraced house. Fee code M

After ten years of courting, Gordon proposes to Sylvia and throws both families into turmoil. Sylvia's parents are hardly the sort of people Gordon's pompous father wants his family connected with and the feeling is mutual. In addition, Sylvia's best friend is all too ready to deflate Sylvia with her cynical, world-weary comments. Against the odds, the two warring families co-operate in the wedding preparations and all looks set for success — but Fate intervenes.
ISBN 0 573 01873 1

Table Manners. Play. Alan Ayckbourn
M3 F3. A dining-room. Fee code M. See the entry under *The Norman Conquests*
ISBN 0 573 01573 2

Take Away the Lady. Play. Jimmie Chinn
M3 (40s, elderly) F4 (30s, 40). A drawing-room. Fee code L

Intriguing glimpses into a cupboard full of family skeletons, together with detective work, combine in this unusual suspense play, to keep everyone guessing until the very last page. Matthew, still protesting his innocence, returns home from prison, after serving fifteen years for allegedly murdering his mother. Who *did* kill Mother? It takes an apparent suicide and a good deal of amateur sleuthing before the truth is revealed and the lady can be taken away.
ISBN 0 573 11453 6

◆ **Taking Sides**. Play. Ronald Harwood
M4 (24, 35-50s, 60) F2 (20s, 32). An office. Fee code M

Wilhelm Furtwängler (1886-1954) was one of the great conductors of this century. It was his misfortune to have been at the height of his career when the National Socialists came to power. While many of his fellow artists were either forced to leave Germany or emigrated as an act of protest, Furtwängler remained. After the war he was accused of having served the Nazi regime.
Period 1946

Taking Steps. Farce. Alan Ayckbourn
M4 (25-40s) F2 (20s, 30s). A lounge, bedroom, attic, hall and stairs. Fee code M

Roland is considering buying an old Victorian House. In the house are his solicitor and the vendor; Roland's wife, who is considering leaving him; her brother; and later the brother's fiancée. In the course of one hectic night and morning, with continual running up and down stairs, these characters try to sort themselves out. All this takes place in a highly ingenious and original setting, in which all the rooms, passages and stairs are on a single level.
ISBN 0 573 11425 0

A Tale of Two Cities. A theatrical adaptation of Charles Dickens' novel by Mark Fitzgibbons M16 F10. The courtyard of an English inn. Fee code M

When Dickens wrote *A Tale of Two Cities* English inns were experiencing hard times. To improve things, inexpensively produced entertainments were presented in the innyards. In this brilliant adaptation the audience are watching the inn's production of Dickens' masterpiece, therefore the problem of different locations is simply solved and the full life and scope of the characters can be absorbed, stunningly presented in this *tour de force* for theatrical organizations everywhere. Period 1860s

A Tale of Two Cities. Play. Matthew Francis, adapted from the novel by Charles Dickens Large mixed cast. Various simple interior and exterior settings. Fee code M

This moving and exciting adaptation of the story of Sydney Carton and Charles Darnay, the English lawyer and French aristocrat caught up inextricably in the violence and bloodshed of the French Revolution, is played on a simple set, with numerous lighting changes and sound effects, minimal props and vivid stage images, making this an atmospheric, fast-moving and satisfyingly theatrical experience which is always true to the original. Period 1780s
ISBN 0 573 01942 8

♦ **The Talented Mr Ripley**. Play. Phyllis Nagy, adapted from the novel by Patricia Highsmith M5 (teenager, 25, middle-age) F2 (young, middle-age). Various simple settings. Fee code M

When Tom Ripley is sent to Italy to track down Richard Greenleaf, the errant son of a wealthy American couple, his mission takes on a sinister twist as their lives become inextricably entwined. Phyllis Nagy's stage adaptation of Patricia Highsmith's novel explores the mind of one of crime fiction's great anti-heroes; an intelligent, suave and charming psychopath whose amorality is at the centre of a plot about duplicity and murder. Period early 1950s

Tales from Hollywood. Play. Christopher Hampton M14 F6. Extras. Various interior and exterior settings. Fee code M

Evening Standard Best Comedy Award winner, this evokes the vagaries of Tinseltown from the late thirties to 1950 McCarthyism, which welcomed the multi-talents of German émigré writers fleeing Nazism and employed them as screenwriters for the major film companies. Mixing fact and fantasy, Hampton presents comical, witty and often moving vignettes of life through the eyes of Austro-Hungarian playwright Ödön von Horvàth whom he sends to America with the Mann and Marx brothers, Garbo, Weismuller, Brecht and many others.
ISBN 0 573 11433 1

Tales of King Arthur. Play. John Chambers M24 F14. Various medieval settings. Fee code M

Tracing Arthur's life from his boyhood, through his magical accession to the throne by means of the sword in the stone, his romance with Guinevere and his search for the Holy Grail, to his death at the hands of the wicked Mordred, *Tales of King Arthur* tells its story clearly and economically, provides good acting opportunities for a large cast and can be staged as simply or as lavishly as circumstances allow.
ISBN 0 573 05110 0

A

Tartuffe. Comedy. Molière. Translated by Christopher Hampton
M8 (young, middle-age) F5 (young, 30, elderly). Interiors. Fee code M

This new translation of Molière's classic depiction of hypocrisy in action into colloquial, English blank verse, was commissioned by the Royal Shakespeare Company and was first presented at The Pit, London in 1983, with Antony Sher as Tartuffe, Alison Steadman as Elmire, and Nigel Hawthorne as Orgon.

Tartuffe. Comedy. Molière. Adapted by Miles Malleson
M8 F4. Interiors. Fee code H

In public, Tartuffe affects every pious excellence; so virtuous is he that every form of pleasure is anathema to him. M. Orgon, a rich merchant, is completely taken in. Inviting Tartuffe to his home, he watches approvingly while Tartuffe 'reforms' his whole family. The besotted merchant even plans to give Tartuffe his fortune and his daughter's hand in marriage. Finally, Mme Orgon exposes Tartuffe for the rogue he is — and M. Orgon for the gullible fool he has been. Period 1664
ISBN 0 573 01437 X

A Taste of Honey. Play. Shelagh Delaney
M3 (20s, 1 Black, 30) F2 (17, 40). Composite setting. Fee code M

Jo, the teenage heroine who lives in a filthy tenement bedsitter, is deserted by her nagging peroxided mother, who is unaware that her daughter is pregnant by a black sailor. Jo's greatest fear is that her illegitimate baby might be mentally deficient like her own father. To soothe, clean and cook for her is Geof, an effeminate art student, with whom she makes a temporary home. Bruised by insensitivity and rejection, the boy and girl find a very real comfort in each other. Period 1958

Teechers. Classroom comedy. John Godber
M1 F2, playing 21 characters. A bare stage. Fee code M

Fast-moving, inventive and highly entertaining, *Teechers* vigorously evokes life at a modern Comprehensive, using the format of an end-of-term play to sketch a drama teacher's progress through two terms of recalcitrant classes, cynical colleagues and obstructive caretakers until he departs for the safer waters of a private school. The play runs the gamut of emotions, climaxing with the final scene which gives a poignant edge to the comedy. '... the style is loud, cheerful, butch and pointedly political.' *Time Out*
ISBN 0 573 01678 X

Temptation. Play. Václav Havel. Translated by George Theiner
M9 F6 or M6 F3, with doubling. Various interior and exterior settings. Fee code M

No longer satisfied with science, Dr Foustka experiments with necromancy, resulting in the appearance of Fistula, a repugnant tramp who offers Foustka three choices. The game of bluff and double bluff which ensues due to his inability to resist and the final ironic revelation of Fistula's identity provide a powerful and witty satire of human pride and give a perspective on life in Eastern Europe as only Havel could.

Ten Times Table. Play. Alan Ayckbourn
M6 (young, 40s, 50s) F4 (young, 30s, 40s, old). A ballroom. Fee code M

The leading lights of the village have decided to hold a pageant of local history based on a somewhat vague event. On the committee is a young left-wing schoolteacher who decides to turn the project into a rally for proletarian revolution. Committee meetings become symbolic battlefields for conflicting views and the event itself turns into a violent confrontation between the two extremes with cataclysmic results. The original production starred Paul Eddington and Julia McKenzie. ISBN 0 573 01531 7

Ten Tiny Fingers, Nine Tiny Toes. Play. Sue Townsend
M5 (30s) F6 (30s), doubling possible. Various simple settings. Fee code M

In the futuristic world of 2001 babies are chosen, bought and paid for before conception. Lucinda and her husband have carefully chosen a blonde-haired, blue-eyed government baby girl. Towards the end of the pregnancy they discover that she has a defect — she has only nine toes — and will be taken at birth for government research. Lucinda joins forces with Dot, who is a lower-class citizen and therefore forbidden to breed, to defeat both State and husbands.

♦ **Tess of the d'Urbervilles**. Play. Michael Fry. Adapted from the novel by Thomas Hardy. Music by Anthony Feldman
M15 F19. Can be played by M3 F4 with doubling. Various simple settings. Fee code M (play) code C (music)

All the tragic majesty of Thomas Hardy's celebrated novel is captured in this arresting and theatrically exciting adaptation, narrated by a masked Chorus in the style of Greek tragedy (Hardy's favoured form of theatre) and using songs to counterpoint and underline the action. Michael Fry's adaptation provides a clear and thrilling experience and an enlightening and fascinating re-evaluation of a familiar text. Period late nineteenth century
ISBN 0 573 01945 2

Thark. Farce. Ben Travers
M6 (20, 30s, middle-age) F5 (young, 25, middle-age, elderly). A library, a dining-room, a bedroom. Fee code M

Sir Hector Benbow invites Cherry, a pretty shop assistant, to dine. Arriving home, he finds not only Cherry but Mrs Frush, to whom he has rented Thark, his niece's Norfolk house. Mrs Frush complains Thark is haunted. To distract Lady Benbow's attention from Cherry, he suggests everyone go to Thark, which lives up to its spinechilling reputation. A wild night, sinister butler and plethora of romantic mix-ups add to the lively proceedings. Period 1927
ISBN 0 573 01528 7

♦ **That Good Night**. Play. N. J. Crisp
M3 (30s, middle-age, 70s) F2 (30s, 40s). A courtyard/patio. Fee code M

Ralph, in his seventies and terminally ill, has two final missions: to be reconciled to his long-abandoned son Michael, and, secretly, to ensure he is not a burden to his younger, devoted wife Anna as he goes 'into that good night'. But Ralph wrecks all hope of reconciliation when he picks a fight with Michael's girlfriend. Later, alone, Ralph receives the 'Visitor' whose services he has hired to provide the painless ending. But the visitor plays a devastating trick.
ISBN 0 573 01913 4

Theft. Play. Eric Chappell
M3 (40s, 50s) F2 (40s). A drawing-room. Fee code M

Imagine returning from a pleasant anniversary celebration to find that your house has been burgled, the burglar is still in the house and has you convinced, for a while, that he is a policeman and then, once his true identity is known, he reveals that he knows all kinds of uncomfortable truths about you. Well, that burglar is none other than Spriggs, who succeeds, in *Theft*, Eric Chappell's witty comedy-thriller, in disrupting two seemingly happy marriages and one formerly strong friendship.
ISBN 0 573 01943 6

There's a Girl in My Soup. Comedy. Terence Frisby
M4 (young, 40s, old) F3 (young). A lounge, kitchen, bedroom in one set. Fee code J

Robert is the newspaper food-and-wine connoisseur who dabbles in female delectations. As the play opens Robert says goodbye to one girl when he's picked up by another who's a match for any roué. The romance bubbles along despite the contrast between sophisticated gourmet and modern girl. Youth wins and Robert finds himself permanently in love while Marion's heart belongs to a pop musician who finally catches up with her and drags her home.
ISBN 0 573 01440 X

They Call It Murder. Play. Bettine Manktelow
M3 (20s, 35, 88) F4 (18, 25, 32, middle-age). A living-room. Fee code K

Despite his lowly origins Mr Dalrymple has done well, and now that he is elderly and ailing speculation inevitably arises as to the disposal of his money among his three granddaughters. One, Peggy, neurotic and inhibited, is driven to take drastic steps to secure the money but becomes involved fatally with the old man's self-seeking male nurse. Peggy's misdeeds rebound on her with a vengeance, and the end is tragic, eerie and savagely ironic.
ISBN 0 573 11449 8

They Came from Mars and Landed Outside the Farndale Church Hall in Time for the Townswomen's Guild's Coffee Morning. Comedy. David McGillivray and Walter Zerlin Jnr
M1 F4. 2 female voices. A vicarage, Mars. Fee code K

The Farndale Avenue ladies and their long-suffering stage manager Gordon attempt lift-off with their dramatic society's unique production of this sci-fi thriller that will have the hysterical audience on the edge of their seats.
ISBN 0 573 01665 8

They Came to a City. Play. J. B. Priestley
M4 F5. One exterior. Fee code M

Just before dawn the play's characters — who represent every stratum of society — come to the wall overlooking a strange city whose gate is shut against them. At daybreak they are admitted and towards the end of the day some have found it to be the ideal earth has never achieved. So that everyone may know of this attainable perfection two of them make the sacrifice of leaving the city to return to their sinful world.
ISBN 0 573 01442 6

They're Playing Our Song. Book by Neil Simon. Music by Marvin Hamlisch. Lyrics by Carol Bayer Sager
M1 F1, chorus. Various interior and exterior settings. Fee by arrangement

America's premier funny man and the Tony-award winning composer have produced this funny, romantic, hit show about an established composer and his relationship with a zany aspiring young female lyricist that is full of laughs and delightful music. First presented in Britain at the Shaftesbury Theatre, it had a long, very successful run. Although a musical, it may be presented equally successfully by small dramatic societies as well as musical societies.
ISBN 0 573 68105 8

◆ **The Thickness of Skin**. Play. Clare McIntyre
M3 (17, 30s, 40s) F4 (30s, 40s). Various simple settings. Fee code M

Roanna sees no reason to get involved with other people's problems. She's furious when her son, Jonathan, tries to help their neighbour. Laura, on the other hand, is determined to help unemployed Eddie. But Eddie smells a rat and thinks Laura should confront the truth. Just who is helping whom? And does 'helping' involve doing what you want to do — or what the other person really needs?

Thieves' Carnival. Play. Jean Anouilh, translated by Lucienne Hill
M9 F5. Two interiors, one exterior. Fee code M. For further details of the music apply to Samuel French Ltd

Two beautiful heiresses provide bait for thieves and adventurers, but things become serious when one girl falls in love with a young thief. Being a man of honour he rejects her love, and keeps his mind firmly on burglary. She, however, outwits him and the play ends happily as love conquers all. This light-hearted play combines ironic dialogue, wise humour, entertaining music and mime.
ISBN 0 573 61652 3

◆ **Things We Do For Love**. Play. Alan Ayckbourn
M2 (40s) F2 (late 30s, 40s). 3 flats. Fee code M

Barbara contentedly occupies the pristine, ordered, male-free ground-floor flat of her Victorian terraced house. Below, lives Gilbert — postman, handyman, bore — who secretly paints a lurid, nude study of Barbara. The top flat Barbara lets to schoolfriend Nikki and her fiancé Hamish, despite the fact that Barbara and Hamish have taken an instant dislike to one another. But, ever life's victim, Nikki is destined to suffer when Hamish and Barbara embark on a night of violent, uninhibited passion. **Available 1st January 2001**
ISBN 0 573 01914 2

This Happy Breed. Play. Noël Coward
M5 (18-21, 30s) F7 (18-20, 30s, 60). A dining-room. Fee code H

Demobbed in 1919, Frank settles in Clapham with his wife Ethel, their three children, Reg, Queenie and Vi, Ethel's mother, and Frank's sister. The respectable working-class home with its commonness, its sterling qualities and its humour is vividly depicted as the family encompass marriage, separation and sorrow in the seventeen year span between the end of the World War I and the looming Second World War. Period 1919-1937
ISBN 0 573 01443 4

Threat! Play. Derek Parkes
M2 (28, 35) F2 (22, 35). A living-room. Fee code K
ISBN 0 573 01572 4

Three Birds Alighting on a Field. Play. Timberlake Wertenbaker
Large mixed cast may be played by M4 F5. Various simple settings. Fee code M

Timberlake Wertenbaker's award-winning play takes a witty, perceptive look at the art world in the boom period of the late Eighties in London. ' ... this rare, rich play for today, which unites the serious and the comical in one dramatic swoop ... a contemporary satire upon the art market, the stinging dealers and wheelers. But in the course of 22 scenes you become aware there is more here than meets the lazy eye.' *Evening Standard*

The Three Musketeers. Play. Willis Hall, from the novel by Alexandre Dumas
M19 F7, may be played by M13 F4. Extras. Various simple interior and exterior settings. Fee code M

Willis Hall brings Dumas' swashbuckling tale to the stage in a lively, tongue-in-cheek version. D'Artagnan, a young Gascon, goes to Paris to join King Louis XIII's Musketeers, is befriended by three valiant members of that force, Athos, Porthos and Aramis, and shares their adventures, foiling the evil plans of Cardinal Richelieu and Milady de Winter to discredit Louis' wife, Anne. ISBN 0 573 01909 6

Three Sisters. Play. Anton Chekhov, translated by Brian Friel
M9 F5. A drawing-room and dining-room, a bedroom, a garden. Fee code M

Brian Friel's translation was undertaken primarily as an act of love and, since the only Chekhov translations available to the Irish theatre at the time (1981) were American and English, in the hope that it might make the unique experience of Chekhov more accessible to Irish audiences. Here he presents brilliantly the social atmosphere, its characters' resolution to return to Moscow, their great passions and epiphanies, and their gradual self-realization.

Thyestes. Play. Seneca, translated by Caryl Churchill
M8, 2M non-speaking. Various simple settings. Fee code M

Taken directly from the Latin, Caryl Churchill's translation is accurate, uncut and faithful to the original.
Atreus is determined to wreak bloodthirsty revenge on his brother Thyestes, who seduced Atreus's wife and usurped his throne and is in exile with his three sons. Feigning reconciliation, Atreus invites them back. He slaughters the sons, serves their flesh to the unwitting father and then tells Thyestes he has eaten his own children.

♦ **Tilting Ground**. Play. Guy Hibbert
M2 (late 20s, early 60s) F1 (mid 50s). A beach-house patio. Fee code M

Nancy, recently widowed, lives in a luxurious beach house overlooking the sea near Puerto Escondido on the Pacific coast of Mexico. When her son, Jack, arrives after a year-long disappearance she is overjoyed to see him but perturbed by his mysterious lifestyle. Fuelled by alcohol, Jack's emotional turmoil begins to disrupt Nancy's peace of mind and to fracture her new relationship with the sensitive Charles. Then Jack discovers that Nancy is financially supporting Charles. One of the men has to go ...
ISBN 0 573 01946 0

Time and the Conways. Play. J. B. Priestley
M4 (20s, 30s) F6 (17, 20s, 40s). A sitting-room. Fee code M

Mrs Conway takes life cheerfully: she and her daughters enjoy entertaining and, although in 1919 war's shadow still lingers, the Conways look forward optimistically. Act II is the same room in 1937 and all the happy homes of 1919 are more or less in ruin. The married girls are miserable, those left spinsters are disillusioned and bitter. Act III returns to 1919 where Mrs Conway and the girls cheerfully look forward to a happy future.
ISBN 0 573 01446 9

Time and Time Again. Comedy. Alan Ayckbourn
M3 (30s, 40s) F2 (20s, 30s). A garden and conservatory. Fee code M

When womanizer Graham meets his employee Peter's fiancée, he makes a bee-line for her as usual. However, the young lady strays instead to Graham's brother-in-law Leonard, a poetic fumbler who holds conversations with the garden gnome. When Leonard half-heartedly tries to tell Peter about the relationship, cricket, football and even draughts supersede all other considerations in Peter's sports-mad mind.
ISBN 0 573 01457 4

Time of My Life. Play. Alan Ayckbourn
M4 (20s, middle-age, 50s) F3 (20s, 50s). A restaurant. Fee code M

Gerry Stratton has organized a family dinner with his sons Glyn and Adam at his favourite restaurant to celebrate his wife Laura's fifty-fourth birthday. The occasion suggests a happy domestic scene, but gradually we are made aware of the family skeletons. The present opens up to have Glyn's story move forward in time and Adam's backward, while at the centre Gerry and Laura pick apart their marriage and recall first love.
ISBN 0 573 11444 7

Time to Kill. Play. Leslie Darbon
M2 (30s) F4 (30s). A living-room. Fee code L

After Maggie's husband Don leaves home on a business trip, Alan arrives at the house expecting an intimate interlude. Instead he finds himself handcuffed and faced by Maggie and three women of their local set. He is to be put on trial for causing the death of another woman. During the trial unforeseen revelations surprise all the participants, including Don who, returning unexpectedly, becomes involved in the Defence. The proceedings culminate in a few moments of violent action.
ISBN 0 573 11445 5

Time Was. Play. Hugh Leonard
M3 (20s, 30s) F3 (30s, 40s). Extras 2M, 1M voice only. A living-room. Fee code M

When Bea and John visit Ellie and P.J., John explains his theory that so many people are longing for the simplicity of bygone days that Time has ruptured and people are disappearing back into the past. Similarly people we want to see again are appearing by the score! The hilarity dissolves later to show the strains of suburbia underneath until P.J. wishes himself back — and disappears.
Period next year

♦ **Tiptoe Through the Tombstones**. Comedy-thriller. Norman Robbins
M4 (25, 30s, 70s) F6 (18, 30s-60s). A library. Fee code L

Some months have passed since the ghastly events in Monument House, well-known to those familiar with Norman Robbins' earlier *A Tomb with a View*. (Previous acquaintance with the Tombs is not required!) Now Mortimer Crayle, the lawyer, has gathered the last remaining Tomb family members (as offbeat a bunch as the original occupants) at the old house, ostensibly to inform them about their inheritance. But Crayle has designs on the inheritance which demand the death of all Tombs ...
ISBN 0 573 01917 7

Tissue. Play. Louise Page
M1 F2 (20s). Open setting. Fee code K

Louise Page has written, in darting, daring, time-chopping structure, a play about breast cancer in which she has to deal with dominant definitions of feminity in order to probe the pain in the problem. As she herself says, 'once I started talking openly about writing a play on mastectomy, women whom I had no idea had had mastectomies began to confide their experiences to me. I began to understand more and more the taboo nature of the subject I was writing about and how much women wanted the subject discussed.'

♦ **To Meet Oscar Wilde**. Play. Norman Holland
M2 (30s, 40s) F1 (30s). Offstage voices. Simple lecture platform setting. Fee code L

'To meet Oscar Wilde' was an inducement printed by Victorian Society hostesses on soirée invitations. In this fascinating play Oscar Wilde gives a dissertation on his life in a lecture in 1899. Supported by his friend, Lord Evelyn, and an actress, Penelope Dyall — who between them enact all the male and female characters mentioned in the dissertation — we are taken, in a series of short scenes, on a journey through Wilde's life. Period Late Victorian
ISBN 0 573 01948 7

A Toe in the Water. Comedy. Derek Benfield
M3 (young, middle-age) F3 (20s, 40s). Composite setting: a poolside and bedroom. Fee code L

Seeking peace and tranquility, Gerald goes to spend a few days in a health farm, presided over by the highly moral Mr Potter. But his hopes are soon dashed by the arrival of his secretary (declaring her undying passion for him), his daughter (intent upon naughty assignations with her boyfriend), and his wife. The resulting mix-ups caused by crafty deceit and misfiring erotic adventures prove more than a headache for the hapless Mr Potter!
ISBN 573 01906 1

♦ **Tom and Clem**. Play. Stephen Churchett
M3 (20s-30s, 62) F1 (mid 30s). A large room. Fee code M

It's 1945 and newly elected, pragmatic Labour Prime Minister, Clement Atlee, arrives in defeated Germany for the Potsdam conference. He encounters his most flamboyant new MP, Tom Driberg, a radical journalist and *bon viveur*. Stephen Churchett's play explores the nature of personal and political compromise, and the conflict between liberty of conscience and totalitarianism, against a backdrop of events which were to shape a country and continent in the second half of the twentieth century. Period 1945

Tom Jones. Comedy. Joan Macalpine. Based on the novel by Henry Fielding
M7 F7. Extras. Composite setting. Fee code M

Tom Jones is rich, ripe and rowdy. Tom, Squire Allworthy's adopted son, falls victim to the charms of one rustic wench after another, until at last the Squire grows tired of the trouble he causes and sends him off to cause it elsewhere. Then Tom becomes entangled with three women at once: Jenny Waters, a lady of warm heart and generous virtue, Mrs Fitzpatrick, a society lady seeking diversion from her oafish husband, and Sophia Western, whom Tom truly loves.
ISBN 0 573 11439 0

A Tomb with a View. Comedy thriller. Norman Robbins
M4 (30s-70s) F6 (20s-60s). A library. Fee code L

The action begins with the reading of the Tomb family will (invoving some millions of pounds) to a pretty sinister family, one member of which has werewolf tendencies, another wanders around in a toga in the style of Julius Caesar, a third is a gentle elderly lady who plants more than seeds in her flower-beds. By the third act there are more corpses than live members left in the cast.
ISBN 0 573 11451 X

Tons of Money. Farce. Will Evans and Valentine
M6 (young, 30s, elderly) F4 (20s, elderly). A library. Fee code M

Aubrey has been left the life interest in a fortune which reverts on his death to his cousin George. Since George is thought to have died in Mexico, Aubrey 'dies' and then resurrects himself as cousin George, thus eliminating his own vast debts. He is obliged to 'die' and take on other identities twice more to avoid complications, until the real George turns up, announcing that the Mexican Government has annexed the fortune. Period 1922
ISBN 0 573 01450 7

Tons of Money. Farce. Will Evans and Valentine, revised by Alan Ayckbourn
M6 F4. For cast and settings see above. Fee code M

Alan Ayckbourn's revised version of the first of the famous Aldwych farces, originally produced in 1922 starring the great farce actor Ralph Lynn, retains the spirit whilst altering some of the original letter of the text — changes to verbal jokes, for instance, or to some of Lynn's uniquely personal gags. The basic story, however, remains the same. The National Theatre produced this version in 1986 with Michael Gambon and Simon Cadell.
ISBN 0 573 01671 2

Top Girls. Play. Caryl Churchill
F7, with trebling. Various simple interior and exterior settings. Fee code M

This play for sixteen women characters was seen at London's Royal Court Theatre. 'Ms Churchill's rich, ambitious play is a powerful exposition of the way in which top girls, like top men, often achieve success at the expense of their less able sisters.' *Time Out*. ' ... brilliantly conceived with considerable wit to illuminate the underlying deep human seriousness of her theme. The play is feminist, all right, but it is an entertaining, sometimes painful and often funny play and not a mere tract.' *Spectator*
ISBN 0 573 13013 2

Torch Song Trilogy. Three plays. Harvey Fierstein. Fees on application

A smash-hit in New York, this trilogy had its British première at the Albery Theatre, London, in 1985, with Antony Sher portraying the alternately moving and hilarious life and loves of a drag queen. '[This play] must be the funniest as well as the most perceptive, exuberant and painful for years about sexuality, inversion and the disorders of modern love.' *Daily Telegraph* '... a remarkably bitchy, waspish and acerbically funny triptych on the nature of homosexuality.' *Punch*

The International Stud
M2 (30s). A black cyclorama.

The first play concerns the agonies of Arnold, a New York drag queen who is picked up in a bar by bi-sexual Brooklyn teacher Ed, and their ensuing on/off relationship until Ed finally leaves Arnold to marry Laurel.

Fugue in a Nursery
M3 (18, 30s) F1 (35). One set to represent various rooms

The second play takes place a year later. Arnold and his new lover, a model called Alan, are invited for a weekend in the country with Ed and his wife with complicated results.

Widows and Children First!
M3 (15, 30s, 40s). F1 (60s). A living-room/kitchenette, a park bench

The third play sees Arnold five years on. Alan has been brutally murdered by a vicious gang and Ed has left Laurel for Arnold's sofa-bed. Another addition to Arnold's household is David, a gay, delinquent teenager who has been rejected by his foster parents and whom Arnold is trying to adopt as his son. Matters are further complicated with the arrival of Arnold's Ma who's not too happy with Arnold.

Total Eclipse. Play. Christopher Hampton
M7 (17, 20s, 43). F4 (18, 31, 50, middle-age). Extras. Various interior and exterior settings. Fee code M

An intelligent treatment of the friendship between the poets Paul Verlaine and Arthur Rimbaud, one of the most extraordinary relationships in the history of literature. With considerable insight into the bourgeois and artistic societies of the nineteenth century, and with a moving understanding of homosexuality, Hampton charts the poets' mutual need for each other as they move through and away from literary life and from Verlaine's family.
ISBN 0 573 61692 2

Touch and Go. Comedy. Derek Benfield
M2 (40s) F3 (20s, 30s). Two living-rooms. Fee code L

Having been encouraged to take up jogging by his wife Hilary, Brian sees his girl-friend, Wendy, in his friend George's flat when he is ostensibly running around the park. However, while Brian is visiting Wendy, helpful George knows that his own affair will not be discovered as the object of his affection is Brian's wife Hilary! It is all plain sailing until George's wife Jessica returns too soon from a business trip to America ...
ISBN 0 573 11301 7

A Touch of Danger. Play. Francis Durbridge
M5 (30s, 40s, middle-age) F4 (20s, 30s). A living-room. Fee code M

When author Max Telligan's secretary, Liz, and his about-to-be ex-wife, Harriet, read that he has been found dead in Munich, they are stunned. When Max walks in, very much alive, they find that the murdered man was Max's friend. Thus begins a sequence of events involving the CID, CIA, security services and a terrorist organization, all of whom seem inordinately interested in Max. ISBN 0 573 01692 5

A Touch of Spring. Comedy. Samuel Taylor
M7 (30s) F2 (young, 30s). An hotel apartment. Fee code M

Diana leaves her husband, Sandy, in Rome to make arrangements for the transfer home of his father's body, killed in Italy in a car crash. While wading through governmental red tape he meets Alison, who is on a similar mission — her mother had died in the same accident. It transpires that the parents' relationship was more than that of co-tourists, and circumstances indicate that a parallel situation will inevitably develop between Sandy and Alison. ISBN 0 573 01592 9

Towards Zero. Play. Agatha Christie
M7 (20s-70s) F4 (20s, 30s, 60s). A drawing-room. Fee code M

The guests at Lady Tressilian's house-party include her nephew, Nevile, his second wife Kay, and his first wife Audrey. When Lady Tressilian is murdered, Nevile appears to have an alibi. The next suspect is Audrey, who stands to inherit some money and is thought to be murderously jealous of Nevile's second marriage. However, the police discover that it was actually Audrey who left Nevile and that Nevile committed the murder to assuage his insane vanity by bringing his unfaithful wife to the gallows.

The Tower, [La Tour de Nesle], or Marguerite de Bourgogne. Play. Alexandre Dumas (Père), in a new version by Charles Wood
M18 F3, may be played by M13 F2. Extras. Various simple settings. Fee code M

Dumas (Père) was commissioned by Parisian theatre manager Harel to write *The Tower* in 1832, a tale of murder, sexual depravity and treachery among the French aristocracy — just what the public wanted. Popularly dubbed as 'anti-monarchist', it played for 800 performances during a French revolution in the 1830s. Over 160 years later, in less turbulent times, lovers of swashbuckling romantic melodrama will not be disappointed. Period 1314

Translations. Play. Brian Friel
M7 (20s-middle-age, 60s) F3 (20s). A hedge-school. Fee code M

In Baile Beag, an Irish-speaking community in County Donegal, a detachment of the Royal Engineers engaged on behalf of the British Army and Government are making the first Ordnance Survey. Lieutenant Yolland falls in love with Maire, a peasant girl, and with Ireland, but when he is murdered Maire goes mad. The British soldiers pillage the countryside in revenge. Period 1833

Traps. Play. Caryl Churchill
M4 (20s, 30s) F2 (20s, 30). A room. Fee code M

First staged at the Royal Court Theatre Upstairs in 1977. Caryl Churchill writes: 'When we were casting *Traps*, we found ourselves repeating the same two things as some kind of introduction to the play. First, that it is like a painting by Escher, where the objects can exist on paper, but would be impossible in life ... Second, that the characters can be thought of as living many of their possibilities at once. There is no flashback, no fantasy, everything that happens is as real and solid as everything else within the play.'

Travels with my Aunt. Play. Adapted by Giles Havergal from the novel by Graham Greene
M15 F9, but very flexible casting. Various simple settings. Fee code M

This stage adaptation of Graham Greene's novel of retired bank worker Henry Pulling and his eccentric Aunt Augusta was first presented at the Citizens' Theatre, Glasgow, in 1989, with a cast of four actors playing all 24 characters. It can be staged with a large or small cast and there are many schemes for doubling to suit the circumstances of the production and the wishes of the director.

Travesties. Play. Tom Stoppard
M5 (20s, middle-age, 60s) F3 (young, 40s). A library, a drawing-room. Fee code M

James Joyce, running a Swiss theatrical company, invites Henry Carr to play in Wilde's *The Importance of Being Earnest*. Carr agrees and scores a success, but later there is a dispute over Carr's claim for reimbursement of the cost of articles of clothing bought for his role. The author uses this factual framework on which to build an extravaganza of political history, literary pastiche, and Wildean parody, even song and dance, introducing Dadaist Tristan Tzara, and Lenin and his wife. Period 1918

Treasure Island. Play. Bernard Miles, Peter Coe and Josephine Wilson from the book by R.L. Stevenson
M21. Various settings on an open stage. Fee code H

The story begins in the Admiral Benbow public house, moving thence to Bristol, the good ship *Hispaniola*, and to the famous island. It concerns a map of buried treasure, the fine old Squire Trelawney and a sea-cook with one leg called Long John Silver among other characters and pirates. This version avoids elaborate staging so it can be performed with a minimum of equipment. ISBN 0 573 04017 6

Treats. Play. Christopher Hampton
M2 (30s) F1 (20s). A living-room. Fee code M

This play consists of the permutations and combinations of Ann and her two lovers. Dave, her previous companion, a journalist, has been away, and on returning finds that he has been replaced by Patrick, amiable but dull. Though Ann rules the roost — and also her two lovers — she herself is weak enough to be unable to do without one of them, and in the end Dave is reinstated and Patrick dismissed. But how long this will last is anybody's guess.

Trelawny of the 'Wells'. Comedy. Arthur W. Pinero
M10 (young, 27, 30, 40, 70, elderly) F8 (19, 20s, 60). Four interiors. Fee code **M**

Actress Rose Trelawny falls in love with the grandson of a snobbish knight. Unfortunately her visit to her lover's home is a humiliating failure and she finds she can no longer act. But the elderly tyrant relents, unexpectedly developing an interest in the theatre; he even finances a play and finally gives his blessing to Rose and his grandson. Period 1860
ISBN 0 573 01459 0

Trespass. Ghost Story. Emlyn Williams
M4 (20, 40, middle-age) F5 (young, 23, 40, 60). The living-room of a castle. Fee code M. Copies available on hire.

When Christine's husband Philip dies she engages a medium to make contact with Philip, a dance band leader. What follows is a night of fear and terror with Philip's music pervading the taut atmosphere, wherein everyone has one foot over the line and must not, under any circumstance, crossover. Secrets are told, spine-chilling events take place and the dawn brings sunshine, peace — and death.

Trivial Pursuits. Play. Frank Vickery
M4 (30s) F6 (20s, 30s). A garden/patio area. Fee code **L**

A summer evening's barbecue is the setting for a meeting of the Trealaw and District Operatic Society. Next season's play is being announced but Nick, the Society's business manager, has promised a different show and the plum roles to four different people. As the evening progresses each character's foibles and talents are revealed and the complex relationships between players emerge as moments of pure slapstick and farce alternate with ones full of real drama and pathos.
ISBN 0 573 11469 2

The Trojan Women. Play. Euripides, translated by Neil Curry
M4 F5, chorus of women. An open stage. Fee code **J**

The play dwells on and enlarges one brief moment at the end of the Trojan War — when all the Trojan men are dead and the women and children are waiting to be shipped into slavery — concentrating attention on the fate of individuals. This classic depiction has survived solely as a veiled reference to distant facts of history; it remains a powerful dramatic exposé of the brutality of war and the pompous nobodies who are responsible for them.

The Trouble With Old Lovers. Play. Angela Huth
M2 (50s) F3 (late 30s-50s). A country-house kitchen. Fee code **M**

Returning somewhat tipsy from a friend's wedding, Alice announces she has met Edward and Laura whom she has invited to dinner. Edward is Alice's old flame and Laura and Tom had a brief pre-marital affair — four ex-lovers meeting after twenty years, where's the harm? But they arrive with Mary with whom Tom had a passionate affair. Will Tom's and Alice's seemingly secure marriage survive the seductive onslaught of Mary who is determined to get Tom?
ISBN 0 573 01941 X

Trumpets and Drums. Play. Bertolt Brecht. Translated by Alan Brown and Kyra Dietz, music by Wagner-Regeny
M21 F12. Interior and exterior settings. Fee code M for play, code C for music

Brecht takes George Farquhar's Restoration comedy *The Recruiting Officer* and transfers it to the period of the American Revolutionary War. Captain Plume, the officer in question, arrives in Shrewsbury from London to enquire how recruitment to fight the rebels is progressing. He receives a discouraging report of military and romantic complications.

Turandot. Play. Bertolt Brecht
Translations: Derek Goldby
                Stefan Lasch and Evelyn Warman
M33 F9. Extras. Various simple interior and exterior settings. Fee code M for play, code C for music

There is no cotton to be bought in China; the Emperor and his brother have a monopoly, but are waiting for a rise in price. A group of futile thinkers is called in to invent excuses for the shortage, the most successful whitewasher to marry the Emperor's daughter Turandot. Gogher Gogh, the gangster, burns half the imperial cotton stock so that the rest can be sold on a rising market, but Turandot does not care to marry him. Set in China at some indeterminate past time.

The Turn of the Screw. Play. Ken Whitmore, adapted from the novel by Henry James
M1 or 2 (35) F3 (20s, 50). 1 boy (12) 1 girl (10). A sitting-room/hall. Fee code L

Shortly after Miss Grey, a governess, arrives at Bly to take charge of Flora and Miles she sees the ghosts of the former valet and governess; it is the children they want. She determines to save the children from destruction and damnation at hands of these 'devils', but her courageous efforts are not enough to save little Miles from tragedy. Period 1875
ISBN 0 573 11454 4

The Tutor. Play. Bertolt Brecht. Translated by Pip Broughton
M10 F10. Extras. Seven interiors, two exteriors. Fee code H

This is a modernized version of the 18th-century drama by Reinhold Lenz about the miseries and humiliations suffered by a young private tutor. Treated as a servant by his employers, he is seduced by the daughter of the house and has to flee from the outraged family. Later, in a similar situation, he lands himself in the same sort of trouble. In desperation he castrates himself, and thereafter finds life easier and is accepted by society. Period 1930s Germany. **NB. Please specify translator when ordering.**

The Tutor. Play. Bertolt Brecht
Translations: Ralph Manheim
                John Willett
                Geoffrey Skelton
                Richard Grunberger
M10 F10. Interior and exterior settings. Fee code M

For synopsis, see above.

Twelfth Man. Comedy. H. Connolly
M7 (teenage, 20s, middle-age) F6 (teenage, 20s, middle-age). A cricket pavilion. Fee code K

When Tetford cricket team are faced with the unexpected challenge of an all women's team their reactions are hardly encouraging. However, despite intrigue and trickery from the Tetford team, the women win the day, calling for some rethinking on the men's behalf on the sanctity of cricket, although not before several major revelations rock the foundations of the cricket club.
ISBN 0 573 01910 3

Twelve Angry Men. Play. Reginald Rose
M13. A jury room. Fee code M

A young delinquent is on trial for the murder of his aggressive father. The judge has directed the jury to find the boy guilty if there is no reasonable doubt. Eleven of the jurors declare there is no reasonable doubt, but one of them, while far from convinced of the boy's innocence, feels that some of the evidence against him has been ambiguous. At the end of a long afternoon he wins all the others round to his view. Period 1950s.
ISBN 0 573 04012 5

Two. Play. Jim Cartwright
M1 F1, playing 14 characters (M6 F7, 1 boy). A pub. Fee code M

Set in a Northern pub owned by a savagely bickering husband and wife, *Two* is a series of short vignettes that skilfully combines pathos and humour, with all fourteen characters played by two actors. During the course of the evening, assorted customers pass through, including a little boy left behind by his father — an event which triggers a movement towards a fragile reconciliation between the pub couple, as their own dark tragedy is revealed.

Two and Two Make Sex. Comedy. Richard Harris and Leslie Darbon
M3 (24, 45, 50) F3 (20, 40). Split set: a drawing-room, a bedsitter. Fee code M

Middle-aged George, having reached the 'virility crisis', seeks reassurance from young Jane. His wife, Clare, finds herself behaving in somewhat the same way with Jane's boyfriend Nick. The action swings between the contrasting rooms (in a split set) until matters are brought to a general confrontation. In a long climactic scene mistaken identities abound and rebound, and a bizarrely humorous game of make-believe is played by all concerned.
ISBN 0 573 01548 1

◆ **Two and Two Together**. Comedy. Derek Benfield
M4 (30s, 50s, 60s) F3 (40s, middle-age) Split set: 2 suburban reception rooms Fee code M

Rachel's husband Victor never suspects that she is keeping an assignation with a young man in the house of her good friend Georgina. Why should he? He has other things on his mind — in the shape of the said Georgina, who he is meeting secretly while her husband Henry, an actor, is safely occupied in the theatre. But Henry returns home unexpectedly and the two couples are forced into a riotous whirlwind of lies and misunderstandings ...
ISBN 0 573 01947 9

Two Into One. Comedy. Ray Cooney
M5 (Oriental, 20s-40s, 60s) F5 (young, 20s, 40s). Extras optional. Multiple settings. Fee code M

While staying at the Westminster Hotel, MP Richard Willey dispatches his wife Pamela to the theatre so that his assistant, George, can arrange a suite where Richard can seduce one of the PM's secretaries. Unfortunately, George bungles the arrangements and Richard finds his illicit love-nest is the suite next to his and Pamela's. From then on George piles one outrageous deceit upon another, accidentally finding himself seducing Pamela, until staff and guests are reeling in confusion!
ISBN 0 573 01607 0

Two of a Kind. Comedy. Hugh Janes
M2 (elderly) F2 (middle-age, elderly). A room, lobby, office and optional inset scene. Fee code M

'Wally' Wallis is hardly the perfect retirement-home resident. When his room-mate, Potts, dies and is replaced with staid, dull George, war is instantly declared! Wally decides he must leave, but before his escape with Potts' ashes he reaches a level of understanding with George and shares some tender moments with May, another resident, who has a soft spot for both men.
ISBN 0 573 01944 4

The Two of Us. Four one-act plays for two players. Michael Frayn
M1 F1. A bedroom, a dining-room, two living-rooms. Fee code J

The four plays are not connected except by the fact that they can all be played by the same two performers. In the first *Black and Silver*, a husband and wife return to the hotel room in which they spent their honeymoon. In *The New Quixote* a young man has spent a night with a girl, to whom the encounter is so casual that he has even forgotten it when he leaves her. However, he returns to take up residence — but will they really be happy together? *Mr Foot*, the third play, concerns a couple — he is in line for a new job, she may be 'vetted' as his wife, by his employer. She creates an imaginary interview. The last play, *Chinamen*, is the longest, and in it the players share five parts. It concerns a dinner party to which friends are invited who at all costs must not be allowed to meet. They do!

Two Planks and a Passion. Play. Anthony Minghella
M12 F4. Extras. Composite setting. Fee code L

Set in York in 1392, this play tells of a performance of the Mystery Plays. For the townspeople the competition is fierce to attract the attention of the Royal Party and to impress them at all costs. But the message of Mystery cycle as performed is strong, clear and truthful. This remarkable and beautifully written play is highly original, often very funny and ultimately deeply moving. '... a play full of bustle, life, satire and at times a most moving account of simple faith.' *Daily Mail*
ISBN 0 573 01604 6

◆ **Uncle Vanya**. Brian Friel, a version of the play by Anton Chekhov
M6 (37, 47, old) F4 (young, 27, elderly) A garden, a dining-room, a drawing-room, a bedroom/office. Fee code M

Brian Friel's version of the Chekhov classic was first produced at the Gate Theatre, Dublin, as part of the Dublin Theatre Festival in October 1998. '*Uncle Vanya* is embedded in a distinctive historical and cultural landscape. The translator's job is to fashion an original repetition of the story that has been shaped by those determinants. ... Such an undertaking is audacious and cheeky. But if it reflects even palely Chekhov's sense and sensibility it is well worth the risk.' Brian Friel
Period 1890s

Uncle Vanya. Play. Anton Chekhov, adapted by David Mamet from a translation by Vlada Chernomirdik
M5 F4. Four settings. Fee code M

This new adaptation by David Mamet of the classic work was premièred in 1988 by the American Repertory Theatre in Massachusetts, USA. It tells the story of an uncle in love with a young lady who is married to an old and ill man. She is attracted to a doctor who attends her husband. These souls are marooned far off in the Russian countryside for one whole season. As they disperse we are left with the memory of deeply human characters.
ISBN 0 573 66212 6

Under Milk Wood. Play for voices. Dylan Thomas. With music by Daniel Jones
69 characters. Extras. Doubling possible. Various settings. Fee code M (to include use of music)

A vigorous and rich narrative, sparkling dialogue, and beautifully simple songs; this play overflows with the author's fecund vision of human experience in the small Welsh seaside town of Llareggub. Although probably the most enchanting work for broadcasting ever written this play is also suitable as a stage play. 'Dylan Thomas's beautiful, bawdy, affectionate, reckless, and deeply original play was justly crowned at its first performance by a storm of cheers ...' *Sunday Times*

Under the Stars. Comedy. Richard Crane
M2 (young) F3 (middle-age). An understudies' dressing-room. Fee code M

Stella and Regina are understudies in a West End production of a classical tragedy. Stella is a Method actress, passionate about the magic of theatre, whilst Regina is her cynically practical opposite, displaying an acerbic wit and resigned to knitting and shopping in Sainsbury's. When their double-crossing director brings in The Known Actress as the understudy for one of the stars, the two rivals unite in their resentment.
ISBN 0 573 01911 8

The Understanding. Play. Angela Huth
M1 (65-75) F4 (18, 65-75). A sitting-room. Fee code M

Three elderly sisters, Lydia, Eva and Acton, live in a rambling London house with Eva's husband, Leonard, to whom she has been married for forty years. Throughout that time he and Acton have nursed a discreet, platonic love for each other. The arrival of a young Girl Friday reminds Leonard of Acton at that age and it appears that Eva knew all about the affair. When Eva dies Leonard has the choice of either marrying Acton or losing her. Seen at the Strand Theatre, London, in 1982 with Sir Ralph Richardson.

♦ **The Undertaking**. Play. Philip Osment
M4 (young, 30s) F1 (30s). Various simple interior and exterior settings. Fee code M

Henry has died of AIDS and his lover, Howard, ex-lover Michael and old friend Sheila — along with Michael's new lover, Eamon — travel to Ireland to scatter his ashes. Conflicts and jealousies arise between the members of the group and are exacerbated by the arrival of Patrick, Michael's straight brother, but the ash-scattering ceremony unites them again. Written with insight, humour and great compassion, *The Undertaking* is a moving and very human play tackling difficult themes with enormous but unobtrusive skill.

A

The Unexpected Guest. Play. Agatha Christie
M7 (19, 30s, 40, middle-age) F3 (30, 50, elderly). A study. Fee code M

Michael Starkwedder stumbles in to Richard Warwick's study to find him dead and his wife Laura standing nearby with a gun. The police are puzzled by a set of fingerprints. Do they belong to MacGregor, the man whose child Warwick killed or are belonging to Julian Farrar, Laura's lover whom Laura has lied to protect? After Warwick's half-brother confesses to the murder and then kills himself the case is closed but then Miss Christie produces one of her surprise endings.
ISBN 0 573 01467 1

Unoriginal Sin. Comedy. David Tristram
M4 (20s, 30s, 50s) F2 (24, 30s). A living-room. Fee code L

Bill and Jenny are divorcing. She tries to catch him in a compromising position while he attempts to seduce the young, innocent Eve who has come to view Bill and Jenny's country cottage. Eve arrives with her fiancé and Jenny proposes to Bill a 'first to the bedpost' competition to establish the divorce settlement. Jenny wins and Bill is humbled into reassessing his profligacy. This riotous comedy is by the author of the famous Inspector Drake farces.

The Unvarnished Truth. Play. Royce Ryton
M4 (middle-age) F4 (middle-age, elderly). 1F voice only. A living-room. Fee code M

One evening Tom and Annabel have a row which leaves Annabel dead. A hectic evening ensues when no woman can enter the cottage without rapidly becoming deceased. Annabel's mother-in-law and Tom's landlady follow, and disposal of bodies becomes an acute problem. The arrival of a grim police inspector complicates matters, until a further corpse involves him too. The hysterical ending finds the stage littered with female corpses, frantic males, and a potential fifth victim banging on the door.
ISBN 0 573 11465 X

Up and Running. Comedy. Derek Benfield
M3 (20s, 50s) F3 (20s, 40s). A living-room. Fee code M

Veteran TV talk-show host Patrick Sumner is desperate to impress his new producer Reg Godfrey, who visits Patrick's smart London flat for drinks. But Patrick reckons without the intervention of Jenny, a pretty girl who arrives on the same evening as Reg, intent upon infiltrating Patrick's private life and even passing herself off as his wife. When Patrick's *real* wife returns unexpectedly from a Paris trip, Patrick is forced into a spiralling series of lies and subterfuge.
ISBN 0 573 01916 9

Up 'n' Under. Comedy. John Godber
M6 F1. A bare stage. Fee code M

Dedicated to the Rugby League fans of Hull and created for the Hull Truck Theatre Company this comedy was premièred at the Edinburgh Festival in 1984 where it won a Fringe First award and subsequently the 1984 Laurence Olivier Award for Comedy of the Year after a successful run in London. Set 'somewhere in the north of England' it centres on the amateur rugby team from the *Wheatsheaf Arms* who can only muster a side of four whose pride lies in their unbroken record of defeat.
ISBN 0 573 01915 0

Up 'n' Under II. Comedy. John Godber
M7 (young, middle-age). F2 (young). May be played by M5 F1 with doubling. A bare stage with basic props. Fee code M

'In Amateur Rugby League, everything is personal.' The truth of this sentiment is proved time and again in *Up 'n' Under II*, the hilarious sequel to John Godber's hit comedy about the mixed bag of players making up the *Wheatsheaf Arms* team. Will the lost honour of the *Wheatsheaf Arms* be retrieved in their match against the *Cobblers Arms*? Audiences will be on the edges of their seats before they find out!
ISBN 0 573 11466 8

Uproar in the House. Farce. Anthony Marriott and Alistair Foot
M6 (30s-50s, elderly) F6 (20s, 30). Extra 1M. A living area. Fee code J

To sell an avant-garde house to the Coopers, his first prospective buyers in years, Lockwood persuades Nigel to pose as the owner and hires an actress to play his wife. But the real complications start when the Coopers are fog bound and have to stay the night — and turn out not to be husband and wife at all!
ISBN 0 573 11468 4

Valued Friends. Play. Stephen Jeffreys
M4 (30s, 40s) F2 (20s, 30s). A living-room. Fee code M

Stephen Jeffrey's observant satire on the eighties' property boom won him the *Evening Standard* Most Promising Playwright Award. Four college friends have lived in harmony for a decade. Their friendship values are questioned when a property developer offers them large sums to vacate their basement flat so he can redevelop the house. Although this money would be welcome they hold out and buy at a bargain price. But relationships collapse, tempers fray and madness takes over as the property boom takes off.
ISBN 0 573 01922 3

The Vanek Plays. Triple bill. Václav Havel. Translated by Vera Blackwell
Fee code M (for triple bill)

The plays in this triple bill (two of which, *Audience* and *Private View*, were presented in the BBC-TV series *Play for Today*), have a central character in Vanek, who, like his creator, is a writer and brewery worker. Although not autobiographical, together they provide a superbly ironic comment on the position of a writer who has incurred the disapproval of an autocratic government. **Please note only translations by Vera Blackwell are licensed for performance by Samuel French Ltd.**

Audience. M2. An office. Fee code E if performed separately. ISBN 0 573 04226 8

Private View. M2 F1. A living-room. Fee code E if performed separately. ISBN 0 573 12212 1

Protest. M2. A study. Fee code E if performed separately

Venus Observed. Play. Christopher Fry
M6 (young, middle-age) F4 (young). An observatory room, a temple by a lake. Fee code M

A stylish comedy of verbal wit and poetry, this autumnal quarter of Fry's 'comedies for the seasons' shows the fifty-year-old Duke of Altair resolving to settle down and marry one of his three mistresses. He is tempted away from this sensible plan by a last attempt to capture youthfulness in the person of the twenty-five-year-old Perpetua, daughter of his bailiff, Reedbeck. Originally written for Laurence Olivier, *Venus Observed* was revived at Chichester in 1992.
ISBN 0 573 01923 1

Verdict. Play. Agatha Christie
M6 (24, 45, middle-age, 60) F4 (23, 30, middle-age). A living-room. Fee code M

Karl and his wife Anya are refugees who return to England to rebuild their lives with the help of Lisa who runs the house. Wealthy Helen arrives to take lessons from Karl and her infatuation for him being unreturned, she doesn't stop at murder to clear the way. When Anya dies Helen commits suicide. Lisa is left to carry the blame but then she is absolved and she and Karl build a new life from the wreckage.
ISBN 0 573 61931 X

Veronica's Room. Thriller. Ira Levin
M2 F2. A bedsitting-room. Fee code M

Susan Kerner and Larry Eastwood are invited to the Brabissant mansion by the Mackeys who are struck by Susan's resemblance to Veronica Brabissant, long-dead daughter of the family for whom they work. Susan goes along with the charade to comfort Veronica's only living relative. But once dressed in Veronica's clothes, Susan finds herself herself locked in the role — and locked in Veronica's room. Or is she Veronica, in 1935, pretending to be an imaginary Susan?
ISBN 0 573 01690 9

Victor's Island. Play. Bryan Stocks
M5 (young, 20s, middle-age, elderly) F3 (young, 20s, 30s). A veranda. Fee code J

Actor Victor Kendrew returns to his Bahamian home from his honeymoon with his young bride Ida, who is rumoured to have left behind an unhappy love affair. Actor Peter Barlow arrives, and it transpires that he is the lover Ida left behind. They both leave together for Hollywood, where Peter's screen test is such a success that he is destined to take the place of fading idol Victor, who has played 'hard to get' once too often.

Vieux Carré. Play. Tennessee Williams
M5 F5. Composite setting: a rooming house. Fee code M

This is an autobiographical portrait of Williams as he recalls, with pain, compassion and wry humour, a sojourn in the French Quarter of New Orleans during 1938. We see a tubercular, homosexual painter, a New York fashion illustrator now suffering from leukaemia, two elderly gentlewomen starving politely, and dominating Mrs Wire, the sentimental and cruel, comically desperate landlady.

The Village Fête. Play. Peter Tinniswood
M4 (30s, 40s) F4 (30s, 40s). Simple settings on an open stage. Fee code M

Nancy is at the helm of the unhappy Empson family who, for the sake of Father's health, move to a small country village. Their new house is in a state of disrepair, but they find that a local handyman, Winston, is keen to help them out. He breaks their resistance to him with his irreverent wit, gourmet cooking, free repairs and liberal doses of sexual advice. Gradually the family are transformed by his presence.
ISBN 0 573 01924 X

Vinegar Tom. Play. Caryl Churchill
14 characters, can be played by a cast of 9. Various simple interior and exterior settings. Fee code L for play, code B for music

Written for Monstrous Regiment in 1976 and first presented at the Humberside Theatre, Hull, this is a history play with a difference. Set loosely in the seventeenth century, it charts the persecution of women in the name of witchcraft showing how fear of female sexuality is one of the motor forces behind the witchhunts — and in its 'modern' songs challenges the audience to examine its own attitudes to women and sexuality.

The Visions of Simone Machard. Play. Bertolt Brecht
Translations: Hugh and Ellen Rank
                Ralph Manheim
M12 F3. Extras. A courtyard. Fee code M

Simone, a teenage girl working as a hostelry servant, spends her time reading about Joan of Arc. The period is 1940 and the Germans are advancing towards the French town. In a series of dreams or visions she sees herself as Joan leading a Resistance movement against the enemy. When she attempts to turn her visions into reality her employers commit her to a mental asylum. However, in the last few lines of the play it appears that she has encouraged others in the town to take action.

The Visit. Drama. Friedrich Dürrenmatt. Adapted by Maurice Valency
M29 F8 (9 principals and 28 small parts). Extras. Composite setting. Fee code L

Claire Zachanassian, the richest woman in the world, returns to her poverty-stricken home town. The townspeople are ready to grovel for favours and select as their representative Anton Schell, for Claire and Anton had once been deeply in love. Claire arrives with a sinister ménage. She soon announces that she has come for revenge on her onetime sweetheart, offering a million marks for his life. In the nightmarish climax Schell's corrupted friends sacrifice him to their greed.
ISBN 0 573 61754 6

Visiting Hour. Play. Richard Harris
M2 F4, playing a variety of roles. A hospital ward. Fee code M (for whole play)

Six interlinked plays set in a National Health hospital during visiting hour. Alternately funny and sad — with elements of tragedy and comedy in each — your audience will be reaching for the Kleenex one minute and rolling in the aisles the next! '... packed with sharp lines and cruel characterization ... It hurts to laugh but laugh we do ... for those who like their comedy black there is much to enjoy.' *Daily Telegraph*
ISBN 0 573 01925 8

Vita and Virginia. Play. Eileen Atkins, adapted from the correspondence between Virginia Woolf and Vita Sackville-West
F2 (30, 40). A bare stage. Fee code M

Virginia Woolf and Vita Sackville-West first met in 1922. Through the course of the next twenty years, until Virginia's suicide in 1941, the extraordinary relationship between them was charted in their letters to one another, providing a remarkable insight into their love affair. Eileen Atkins has made a supremely skilful dramatization of their correspondence in which they speak of everyday life, friends, literature and, above all, themselves.
ISBN 0 573 13012 4

A

Vivat! Vivat Regina! Play. Robert Bolt
M27 F4. Extras. Doubling possible. Unit setting. Fee code J

The play follows the relationship between Mary, Queen of Scots and Elizabeth I, from shortly before the former's return to Scotland, through her marriage to Darnley, Rizzio's death, the scandal over Bothwell, Mary's imprisonment, Catholic plots, until her execution, closing as Spain's Armada is in active preparation.
ISBN 0 573 01489 2

A Voyage Round My Father. Play. John Mortimer
M10 (boys, middle-age, 60s) F6 (girl, 50s), with doubling. Fee code M

The author traces his life from the point of view of his relationship with his father. Near the start of the action the latter is blinded by an accident and the play ends with his death. The story is presented with humour, affection and, finally, deep pathos. The setting is a bare stage, with properties brought on and off by cast or stage management, and changes of milieu indicated, where necessary, by alterations in the lighting.
ISBN 0 573 01481 7

Wait Until Dark. Play. Frederick Knott
M6 (20s, 30s) F2 (12, 30). A basement flat. Fee code M

A drug-filled doll has disappeared from a London flat and three petty crooks try to find it. They plot to compel the owners to give away its whereabouts. The owner's wife is blind; the crooks tell her a frightening story involving her husband's supposed infidelity. She, however, becomes suspicious. In a terrifying climax she makes uses of the fact that in the dark the blind have an actual advantage over those who can normally see.
ISBN 0 573 01050 1

Waiting for Godot. Tragic comedy. Samuel Beckett
M4 1 boy. A country road. Fee code M

Two tramps, Vladimir and Estragon, are waiting for someone. To pass the time they indulge in cross talk, they argue, they play bizarre games. Lucky, more animal than human, enters, driven by Pozzo, a wealthy, blubbering creature. Another visitor is a small boy who says he works for Mr Godot and tells the tramps his master will come *tomorrow*. The following day Pozzo and Lucky visit again, as does the small boy with another message: Mr Godot will certainly be coming *tomorrow*. The tramps wait on.
ISBN 0 573 04008 7

Waiting For Yesterday. Play. Duncan Greenwood
M2 (30s, elderly) F6 (30s, elderly). A lounge. Fee code L

This is a sensitive and perceptive look at the elderly residents of a small private hotel which is set to close. Although most of them have lived there for a number of years, they are all just biding their time. All their dreams and hopes for the future are based in the past. They will soon be homeless; this fact, and an attempted suicide, force all the residents to admit that they have been living an illusion. They toast the future, no longer waiting for yesterday.
ISBN 0 573 01602 X

Waiting in the Wings. Play. Noël Coward
M4 (30s, 40s, 70s) F14 (20s-80s). A lounge. Fee code M

'The Wings' is a charity home for retired actresses. Here these aged ladies grow older ungracefully amidst squabbles, jealousies and grandiose memories. The once-great actress Lotta Bainbridge arrives; years ago she married the ex-husband of one of the inmates, May Davenport, and her arrival sparks off a feud. It is only resolved when one deranged old lady sets fire to her room. After this tragedy, Lotta and May spend what little time is left to them in peace and harmony.
ISBN 0 573 01470 1

Walk On Walk On. Play. Willis Hall
M6 (young, 40s, elderly) F2 (18, 30s). An office. Fee code L

The action passes in a single afternoon, during the course of a football match. It is a match of vital importance for the somewhat uninspired record of a Third Division club and it also affects the lives of several of the people connected with it, in particular Gillian Dugdale, who runs the office, and her association with Bernie Gant, club manager. By the end of the match more than the future of the club itself has been decided.
ISBN 0 573 01594 5

The Waltz of the Toreadors. Play. Jean Anouilh. Adapted from the French by Lucienne Hill
M4 (young, middle-age) F7 (young, 18, 30s). A landing/study. Fee code M

Now retired, General St Pé tries to keep old age at bay by dallying with every available pretty woman. His wife Emily, a determined invalid, perpetually complains of her husband's peccadilloes. Seventeen years ago, as they danced to the Waltz of the Toreadors, the General and Ghislaine de Ste Euvert fell in love. Ghislaine has waited, chaste and faithful, for the day when the General will be free of Emily. Now she comes to claim her man, armed with letters that prove Emily has been unfaithful.
ISBN 0 573 01471 X

Warrior. Play. Shirley Gee
M8 F3 or M5 F3. Opportunities for many extras. Composite setting. Fee code M

This powerful, moving drama is based on a true story. In 1750 Hannah Snell, disguised as a boy, goes to sea in search of her errant husband. For seven years she lives as a man, boldly braving wounds, bloody battles and her own troubling visions. Back home, a woman again, penniless, she and two fellow marines form a successful stage act. But apocalyptic visions force her publicly to proclaim the horrors of war and the authorities imprison her in Bedlam. Rescued, she sails away to speak out for life.
ISBN 0 573 01931 2

Was He Anyone? Play. N. F. Simpson
M14 (can be played by M3 or more) F13 (can be played by F4 or more). Acting area with a ramp. Fee code G

An extremely witty study of a bookmaker's runner who takes a long walk off a short ship. The drowning man's cause is taken up by various charitable institutions and well-wishers, so immersed in the paraphernalia of bureaucratic machinery that they omit to rescue the 'drownee'. Playing time approximately 75 minutes

◆ **Wasted**. Play. Simon Bent
M5 F3. In and around a North London house. Fee code M

A housing co-op in North London is the setting for Simon Bent's play which seethes with the frustrations and intrigues of its eight young occupants. An affectionate but satirical eye is cast over this none-too-happy commune, from the uncooperative co-op meeting to the profounder subjects of oppressive jealousy and latent homosexuality. A series of short scenes conveys the rapidly changing tensions, moods and frustrations of this group who seem forever to be swimming against the tide.

Watcher in the Shadow. Play. Norman Holland
F9 (20s, 40s, middle-age). A housekeeper's room. Fee code J

Kesiah, the gypsy, is determined to ensconce herself in the Old Manor House, and is totally unscrupulous in her methods to achieve this. First she contrives the housekeeper's death and takes her place. Then she gets the sharp-eyed servant girl dismissed. Finally she persuades the ageing, drink-shaky Mrs Sumner to make the house over to her and away from the old woman's niece. Installed as owner, Kesiah provides herself with a maid, but here she meets Nemesis. Period 1908
ISBN 0 573 03019 7

Way Upstream. Play. Alan Ayckbourn
M3 (30s) F4 (young, 30s, 40). A boat and surrounding river and banks. Fee code M

What could be more pleasant than a holiday on the river? Unfortunately, things do not go quite as smoothly as Keith, self-appointed skipper, has anticipated. The last straw comes when Vince, hitching a ride upstream, is elected skipper in his place. This dark comedy was presented at the National Theatre, London, in 1982, where real water, rain and a moving boat were used; these are not essential, however, and the play can be produced using simulated or imagined water.
ISBN 0 573 11504 4

The Wayward Spirit. Play. Charlotte Hastings
M6 (20s-50s, elderly) F6 (18, 20s, 40s-50s). A hospital room, an office. Fee code M

Captain Anthony Cole, confined to a wheelchair, dreams of being able to walk again and marry his beloved Chrissy. When he is informed that he won't regain the use of his legs, he lashes out at Chrissy, declaring that he will never marry her. Sister Winifred, who combines professionalism as a nurse with a slightly unorthodox vocation as a nun, saves the day, ensuring that the couple get the wedding they have longed for.
ISBN 0 573 01938 X

We Found Love and an Exquisite Set of Porcelain Figurines Aboard the SS *Farndale Avenue*.
Comedy. David McGillivray and Walter Zerlin Jnr
M2 (20s, any age) F3 (20s, 40s, 50s). Various simple settings. Fee code K

Flushed and following on from their previous successes (?), the stalwart veterans of the F.A.H.E.T.G. Dramatic Society are poised to conquer another dramatic idiom. In romantic vein aboard an ocean-going liner for their excursion into the world of thirties' musical comedy *à la* Noël and Gertie, the ladies prove that the age of elegance, glamour and enchantment is not dead ... well, not quite anyway.
ISBN 0 573 01933 9

Webster. Play. Robert David MacDonald
M10 F4. A theatre corridor. Fee code M

Premièred at the Citizens', Glasgow, and revived at the Old Red Lion in London, this Grand Guignol is based on the few known facts of the great Jacobean playwright's life and on conjecture about his lost play *The Guise*. Trapped and embittered by an appalling family, Webster seeks solace with the attractive boy actors in his company. But then he disagrees with his patron and the theatre manager ... 'This brawling, sprawling play makes a wonderfully entertaining evening ... The language is scatalogical and downright.' *Financial Times*

Wedding of the Year. Comedy. Norman Robbins
M4 (20s, 30s, 50, 70s) F6 (20s, 40s, 70s, 80s). A living-room. Fee code K

Alison Murchison, fat, straight-haired, bespectacled, is the last sort of girl one would visualize as a heroine, but Uncle Frank decides to make her one by entering her as a prospective candidate for a Wedding of the Year competition, selecting a designer to create her wedding dress even before he has found her a suitable husband. His eye falls on Walter Thornton's son, Melvyn, a frustrated inventor and an appallingly clumsy young man. However, the best-laid plans ...
ISBN 0573 11473 0

The Weekend. Play. Michael Palin
M4 (30s, 60s) F5 (teenage, 30s, 50s, 60s). A dog. M1 voice only. A living/dining-room. Fee code M

Cantankerous, misanthropic, miserable, world-weary ... think of an adjective synonymous with 'crabby' and it will apply to Stephen Febble. All he wants is to be left alone, but, to his horror, his long-suffering wife Virginia fills the house with guests for the weekend. Stephen responds in the only way he knows how — with a monstrous display of rudeness. A riot of a comedy with an ever-present dark side.

♦ **Weekend Breaks**. Play. John Godber
M2 (30s, 60s) F1(60s) A voice. An empty stage. Fee code M

John Godber's striking, easily staged play explores the complex relationship between a thirty-three year old theatre studies teacher and his elderly parents. Martin Dawson has invited his parents, Joan and Len, to visit him in the Lake District. This 'enjoyable' weekend break evolves into an opportunity for the release of the pent-up frustrations of a lifetime. Godber successfully combines biting humour with serious intent in this thought-provoking comment on age, communication and life in general.
ISBN 0 573 01940 1

Whale Music. Play. Anthony Minghella
F10 (17, 20s, 40s). Various simple settings. Fee code L

An acutely sensitive, moving portrayal of the lives of a group of women which reflects the attitudes and feelings of women today, depicted in a series of settings which flow gently into each other. Caroline, pregnant by one of her boyfriends, escapes to her seaside birthplace where she is visited by friends. The reaction of these women to each other whilst awaiting the birth is sympathetically told and we become totally involved in the heights and depths of their collective emotions and thoughts.
ISBN 0 573 13015 9

A

What Are Little Girls Made Of? Comedy. Peter Coke
M4 (20s, 60s, old) F6 (young, 40, middle-age). An antiques showroom. Fee code K

Isabel Merryweather runs an antique shop with her Rear-Admiral father. One of her eccentric customers leaves a baby temporarily in the shop and Isabel's strong maternal instincts are aroused. Assisted by her most eccentric visitor of all she sets about an unconventional adoption plan. The unexpected results are astonishingly successful, and the ensuing flood of babies leads to frenetic complications and eventually to a highly original, if questionable, plan of operation, affecting not least the Rear-Admiral.
ISBN 0 573 11483 8

What Every Woman Knows. Comedy. J. M. Barrie
M7 (20s-40s, 60s) F4 (young, 20s). Four interiors. Fee code M

The Wylie family are concerned about Maggie who is still unmarried. Then one night Maggie finds the local railway porter, John Shand, surreptitiously studying in their library. Alick, Maggie's father, offers to help, provided that after five years John will offer himself to Maggie as a husband. Years later, Maggie finally wins John's heart for real by proving just how much his success has been owed to her wit and humour. Period 1900
ISBN 0 573 01475 2

What I Did in the Holidays. Play. Philip Osment
M5 (11, 17, 19, 20s, 60s) F3 (20s, 40s). Various simple interior and exterior settings. Fee code M

On a dilapidated West Country farm in 1963, Morley is coping with puberty and the tangles of love within his family. Mother has temporarily walked out and Morley is drawn to Andy, one of a pair of Scottish hitchhikers who seek shelter at the farm. But things are not as they seem on the surface and Morley's habit of telling tales on his seniors hastens the crisis. (*Slightly restricted*)
ISBN 0 573 01937 1

What the Butler Saw. Black comedy. Joe Orton
M4 (middle-age) F2 (young, middle-age). A room in a private clinic. Fee code M

Dr Prentice is a psychiatrist who believes that the best way to interview a girl for a job is to seduce her. Geraldine does her best to comply. Mrs Prentice, who has seduced a page boy, brings him home with her, just as a state inspector pays a visit. What ensues is a wild mêlée of disappearances, disguises and discoveries as husband and wife try to hide their prizes from one another and the state inspector.

When Did You Last See Your Trousers? Farce. Ray Galton and John Antrobus. Based on a story by Ray Galton and Alan Simpson
M6 F3, with doubling. An apartment. Fee code M

This hilarious farce begins quietly enough with Howard and Penny asleep in bed, when a burglar enters and steals various items, including Howard's suit! Awakening, Howard announces his intention to get back to the wife; but how is he to make it to Esher without his trousers, having been left only vest and pants by the burglar? '... Brilliantly constructed farce ... achingly funny ...' *Guardian*
ISBN 0 573 01667 4

When I was a Girl, I Used to Scream and Shout ... Play. Sharman Macdonald
M1 (young) F3 (30s, middle-age). Split set: a rocky beach and prom. Fee code M

'Sharman Macdonald recounts with sympathy and deliciously rude detail, the sexual misadventures and misconceptions of Fiona, growing up with her repressive mother and best friend Vari in 1950s Scotland. She shows how the girls' excitement and expectations atrophy, so that in their thirties they have become sober stereotypes of the modern woman.' *Time Out*. Sharman Macdonald won the *Evening Standard* Drama Award for the Most Promising Playwright in 1984.

When She Danced. Play. Martin Sherman
M3 (19, 20s, 30s) F5 (17, 40s). A large room. Fee code M

Isadora Duncan, way past her prime as a dancer and haunted by the death of her two children, has to rely on her legendary reputation to raise money for the founding of dancing schools in Europe. Her marriage to Russian revolutionary poet Esenin and her multi-lingual Bohemian household in 1923 Paris are deftly recreated and a sprightly dialogue illuminates a wide variety of subjects: the thrill of destructive passion; language and understanding; and the transience of fame.
ISBN 0 573 01934 7

When the Barbarians Came. Play. Don Taylor
M8 (20s-50s, 70s) F4 (20s, 70s). Various simple settings. Fee code M

In an unnamed country at an unspecified time, the Barbarians seize power in a bloodless coup. Insidiously, they take over institutions, reintroducing slavery with the weak crushed and democracy dead. Adrian, a playwright/artistic director, fears for theatre's survival and sells his soul to provide the bloodthirsty, crude, vulgar fare the Barbarians demand — a gala performance of *Oedipus* with the actor on stage literally blinded and *Richard III* with a real death.

When the Cat's Away. Comedy. Johnnie Mortimer and Brian Cooke
M2 (middle-age) F4 (25, middle-age). A living-room. Fee code M

Based on the popular TV sit-com *George and Mildred,* this is a riotously funny comedy. Mildred has organized a second honeymoon in France for herself and George but he is not keen on her idea. Mildred's sister, Ethel, turns up, having left her husband Humphrey. Then Humphrey arrives, so the *women* set off for France. It isn't long before Humphrey gets George into trouble involving a date with two girls and the unexpected return of their wives!
ISBN 0 573 69131 2

When the Wind Blows. Play. Raymond Briggs
M1 (60s) F1 (60s). Extras. A small cottage and garden. Fee code M

Raymond Briggs's stage version of his famous anti-nuclear cartoon parable is passionately on the side of sanity and survival. Jim and Hilda Bloggs, a retired couple, hear on the radio that a pre-emptive strike is on the way. Armed with Government leaflets, in which he places all his faith, Jim constructs a refuge for them both, and gathers emergency rations. They emerge after the bomb to find a devastated post-holocaust world.
ISBN 0 573 11496 X

When We Are Married. Yorkshire farcical comedy. J. B. Priestley
M8 (young, middle-age) F7 (young, 20s, middle-age). A sitting-room. Fee code M

Twenty-five years ago, the Helliwells, the Parkers and the Soppitts were married on the same day by the same parson. They gather at the Helliwell home to celebrate their silver wedding. The new chapel organist tells them that he recently met the parson who conducted the triple wedding ceremony — he was not authorized to do so. Pandemonium breaks out when these pillars of society believe they have been living in sin for twenty-five years. Period 1900
ISBN 0 573 01476 0

Who Goes Bare? Farce. Richard Harris and Leslie Darbon
M6 (40, middle-age) F4 (young, 20s, 30s, middle-age). An entrance hall. Fee code J

Running a Health and Strength Home in a large mansion can be a hazardous undertaking, as Eddie Manchip knows. He is beset by a sinister crook, a complete desertion of the staff except for one half-witted and hysterical maid, an erring, pompous brother, his suspicious wife, a nude tennis-player, a quick-change artist, the tennis-player's kilted husband and a hearty countrywoman grabbing second-hand clothing for charity. The result? Chaos!
ISBN 0 573 01546 5

Who Killed Santa Claus? Play. Terence Feely
M6 (young, 20s, 30s) F2 (30s). A Chelsea house. Fee code M

Barbara Love is a popular television 'auntie'. It is Christmas, and a number of men connected with her are coming to a party. Her secretary, Connie, is also there. Before they arrive she is threatened by a disguised voice on her Ansaphone, and is sent a grotesque 'murdered' doll in a coffin, in a dress resembling one of her own. It becomes apparent that one of her guests is planning to kill her ...
ISBN 0 573 01510 4

Who Saw Him Die? Play. Tudor Gates
M3 (30s, middle-age) F1 (20-30). Extras M. Composite setting: a surgery, a living-room, a cellar. Fee code M

Former Police Superintendant Pratt is a man with an obsession — to track down the criminal John Rawlings who has eluded him so long. When summoned to Dr Adcock's surgery and presented, apparently, with Rawlings' body Pratt is totally defeated, his purpose in life gone. Things are not what they seem and as a result of a intricate and cunning criminal plot Pratt finds himself engaged in a ruthless duel of wits and bluff that leads to a grim and tense climax.
ISBN 0 573 01568 6

Whodunnit. Comedy thriller. Anthony Shaffer
M7 F3. An eighteenth-century library. Fee code M

This witty, wickedly funny satire, a long-running success on Broadway, is firmly in Agatha Christie country of the 1930s, complete with her stock characters and situations. A group of six strangers have gathered for dinner at Orcas Champflower Manor. One of the guests, an oily Levantine, informs each of his fellow guests that he has the means to blackmail them. Not suprisingly he gets murdered — but whodunnit? In Act II the surprise is unveiled.
ISBN 0 573 61823 2

Whoops-a-Daisy. Play. Keith Waterhouse and Willis Hall
M3 (middle-age) F3 (young, middle-age). A living-room and patio. Fee code L

James and Iris live comfortably in their green-belt bungalow enjoying a placid existence in which a discussion on cornflakes can take on major significance. With them is their daughter, about to divorce her husband for his 'certain habits'. They await the arrival of their new neighbours, the Smedleys, with interest which turns to dismay when the Smedleys turn out to be brash aggressive intruders who start by taking over their phone and continue by trying to run their entire lives.
ISBN 0 573 11486 2

Who's Afraid of Virginia Woolf? Play. Edward Albee
M2 (30, 40) F2 (26, 52). A living-room. Fee code M

George, an assistant professor of history, and his wife, Martha, invite Nick and Honey to their home on the campus of a small New England college. Throughout the long liquor-drenched night, the strangers are forcibly initiated into the demoniac misery of George and Martha's eternal matrimonial *corrida*. Martha exposes a secret, which George cannot forgive, and the guests slip away, leaving George and Martha, who love each other but hate themselves and therefore can only hurt each other.

Who's Under Where? Farce. Marcia Kash and Doug Hughes
M5 (20s, 40s, 50s) F2 (30s). An hotel suite. Fee code M

Jane and Sybil are on the verge of the deal of their lives. They plan to convince the world famous Italian designer Bruno Fruferelli to buy their 'Passion Fashion Wear' line of lingerie. They arrange to give him a private fashion show in a fancy hotel suite. The models are booked, the champagne is on ice, the sexy samples are on display — and then their jealous husbands arrive, inevitably jumping to the wrong conclusions!
ISBN 0 573 69389 7

Whose Life Is It Anyway? Play. Brian Clark
M9 F5. Multiple set. Fee code M

Ken Harrison has been so severely injured in a car crash that he is totally paralysed; only his brain functions normally. He is being kept alive by the miracles of medicine, but wishes to die. This he could achieve by discharging himself from hospital but being wholly helpless has to gain the authorities' consent. The play examines the moral and legal aspects of the situation and the reactions of the hospital staff.
ISBN 0 573 01587 2

Why Me? Comedy. Stanley Price
M3 (19, 30, middle-age) F3 (30, 40, 60). A living-room, a dining area. Fee code M

A very funny comedy of unemployment which starred Richard Briers as redundant civil engineer John, a bitter recipient of a 'tarnished chrome' handshake. During the ensuing summer he struggles bravely with job rejections; loss of dignity in the face of his wife's hugely successful pizza business; an adulterous affair; the incipient break-up of his marriage and repeated forays into his house by his mother-in-law who refuses to stay in her granny flat!
ISBN 0 573 01622 4

Why Not Stay for Breakfast? Comedy. Gene Stone and Ray Cooney
M3 (young, 30s) F2 (17, young). A flat. Fee code L

George, respected member of the Establishment, once married, now alone, lives in Hampstead. The apartment above his is inhabited by hippies and one night the very pregnant Louise arrives on his doorstep having rowed with Davey in their pad upstairs. The clash between the hippies and the square type is at full strength when Louise starts labour pains! George takes charge and both the baby and Louise remain in the flat for the time being. Period 1970
ISBN 0 573 01580 5

◆ **Widows**. Play. Ariel Dorfman, with Tony Kushner
Large, flexible cast, may be played by M6 F8. Various simple settings. Fee code M

In a war-torn village the men have disappeared. The women — their mothers, wives, daughters — wait by the river, hope and mourn. Their anguish is unspoken until bruised and broken bodies begin being washed up on the banks and the women defy the military in the only form of protest left to them. Ariel Dorfman's smouldering political allegory, written in collaboration with Tony Kushner, was given its European première by the Traverse Theatre in Cambridge, Oxford, Newcastle and Edinburgh.

Wife Begins at Forty. Comedy. Arne Sultan, Earl Barret and Ray Cooney
M4 (16, 40s, 75) F2 (30, 40). 1 dog. A living-room. Fee code M

This delightful comedy was premièred by Ray Cooney's Theatre of Comedy. Forty is a traumatic age for some people, especially Linda Harper who starts worrying about it three years before the date! Dissatisfied spiritually and physically with marriage to the staid George, Linda decides to leave. George moves out, giving Linda a chance to 'find herself', but returning to discuss maintenance they discover the flames of passion are not quite dead!
ISBN 0 573 01636 4

The Wild Duck. Play. Henrik Ibsen, translated by Christopher Hampton
M12 F3. 8M 2F extras. A study, a studio. Fee code M

Here is the greatest account ever written of the destructiveness of missonary zeal. Gregers Werle enters the house of photographer Ekdal preaching 'the demands of idealism' (a nicely ambiguous phrase in Hampton's translation) and systematically destroys a family's happiness. 'If Ibsen's play is not a masterpiece, then the word is devoid of meaning.' *Guardian*
ISBN 0 573 61820 8

Wild Goose Chase. Farce. Derek Benfield
M5 (20s, middle-age) F5 (young, 20s, 40s, middle-age). A baronial hall. Fee code K

Chester Dreadnought bluffs his way into the crumbling stately home of an impecunious aristocratic family, and even a trigger-happy belted Earl suffering from hallucinations cannot keep at bay the enterprising pair of jewel thieves who are pursuing their loot — not to mention Chester — round the castle. Suits of armour and secret doors, mistaken identities and dotty servants all help to provide the variety of fare that goes to the making of this wild goose chase.
ISBN 0 573 11501 X

Wild Honey. Play. Anton Chekhov, translated and adapted by Michael Frayn
M12 (young to elderly) F4 (young, middle-age). Four settings. Fee code M

A dazzling version of this dark comedy (sometimes called *Platonov*) premièred at the National Theatre in 1984 starring Ian McKellen as the complex, but hapless schoolmaster Platonov who lurches from one amorous chaos to the next, until, tormented, self-recriminating and suffering from delirium tremens he dies in the path of an oncoming train. Frayn has subtly cut and remodelled the original six-hour running time whilst staying close to Chekhov's original.

Wildest Dreams. Play. Alan Ayckbourn
M4 (young, middle-age) F4 (young, middle-age), 1M 1F, voices only. Three acting areas. Fee code M

Four typical Ayckbourn misfits are playing a Dungeons-and-Dragons type game in a suburban living-room. The repressed Hazel and Stanley, her meek, sex-starved husband, are joined by emotionally-retarded, computer-freak schoolboy, Warren, and Rick, a taciturn lesbian. The game offers the chance for them to be beautiful, wise and heroic — qualities they will never possess in reality. The advent of Marcie, escaping from her violent husband, blows apart their foursome. ISBN 0 573 01932 0

Will You Still Love Me in the Morning? Farce. Brian Clemens and Dennis Spooner
M4 (30s-50s) F3 (25-40s), or M3 F4, 1M voice only. A country cottage. Fee code M

Jeremy and Celia return early from their honeymoon to find that both Jeremy's working partners have accepted his offer to stay in his house while he is away; unfortunately they have each brought the other's wife with them. Jeremy discovers one illicit couple, Celia the other, and both issue invitations to dinner. Desperate to make a good impression, they then must stage two dinner parties — simultaneously! ISBN 0 573 01935 5

◆ **The Wind in the Willows**. Kenneth Grahame. Adapted for the stage by Alan Bennett. Music by Jeremy Sams
24 characters. Extras. Various settings. Fee code M (play) code C (music)

The characters of Ratty, Mole, Toad and Badger have delighted generations of readers. Alan Bennett's version is true to the original and yet carries the distinctive Bennett hallmark. It was first performed at the Royal National Theatre in 1990 and subsequently at the Old Vic Theatre, London, in a shortened version adapted for proscenium staging. This is the version given here. The music by Jeremy Sams is available in a separate songbook. ISBN 0 573 01930 4

The Wind in the Willows. Family entertainment. John Morley, adapted from the novel by Kenneth Grahame
22 characters, chorus. Doubling possible. Various interior and exterior settings. Fee code L

John Morley has taken the well-loved characters of Toad, Mole, Ratty and Badger from Kenneth Grahame's classic tale and woven their exploits into an exciting adventure story for all the family. Designed to be staged simply or elaborately, the casting is also very flexible with choice of music left up to individual producers. This delightful play will provide an evening of magic and joy for all. ISBN 0 573 05073 2

The Wind of Heaven. Play. Emlyn Williams
M4 (13, 30-50) F4 (20, 30s). A lounge. Fee code M

Dilys Parry, an inconsolable Crimean War widow, lives in Blestin, a village which has no children, sings no songs, and worships no god since a disaster snatched away all its youth. She is gradually re-awakened to life once a Miracle boy's influence begins to permeate her home and the village. A flashy showman turns up intending to exploit the boy but becomes his world-forsaking disciple. The boy restores a dead man to life but dies himself in agony. Period 1856
ISBN 0 573 01653 4

Wings. Play. Arthur Kopit
M4 (30, elderly) F5 (elderly, 70s). Extras. A hospital recreation room and other locations. Fee code M

Emily Stilson, once an aerial acrobat, has suffered a stroke and is in hospital. The play takes us into her strange, shattered world and concerns her gradual, painful, struggle to bring together the pieces of an existence in which time, place, language and thought have become terrifyingly dislocated. A human story of the utmost compassion, and even of hope.

The Winslow Boy. Play. Terence Rattigan
M7 (14, 20-40, 60) F4 (30-50, elderly). A living-room. Fee code M

Cadet Ronnie Winslow is expelled from the Royal Naval College accused of stealing. His father, refusing to believe his guilt and dissatisfied with the manner in which the investigation was conducted, demands a new inquiry. This is refused and Arthur Winslow settles down to fight for his son's honour. Following an independent inquiry the matter is taken to the House of Commons but Arthur ruins himself financially and in health in the process. But his stubbornness wins, a civil trial is allowed and Ronnie is acquitted. Period Edwardian
ISBN 0 573 01494 9

Winter Glory. Comedy. Peter Coke
M1 (elderly) F7 (25, middle-age, elderly). Extras 2M. A drawing-room. Fee code L

We meet once again the redoubtable quartet of Dame Beatrice and her lodgers — Nan, Hattie and the Brigadier — who featured in Peter Coke's earlier comedies *Breath of Spring*, *Midsummer Mink* and *Autumn Manoeuvres*. This, however, will be positively their last appearance, as due to an unfortunate slip-up in their schemes to put a pathetic pet out of its misery and to help an ageing actress fade away at a peak of happiness, they dispatch themselves heavenwards as well!
ISBN 0 573 01674 7

♦ **The Winter Guest**. Play. Sharman Macdonald
M3 (young) F5 (young, 30s, elderly). A seaside promenade and beach. Fee code M

The play is set on a seaside promenade and intermingles the lives of several sets of people found there. A grandmother is still clings on to her daughter, a young photographer, who is trying to come to terms with the death of her husband, while the photographer's son pursues love. Two young truant boys are concerned with the onset of puberty. And an elderly pair of ladies discuss their favourite pastime, funeral attendance. NB. Contains explicit language.

The Winter Wife. Play. Claire Tomalin
M1 (30s) F3 (30s, 50s). A *wagon-lit* compartment, a surgery, a salon and terrace. Fee code M

In the winter of 1920-21, the consumptive Katherine Mansfield went to Menton in the South of France in the vain hope of recuperating, accompanied by her lifelong friend and devoted companion Ida Baker, whom Katherine frequently treated abominably and called her 'wife'. Claire Tomalin's play concentrates on this episode, tracing the relationship between the two women as well as Katherine's role as wife to John Middleton Murry.

Witness for the Prosecution. Play. Agatha Christie
M: 9 principals, 15 extras. F: 4 principals, 2 extras. Justice's chambers. Law Courts. Fee code M

Although circumstantial evidence is damning, Leonard Vole convinces even the perceptive Sir Wilfred that he is innocent of murder. In the mounting tension of the trial there are three amazing developments. Vole's wife takes the stand and coldly swears away her husband's alibi. A brassy young woman then sells Sir Wilfred's letters proving Mrs Vole has committed perjury. Vole is acquitted but only then does Sir Wilfred discover how this acquittal has been engineered by Mrs Vole. But there is still the dramatic finale ...
ISBN 0 573 01500 7

Wolf at the Door. Original play (*Les Corbeaux*) by Henry Becque, translated by David Walker and adapted by Alan Ayckbourn
M9, F6 plus M3 (non-speaking). A drawing-room. Fee code M

When a sudden heart attack claims the life of the father of the Vigneron household, the family is plunged into economic turmoil. Madame Vigneron and her children are forced to rely on the advice of others in sorting out the complicated estate, and find they are surrounded by wolves at every turn in the form of creditors, business associates and 'friends'. Period nineteenth century
ISBN 0 573 01936 3

Wolfsbane. Play. Georgina Reid
M2 (20, 50) F4 (16, 45, 50s). A kitchen. Fee code L

Joan, a renowned sculptor, forgets she has engaged Mrs Bond as cook, until the lady and her daughter, Sarah, turn up. Put off by Mrs Bond's attitude, they are won over by her cooking and the charming Sarah (who sits for Joan). Mrs Bond is furious when she finds out and a sequence of sinister events is set in train leading to the near-death of Gran. Mrs Bond is arrested for attempted murder, but it is up to Gran to reveal the would-be killer.
ISBN 0 573 11503 6

Woman in Mind. Play. Alan Ayckbourn
M5 (20, 30, 40) F3 (20, 40s). A garden. Fee code M

Seen at the Vaudeville, London, in 1986 with Julia McKenzie and Martin Jarvis this is one of Ayckbourn's blacker comedies, dealing with the gradual mental collapse of Susan. Starved of affectionate companionship and understanding love by an appalling husband and priggish son, Susan conjures up an ideal family. But gradually she loses control over this dream and finally breaks down in a nightmarish fantasy involving her real and imaginary families.
ISBN 0 573 01662 3

The Woman in White. Play. Constance Cox, adapted from the novel by Wilkie Collins
M6 (20s to elderly) F5 (20s to elderly). A drawing-room. Fee code H. Typescript on hire

The story of unhappy Laura Fairlie and the plot to deprive her of her fortune is as gripping now as
when Collins first wrote it. Lovers of period drama will welcome Constance Cox's admirable
dramatization, neatly constructed as to allow presentation in one set. Period 1861-2

The Women. Play. Clare Booth Luce
F44: 11 principals and 33 small parts; doubling and trebling possible. Twelve interiors. Fee
code J

Mary Haines's friends are cynical about her happy, successful marriage. When news reaches the
friends that Stephen, Mary's husband, is enjoying a dalliance with the gold-digging Crystal Allen,
Mary is soon informed. Her mother, wise and worldly, advises her to forgive him, but she feels
divorce is the only solution. Eventually, having learned from her friends the laws of the female
jungle, Mary sharpens her claws, and prepares to win back the man she still loves.

◆ **Women on the Verge of HRT.** Play. Marie Jones. Music by Neil Martin
M1 (early 30s) F2 (40s). A hotel bedroom, a beach. Fee code M

Vera and Anna have made the trip to Donegal to see their singing idol Daniel O'Donnell. Vera has
been abandoned by her husband and Anna is content to dream of Daniel whilst sustaining a
loveless marriage. Singing waiter, Fergal, invites the women to join him at dawn. In a series of
dream-like meetings the women confront their spouses and each other. Neil Martin's country-
style songs enhance this easily-staged, telling look at the spirit of women.
ISBN 0 573 01939 8

◆ **A Word from Our Sponsor.** Words by Alan Ayckbourn. Music by John Pattison
M4 F5. A disused railway station. Fee by arrangement

This futuristic musical is set in a small-town railway station, sometime all too soon. Harry Wooller,
a vicar, is looking for sponsorship for his group's musical Mystery play. His call is intercepted by
a dubious but immensely powerful source — Valda/Valder who alternates between male and
female forms. Artistry is soon compromised; this drastic interference forces the group to reveal
their past deeds, and recognize the need for change.
ISBN 0 573 08105 0 Vocal score ISBN 0 573 08603 6 Perusal material available

Woyzeck. Play. Georg Büchner, translated by John Mackendrick
M10 F3, with doubling. Various interior and exterior settings. Fee code M

This anti-romantic and starkly realistic tragedy is about a common soldier, Woyzeck, who attempts
to make sense out of life in the face of the intolerance of those about him who think him stupid.
Driven mad by external forces — inhuman military discipline, environment, class and religion —
he slaughters his wife and then drowns himself. Büchner's portrayal is ironic and compassionate:
the play was a remarkable nineteenth-century call for the need for social reform.

Wuthering Heights. Play. Emily Brontë, adapted for the stage by Charles Vance
M6 F4. Composite setting. Fee code M

A new version of Emily Brontë's great classic, the immortal love story set amid the bleak beauty of Haworth Moor, the landscape over which towers the wild, terrible figure of Heathcliff. The tale of his searing passion for the beautiful Catherine Earnshaw has the vividness of nightmare, the beauty and simplicity of an old ballad and the depth and intensity of ancient tragedy. Period nineteenth century
ISBN 0 573 11474 9

A Yard of Sun. Play. Christopher Fry
M9 (young to middle-age) F3 (young, middle-age). A courtyard. Fee code M

A 'summer comedy' set in Sienna just after World War II. Preparations are in hand for the renewal of the Palio fiesta — a horse race which has been held in the town for hundreds of years. Angelino is one of two central characters whose families are unexpectedly reunited after the war, and the play deals with the effects of the reunion both on individuals and on the group as a whole. Period 1946

The Year After The Fair. Play. Donald Madgwick
M4 (20-50) F4 (18, 20, 30s). A drawing-room. Fee code L

Thomas Hardy's story *On The Western Circuit*, dramatized so successfully by Frank Harvey under the title *The Day After The Fair,* is the starting point for this delightful play. Charles and Anna's wedding goes ahead although Charles is still unaware that the writer of the letters with whom he is so in love is Edith and not Anna, her former servant. On the eve of Edith's departure to Europe she spends the night with Charles in an attempt to escape her desolate world. The events unfold in the high summer of the British Empire, 1893, under the watchful eye of Thomas Hardy himself.
ISBN 0 573 01683 6

Yerma. Play. Federico García Lorca. Translated by Peter Luke
M3 F13. Stark set. Fee code M

Peter Luke's translation of this powerful and passionate play was performed at the National Theatre in 1987 with Juliet Stevenson and Roger Lloyd-Pack. It tells the tragic tale of Yerma, an Andalusian woman trapped by circumstance and social obligations in a joyless and barren marriage. The play revolves around two central obsessions — Yerma's desperate need for a child and the indifference and impotence of her husband. In a passionate frenzy Yerma murders her husband in response to her frustrated desires.

You Say Tomatoes. Comedy. Bernard Slade
M2 (50s, 70) F2 (20s, 50s-60s). 2 living-rooms. Fee code M

Giles, quintessentially English, doesn't take kindly to the intrusion of Americans Libby and Daisy. Libby needs to contact T. J. Walbourne, the famous mystery writer, to put together a film deal. Walbourne is, of course, Giles, and he musters all his reserve to thwart Libby. Finally, she admits defeat. But Libby has aroused passions in Giles and within days he is knocking at her door with a neat romantic compromise!
ISBN 0 573 69540 7

You Should See Us Now. Play. Peter Tinniswood
M2 (40s) F4 (30s, 60). Composite setting. Fee code M

Divorcé Graham asks friends Ernest and Pamela to help out with the holiday visit of his children. The children are brought by his ex-wife and her mother, who disapproves of Graham's lifestyle. Pamela, although childless, has strong views on children and organizes a party for them. By having the adults play both the party guests and themselves as children we are given fascinating and funny glimpses of their pasts, making their scenes as grown-ups all the more pertinent.
ISBN 0 573 11512 5

Zack. Comedy. Harold Brighouse
M6 (20, 30, middle-age) F4 (18, young, 50s). A parlour/refreshment room. Fee code M

Harold Brighouse manages to extract the maximum of comedy from a farcical situation. Zack is the half-witted son of a wedding purveyor whose cheerfulness and goodheartedness are a greater asset than his brother's crafty greed, and the story shows in most amusing fashion how he eventually wins self-respect and a bride. Period 1920s
ISDBN 0 573 01710 7

Zigger Zagger. Play. Peter Terson
M34 F5. Extras. Composite setting. Fee code M

Specially written for the National Youth Theatre the play depicts with enormous vigour the story of Harry, a 'football hooligan' and his progress forwards from the end of his schooldays. Football is in fact only the background to the author's real concern, which is the emptiness and futility facing so many youngsters today when they leave secondary school at fifteen, only to find themselves in a series of dead-end jobs. The play may indeed be called an important social document but its essential appeal lies in its exhilarating theatrical life.

How to Order Your Books

Retail Mail Order

RETAIL MAIL ORDER

Unless you already have an Account with us, pre-payment is required for ALL orders, either

a) by cheque or postal order made out to Samuel French Ltd

OR

b) by credit/debit card when the number and expiry date of the registered card MUST be quoted.

Please send your order to:

Mail Order Department
Samuel French Ltd
52 Fitzroy Street
London W1P 6JR

Or you may telephone your order on 020 7255 4300 or fax on 020 7387 2161 and quote your credit/debit card number.

Credit/debit card orders may also be left on our telephone answering service outside office hours. Please leave a daytime telephone number should we need to contact you during office hours (Monday to Friday 9.30 a.m. to 5.30 p.m.).

Please ensure when ordering by credit/debit card that your card number is correctly quoted, together with the date of expiry and the address of the registered card owner.

Trade Customers

TRADE CUSTOMERS

Please enquire for trade terms and conditions.

The current prices of the plays in this Guide, together with postage rates for inland and overseas customers, can be found in our Price List, issued separately.

Orders for books may also be addressed to our authorized agents whose names and addresses appear on page ix of this Guide.

SECTION B

One Act Plays and Revue Sketches

B

CONTENTS

B

Classified Index

B

Plays arranged according to the number of characters

ONE CHARACTER

MALE
Chip in the Sugar
Krapp's Last Tape
Lady Bracknell's Confinement
Leslie
Time of Wolves and Tigers
Wendlebury Day

FEMALE
Bed Among the Lentils
Cream Cracker Under the Settee
Her Big Chance
Human Voice
Lady Bracknell's Confinement
Lady of Letters
Maureen
Medea
Post Mortem
Same Old Story
Soldiering On
Waking Up
Woman Alone
Woman of No Importance

TWO CHARACTERS

Last Call for Breakfast (*variable cast*)

COMEDIES

M1 F1
Alas Poor Fred
Extraordinary Revelations of Orca
  the Goldfish
Heir's Return
Joining the Club
Plaster
Waiting

M2
Victoria Station
Yes and No

F2
Dancers
Day Trippers
Doggies
Indian Summer
Theatrical Digs

PLAYS

M1 F1
Evergreens
Green Favours
Last Things
Lifelines
Rialto
Stuttgart
Talk to Me Like the Rain ...
This Property is Condemned
Visit From Miss Protheroe

M2
Acting Exercise
Audience (Havel)
Bookends
Duck Variations
Man of Letters
Me and My Friend
Memento Mori
Out of the Flying Pan
Stanley Parkers

F2
Early Blight
Me and My Friend
Shoppers

SERIOUS PLAYS

M1 F1
Abortive
Ashes
Close to Croydon
I Can't Imagine Tomorrow
Poor Old Simon
Silver Wedding
Then
Whence

M2
New World Order
Protest

F2
Keeping Mum

DRAMAS

M1 F1
Auto-Da-Fé
Bar and Ger
Dead End
Forward to the Right
Galway Girl
Humour Helps
Moony's Kid Don't Cry
Mortmain
Neighbours
Sound of Silence

M2
Death Artist
Dock Brief
Dumb Waiter
Zoo Story

F2
Effie's Burning
Guilt Card
Late Frost
Short Changed
Something Unspoken

THREE CHARACTERS

Edge (*variable cast*)
Tryst (*variable cast*)

COMEDIES

M1 F2
Genteel
Mutatis Mutandis
Say Something Happened
Slight Accident
What Shall We Do With The Body?

M2 F1
Albert
Boundary
Edwin
Maria Marten (Dennis)
Matchstick Dreams
Smell of Burning

M3
Molecatcher

PLAYS

M1 F2
Big Cats
Commitment
Consequences
Hitting Town
Kind of Alaska
Lady of Larkspur Lotion
Lunch Hour
Office Song
Phoenix Too Frequent
Rape of Bunny Stuntz
Resounding Tinkle
Roman Fever
Seagulls

B

M2 F1
Drag Factor
Family Voices
From Here To The Library
Is It Something I Said?
Last Munro
Meat and Two Veg
Private Ear
Private View
Proposal
Public Eye
View from the Obelisk
Waiting for a Bus
White Liars

M3
Kind of Vesuvius

F3
Christmas Incorporated
Leaving
Who Was Hilary Maconochie?

SERIOUS PLAYS

M1 F2
Dark Room
Epitaph For A Hard Man
I Rise in Flame, Cried the Phoenix
Lesson
Long Stay Cut Short
Sins of the Father
Sunbeams
Too Hot to Handle

M2 F1
Birdsong
Chairs
Escapologist
Field of Olives
Little Brother, Little Sister
Lover
Nothing Personal
Not Not Not Not Not Enough Oxygen
Old One-Two
One-Sided Triangle
River

Slight Ache
Twenty-Seven Wagons Full of Cotton
Wall

F3
And Go to Innisfree
Cecily
Chimera
Last of My Solid Gold Watches

M3
Last of My Solid Gold Watches
Vigil

DRAMAS

M1 F2
Cut in the Rates (*min. cast*)

M2 F1
Edge

M3
Dwarfs
Edge

F3
Donahue Sisters

FOUR CHARACTERS

Properly Processed (*variable cast*)
Savoury Meringue (*variable cast*)

FARCES

M2 F2
As You Were
Better Late
Master and the Maid
Pastiche
Space Between the Years
Upstairs Cuckoo

COMEDIES

M1 F3
Don't Blame It on the Boots
Fumed Oak

M2 F2
Bang, You're Dead!
Cards
Come into the Garden Maud
Different Way to Die
Drunkard's Wife
Figuring Things
Fluff
Getting and Spending
Hitman
House Plant
Intruders
Jolly Sinister Jape
Last Panto in Little Grimley
Last Tango in Little Grimley
Night Errant
Night Out (Vickery)
Other People
Save My Child!
Sense of the Ridiculous
Sexual Perversity in Chicago
Sparrows
Split Ends
Trouble Shared
Twelve-Pound Look

M3 F1
Before Dawn
Bells
Drunkard's Dilemma
Every Picture Tells A Story
Maria Marten (Austin)
Mayhem at the Mill
Wages of Sin

F4
What Ho Within

PLAYS

Teddy Bear's Picnic (*variable cast*)

M1 F3
After I'm Gone
Departure
Interior Designs
Lord Byron's Love Letter
Pity About Kitty
Respectable Funeral
Sweet Caroline Sweet

M2 F2
Café
Case of the Crushed Petunia
Form
I Never Thought It Would Be Like This
In Room Five Hundred and Four
Joggers
Knightsbridge
One Careful Owner
Patio Window
Perfect Partners
Sandcastles on the Beach
Stop the Nightmare
Sweet Caroline Sweet

M3 F1
Railwayman's New Clothes
Strangest Kind of Romance
Young Guy Seeks Part-Time Work

M4
Bespoke Overcoat

F4
Café Society
People Like Us
Relics
September Revisited
What Brutes Men Are

SERIOUS PLAYS

M1 F3
Branwell
Everybody's Friend

B

M2 F2
Hyde Park
In Need of Care
On the Verandah
Ritual for Dolls
Secrets
Shadows of the Evening
Train
Three More Sleepless Nights
Yesterday Man

M3 F1
Collection
Endgame
One for the Road
Receive This Light
Soldier and the Woman

F4
Everybody's Friend

M4
Bright Boy

DRAMAS

M1 F3
Cut in the Rates

M2 F2
Bottles With Baskets On
Company Come
Daddy's Gone A-Hunting
Love Course
Murder Play
Nightingale and Not the Lark
Rats

M3 F1
One Season's King

M4
Hebrew Lesson
Loophole
Sleep of Prisoners

F4
Flowers for Mrs Hopkins
Garden Room
Hello from Bertha
Visitor

FIVE CHARACTERS

Kids (*variable cast*)

FARCES

M1 F4
Housekeeper Wanted
Music Lovers

M3 F2
After Magritte

M4 F1
Don't Walk About With Nothing On
Englishman Abroad
Put Some Clothes On, Clarisse!

F5
Day of Reckoning

COMEDIES

M1 F4
Shop for Charity

M2 F3
Babysitting Calvin
Barnstable
Cahoot's Macbeth
Caught on the Hop
Temptation Sordid

M3 F2
Double, Double
Getting Along
I Spy
Last of the Last of the Mohicans
Monmouth
Push
What's for Pudding?

M4 F1

Black Eye'd Susan
Brave Bugler
Husbands Are a Girl's Best Friend
Little Lights of Kimberley

F5

Costa del Packet
Crowing Hen
Face the Music
From 5 to 5.30
In by the Half
Skip

PLAYS

M1 F4

Not Bobby

M2 F3

Green Forms
Hot Fudge
House Without Windows
Old Quebec
Olive and Hilary
Pizzazz
Sour Grapes and Ashes
Twenty-Five Not Out

M3 F2

Frosted Glass Coffin
Humphrey Pumphrey Had A Great Fall
London Vertigo
Perfect Analysis Given by a Parrot
Tippers
Waiting Room

F5

Cards Cups and Crystal Ball
Rialto Prom
Smile
Think the Beautiful Thoughts
Whose Wedding Is It Anyway?

SERIOUS PLAYS

M2 F3

American Dream
But Yesterday
Janna Years

M3 F2

David's Birthday
Day of the Dog
Dreamjobs
Going All the Way
Mobile 4
Rattling the Railings
Something in the Genes

M4 F1

Measures Taken
If Yer Take A Short Cut

DRAMAS

M1 F4

Failed Investments
In by the Half
Parentcraft
Permission to Cry
Under the Twelfth Sign

M2 F3

Baby Love
Have a Nice Day
Last Wife
Mum's the Word
Permission to Cry
Tunnel Vision
Walking Dead!

M3 F2

Mantrap
Night's Candles
Overtime
Sequence of Events

B

F5

Alas Dear Reader
Ghost of a Chance
Little Benjamin
Long Home
Nasty Things Murders
Permission to Cry
Quake
Shindig
Trial

SIX CHARACTERS

Can You Hear the Music? (*variable cast*)
Singing in the Wilderness (*variable cast*)
Winter of 1917 (*variable cast*)

FARCES

M2 F4
Magic
One Month Early

M3 F3
Take Your Medicine Like a Man
Tram-Track Tragedy
What the Dinosaur
Who Will Man the Lifeboat?

M4 F2
Crimson Coconut

COMEDIES

M1 F5
Careful Rapture

M2 F4
Curses, Foiled Again!
Distracted Globe
Separate Peace
Showbusiness (*min. cast*)

M3 F3
Brenton Versus Brenton
Gypsy Curse

Miasma in Mostyn Mews
One Month to Pay
School Ties
Thermal Underwear

M4 F2
Code of the West
Double Dealing
Fanny's Prayer
Fifteen Minute Hamlet
Red Peppers

M5 F1
Set a Thief to Catch a Thief

F6
Darlings You Were Wonderful
Flesh Game

PLAYS

M1 F5
Bedside Manner

M2 F4
Droitwich Discovery
Going Home
Heart's Desire (min.cast)

M3 F3
Happy Journey
Hunting Pink
It's All in the Game

M4 F2
Lovesick

F6
Country Rebel
Mrs Meadowsweet
Now and Then
Once and for All
Our Branch in Brussels
Slight Misunderstanding

SERIOUS PLAYS

M2 F4
Asylum

M3 F3
Bald Prima Donna
Birds Stopped Singing
Bye Bye Blues
Fallen Heroes
No Picnic

M4 F2
Aftermath
Are You Normal, Mr Norman?
Do-Gooders
Portrait of a Madonna
Room
Two Summers

M5 F1
Aftermath

DRAMAS

Our Man (*variable cast*)

M2 F4
After Midnight—Before Dawn
Exiles

M3 F3
Conversations with a Golliwog
Gnädiges Fräulein
Goodbye Iphigenia

M4 F2
Return

M5 F1
Question of Attribution

M6
Fourth Prisoner

F6
Borderline
Just a Little Word
Terrace Talk
Who Calls?

SEVEN CHARACTERS

Stalag 69 (*variable cast*)

FARCES

M4 F3
This Desirable Cottage

COMEDIES

M1 F6
Orchestra
Womberang

M2 F5
Easy Stages
Last Bread Pudding
Nudes in Waning Light

M3 F4
Courting Disaster
Easy Stages
Last Bread Pudding
World Première

M4 F3
Chinese Pendant
Nellie's Nightlights
Vin Extraordinaire

M6 F1
Green Eye of the Little Yellow Dog

PLAYS

M2 F5
Last Scene of All
Reading Group
Shadows

M3 F4
For the Love of Norman
Shadows
Too Long an Autumn

M4 F3
Cup Final
There's None So Blind

M5 F2
Fear of Heaven
Foreign Bodies
Game of Soldiers
Hiss the Villain!
Hole

F7
Bus Stop
None the Wiser
Tea Dance

SERIOUS PLAYS

M2 F5
Suddenly Last Summer

M3 F4
Beata Beatrix
Judge's Wife
Philip and Rowena
Umjana Land
Victory of the Cross

M4 F3
Play for Yesterday

M5 F2
Browning Version
Mountain Language

F7
Gathering of Doves
Second Easter

DRAMAS

M2 F5
Long Noon

M3 F4
Demon

M4 F3
No Why

F7
Crossways

EIGHT CHARACTERS

FARCES

M1 F7
Husbands Supplied

COMEDIES

Top Table (*variable cast*)

M4 F4
Little Red Whittington
New Leaf

M5 F3
Black Comedy
Real Inspector Hound
Red Hot Cinders

PLAYS

M3 F5
Two Fat Men

B

M4 F4
Albert's Plot

M5 F3
Parochial Problems

F8
Lovesome Thing
Person of No Consequence

SERIOUS PLAYS

Cagebirds (*variable cast*)

M3 F5
Parcel
Random Moments in a May Garden

M5 F3
Parcel
Ringing for You (*min. cast*)

DRAMAS

M2 F6
Blue Kettle

M4 F4
Is There Anybody There?

NINE CHARACTERS

Christmas Incorporated (*variable cast*)
Do-it-Yourself Frankenstein Outfit (*variable cast*)
Growing Pains (*variable cast*)
Melons at the Parsonage (*variable cast*)
Present Slaughter (*variable cast*)

COMEDIES

M2 F7
Sold to the Gypsies

M3 F6
Merry Regiment of Women

M4 F5
George
Hidden Meanings

M5 F4
Frankenstein's Guests
Hands Across the Sea
Out for the Count
Ways and Means

B

LIGHT PLAY

Zartan (*variable cast*)

M6 F3
Right Place

SERIOUS PLAYS

M1 F8
Waiting for Alec

M2 F7
Waiting for Alec

M5 F4
Martyred Wives
Party Time

M7 F2
Long Goodbye

DRAMAS

M5 F4
Patient

M6 F3
Señora Carrar's Rifles

TEN CHARACTERS

Streuth (*variable cast*)

B

COMEDIES

M4 F6
Albert Laddin
Fiesta Fandango
Puss in Slippers

M6 F4
Double, Double
Fishy Business
Piccalilli Circus
Way Out West

F10
Clara's on the Curtains!
Speeches and Cream

PLAYS

M5 F5
Dial 10 Amazing Little Boyfriends
Hot Fudge

M6 F4
Dispute

SERIOUS PLAYS

M7 F3
One Thing More

M9 F1
Exception and the Rule

DRAMAS

M4 F6
Cold Salmon

M5 F5
LittleBro Morning and BigSis Afternoon
What Are You Doing Here?

ELEVEN CHARACTERS AND OVER

After-Dinner Joke
Afternoon at the Seaside
Albert's Bridge
Ali's Barbara
All's Well That Ends As You Like It
'As With Gladness ...'
Ask a Silly Question
Audience
Baby Love
Blah Blah Blah
Boy With a Cart
Cahoot's Macbeth
Cherry Sisters
Cock Robin Hood
Collier's Tuesday Tea
Death
Definitely Eric Geddes
Dogg's Hamlet
Ernie's Incredible Illucinations
Everyman
Everywoman
Fans or Don't Clap ...
Festival Play
Field of Fashion
Fish in her Kettle
Forty Winks Beauty
God
Great Jowett
Half an Idea
Hamelin Incident
Harlequinade
Henry the Tenth
Hi-Fi Spy
If You're Glad I'll Be Frank
Il Fornicazione
Julius and Cleopatra
Lady Audley's Secret
Long Christmas Dinner
Maria Marten (Cox)
Moby Dick
Mutilated
Night Out
One Thing More
Play the Game
Pullman Car *Hiawatha*

Purification
Present Slaughter
Sea Side Trippers
Showbusiness
Small Affair
Snow White Special
Spring Song Singers
Stalag 69
Still Life
Summoning of Everyman
Thor With Angels
Trial of Joan of Arc at Rouen, 1431
Trial of Lucullus
Unhand Me Squire!
Urban Cycles
Us and Them
Vagabond Prince
Who's Bean Stalking?

B

Plays arranged under specific headings

BURLESQUES/MELODRAMAS

Ah, Cruel Fate
Bells
Black Eye'd Susan
Brave Bugler
Chinese Pendant
Code of the West
Curses, Foiled Again!
Day of Reckoning
Double Dealing
Drunkard's Dilemma
Drunkard's Wife
Every Picture Tells a Story
Fanny's Prayer
Frankenstein's Guests
Green Eye of the Little Yellow Dog
Gypsy Curse
Heir's Return
Hiss the Villain
Husbands are a Girl's Best Friend
Lady Audley's Secret
Little Lights of Kimberley
Maria Marten (Austin)
Maria Marten (Cox)
Maria Marten (Dennis/Kilgarriff)
Master and the Maid
Mayhem at the Mill
Molecatcher
Nellie's Nightlights
One Month to Pay
Out for the Count
Save My Child!
Set a Thief to Catch a Thief
Sold to the Gypsies
Temptation Sordid or Virtue Rewarded
Tram-Track Tragedy
Trouble Shared
Unhand Me Squire
Wages of Sin
Who Will Man the Lifeboat?

MINI-DRAMAS

Ah Cruel Fate
Albert Laddin
Ali's Barbara
Ask a Silly Question
Cock Robin Hood
Field of Fashion
Fiesta Fandango
Forty Winks Beauty
Hi-Fi Spy

Iron Hot Strikers
Little Red Whittington
Piccalilli Circus
Puss in Slippers
Red Hot Cinders
Sea Side Trippers
Snow White Special
Spacewoman
Speeches and Cream
Spring Song Singers
Unhand Me, Squire
Way Out West
What Ho Within
What the Dinosaur
Who's Bean Stalking?

COSTUME PLAYS

(Dates are given in round figures as an approximate guide)

Ancient Greek
Goodbye Iphigenia
Medea
Phoenix Too Frequent

Ancient Roman
Trial of Lucullus

Biblical
Second Easter
Soldier and the Woman
Victory of the Cross

Anglo Saxon
Thor, with Angels

Medieval
Boy With A Cart
Everyman (Cox)

Gothic 1200-1450
Forward to the Right
Hamelin Incident
Healer
Trial of Joan of Arc at Rouen

Tudor 1500-1550
Last Wife

Elizabethan 1550-1620
Crossways

Fifteen Minute Hamlet
Merry Regiment of Women

Louis XIV 1660 onwards
After Midnight—Before Dawn

Late Georgian 1750 onwards
Before Dawn
Gideon and the Sea Witch
London Vertigo

Regency 1810 onwards
Martyred Wives
Path to Liberty (Greek)
Person of No Consequence

Early Victorian 1840-1865 (Crinoline)
Branwell
Lady Audley's Secret
Maria Marten
Temptation Sordid

Late Victorian 1865-1900 (Bustle)
Alas, Dear Reader
As You Were (Austrian; to 1950)
Cards, Cups and Crystal Ball
Day of Reckoning
Great Jowett
Hiss the Villain
Is There Anybody There?
Lady Bracknell's Confinement
Music Lovers
Our Branch in Brussels
Proposal
Purification
Ritual for Dolls
Smile
Who Calls?

Edwardian 1900-1910
Better Late (French)
Borderline
Country Rebel
Don't Walk About With Nothing On (French)
Night Errant (French)
Old Quebec
One Month Early (French)
Put Some Clothes On, Clarisse! (French)
Sequence of Events
Take Your Medicine Like a Man (French)
Terrace Talk
Twelve-Pound Look

1st World War
Fallen Heroes

1920s
Dial Ten Amazing Little Boy Friends
Exiles
Hebrew Lesson
Jolly Sinister Jape

1930s
Anastasia — the Recognition Scene
Birds Stopped Singing
Fumed Oak
Hands Across the Sea
No Picnic
Red Peppers
Roman Fever
Señora Carrar's Rifles
Still Life
Tea Dance
Ways and Means

1940s
Dark Room
I Rise in Flames Cried the Phoenix

1950s
Asylum
Browning Version
Different Way to Die
Englishman Abroad

1960s
Foreign Bodies
Game of Soldiers
If You're Glad I'll Be Frank
Kind of Alaska
Rialto Prom

Modern and Period
As With Gladness ...
At the Changing of the Year
But Yesterday
Curses, Foiled Again!
Droitwich Discovery
Ghost of a Chance
God
Hidden Meanings
In Room Five Hundred and Four
Long Christmas Dinner
Now and Then
Random Moments in a May Garden
September Revisited
Train
Two Summers
Winter of 1917

Futuristic
Aftermath
If Yer Take a Short Cut

B

It's All in the Game
Little Brother, Little Sister
Not Not Not Not Not Enough Oxygen
Return
Space Between the Years
Whence

B

PLAYS SET IN HOSPITALS

Bedside Manner
Drag Factor
Effie's Burning
Fear of Heaven
George
Going Home
Just a Little Word
Keeping Mum
Kind of Alaska
Magic
Parentcraft
Philip and Rowena
Plaster
Separate Peace
Showbusiness
Waiting
Waiting for Alec
Walking Dead!
Woman of No Importance
Womberang

PLAYS WITH A NATIONAL OR REGIONAL SETTING OR INTEREST

AMERICAN

American Dream
And Go To Innisfree
Auto-Da-Fé
Brenton Versus Brenton
Case of the Crushed Petunia
Dark Room
Death
Duck Variations
Frosted Glass Coffin
Happy Journey
Hello from Bertha
I Can't Imagine Tomorrow
Last of My Solid Gold Watches
Long Goodbye
Long Stay Cut Short
Lady of Larkspur Lotion
Lord Byron's Love Letter
Moony's Kid Don't Cry
Mutilated
Old One-Two
Perfect Analysis Given By A Parrot

Portrait of a Madonna
Pullman Car *Hiawatha*
Purification
Rape of Bunny Stuntz
Sexual Perversity in Chicago
Something Unspoken
Strangest Kind Of Romance
Suddenly Last Summer
This Property is Condemned
Twenty-Seven Wagons Full of Cotton
Zoo Story

FRENCH

Better Late
Dispute
Don't Walk About With Nothing On
Establishment at Arles
Field of Olives
Forward to the Right
Human Voice
Lesson
Music Lovers
Night Errant
One Month Early
Orchestra
Put Some Clothes On, Clarisse!
Sound of Silence
Take Your Medicine Like a Man
Trial of Joan of Arc at Rouen

IRISH

Comedies
Last of the Last of the Mohicans
Pizzazz

Dramas
Fallen Heroes
Galway Girl
Hebrew Lesson
London Vertigo
Nightingale and Not the Lark
Nothing Personal
Olive and Hilary
Time of Wolves and Tigers
View from the Obelisk

WELSH
(in English)

Bedside Manner
New Leaf

PLAYS WITH AN ENVIRONMENTAL INTEREST

Do-Gooders
Not Not Not Not Not Enough Oxygen
River
Singing in the Wilderness
Sleep Tight Tonight
Sparrows
Tippers

PLAYS WITH A THEATRICAL INTEREST

Acting Exercise
Anyone for Drama?
Audience (Frayn)
Cahoot's Macbeth
Clara's on the Curtains!
Curses, Foiled Again
Darlings, You Were Wonderful!
Distracted Globe
Dogg's Hamlet
Don't Blame It on the Boots
Droitwich Discovery
Easy Stages
Festival Play
Fifteen Minute Hamlet
Game of Soldiers
Half an Idea
Harlequinade
Her Big Chance
Hidden Meanings
Humour Helps
In by the Half
Lady Bracknell's Confinement
Last Bread Pudding
Last Panto in Little Grimley
Last Scene of All
Last Tango in Little Grimley
Last Things
Melons at the Parsonage
Merry Regiment of Women
Night's Candles
Nightingale and Not the Lark
Real Inspector Hound
Red Peppers
Small Affair
Theatrical Digs
Too Long an Autumn
Waiting for a Bus
World Première
Yes and No

MUSICAL PLAYS

Blah Blah Blah
Dial 10 Amazing Little Boy Friends
Maria Marten
Orchestra
Play the Game
Purification
Red Peppers

MYSTERY AND SUSPENSE PLAYS

Afternoon at the Seaside
Alarm Call
Daddy's Gone A-Hunting
Dead End
Demon
Flowers for Mrs Hopkins
Jolly Sinister Jape
Mantrap
Mum's the Word
Murder Play
Nasty Things Murders
Patient
Rats
Visitor
Walking Dead!
What Shall We Do with the Body?
Who Calls?

PLAYS ABOUT THE SUPERNATURAL, GHOSTS AND WITCHCRAFT

After Midnight — Before Dawn
At the Changing of the Year
Cards, Cups and Crystal Ball
Company Come
Crossways
Cut in the Rates
Demon
Droitwich Discovery
Edge
Epitaph for A Hard Man
Frankenstein's Guests
Genteel
Ghost of a Chance
Gideon and the Sea Witch
Is There Anybody There?
Last Things
Last Wife
Night's Candles
Now and Then
Olive and Hilary
Return
Seagulls

B

Sense of the Ridiculous
Tunnel Vision
Under the Twelfth Sign
View From the Obelisk

RELIGIOUS INTEREST AND MORALITY

Abortive
Aftermath
As With Gladness ...
Boy With A Cart
Cathedral—Ten Minutes
Deterrent
Different Way to Die
Effie's Burning
Everyman
Everywoman
Great Jowett
Hamelin Incident
Happy Journey
Hole
Long Christmas Dinner
No Why
One Thing More
Public Eye
Pullman Car *Hiawatha*
Receive This Light
Second Easter
Sleep of Prisoners
Soldier and the Woman
Something in the Genes
Stop the Nightmare
Summoning of Everyman
Thor, With Angels
Victory of the Cross
Vin Extraordinaire

ALL MALE

Acting Exercise
Audience
Ball Boys
Bespoke Overcoat
Blood Sports
Bookends
Bright Boy
Chip in the Sugar
Death Artist
Dock Brief
Do-It-Yourself Frankenstein Outfit
Duck Variations
Dumb Waiter
Dwarfs
Edge

Fourth Prisoner
Hebrew Lesson
Kind of Vesuvius
Krapp's Last Tape
Lady Bracknell's Confinement
Last of My Solid Gold Watches
Leslie
Loophole
Man of Letters
Me and My Friend
Memento Mori
Molecatcher
New World Order
Out of the Flying Pan
Protest
Sea Side Trippers
Sleep of Prisoners
Spring Song Singers
Stanley Parkers
Time of Wolves and Tigers
Top Table
Victoria Station
Vigil
Wendlebury Day
Yes and No
Zoo Story

ALL FEMALE

Alas Dear Reader
Anastasia — Recognition Scene
And Go To Innisfree
Ask a Silly Question
Bed Among the Lentils
Borderline
Bus Stop
Café Society
Cards, Cups and Crystal Ball
Cecily
Chimera
Christmas Incorporated
Clara's on the Curtains
Costa del Packet!
Country Rebel
Crossways
Crowing Hen
Dancers
Darlings, You Were Wonderful
Day of Reckoning
Day Trippers
Do-It-Yourself Frankenstein Outfit
Doggies
Donahue Sisters
Dreamjobs
Early Blight
Effie's Burning

Everybody's Friend
Everyman
Face the Music
Field of Fashion
Flesh Game
Flowers for Mrs Hopkins
From Five to Five-Thirty
Garden Room
Gathering of Doves
Ghost of a Chance
Guilt Card
Hello from Bertha
Her Big Chance
Human Voice
In by the Half
Indian Summer
Iron Hot Strikers
Just a Little Word
Keeping Mum
Lady Bracknell's Confinement
Lady of Letters
Late Frost
Leaving
Little Benjamin
Long Home
Lovesome Thing
Maureen
Me and My Friend
Medea
Mrs Meadowsweet
Nasty Things Murders
None the Wiser
Now and Then
Once and for All
Our Branch in Brussels
People Like Us
Permission to Cry
Person of No Consequence
Post Mortem
Quake
Relics
Rialto Prom
Same Old Story
Sea Side Trippers
Second Easter
September Revisited
Shindig
Shoppers
Short Changed
Skip
Smile
Soldiering On
Something Unspoken
Spacewoman
Speeches and Cream
Spring Song Singers
Tea Dance

Terrace Talk
Theatrical Digs
Think the Beautiful Thoughts
This Village I Know
Top Table
Trial
Visitor
Waking Up
What Brutes Men Are
What Ho Within!
Who Calls?
Who Was Hilary Maconochie?
Whose Wedding Is It Anyway?
Woman Alone
Woman of No Importance

B

DOUBLE BILL PLAYS (Long one act plays and some others that make a double bill)

B

Acting Exercise
Actor's Nightmare
Afternoon at the Seaside
Albert's Bridge
The American Dream*
Ashes to Ashes*
Bald Prima Donna
Ball Boys
Black Comedy*
Blood Sports
Blue Kettle
Browning Version*
Cahoot's Macbeth
Chairs*
Collection*
Come into the Garden Maud*
Dock Brief
Dogg's Hamlet
Dumb Waiter
Endgame*
Englishman Abroad
Family Voices
Foreign Bodies
Form
Fumed Oak
Game of Soldiers
Green Forms
Half an Idea*
Hands Across the Sea
Harlequinade*
Heart's Desire
Hole*
Hot Fudge
Humour Helps
Hunting Pink
I Spy
Kind of Alaska
Last Panto in Little Grimley
Last Tango in Little Grimley
Last Things
Leslie
Lesson
Lover
Lunch Hour
Maureen
Mountain Language
Night Out* (Pinter)
Office Suite
One for the Road (Pinter)
Party Time
Patient
Private Ear
Public Eye

Question of Attribution
Rats
Real Inspector Hound*
Red Peppers
Resounding Tinkle
Room
Sexual Perversity in Chicago*
Shadows of the Evening*
Sister Mary Ignatius Explains It All For You*
Slight Ache
Small Affair*
Soldier and the Woman*
Still Life*
Victoria Station
Waiting for a Bus
Waiting Room
Ways and Means
White Liars
Zoo Story

*Indicates a playing time of one hour or longer

Authors' Index

B

Entries in italics refer to novels by well-known authors which have been dramatized either under their own name or under another title which is given in parethesis

B

Albee, Edward
American Dream
Zoo Story

Aldrich, Arthur
Shindig

Allen, Woody
Death
God

Anouilh, Jean
Orchestra

Armstrong, Ian
Fallen Heroes
Growing Pains

Aron, Geraldine
Bar and Ger
Donahue Sisters
Galway Girl
Joggers
Olive and Hilary
Stanley Parkers

Austin, Harry
Brave Bugler
Chinese Pendant
Every Picture Tells
Green Eye of the Little Yellow Dog
Husbands Are a Girl's Best Friend
Little Lights of Kimberley
Maria Marten
Nellie's Nightlights

Ayckbourn, Alan
Cut in the Rates
Ernie's Incredible Illucinations

Bailey, Michele
Going All the Way

Baker, Lawrence
Birds Stopped Singing

Barnes, Peter
Acting Exercise
Humour Helps
Last Things
Waiting for a Bus

Baron, Alec
Asylum
Big Cats
Chimera
Company Come
Push

Barrie, J. M.
Twelve-Pound Look

Beard, Paul
Meat and Two Veg

Beckett, Samuel
Endgame
Krapp's Last Tape

Bennett, Alan
Bed Among the Lentils
Chip in the Sugar
Cream Cracker Under the Settee
Englishman Abroad
Green Forms
Her Big Chance
Lady of Letters
Question of Attribution
Say Something Happened
Soldiering On
Visit From Miss Protheroe
Woman of No Importance
(See also *Beyond the Fringe* in the Revue section)

Blackwell, Vera
Audience (trans.)
Private View (trans.)
Protest (trans.)

Bolton, Guy
Anastasia, Recognition Scene

Booth, Anthony
Costa Del Packet!
Ladies, This Is War!
None the Wiser
Quake
This Desirable Cottage
Trial

Bowen, John
Cold Salmon
Silver Wedding
Waiting Room
Young Guy Seeks Part-Time Work

Bower, Margaret
Animal Connection
Tea Dance
Whose Wedding is it Anyway?

Bowskill, Derek
Long Home

Braddon, Mary
Lady Audley's Secret

Brecht, Bertolt
Exception and the Rule
Measures Taken
Señora Carrar's Rifles
Trial of Joan of Arc at Rouen, 1431
Trial of Lucullus

Brittney, Lynn
Different Way to Die
Failed Investments
Have a Nice Day
Last Wife
Properly Processed

Brockhill, George
Nudes in Waning Light
School Ties

Brook, J.C.W.
Hitman

Burton, Brian J.
Double Dealing
Drunkard's Wife
Fanny's Prayer
Foiled Again!
Ghost of a Chance
Gypsy Curse
Mayhem at the Mill
Murder Play
One Month to Pay
Save My Child
Sold to the Gypsies
Trouble Shared

Campton, David
After Midnight — Before Dawn
Cagebirds
Can You Hear the Music?
Cards, Cups and Crystal Ball
Do-It-Yourself Frankenstein Outfit
Evergreens
Everybody's Friend
Getting and Spending
Little Brother, Little Sister
Memento Mori
Mrs Meadowsweet
Mutatis Mutandis
Now and Then
Our Branch in Brussels
Out of the Flying Pan
Parcel
Permission to Cry
Relics

Right Place
Singing in the Wilderness
Smell of Burning
Smile
Then
Us and Them
What Are You Doing Here?
Who Calls?
Winter of 1917

Carley, Steve
Edge

Cary, Falkland L.
Husbands Supplied

Cary, Falkland L and King, Philip
Housekeeper Wanted

Chekhov, Anton
Proposal

Chinn, Jimmie
But Yesterday
From Here to the Library
In by the Half
In Room Five Hundred and Four
Interior Designs
Leslie
Maureen
Pity About Kitty
Respectable Funeral
Too Long An Autumn

Chown, Patricia
Long Noon

Christie, Agatha
Afternoon at the Seaside
Patient
Rats

Churchill, Caryl
Abortive
After-Dinner Joke
Blue Kettle
Heart's Desire
Hot Fudge
Judge's Wife
Lovesick
Not Not Not Not Not Enough Oxygen
Seagulls
Three More Sleepless Nights

Clark, Brian
Post Mortem

B

B

Climie, David
(See *Intimacy at 8.30* in the Revue section)

Clucas, Daniel
Our Man

Cocteau, Jean
Human Voice
Sound of Silence

Cole, Giles
Secrets

Coles, Enid
Just A Little Word
Little Benjamin
Once and for All
September Revisited
Under the Twelfth Sign

Connolly, H
Daddy's Gone A-Hunting
One Careful Owner
Overtime

Cook, Peter
(See *Beyond the Fringe* in the Revue section)

Cossons, W. Ernest
(*See* Taylor and Cossons)

Coward, Noël
Come into the Garden Maud
Fumed Oak
Hands Across the Sea
Red Peppers
Shadows of the Evening
Still Life
Ways and Means

Cox, Constance
Everyman
Lady Audley's Secret
Maria Marten
What Brutes Men Are

Creagh-Henry, M.
Victory of the Cross

Crowther, Colin
Tryst

Davies, Andrew
Thermal Underwear

Davis, Wyn
Borderline

Day, Doris M.
Crowing Hen
Gathering of Doves

de Maupassant, Guy
(*See* Stocks, Bryan)

Dennis, Richard
Maria Marten

Dennis, Richard, and Kilgarriff, Michael
Bells

Doust, Paul
Lady Bracknell's Confinement

Downing, Martin
Demon
Frankenstein's Guests
Out for the Count

Durang, Christopher
Actor's Nightmare
Sister Mary Ignatius Explains It All For You

Eccles, Frank
Waiting for Alec

Eden, Roy
Fans

Edwards, Tony
Return
Sweet Caroline Sweet

Emmet, Alfred (adapt.)
Proposal

Evans, E. Eynon
New Leaf

Exton, Clive
(*See* Stoppard and Exton)

Feydeau, Georges
Feu la Mère de Madame
(see *Better Late* and *Night Errant*)
Lèonie est en Avance
(see *One Month Early*)
Mais N'te Promène Donc Pas Toute Nue! (see
Don't Walk About with Nothing On and *Put
Some Clothes On, Clarisse*)
On Purge Bébé
(see *Take Your Medicine Like a Man*)
(*See* Meyer, Peter; Oliver, Reggie; *and* Pilch,
Michael)

Firth, Tim
Man of Letters

Flewitt, Lee
Is There Anybody There?

Fo, Dario and Rame, Franca
Medea
Same Old Story
Waking Up
Woman Alone

Fosbrook, Michael
Figuring Things

Foxton, David
Caught on the Hop

Frayn, Michael
Audience
(See also *Listen to This* in the Revue section)

Friel, Brian
London Vertigo

Fry, Christopher
Boy With A Cart
One Thing More
Phoenix Too Frequent
Sleep of Prisoners
Thor With Angels

Grahame, Alec
(See *Intimacy at 8.30* in the Revue section)

Green, George MacEwan
Goodbye, Iphigenia
No Picnic
One Season's King
Ritual for Dolls
Sequence of Events
Stop the Nightmare
Terrace Talk

Green, Lily Ann
Forward to the Right

Green, Michael
All's Well That Ends As You Like It
Cherry Sisters
Collier's Tuesday Tea
Fish In Her Kettle
Henry the Tenth (Part Seven)
Il Fornicazione
Julius and Cleopatra
Last Call for Breakfast
Moby Dick

Present Slaughter
Stalag 69
Streuth
Vagabond Prince

Greenaway, Alfred
Humphrey Pumphrey Had A Great Fall

Greene, Graham
Great Jowett
Yes and No

Grenfell, Joyce
Old Tyme Dancing
The Whizzer

Grenfell-Hill, Jeffrey
Country Rebel
Exiles

Gurney, A. R.
Love Course
Old One-Two
Rape of Bunny Stuntz

Guyan, Alexander
Conversations with a Golliwog

Hall, Nick
Pastiche

Hall, Willis
Railwayman's New Clothes

Harris, Richard
Albert
Going Home
Is It Something I Said?
Keeping Mum
Magic
Plaster
Showbusiness
Waiting

Hartwell, Bob
Albert's Plot

Havel, Václav
Audience
Private View
Protest

Hawkins, Jim
Too Hot to Handle

Hay, Ian
Crimson Coconut

B

B

Hayward, Jean M.
Our Furry Friends

Hickman, Derek
George

Hillman, Barry. L
Face the Music

Hodgson, Sheila
Tunnel Vision

Hogg, Gladys M
Flowers for Mrs Hopkins

Holland, Norman
Second Easter

Hood, Evelyn
Curses, Foiled Again!
Epitaph For A Hard Man
Genteel
I Never Thought It Would Be Like This

Horsler, P. H.
Christmas Incorporated
Intruders
Upstairs Cuckoo

Ionesco, Eugene
Bald Prima Donna
Chairs
Lesson

Jarvis, Martin
Bright Boy

Jeffreys, Stephen
Mobile 4

John, Miriam
Orchestra (trans.)

Johnson, Philip
From Five to Five-thirty

Johnston, Jennifer
Nightingale and Not the Lark

Jones, Graham
Do-Gooders
Dreamjobs

Jordan, Kay
For the Love of Norman

Kilgarriff, Michael
Black-Eye'd Susan
Code of the West
Day of Reckoning
Heir's Return
Master and the Maid
Molecatcher
Tram-Track Tragedy
Who Will Man the Lifeboat?
(*See* Dennis, Richard; Sachs, Andrew
and Ventham, Peter)

King, Paul
Teddy Bear's Picnic

King, Philip
(*See* Cary and King)

Lambe, Michael
Walking Dead!

Larbey, Bob
Half an Idea
Small Affair

Lee, Maureen
Visitor

Leonard, Hugh
Last of the Last of the Mohicans
Nothing Personal
Pizzazz
Roman Fever
Time of Wolves and Tigers
View From the Obelisk

Leviticus, Louis I
Train (trans.)

Lomas, Derek
Darlings, You Were Wonderful!

Lovegrove, Arthur
Clara's on the Curtains!
Nasty Things, Murders

Lowe, Stephen
Cards

Macrae, Arthur
(See *Living for Pleasure* in Revue section)

Macklin, Charles
(*See* Friel, Brian)

Mamet, David
Duck Variations
Sexual Perversity in Chicago

Mander, Charles
Deterrent
Getting Along
Monmouth
River
Shop for Charity
Sparrows
World Première

Mankowitz, Wolf
Bespoke Overcoat
Hebrew Lesson

Manktelow, Bettine
Branwell

Marcus, Fiz
Matchstick Dreams

Marivaux
La Dispute

Marshall, Brian
Blah Blah Blah

Maskell, Valerie
Alas, Dear Reader
It's All in the Game

Mason, Rosemary
Sunbeams

Maurette, Marcelle
Anastasia Recognition Scene

Maurice, Lucy
Indian Summer

Mayall, John
Festival Play

McColl, John
Sandcastles on the Beach

McConnell, Jean
Dancers
Day Trippers
Doggies
Early Blight
Guilt Card
Late Frost
Lovesome Thing
Shoppers
Short Changed
Theatrical Digs

Meyer, Peter
Better Late
Don't Walk About With Nothing On
One Month Early
Take Your Medicine Like a Man

Miller, Brian
Mum's the Word

Miller, Jonathan
(See *Beyond the Fringe* in Revue section)

Moore, Dudley
(See *Beyond the Fringe* in Revue section)

Morgan, Elaine
Soldier and the Woman

Morgan, John
Kids

Mortimer, John
Dock Brief
Edwin
Fear of Heaven
I Spy
Knightsbridge
Lunch Hour
(See also *One to Another* in Revue section)

Myers, Peter
(See *Intimacy at 8.30* in Revue section)

Nestroy, Johann
As You Were

Newmeir, John H.
Babysitting Calvin

Nichols, Peter
Foreign Bodies
Game of Soldiers

Norfolk, William
Hunting Pink
Old Quebec

Ogden, Alan
Miasma in Mostyn Mews

Oliver, Reggie (adapt.)
Music Lovers
Put Some Clothes On, Clarisse!

Parry-Davis
Crossways

B

Parsons, Richard
Dead End
Mortmain
Rialto

Payne, Herbert
Summoning of Everyman

Perry, Scott
Bookends

Phelps, Winifred
Temptation Sordid or Virtue Rewarded

Pilch, Michael
Night Errant

Pinter, Harold
Ashes to Ashes
Collection
Dumb Waiter
Dwarfs
Family Voices
Kind of Alaska
Lover
Mountain Language
New World Order
Night Out
One for the Road
Party Time
Room
Slight Ache
Victoria Station
(See also *One to Another* and *A Slight Ache and Other Plays* in the Revue section)

Plowman, Gillian
Beata Beatrix
Cecily
Close to Croydon
David's Birthday
Janna Years
Kind of Vesuvius
Me and My Friend
Philip and Rowena
There's None So Blind
Tippers
Two Fat Men
Two Summers
Umjana Land

Poliakoff, Stephen
Hitting Town

Popplewell, Jack
Careful Rapture

Raif, Ayshe
Café Society

Rame, Franca
(*See* Fo, Dario)

Rattigan, Terence
Before Dawn
Browning Version
Harlequinade

Reakes, Paul
Bang, You're Dead!
Mantrap

Rensten, Mary
Skip

Richardson, Alan
Perfect Partners

Roberts, Don
Garden Room
Isabeau

Robinson, Patricia
Red Hot in Amsterdam

Rosenthal, Amy
Lifelines

Ross, Stella
Vin Extraordinaire

Rowley, David E.
In Need of Care

Sachs, Andrew
Drunkard's Dilemma
Wages of Sin

Saunders, Geoff
Other People

Saunders, James
Alas Poor Fred
Barnstable
Birdsong
Bye Bye Blues
Double, Double
Neighbours
Over the Wall
Play for Yesterday
Poor Old Simon
Random Moments in a May Garden
Savoury Meringue
Slight Accident
Who Was Hilary Maconochie?

Scholes, John
Fluff
Space Between the Years

Sell, Colin
Dial Ten Amazing Little Boy Friends

Sellars, Charles H.
As With Gladness ...

Shaffer, Peter
Black Comedy
Private Ear
Public Eye
White Liars

Shirley, Rae
Bus Stop
Flesh Game
Merry Regiment of Women
Think the Beautiful Thoughts
What Shall We Do with the Body?

Simpson, N. F.
Form
Hole
Resounding Tinkle
(See also *One to Another* in Revue section)

Skelton, Geoffrey
As You Were (trans)

Slotboom, Carl
Train

Smith, Leo
Sins of the Father
Whence

Smith, Stephen
Departure
One-Sided Triangle
Parentcraft

Snelgrove, Michael
Definitely Eric Geddis
Hidden Meanings
Urban Cycles

Stocks, Bryan
Field of Olives
On the Verandah

Stoppard, Tom
After Magritte
Albert's Bridge
Cahoot's Macbeth

Dogg's Hamlet
Fifteen Minute Hamlet
If You're Glad I'll be Frank
Real Inspector Hound
Separate Peace

Stoppard, Tom and Exton, Clive
Boundary

Strange, Elliot
Jolly Sinister Jape

Stubbs, Norman
Patio Window
Ringing For You

Swannell, Graham
Commitment
Consequences
Day of the Dog
Hyde Park
Stuttgart

Taylor, A.R.; and Cossons, W. Ernest
Hiss the Villain

Terence, Rae
Aftermath
Sense of the Ridiculous

Terson, Peter
Rattling the Railings

Tibbetts, Mike
Bottles With Baskets On
LittleBro Morning and BigSis Afternoon

Toddie, Jean Lennox
And Go To Innisfree

Tordoff, Bill
Play the Game

Townsend, Sue
Womberang

Tristam, David
Brenton Versus Brenton
Extraordinary Revelations of Orca the
    Goldfish
Joining the Club
Last Panto in Little Grimley
Last Tango in Little Grimley
What's For Pudding?

B

Tydeman, Richard
Ah Cruel Fate
Albert Laddin
Ali's Barbara
Ask a Silly Question
Cock Robin Hood
Field of Fashion
Fiesta Fandango
Forty Winks Beauty
Hi Fi Spy
Iron Hot Strikers
Little Red Whittington
Piccalilli Circus
Puss in Slippers
Red Hot Cinders
Sea Side Trippers
Snow White Special
Spacewoman
Speeches and Cream
Spring Song Singers
Unhand Me, Squire
Way Out West
What Ho Within!
What the Dinosaur
Who's Bean Stalking

Valentine, Joe
House Without Windows

Ventham, Peter and Kilgarriff, Michael
Set a Thief to Catch a Thief

Vickery, Frank
After I'm Gone
Bedside Manner
Drag Factor
Green Favours
Night Out
Split Ends

Vooght, Cherry
People Like Us

Walker, Graham
Hamelin Incident

Warboyes, Sally
House Plant

Warburton, N. J.
Distracted Globe
Don't Blame It on the Boots
Droitwich Discovery
Easy Stages
Last Bread Pudding
Loophole
Melons at the Parsonage

Not Bobby
Office Song
Receive This Light
Sour Grapes and Ashes
Zartan

Watchurst, Neville
Café

Watson, Dave
Last Munro

Watson, Donald
Bald Prima Donna (trans.)
Chairs (trans.)
Lesson (trans.)

Weldon, Fay
Reading Group

Wertenbaker, Timberlake
La Dispute (trans.)

West, Don
Vacant Possession

Whiting, John
No Why

Wilder, Thornton
Happy Journey
Long Christmas Dinner
Pullman Car *Hiawatha*

Williams, Emlyn
Vigil

Williams, Hugh Steadman
Everywoman

Williams, Tennessee
Auto-Da-Fé
Case of the Crushed Petunia
Dark Room
Frosted Glass Coffin
Gnädiges Fraulein
Hello from Bertha
I Can't Imagine Tomorrow
I Rise In Flame Cried the Phoenix
Lady of Larkspur Lotion
Last of My Solid Gold Watches
Long Goodbye
Long Stay Cut Short
Lord Byron's Love Letter
Moony's Kid Don't Cry
Mutilated
Perfect Analysis Given By a Parrot

Portrait of a Madonna
Purification
Something Unspoken
Strangest Kind of Romance
Suddenly Last Summer
Talk to Me Like the Rain ...
This Property Is Condemned
Twenty-Seven Wagons Full of Cotton

Wilson, David Henry
Are You Normal, Mr Norman?
Death Artist
Escapologist
Fourth Prisoner
If Yer Take A Short Cut
Wall
Wendlebury Day

Windsor, Valerie
Effie's Burning

Wood, Anthony
Human Voice (trans.)
Sound of Silence (trans.)

Wood, Margaret
Courting Disaster
Fishy Business
Last Scene Of All
Martyred Wives
Parochial Problems
Person of No Consequence
Top Table

Woods, Don
Leaving
Something in the Genes

Wye, Angela
Rialto Prom

Wyld, Hazel
Night's Candles
Twenty-Five Not Out

Wymark, Olwen
Medea (trans.)
Same Old Story (trans.)
Waking Up (trans.)
Woman Alone (trans.)

Young, Malcolm
At the Changing of the Year

B

B

One Act Plays

B

Abortive. Play. Caryl Churchill
M1 F1. A bedroom. Fee code D

Roz and Colin lie in bed discussing the effect on them of Roz's recent abortion. The father of the child was not Colin but Billy, a pathetic under-privileged character whom they befriended for three months. Billy and Roz's sexual encounter began as rape but ended differently, and as she and Colin recall the events leading to it the gulf between the couple is revealed.

Acting Exercise. Play. Peter Barnes
M2. (20s, 40s) A rehearsal room. Fee code B

Rowan, an actor, is rehearsing. A distraught husband demands the actor give him back his wife. With a superlative performance, Rowan convinces the husband he is mistaken, but alone again he crows: 'I could sell electric fans to Eskimos!' May be presented as part of the full-length entertainment *Corpsing*. For details, please see the entry in Section A.
ISBN 0 573 10006 3

Actor's Nightmare. Play. Christopher Durang
M2 (20s, 30s) F3 (20s, 30s). An empty stage. Fee code E

See full synopsis in Section A under *Sister Mary Ignatius Explains It All For You.*

The After-Dinner Joke. Play. Caryl Churchill
Large mixed cast. Various simple settings. Fee code G

A secretary decides to quit her job and become a fundraiser for an international charity. She is determined to remember that 'A charity is by definition nonpolitical. Politics is by definition uncharitable.' But everything she experiences in her new job makes this precept untenable. The play has a large cast with a wide age range and provides excellent opportunities for multiple role playing.

After I'm Gone. Play. Frank Vickery
M1 (late middle-age) F3 (37, middle-age). A living-room. Fee code D

Mam does not want her daughter Matti to marry and leave her on her own; Matti, however, is determined, and her marriage brings into Mam's house the undertaker husband and his deaf and ageing father. Unexpectedly, Mam and Dad hit it off and get married themselves. Later Dad gives them all a surprise present: a world cruise!
ISBN 0 573 12003 X

After Magritte. Farce. Tom Stoppard
M3 (40) F2 (30s, old). One interior. Fee code F

Harris and his family are eccentrics. Two police officers place them under arrest. It is not clear why: something about a parked car, a bunch of .22 calibre shells in the waste basket and a robbery of the box office of a minstrel show. From there, the plot goes haywire.

After Midnight—Before Dawn. Play. David Campton
M2 (late teenage, middle-age) F4 (late 20s, 30s, middle-age, old). A prison cell. Fee code D

Six characters, sentenced for witchcraft, await death. The Calm Woman remains unmoved; she will not hang as the Devil looks after his own. The others beg her to tell them how they may gain Satan's protection. The Girl protests: they kill her and set on the Calm Woman also — fulfilling her prophecy. Period late 1600s-early 1700s
ISBN 0 573 12002 1

B

Aftermath. Play. Rae Terence
M5 (30-middle-age) F1 (30s), or M4 F2. Simple settings on a bare stage. Fee code D

This provoking, poignant play centres on the anguished existence of survivors in a village whose numbers dwindle in the aftermath of the nuclear holocaust. Their leader, John, angered by futile orders issued from the Regional Centre of Government, enters the centre and despatches its survivors above ground to begin a new life.
ISBN 0 573 12005 6

Afternoon at the Seaside. Play. Agatha Christie
M7 (25-elderly) F5 (25, 34, 52, 60). A beach. Fee code F

Inspector Foley arrives on the beach in pursuit of a stolen emerald necklace. It turns up in the trouser pocket of the timid Percy. An attempt to snatch the necklace from Percy is foiled by a disguised policewoman. The emeralds are paste; the real necklace is safely in the hands of the two most respectable-looking thieves.
ISBN 0 573 02004 3

Ah Cruel Fate. Minidrama. Richard Tydeman
M5 Extras 4F. Fee code B

A tale (with compère) of a cruel father, a wronged daughter, a shipwrecked mariner and some unconventional pirates. All set to traditional music with, of course, the traditional happy ending. Running time: 15-20 minutes
ISBN 0 573 12033 1

Alas, Dear Reader. Play. Valerie Maskell
F5 (12, 18-40s). 1 male voice. A Victorian parlour. Fee code D

Tyrannized by Mr Bristow, the female members of his household are horrified to hear he has retired to devote his time to them. Agnes and Lucy doctor his medicine; Dora hunts for a pair of scissors while Hattie disappears upstairs with her melted wax doll. In the midst of all this Mr Bristow dies inexplicably of heart failure. Period Victorian
ISBN 0 573 13202 X

Alas, Poor Fred. Play. James Saunders
M1 (middle-age) F1 (middle-age). A drawing-room. Fee code E

The play begins with a peaceful armchair conversation between Ernest and Ethel, who are chatting about how funny it must be to get cut in half, as Fred was. The murder is placed in the past and these two conventional people talk about it as if it didn't interest them all that much. The fact is, it was Ernest that killed Fred ...

Albert. Comedy. Richard Harris
M2 (20s) F1 (20s). A sitting-room. Fee code C

If it were not for the thoughtfulness of the author who has kindly translated the dialogue of two of the characters into English, the audience would be as confused as the actors, who play a Finn, an Italian and an Englishman — none of whom speak a word of the other's languages.
ISBN 0 573 12021 8

Albert Laddin. Minidrama. Richard Tydeman
M4 F6. Fee code B

A new angle on the old Aladdin fable, with a very determined and independent Widow Twankey, who will not conform to the time-honoured rule of speaking in rhyme and as a result says 'Yes, yes' when she should have said 'No, no'. Running time: 15-20 minutes
ISBN 0 573 06617 5

Albert's Bridge. Play. Tom Stoppard
M10 F2. Composite setting. Fee code E

Albert is a painter who takes an immense pride in his work on a huge girdered railway bridge. To him it is 'his' bridge. The play follows, in a series of brief sequences, Albert's life at home and at work. The bridge eventually collapses under the tramping feet of an army of 'ordinary' people mounting it because 'it is the only direction left'.
ISBN 0 573 02321 2

Albert's Plot. Play. Bob Hartwell
M4 (40s-60s) F4 (teenage, 30-50s). An allotment, and a street. Fee code D

To Albert, retired miner, his allotment is his piece of England, his escape from the world. The Council places a repossession order on the land; Albert is determined to keep his tenancy. Several people urge him to give up and familiar facets of human behaviour are revealed. Eventually nature takes its course in this gently amusing 'slice of life'.
ISBN 0 573 12024 2

Ali's Barbara. Minidrama. Richard Tydeman
M6 F7. Fee code B

Described as an Arabian nightmare, this minidrama has Ali surrounded by females instead of the more usual forty thieves. Running time: 15-20 minutes
ISBN 0 573 12006 4

All's Well That Ends As You Like It. A play for Coarse Actors. Michael Green

See the entry for *Four Plays for Coarse Actors*.

The American Dream. Play. Edward Albee
M2 (20, 30) F3 (45, 86). A living-room. Fee code F

In this vicious parable about America, Mommy and Daddy live in gilt-edged insecurity, Mommy ruling with an unholy vitality that has reduced Daddy to a terrible, contented impotence. Into the house strays a beautiful young man — an American dream — except that he can feel nothing because he is the twin of the child they killed years before.
ISBN 0 573 02007 8

Anastasia — the Recognition Scene. Adapted by Guy Bolton from the play by Marcelle Maurette
F2. A drawing-room. Fee code A

The Dowager Empress of Russia is brought face to face with a young woman who claims to be her granddaughter and to have escaped the massacre of Ekaterinburg in 1918.
ISBN 0 573 03203 3

♦ **And Go to Innisfree.** Play. Jean Lennox Toddie
F3 (young, middle-age, older). A bare stage. Fee code D

A woman appears, her long skirt sweeping the sand of the deserted New England beach. She must make a decision, but will she make it alone? The middle-aged matron she was argues for the comfort of a retirement home. The child she was urges her to sit again and eat blackberries and to arise at long last and go to Innisfree.
ISBN 0 573 62620 0

Are You Normal, Mr Norman? Play. David Henry Wilson
M4 (27, 50s) F2 (20s). A dentist's waiting-room and surgery. Fee code C

Mr Norman Norman is waiting his turn to see the dentist when horrific screams are heard from the surgery. Confronted by a lunatic dentist who considers himself the Saviour, Norman soon realizes that much more than his teeth is at stake ... This stimulating play shows how the borderline between madness and normality is often fuzzy.

'As With Gladness ...' Nativity play. Charles H. Sellars
M15 F6. Children. Various simple settings on an open stage. Fee code E

The play recounts the Nativity story mainly from the point of view of the three Wise Men. Realism and humour are shown in such scenes as the disreputable Bethlehem Inn and, in a more fanciful interlude Herod and Judas are envisaged meeting in Hell. The whole story is told between a Prelude and Epilogue of a present-day children's nativity play.
ISBN 0 573 06242 0

♦ **As You Were**. Farce. Johann Nestroy. Translated from the German and adapted by Geoffrey Skelton
M2 (young, middle-age) F2 (young, middle-age). An elegant living-room. Fee code D

Michael and Helena Hoffmann have a precarious marriage, not least because of servant trouble. Josie conveniently arrives and takes the post of maidservant. But it is when Muffett, Michael's former master, responds to an advertisement for a new manservant that the trouble begins. Period mid 19th to mid 20th century
ISBN 0 573 12138 9

Ashes to Ashes. Play. Harold Pinter
M1 (40s) F1 (40s). A living-room. Fee code G

A man interviews a woman. She has been sexually brutalized in the past; is he her torturer and her nation's political scourge? 'Pinter ... allies his fascination with isolation and separateness to his instinctive hatred of barbarism; he is exploring the apparent link between sexual and political fascism and the way one echoes, or even contradicts, the other.' *Guardian*. Running time approximately one hour.

Ask a Silly Question. Minidrama. Richard Tydeman
F12. Extras. Fee code B

A hilarious meeting of a PTA brains trust which can be made to involve the audience as much as the actors. Running time: 15-20 minutes
ISBN 0 573 06621 3

Asylum. Play. Alec Baron
M2 F4. An office. Fee code D

In this compelling play about the continuing effects of the Second World War, Dr Kirshner, head of a sanatorium in Germany, has to make a decision on whether or not Bauermann, whose obsessional paranoia results from losing his wife and son in an air-raid, can be released into society after spending a year in her care. Following an emotional reunion with his daughter, Bauermann viciously attacks Dr Kirshner.
ISBN 0 573 12010 2

Audience. Play. Michael Frayn
M6 (late teenage, middle-age, American 70s) F7 (17, middle-age, American 50s, 60s). Theatre stalls. Fee code F

In this amusing satire Michael Frayn turns the tables on us, the audience, and presents us with a picture of — an audience! A hapless playwright must contend with coughing fits, electronic watch alarms, noisy chocolate wrappers and latecomers as he tries to watch a performance of his play.
ISBN 0 573 62068 7

Audience. Play. Václav Havel. Translated by Vera Blackwell
M2 (middle-age, any age). An office. Fee code E

Forming part of the *Vanek Plays* trilogy, *Audience* is a cleverly-constructed satire on power and those who wield it. Vanek is summoned to a meeting with the Head Maltster and offered promotion, but only if he informs on himself! NB. Please specify author when ordering this title.
ISBN 0 573 04226 8

Auto-Da-Fé. Tragedy. Tennessee Williams
M1 (late 30s) F1 (elderly). A cottage porch. Fee code E

This is a tragic story of fanaticism. Madame Duvenet's son Eloi is wildly obsessed with the wickedness of the district in which they live. He rails against his mother's lodgers and tells her of an indecent picture which fell out of a envelope in the mail. His mother says he must burn it at once; he deliberately sets fire to the entire house.

◆ **Babysitting Calvin.** Play. John H. Newmeir
M2 (baby, 40s) F3 (young, 40s). A living-room. Fee code E

Baby Calvin (acted by an adult) can remember his previous life when he was happily married to Laura. Calvin will lose his blissful memories when he reaches his first birthday — or speaks — so he determines not to talk! His babysitter is Laura but she has brought along lecherous Bob. Calvin sets about thwarting Bob but can he prevent the unthinkable happening ... without speaking?
ISBN 0 573 12152 4

The Bald Prima Donna. Anti-Play. Eugene Ionesco. Translated from the French by Donald Watson
M3 F3. A typical middle-class English interior. Fee code E

This is a hilariously maniacal assault on the banality of English suburbia. A family is discussed, every member of which is called Bobby Watson; a young couple is alarmed to find that they have been married for years. For such people, words can have no meaning. The play ends in a crescendo of non-sequiturs.
ISBN 0 573 02013 2

B

Bang, You're Dead! Comedy thriller. Paul Reakes
M2 (late 20s, early 40s) F2 (30s, 45). A living-room. Fee code D

Lydia and her boyfriend Marcus rehearse the murder of Theo, Lydia's husband, which they are to commit that evening. When the victim and 'perfect witness' arrive all goes according to plan except that Marcus kills Lydia. A ghastly mistake — or are there some deviations from the original plot? In reality Marcus is Theo's boyfriend and Lydia the intended victim all along.
ISBN 0 573 12023 4

Bar and Ger. Drama. Geraldine Aron
M1 (young) F1 (young). A rostrum with cushions. Fee code E

In brief flashes of dialogue the growing-up relationship of a brother and sister is traced through the years. At the beginning, Bar (Barry) is newborn, Geraldine (Ger) is about ten years old. The relationship is developed in a simple, realistic and tender style as they age gradually through the play — not necessarily at the same time — until Bar is seventeen.

Barnstable. Play. James Saunders
M2 (60s) F3 (30, 60s). A drawing-room. Fee code C

The Carboy household is frantic: chimneys are crashing to the ground, dead moles strew the lawn and Barnstable is persistently shooting thrushes. A mystery faces them all: each time there is a shot, a chimney falls. Is Barnstable shooting at the chimneys or does each crashing chimney precipitate a shot? A most disturbing problem, this, to them all.
ISBN 0 573 02015 9

Beata Beatrix. Play. Gillian Plowman
M3 (any age, middle-age). F4 (any age, young). An art gallery. Fee code D

Touring an art gallery, Beatrice notices a lone man, Jon, crying before a painting created out of remorse for a tragedy in the artist's life. Intrigued, Beatrice offers help, and it transpires that for Jon, whose wife had died of leukæmia while he was with another woman, the painting tells his own story. Beatrice, also, has her own haunting secret ...
ISBN 0 573 12136 2

♦ **Bed Among the Lentils.** Monologue. Alan Bennett
F1 (40s). A kitchen. Fee code F

Susan is a failure when it comes to jam-making and flower-arranging and isn't at all sure about God; how unfortunate for her that she is married to Geoffrey, a popular and respected vicar who treats her in an intensely patronizing manner and expects her to conform to her role as vicar's wife. A bleakly hilarious, dark and painful monologue, packed with insights and sparkling satire.
ISBN 0 573 13224 0

Bedside Manner. Play. Frank Vickery
M1 (70s) F5 (20s, middle-age, 60s, 70s). A hospital ward. Fee code D

The lovable, gutsy, human bulldozer, Marlene, finds herself hospitalized once more. Will she be discharged in time for her daughter's wedding? Will the result of the two forty-five at Windsor arrive before the Minister comes to collect the proceeds from the raffle? In true Marlene form, things just never quite go according to plan.

B

Before Dawn. Play. Terence Rattigan
M3 (young, middle-age) F1 (early middle-age). A room in a castle. Fee code E

An hilarious retelling of the play and opera *Tosca*, with Scarpia as a swaggering villain who proves to be impotent, Tosca as a proud beauty and a Captain who gets confused as to whether Scarpia means that Tosca's lover should *really* be executed ... or only appear to be. Tosca's attempt to stab Scarpia is foiled by his knife-proof vest. Period 1800
ISBN 0 573 12017 X

The Bells. Melodrama. Richard Dennis and Michael Kilgarriff
M3 F1. Fee code C

A short melodrama for Music Hall. Contained in *Three More Melodramas*.
ISBN 0 573 00019 0

The Bespoke Overcoat. Play. Wolf Mankowitz
M4 (young, middle-age, 60s). Three acting areas. Fee code C

A minor classic, the play concerns Morry, a Jewish tailor who, in a drunken stupor, sees his dead friend, Fender. Fender has returned to take his due of the living — the harsh employer who dismissed him for being too old. Nothing will satisfy him but a coat from his employer's stock, and Morry in his dream helps his friend to raid the warehouse.
ISBN 0 573 04223 3

♦ **Better Late**. Farce. Georges Feydeau, translated by Peter Meyer
M2 (40s, elderly) F2 (20, 40s). A bedroom. Fee code E

Returning home at 4 a.m. Lucien wakes up his wife, Yvonne, having forgotten his key. The manservant announces that Yvonne's mother has died: Lucien's unfortunate comments infuriate Yvonne. The mother is not dead, they discover, but things do not calm down for poor Lucien ... Translated from Feydeau's *Feu la Mère de Madame* (see also *Night Errant*). Period 1910

Big Cats. Play. Alec Baron
M1 (50) F2 (25, middle-age). A living-room. Fee code D

Lily's dead husband, Joe, is very much alive in Lily's mind. When Lily learns that the house in which she and Joe shared their married life is to be demolished and that she is to be rehoused she flatly refuses to budge believing that her memories of the life she shared with Joe will be buried under the rubble. Eventually she bows to the 'big cats' but at least she has the chance of saying goodbye to Joe.
ISBN 0 573 12060 9

The Birds Stopped Singing. Play. Lawrence Barker
M3 (young, 40s, 50s) F3 (30, 50). Fee code D

When visited by a salesman, Liszt, Pavel reveals how troubled he is by having assisted at the murder of Tsar Nicholas. It has haunted him ever since. His story leads to him revealing his suspicions that he believes that Anastasia, the Russian princess, is working as a prostitute in a local inn. The denouement is even more surprising but by then Pavel is too sunk in 'alcoholic oblivion' to realize it. Period 1930
ISBN 0 573 12028 5

Birdsong. Play. James Saunders
M2 F1. A birdcage. Fee code E

Although set inside a birdcage, with birds as the characters, this play has universal connotations. Joey and Tinker are happy companions, sharing a cage. Into their lives is thrust Trixie — an unhappy, foul-mouthed trouble-maker who only wants to be free. Tinker cannot convince Trixie that the outside is horrid but Joey evolves a plan whereby they can secure her escape by faking a fight. However, Tinker has been thoroughly rattled by Trixie's chanting and strangles her in the mock fight.

Black Comedy. Comedy. Peter Shaffer
M5 (30s, middle-age) F3 (20s, middle-age). An apartment. Fee code H

In this play the usual conditions of light and dark are reversed: when the lights are 'on', we see nothing but darkness; when they are 'off', we see the characters behaving as if they were in a black-out. Carol and Brindsley have invited a millionaire to see Brindsley's sculpture and to impress him have 'borrowed' antiques from a neighbour. Carol's formidable father is also expected. The lights fuse, and the arrival of several unexpected visitors effectively wrecks the evening.
ISBN 0 573 02303 4

Black-Ey'd Susan. Melodrama. Michael Kilgarriff
M4 F1. Fee code C

A short melodrama for inclusion in a Music Hall. Contained in *Three More Melodramas*. Music for this sketch is included in the copy.
ISBN 0 573 00019 0

◆ **Blah Blah Blah.** Play with songs. Brian Marshall
Large variable cast. A bare stage. Fee code E

Id illustrates, with the help of the Chorus, the unfathomable path a life can take, from bewildered childhood, across rebellious adolescence to the mid-life crisis and, finally, dotty old age. 'A zestful and inventive piece of writing, teeming with humour, accurate but suitably ironic observation.' *Irene Rostron, GODA.* (Music available separately on hire)
ISBN 0 573 15210 1

◆ **Blue Kettle**. Play. Caryl Churchill
M2 (40, 70s) F6 (30, 50s-80s). Various simple settings. Fee code E

Derek, a con-man, approaches five different women and claims to be the illegitimate son they gave up for adoption. The hurt this engenders is mirrored in the gradual disintegration of the play's language as the words 'blue' and 'kettle' come to replace the words the characters mean to say. Together with *Heart's Desire*, this forms the double bill *Blue Heart* (see Section A).

◆ **Bookends.** Play. Scott Perry
M2 (old). A park bench. Fee code E

Ron and Bill haven't met up for three weeks — Bill has been in Scarborough, reliving his honeymoon and Ron, having escaped from his old people's home, has been living it up on the ferry to Amsterdam. Funny and touching simultaneously, *Bookends* is a perceptive portrait of old age.
ISBN 0 573 14208 4

Borderline. Play. Wyn Davis
F6 (teenage, 30s, 40s, elderly). A study. Fee code D

Margaret Summers, the dominant headmistress of a girls' school, rules with a rod of iron. When Miss Leigh announces her philanthropic intention of giving the young servant Tansy an education in the school, Miss Summers schemes to force Tansy to leave. The satisfying dramatic ending sees the tables well and truly turned on the jealous headmistress. Period 1905
ISBN 0 573 13214 3

Bottles with Baskets On. Play. Mike Tibbetts
M2 (20s, middle-age) F2 (20s, middle-age). A suburban living-room. Fee code D

It is the eve of Nicola Thompson's wedding day; the festivities are prepared, the presents are wrapped. The groom-to-be, Tom, arrives with a raffia-covered bottle of Chianti for his prospective father-in-law, David, and a night of humorous banter and reminiscence ensues. When David opens the wine, however, things take a dramatic and surprising turn.
ISBN 0 573 12001 3

The Boundary. Comedy. Tom Stoppard and Clive Exton
M2 (elderly) F1. Extras. A lexicographer's library. Fee code E

Johnson is horrified to discover that his library, where he is working on his dictionary, appears to be ransacked. Paper is everywhere, so that even the body of his wife, Brenda, is hidden. With his collaborator Bunyon, he concludes that Brenda is responsible, but the true explanation lies beyond the window. Originally produced for television, this play combines wit, wordplay and a slight touch of comic absurdity.
ISBN 0 573 12046 3

The Boy with a Cart. Play. Christopher Fry
M8 F5. Extras. The open countryside. Fee code F

A retelling of the story of young Cuthman, Saint of Sussex. When his father dies he decides to spread the gospel through southern England: unable to leave his invalid mother, he pulls her along with him in a cart. Eventually he reaches Steyning, in Sussex, where he determines to build a church. Despite some opposition, he succeeds in his plan, aided in the final moments by an apparent miracle. Period early Britain.

Branwell. Play. Bettine Manktelow
M1 (29) F3 (26, 28, 30). A dining-room. Fee code D

We see the Brontë family on a windy autumn evening at a time before the fame of their books has arisen. The play deals with the problem of Branwell, his rapidly accelerating deterioration, the attitude towards him of the three sisters. His weakness, and the tragic waste of his potentially fine intelligence and creative ability are brought out, against the background of the close-knit family circle and the grim moorland landscape which surrounds the Parsonage. Period 1846
ISBN 0 573 02350 6

The Brave Bugler or Up the Khyber Pass. Melodrama. Harry Austin
M4 F1. 1M Extra. Fee code B

Spurred on by the voluptuous Daphne, the diminutive but brave Bugler attempts to repulse single-handedly an attack on the British fort by marauding Indian tribesmen, only to lose Daphne to the suave officer who appears once the fighting is over. Playing time approximately 12-14 minutes. Contained in *The Little Lights of Kimberley*.
ISBN 0 573 10023 3

Brenton Versus Brenton. Comedy. David Tristram
M3 (middle-age) F3 (20s, middle-age). An office. Fee code E

What is the dark secret which inflames the Brenton family feud? Who is the mysterious Eddie? Why are Lana's shoulder-pads wider than the door? And just what was Deke Brenton doing down on the farm? All this, and more, is revealed in this outrageous spoof of American soaps and blockbluster mini-series, set in the manic world of Chicago's biggest advertising agency.

Bright Boy. Play. Martin Jarvis
M4 (young, 30s, 40s). Composite set. Fee code D

Haddleton is on business in Germany. At the hotel bar he is accosted by Grey, another Englishman, with whom he was at school. But Grey has more on his mind than schoolboy reminiscences. Gradually he undermines Haddleton's self-confidence until he has wreaked a terrible vengeance for the equally terrible treatment he received at his hands as a boy.
ISBN 0 573 04202 0

The Browning Version. Play. Terence Rattigan
M5 (16, 22, middle-age) F2 (20, 30s). A living-room. Fee code F

Ill-health is forcing Andrew Cocker-Harris to retire from school-teaching. His wife despises him for being a failure and has been finding consolation with a master, Frank Hunter. As Andrew prepares to leave she openly taunts him. Frank, witnessing this, is disgusted and bitterly ashamed. As the full story of the marriage is revealed, he warms to Andrew. Millie knows she has lost Frank, but even more bitter is the realization that he is now Andrew's fast friend.
ISBN 0 573 02025 6

Bus Stop. Comedy. Rae Shirley
F7 (middle-age). Extra 1M optional. A bus stop. Fee code C

A group of women gather at a bus stop and indulge in gossip to pass the time. Two well-dressed and not very frequent bus users arrive and there is a touch of class conflict. Finally they are confronted by a 'Bookworm', who informs them that they will have a long wait — there is a bus strike!
ISBN 0 573 13209 7

But Yesterday. Play. Jimmie Chinn
M2 F3. Extras 2M. A garden. Fee code D

A haunting, enigmatic play set in the fifties and before. Prior to leaving on a journey Robert comes back to the garden of his childhood and relives moments from his past, which become mingled with the present. Sound and light do much to evoke the atmosphere and we learn of Robert's gradual desertion of his childhood beliefs and hopes. Two men in shadow have accompanied him on this last visit and they escort him to his new life leaving behind a hurt, bewildered family.
ISBN 0 573 12048 X

B

Bye Bye Blues. Play. James Saunders
M3 F3. Fee code D

Bye Bye Blues deals with the conflicts between freedom, control and responsibility, discussed by three pairs of strangers 'caught in an accidental confrontation', who are 'linked to each other, responsible to each other', although independent and struggling to preserve their freedom. Ultimately, living cannot be operated like a machine, and demands involvement between self and others.

The Café. Play. Neville Watchurst
M2 (elderly) F2 (60s, elderly). A ballroom. Fee code D

In July 1990, the Café de Paris, a ballroom off Leicester Square, opened its doors for the last time in its sixty-six year history. *The Café* focuses on four elderly people who have met and danced together for many years and are viewing life without their regular meetings with sadness. Bittersweet, sad and romantic, this is a charming and moving play for older actors.
ISBN 0 573 12088 9

Café Society. Play. Ayshe Raif
F4 (70s, any age). A café. Fee code D

Three elderly ladies meet in the same café each morning until the café announces it is closing down. Dolly attempts to interest the others in a new meeting place but Hetty is offered a council flat some miles away and Amy accepts a proposal of marriage. The end of the play shows a happy solution for all.
ISBN 0 573 13218 6

The Cagebirds. Play. David Campton
8 characters. A room. Fee code D

In this allegorical play six birds live in a cage, each totally absorbed in her own particular characteristics. When the Wild One is introduced into their midst by their Mistress, she endeavours to persuade them to break out from their self-imposed dependence and imprisonment into the wider world outside — but her efforts result only in her own destruction at their hands.
ISBN 0 573 03366 8

Cahoot's Macbeth. Tom Stoppard

Please see the entry for *Dogg's Hamlet* in this section.

Campfire's Burning. Play. Jean M. Hayward
M2 (17, middle-age) F3 (17, middle-age). An open stage. Fee code C

This light and lively play, set on an English campsite, contrasts the lifestyle of well-to-do Monty, his wife Ruth and son Tarquin (who camp here every year) with that of Debbie and Shirleen, young girls from a depressed background, trying camping for the first time. The girls breathe fresh air into the 'every year' routine of the others' lives.
ISBN 0 573 12073 0

B

Can You Hear The Music? Play. David Campton
6 characters. A loft. Fee code D

Everyone has their dream, and this is no exception for the six mice living in the loft. Their dreams are conjured up by music as each hears a different tune played by an invisible Piper and each has to answer his call until only Tattymouse, who is completely deaf, is left. A highly original and thought-provoking play.
ISBN 0 573 12042 0

Cards. Play. Stephen Lowe
M2 (20, middle-age) F2 (20s, middle-age). Extras. Boy and 1M voices only. A seaside front. Fee code E

Cards brings to life the vulgar characters of traditional seaside postcards painted by artist Donald McGill. The models for these cards — Big Fat Mam and Wiry Old Dad — reminisce nostalgically of the days of honest, innocent vulgarity. Hurt, angry and appalled by a changing postcard trade, Mam and Dad find themselves dumped on the inevitable scrap-heap.
ISBN 0 573 12029 3

Cards, Cups and Crystal Ball. Play. David Campton
F5 (middle-age). A drawing-room. Fee code D

The Weerd sisters try to make ends meet through fortune-telling. When Lady M calls, Flora discovers she indeed has the gift of foresight, although she does not like what she sees. The sisters' fortunes are turned. Lady M returns to learn more but this time the truth is held back. Period late nineteenth-early twentieth century
ISBN 0 573 13215 1

Careful Rapture. Comedy. Jack Popplewell
M1 (43) F5 (18, 19, middle-age, 70). A living-room. Fee code D

Ted is engaged to Peggy, but before taking the final step, he insists on vetting his future mother-in-law. To his pleasant surprise, Peggy's widowed mother Jean is a very attractive woman, so attractive that Ted breaks his engagement to the daughter to marry the mother. Jean is happy, until *her* mother arrives on the scene ...
ISBN 0 573 02030 2

Case of the Crushed Petunia. Play. Tennessee Williams
M2 (young) F2 (26, middle-age). A shop. Fee code E

Primanproper, Massachusetts: Dorothy owns a shop called Simple Notions which is barricaded behind a double row of petunias. One morning she is distraught to find the flowers trampled down. A young man admits he trod down the flowers, reluctant to live a full life. Finally she makes an assignation with him and changes the name of her shop to Tremendous Inspirations.

Caught on the Hop. Comedy. David Foxton*
M2 F3. A room in a Paris apartment. Fee code D

Returning home unexpectedly early from a rendezvous with her lover, Sophie Fontaineau finds that her husband Étienne is absent and immediately suspects him of philandering. Étienne's lover 'Esmeralda' appears and recognizes the porter — by now disguised as Sophie's aged aunt in order to escape Étienne — as her husband. Clothilde, the long-suffering maid, provides the final twist to this delightful comedy. (*State author when ordering)
ISBN 0 573 12059 5

B

Cecily. Play. Gillian Plowman
F3 (20s, 40s). Interior setting. Fee code D

Intense complicated family relationships are put to the test when Cecily becomes brain damaged following a motor-cycle accident and the problems of carers are highlighted. Flashbacks of Cecily before the accident are shown, her lively personality contrasting cruelly with her wheelchair-bound reality. Fiery, forthright and honest, this moving play has three excellent roles for women.
ISBN 0 573 13227 5

The Chairs. Tragic farce. Eugene Ionesco. Translated from the French by Donald Watson
M2 (45-50, 95) F1 (94). A room. Fee code E

An old man invites all the world to hear his message — the vindication of his existence. His wife has to bring in more and more chairs for the guests. The Orator arrives. The couple announce that their mission is completed and jump to their deaths. The voice of the Orator is that of a deaf mute.

The Cherry Sisters. A play for Coarse Actors. Michael Green

See the entry for *The Coarse Acting Show 2*.

Chimera. Play. Alec Baron
F3 (29, 50). 1 voice. A living-room/bedroom. Fee code D

Kate, paralysed from the waist down, copes bravely with daily help from her 'treasure' Mrs Ponsello, until Mrs Ponsello is to move. Then Emma, Kate's closest friend, arrives. Emma's glamorous Californian lifestyle is a sham and now she cannot face returning to America, pregnant and alone. But Kate has the perfect solution, if only Emma will agree ...
ISBN 0 573 13226 7

The Chinese Pendant. Melodrama. Harry Austin
M4 F3. Chairman. Fee code B

Sir Geoffrey arrives home from the Orient bringing a pendant on which is inscribed the location of secret treasure. Evil Dr Fu Man Chu attempts to recover it but is thwarted by the British Secret Service. A short play suitable for inclusion in a Music Hall evening or similar compilation. Contained in *The Chinese Pendant and Other Plays*.
ISBN 0 573 00029 8

A Chip in the Sugar. Monologue from *Talking Heads*. Alan Bennett
M1 (middle-age). A bedroom. Fee code F

Graham, a middle-aged bachelor, emotionally retarded and chronically dependent on his mother, finds life difficult enough at the best of times; when Mother meets an old flame and seems set to marry him, however, Graham's old insecurities rear their ugly heads again. Fate, eventually, rescues Graham and he resumes his normal life of banal muddle under his mother's amnesiac tyranny.
ISBN 0 573 04212 8

Christmas Incorporated. Satirical comedy. Peter Horsler
F3. Extras. 6 M or F. A child's bedroom. Fee code D

'What's the Christmas spirit?' asks the Child as she settles down to write the customary letter to Father Christmas. Before her, the Educational Psychologist and Father Christmas's Personal Assistant battle over what toys the Child ought to have, considering science versus commercialism. The Child is so confused she discards all the toys in a tantrum.
ISBN 0 573 12034 X

Clara's on the Curtains! Comedy. Arthur Lovegrove
F10 (16, young, middle-age). A bare stage. Fee code D

Just before the Curtain Up on the Wickley Women's Guild variety and dramatic show, one of the leading performers loses her voice. This is only the start of a series of calamities, not lessened by well-meant but embarrassing offers of help from others. Everything works out, however, and Clara even learns how to work the curtains.
ISBN 0 573 03352 8

Close to Croydon. Play. Gillian Plowman
M1 F1. M1 F1 voices only. An overturned railway carriage. Fee code D

Hugo, a PR consultant on his way to an important meeting, and Martha, a Museum Education Officer with a case full of liberty bodices, are trapped in an overturned railway carriage following a rail crash, waiting tensely to be rescued. A touching relationship begins to develop between them but they are torn apart by tragedy.
ISBN 0 573 12012 9

THE COARSE ACTING SHOW 2 (Further Plays for Coarse Actors)

Michael Green
M9 F4. Extras. Various interior and exterior settings. Fee codes A, B, C and D.

The number of characters given above would be sufficient, with doubling, to cover the presentation of all four plays by the same cast. Ages can vary from young to practically senile.
The Coarse Acting Show 2 contains further plays for Coarse Actors. Like the plays in the previous volume, *Four Plays for Coarse Actors*, these four plays show different aspects of Coarse Theatre. *Moby Dick* is a rather over-ambitious attempt to reduce the epic novel (685 pages long) into a series of quick-fire scenes. *The Cherry Sisters*, a hitherto undiscovered fragment of Chekhov, is a desperately sincere piece, with a real tear-jerker of an ending, spoiled only by the fact that someone has to die standing up in order to cope with a faulty prop. *Last Call for Breakfast* is full of symbolism, a short avant-garde piece made shorter by the simple mischance of one of the actors getting himself in the wrong position during a black-out. *Henry the Tenth (Part Seven)* is a rarely-performed masterpiece (from a suggestion by William Shakespeare) with battle scenes of which the Bard would have been proud. In all four, everything which can conceivably go wrong does so: sets collapse, actors fail to appear on stage, props fall to pieces — but the Coarse cast carry on, firmly believing that the audience won't notice a thing.
ISBN 0 573 10005 5

Cock Robin Hood. Minidrama. Richard Tydeman
M10 F3. Extras. Fee code B

With the illiterate Arfur Mo doing verbal battle with his compère and the Merrie Men almost getting round to doing battle with the Sherriff and his men, the story of Robin Hood and Maid Marion is lost — almost. Running time: 15-20 minutes
ISBN 0 573 12027 7

The Code of the West. Comedy Sketch. Michael Kilgarriff
M4 F2. Chairman. Extras. Fee code B

This is a mime piece with actions by the cast accompanying the recitation of a poem of truly epic stature. The Ranch Boss, the Wicked Mayor, the Gunslinger, the Hero, the Heroine and the Saloon Gal — a rich canvas of life in the old Wild West is starkly depicted in these unforgettable stanzas. Michael Kilgarriff has included helpful production notes and song suggestions for this sketch as well as technical plots. Contained in *Three Comedy Sketches*.
ISBN 0 573 00028 X

◆ **Cold Salmon**. Play. John Bowen
M4 (20s, 40s, 60s) F6 (14, 30s-50s, 70s, 90s) A graveyard. Fee code D

In a neglected graveyard, deceased Harry is waiting for his wife, Beth, to join him. He can only watch helplessly as his daughter Angie wheels the deaf and ailing Beth to the graveside for their monthly visit. Then a five-strong family arrives to scatter Dad's ashes and Harry sees his chance to reach out to Beth ...
ISBN 0 573 12032 3

The Collection. Play. Harold Pinter
M3 (28, 35, middle-age) F1 (35). Composite setting. Fee code F

Stella returns from her dress collection in Leeds to tell James, her husband, that she has been unfaithful. James confronts Bill, pressing for the truth, already determined to believe the worst. Bill confesses that he and Stella had only talked about spending the night together. It had amused him to perpetuate Stella's story — to hurt his friend Harry. Is this the truth? Stella is silent.
ISBN 0 573 02036 1

A Collier's Tuesday Tea. A Play for Coarse Actors. Michael Green

See the entry for *Four Plays for Coarse Actors*.

Come into the Garden Maud. Comedy. Noël Coward
M2 (28, 55) F2 (late 40s, early 50s). A Swiss hotel suite. Fee code F

For years the affable Verner Conklin has placidly endured his ill-humoured wife, Anna-Mary. When one of her dinner guests falls ill she is left with thirteen at table; she orders Verner to dine in their suite. He has excellent company in Maud Caragnani. When Anna-Mary snappishly tells Verner to go away Verner complies — with Maud.
ISBN 0 573 02308 5

Commitment. Play. Graham Swannell
M1 F2. A kitchen. Fee code D

See the entry under *A State of Affairs* in Section A.

B

Company Come. Play. Alec Baron
M2 (20s, 50) F2 (late 30s, 40-70). A farmhouse kitchen. Fee code D

Martha apparently lives alone in her remote farmhouse, but is she, in fact, alone? First Jesse, her husband, then Tim, her son — both dead — enter, apparently through a bolted door. The story moves back and forth in time and reveals the lives of all three, lives in which Mary Lee, their neighbour, also turns out to be closely involved. The borders between past and present, life and death are blurred.
ISBN 0 573 12022 6

Consequences. Play. Graham Swannell
M1 F2. An hotel bedroom. Fee code D

See the entry under *A State of Affairs* in Section A.

Conversations with a Golliwog. Play. Alexander Guyan
M3 (15-20s) F3 (14-19, middle-age). A bedroom with hospital ward inset. Fee code E

As a fourteen-year-old, Canny had insulated herself against reality, confiding only in her golliwog, Boswell. Her brother, Mike, inadvertently forced her out of her fantasy world and thereafter Boswell was silent. A shock pushes Canny over the borderline into insanity, but there is one comfort: Boswell is once more conversing with her.
ISBN 0 573 02040 X

Costa del Packet! Farce. Anthony Booth
F5. A hut. Fee code D

Four women arrive at Del Sol on a package tour. They find themselves stranded in a workman's hut on the site of their hotel, which is not even constructed yet. Determined not to let their husbands know that they have been conned, they decide not to return home and determinedly try to make the best of everything. It is, however, far from easy!
ISBN 0 573 03357 9

A Country Rebel. Play. Jeffrey Grenfell-Hill
F6 (young-elderly). A simple cottage room. Fee code D

This humorous and well-crafted play deals with the class divisions of Edwardian England and is set before the Old Age Pensions Act was passed. It skilfully depicts the battle of Sarah Dawkins and her mother, Gran Twigden, to outwit the local gentry, whose attitude is paternalistic but patronizing. Period 1908
ISBN 0 573 13222 4

Courting Disaster. Comedy. Margaret Wood
M3 (20s, 30, middle-age) F4 (20, 30, middle-age). A farmhouse kitchen/living-room. Fee code D

Meg, housekeeper to the tyrannical Trevor Lloyd, is sweet on Trevor's younger brother Hughie, who feels the same about her but lacks confidence. Trevor, too, has love problems, although in his case it is land which brings the light of love into his eyes. Meg decides it's time to act and the results are lively!
ISBN 0 573 12037 4

◆ A Cream Cracker Under the Settee. Monologue. Alan Bennett
F1(70s). 1 M, voice only. A living-room. Fee code F

Doris, a widow, lives alone. Refusing to relinquish her independence, she surreptitiously cleans when her home help, Zulema, is absent; when we meet her, she has just fallen over whilst attempting to dust a picture frame high on the wall. The day goes on; unable to get help, Doris reminisces about her quiet, uneventful life with its joys and sadnesses.
ISBN 0 573 13225 9

The Crimson Coconut. Farce. Ian Hay
M4 (young, middle-age, old) F2 (young, middle-age). A Soho restaurant. Fee code C

Jack Pincher has come to a decrepit restaurant where two anarchists are expected to rendezvous. Scotland Yard has word that a plan is afoot to blow up the Bank of England. Robert the waiter is more concerned with wooing the cook, but agrees to help Pincher foil the anarchists. The would-be bombers are arrested; Pincher and Robert share the reward.
ISBN 0 573 02041 8

Crossways. Play. Jane Parry-Davis
F7 (20s, middle-age). A cottage sitting-room. Fee code D

When widowed Elizabeth moves into the ancient, thatched-roof cottage, Crossways, in the village where her parents and closest schoolfriend, Caroline, live, she feels drawn to Crossways through a distinctly psychic feeling. When Caroline brings another village newcomer, a psychiatrist with a special interest in regression, a chilling sixteenth-century witch-hunt begins with Elizabeth as the victim.
ISBN 0 573 13228 3

A Crowing Hen. Comedy. Doris M. Day
F5 (20, 40s, 50, 70s). A dining-room. Fee code D

Rita has invited the Dawsons to discuss the wedding of their respective children. Mrs Dawson has grandiose ideas, and simmering disagreements boil up into a first-class row. Things are smoothed over, but a phone call makes all the fuss unnecessary: the young couple have been married quietly and in secret.
ISBN 0 573 03374 9

Curses, Foiled Again! Play. Evelyn Hood
M2 F4. A drawing-room. Fee code D

The eve-of-performance dress rehearsal of Henry's send-up of a Victorian tragedy is running anything but smoothly as the cast constantly step out of character to bicker. Feuds simmer beneath the surface and the pretty heroine cannot remember her lines! However, when all seems lost, and the play likely to be cancelled, the cast rally like true troopers for 'the show must go on'!
ISBN 0 573 12020 X

A Cut in the Rates. Play. Alan Ayckbourn
M1 F3, may be played by M1 F2. A street, a study, a cellar. Fee code D

When Miss Pickhart visits Ratchet, an illusionist, at his home she discovers some dark, sinister secrets from his past. She is asked for help by Rosalinda's ghost, who died when they performed the saw-the-woman-in-half trick, but this means Miss Pickhart reliving that fateful night. Will she also meet a grim death?
ISBN 0 573 12084 6

Daddy's Gone A-Hunting. Play. H. Connolly
M2 (late 20s, 30) F2 (early 20s, 25). 1F, voice only. A living-room. Fee code D

Simon, Liz and their new baby, Max, are visited by Simon's younger sister Rebecca and her new boyfriend, who turns out to be an important figure from Liz's past. This tautly-written play moves from comedy to terror as Max becomes a pawn in a deadly game of jealousy and attempted murder.
ISBN 0 573 12035 8

Dancers. Comedy. Jean McConnell
F2 (middle-age). A seaside promenade. Fee code B

See the entry for *Deckchairs I*.

The Dark Room. Play. Tennessee Williams
M1 (boy) F2 (middle-age). A kitchen. Fee code E

Miss Morgan, a social worker, is interviewing Mrs Pocciotti, whose daughter of fifteen, Tina, has remained shut in a dark room for six months after being jilted by a young German. Further surprises follow: the boy, Max, visits her regularly, the girl fights and screams if he does not arrive. The biggest surprise of all comes as the curtain slowly falls. Period 1946

Darlings, You Were Wonderful! Comedy. Derek Lomas
F6. 1 male voice. The dressing-room of a small theatre. Fee code D

The Amazon Theatre Group are to perform a little-known, passionate, Spanish drama in a festival. Amid multiple tensions and general chaos backstage, Lesley, the missing member, staggers in paralytically drunk and dressed in motor-cycle gear. The adjudicator is impressed with the cast's seething passion and pronounces Lesley's motor-cycle regalia a stroke of genius!
ISBN 0 573 13231 3

David's Birthday. Play. Gillian Plowman
M3 (30s, 40s) F2 (30s). A sitting-room. Fee code D

David, a mentally-handicapped young man, forms the catalyst between two couples — his sister, Liz, and her husband, John, and his other sister Maggie and her partner Paul. Both sisters bear conflicting emotions of love, hate, compassion and guilt towards David — highlighted in the flashbacks to childhood sequences.
ISBN 0 573 12062 5

The Day of Reckoning. Comedy. Michael Kilgarriff
F5 (20s, 50s). A kitchen. Fee code D

With a plot of ludicrously labyrinthine complexity and a plethora of Gilbertian coincidences this one-act play charts the startling changes in fortunes of a poor but honest widow and her daughter — not to mention their eccentric neighbour. Or is she more than just a neighbour? Period Victorian. Contained in the volume *Three Comedy Sketches.*
ISBN 0 573 00028 X

Day of the Dog. Play. Graham Swannell
M3 F2. A pub courtyard. Fee code D

See the entry under *A State of Affairs* in Section A.

♦ **Day Trippers**. Short play (From *Deckchairs II*). Jean McConnell
F2 (elderly). A seafront. Fee code C

Confident Beryl and prudish Doris, on an annual works outing, learn a little more about themselves and their work colleagues than they perhaps ought to. When they discover that they have come to a nudist beach, the result is a brilliantly funny scene of hilarious antics.
ISBN 0 573 10004 7

Dead End. Play. Richard Parsons
M1 (30s) F1 (30s). A cottage interior. Fee code C

Is Arabella Snelgrove, isolated and apparently alone in her typical English cottage, the perfect, upright, law-abiding citizen? Brian Wedmore, an inspector from the Department of Social Security, throws grave suspicions on Arabella's honesty. He wonders if her elderly mother, for whom she claims a pension, exists at all: why is she never seen? A tense, tantalizing, psychological thriller with the most unexpected twist.
ISBN 0 573 10001 2

Death. Comedy. Woody Allen
M18 F2. Various settings on an open stage. Fee code F

Kleinman is awakened in the middle of the night and summoned to join a party of vigilantes hunting a murdering maniac. He finds himself in a series of encounters which become increasingly mystifying and menacing. Is he even suspected of being the maniac himself? When the strangler eventually appears he resembles Kleinman just as — oddly — one of the murdered had said the maniac resembled *him.*
ISBN 0 573 62129 2

The Death Artist. Play. David Henry Wilson
M2 (30s, 60s). One interior. Fee code C

The central issue of this thought-provoking play is death and punishment. Deliberately retreating from the world to avoid evil and injustice, the sinner, on the verge of monetary success, is visited by the death artist who instils the fear of dying into the victim's mind and leaves him a complete wreck.
ISBN 0 573 62364 3

Deckchairs I. Five short plays. Jean McConnell
F2. A seaside promenade. Fee code B per play. (For productions of two or more of these plays in one performance please apply for details)

These five twist-in-the-tail playlets for two women — all set on a seaside promenade — are by turns funny and poignant. In *Shoppers*, two well-to-do shopaholics have a rather surprising secret. *Early Blight* is a heart-breaking exploration of a doomed mother/daughter relationship. *Dancers* wittily dissects the tea-dancing world of two skittish widows. *Late Frost* is a drama in which a woman finds out her best friend had an affair with her late husband. And *Doggies* is an hilarious tale about two very different types of dog-owner. These delightful plays run for approximately fifteen minutes each and may be performed as a set or individually.
ISBN 0 573 10003 9

◆ **Deckchairs II**. Four short plays. Jean McConnell
F2. Fee code C per play
See *Day Trippers, The Guilt Card, Short Changed, Theatrical Digs*

Definitely Eric Geddis. Satire. Michael Snelgrove
M21 F14, doubling possible. Simple settings on a bare stage. Fee code D

Eric decides to seek fame and fortune by persuading Rodney, the executive of his firm's advertising agency, to market him as a superstar. There follows a glimpse of the crazy, cut-throat world of finance and promotion where Eric, his family and the advertising agency fall victims to the fickle nature of the public.
ISBN 0 573 12043 9

The Demon. Thriller. Martin Downing
M3 (30s, 40) F4 (20s, 30s). A lounge. Fee code D

Escaping a torrential rain-storm, six friends meet in a high-rise flat and hear a terrifying announcement: one of them may well be a serial killer, possessed by the Devil! This hypothesis is soon proved when one of their number meets a hideous death, and from then on the survivors embark on a desperate quest — to find and destroy the fiend in their midst before more blood is spilled.
IBSN 0 573 12090 0

Departure. Play. Stephen Smith
M1 (40s) F3 (20, 40s). An airport lounge. Fee code D

Stranded in an airport lounge during the delay of a holiday flight to Spain, Rosemary and her carbon-copy daughter, Mandy, draw the reluctant Dennis and Sheila Tippit into conversation. The comic tone of the play shifts continually between Rosemary's malapropisms and Dennis's grimly humorous bigotry with the close of the play finding Rosemary unmoved by the chaos she has caused and Dennis near to a nervous breakdown!
ISBN 0 573 12075 7

Dial Ten Amazing Little Boy Friends. Musical play. Colin Sell
M5 F5. A library. Fee code F

This musical play is a zany combination of the most popular genres of British Theatre, the murder mystery and musical. Ten people find themselves under the roof of Mr Jacobs's country house in 1924. It transpires that eight of them have grievances against Jacobs, but as they never see him their revenge must be on his son ... Period 1924
ISBN 0 573 12053 6

A Different Way to Die. Play. Lynn Brittney
M2 (35), F2 (20, 30). An hotel room. Fee code D

Anna Gruber, a concentration camp survivor, arrives in Israel in 1950 to start afresh — but first she must relive the horrifying events of her past as Dr Feldman, a psychiatrist, interviews her about her experiences. Anna dreads revealing an intimate secret and this dilemma, and the appalling story of her imprisonment, form the heart of this compelling and moving drama.
ISBN 0 573 12052 8

La Dispute. Marivaux. Translated by Timberlake Wertenbaker
M6 F4. Extras. Country settings. Fee code E

Nineteen years ago, the Prince's father had found four new-born babes (two of each sex) and had them brought up in separate houses. Now the Prince and Hermiane are to view the couples' first meeting, to view love as it must have first happened and to discover whether man was the first to be unfaithful, or woman. Will the eternal dispute be settled now?

Distracted Globe. Comedy. Nick Warburton
M2 (40, middle-age) F4 (young). The set of *Hamlet*. Fee code D

A very funny completion to Nick Warburton's trilogy of the Drama Club's production of *Hamlet* (seen on stage in *Don't Blame It on the Boots* and backstage in *Easy Stages*) which progresses to the after-show party! Meticulous stage-manager Gerry, in charge of the refreshments and music, marshals poor Patsy into artistically arranging bridge rolls, to the accompaniment of *Peer Gynt*!
ISBN 0 573 12102 8

Do-Gooders. Play. Graham Jones
M4 (16, 40s) F2 (16). A bare stage. Fee code D

This play, ideally suited to younger actors, concentrates on a very important topical issue — pollution. Nora, a member of her school's Environmental Studies Society, attempts to have analysed samples of water from local caves which she suspects is being contaminated by a factory of which her father is a director. Excitement and tension mount when Nora threatens to drink the water.
ISBN 0 573 12054 4

The Do-It-Yourself Frankenstein Outfit. Play. David Campton
M9 or F9. Extras. A bare stage. Fee code D

The Demonstrator is showing the audience a kit for making your own robot. To demonstrate how far advanced this model is he exhibits various earlier models but is increasingly interrupted by a voice in the audience, who could be a Government agent sent to discover who is selling robots to the public — a practice that is not allowed.
ISBN 0 573 12056 0

The Dock Brief. Play. John Mortimer
M2 (middle-age, old). A prison cell. Fee code E

Morgenhall, a seedy broken-down barrister, is chosen to defend Fowle, accused of murdering his wife. In the first scene Morgenhall takes him through the probable course of the trial. In the second scene the case has been lost. Morgenhall hopes for an appeal but Fowle is put out — there is no need to appeal, he has already been reprieved on account of the ineptitude of his defence.
ISBN 0 573 04209 8

Doggies. Comedy. Jean McConnell
F2 (any age). A seaside promenade. Fee code B

See the entry for *Deckchairs I.*

Dogg's Hamlet, Cahoot's Macbeth. Tom Stoppard
Fee code M when performed as a double bill, fee code F when performed separately

Dogg's Hamlet is an exercise in nonsensical language for 22 characters (much doubling possible), which leads to *The Dogg's Troupe 15-Minute Hamlet* (available separately under the title *The Fifteen Minute Hamlet*)

Cahoot's Macbeth is a play for 19 characters (with doubling, M2 F3) dedicated to the Czechoslovakian playwright Pavel Kohout. At its core is a performance of *Macbeth* taking place in a private home because the actors have been forbidden to perform in public.

The Donahue Sisters. Play. Geraldine Aron
F3 (30s, 40s). An attic room. Fee code E

Gathered together the sisters talk of their unhappy lives into the night until the time comes for the ritual re-enactment of a disturbing incident from their childhood. Departing from the hitherto naturalistic style of the play the sisters in unison create the persona of Dominic and with this creation would appear to come an answer to their problems. A challenge to both actors and director.
ISBN 0 573 13234 8

Don't Blame It on the Boots. Comedy. N. J. Warburton
M1 (40) F3 (young, 30, 40). A stage, a dressing-room. Fee code D

No-one would have blamed it on the boots if only Kate had produced *Macbeth* instead of *Hamlet*; Ophelia hadn't been so attractively naïve; Eric had been blessed with smaller feet and wasn't the drama group's prize flirt; and Liz's father hadn't once trod the boards at Stratford in those self-same boots.
ISBN 0 573 12086 2

◆ **Don't Walk About with Nothing On**. Farce. Georges Feydeau, translated by Peter Meyer
M4 (40s) F1 (30s). 1 boy (voice only). A drawing-room. Fee code E

Clarisse has removed her dress and donned a nightdress in daytime. A quick succession of unexpected influential visitors seems set to destroy her husband's promising political career — especially when a wasp stings Clarisse in a very delicate place. Translated from Feydeau's *Mais N'te Promène Donc Pas Toute Nue!* (see also *Put Some Clothes On, Clarisse!*). Period 1910

Double Dealing, or, **A Little Horse Play**. Melodrama. Brian J. Burton
M4 F2. Simple interior setting. Fee code B

A mini melodrama for inclusion in a Music Hall Evening, with the emphasis on comedy with a difference. Contained in *Foiled Again!*

Double, Double. Play. James Saunders
M6 (young, middle-age) F4 (young, middle-age) or M3 F2. A busmen's canteen. Fee code C

In the depressing atmosphere of the busmen's canteen, minor irritations become insurmountable problems. The Inspector is twittering with nerves; buses are late, staff missing and a number 642 has disappeared completely. The missing bus eventually reappears, Bert having catastrophically driven under too low a bridge; now his bus is the first open-top double decker in the fleet.
ISBN 0 573 02055 8

B

◆ **The Drag Factor**. Play. Frank Vickery
M2 (youngish, mid 50s) F1 (mid 50s). A hospital corridor. Fee code D

Set in a hospital corridor, *The Drag Factor* is a poignant and blisteringly funny account of a husband and wife coming abruptly to terms with the fact that their son is gay. NB. *The Drag Factor* is Act I Scene 1 of Frank Vickery's full length play *Roots and Wings*.

Dreamjobs. Play. Graham Jones
F5 (15). A waiting-room. Fee code D

Waiting for interviews with a Youth Employment Service, five teenage girls dream of romantic, exciting jobs derived from sentimental television series and films. The dreams are enacted, and in each case there is a rude awakening. Finally Beverly, clearest-sighted, brings them down to earth, forcing them to realize that their characters and abilities will fit them for only the drabbest of occupations.
ISBN 0 573 03379 X

The Droitwich Discovery. Play. Nick Warburton
M2 (young) F4 (young, middle-age). An attic. Fee code D

Four thespian enthusiasts find themselves in a dusty attic in Droitwich. Their guide explains that Shakespeare, aged ten, lived there. Then there emerges a Tudor-looking man, the ghost of Terry Shakespeare, embittered by his brother William's literary thievery. To prove his point, he puts the visitors in a trance, making them perform scenes from the plays *he* had written.
ISBN 0 573 12146 X

The Drunkard's Dilemma. Melodrama. Andrew Sachs. Edited by Michael Kilgarriff
M3 F1. Fee code A

The near-deflowering of a sweet young thing by her drunken uncle's wicked landlord, and her last-minute rescue by the upright hero. For inclusion in a Music Hall Evening. Contained in *Three Melodramas*. Music available separately.
ISBN 0 573 00018 2

The Drunkard's Wife or **The Tables Turned**. Melodrama. Brian J. Burton
M2 F2. One interior. Fee code D

A temperance drama, employing the Victorian device of the occasional overuse of long or obscure words, which it is doubtful if the actors understand, let alone the audience! Contained in *Three Hisses for Villainy*.

Duck Variations. Play. David Mamet
M2 (60s). A park. Fee code E

Two elderly gentlemen meet in a park and proceed to discuss life, death and ducks. The ducks form a sort of sounding-board from which their flights of fancy take off, providing parallels, analogies and equivalents for their more serious, or less worldly, topics. The play is presented in the form of fourteen variations with an interval between each variation to allow the actors to prepare.

The Dumb Waiter. Play. Harold Pinter
M2. A basement room. Fee code F

Gus and Ben are on the job, waiting and listening. Into the waiting silence rattles the dumb waiter with extraordinary demands for dishes they cannot supply — and who is operating the dumb waiter in an empty house? In a while their victim will come and they will know what to do.
ISBN 0 573 04210 1

The Dwarfs. Play. Harold Pinter
M3 (20s). Composite set. Fee code E

Len and Peter are drinking tea in Mark's flat at midnight. As Mark arrives the scene changes to Len's house. Len, a neurotic young man, is haunted by dwarfs. At great length he describes their extraordinary and seemingly nonsensical behaviour. The other two believe he gets too excited by life and his delusions. The explanation of Len's haunting is left in the air.

Early Blight. Play. Jean McConnell
F2 (middle age, elderly). A seaside promenade. Fee code B

See the entry for *Deckchairs I*.

Easy Stages. Comedy. N. J. Warburton
M3 (40s) F4 (30s) or M2 F5. A stage. Fee code D

This is an amusing, subtle parody of the backstage goings-on of an amateur dramatic society. While N. J. Warburton's play *Don't Blame It on the Boots* centred on the onstage difficulties of the amateur dramatic society's production of *Hamlet*, here we see the stage crew struggling to play their part against all the odds.
ISBN 0 573 12066 8

◆ **The Edge**. Play. Steve Carley
M3 (any age, 50) or M2 F1. Composite set: 2 offices. Fee code E

Marcus Wade has found himself saddled with a curious gift: he can see into the future. At first he can use this power to his advantage but his pleasure turns to terror when he finds his vision only extends a certain distance into the future. What lies beyond 'the edge' he sees coming rapidly towards him?
ISBN 0 573 12151 6

Edwin. Play. John Mortimer
M2 (elderly) F1 (elderly). Extras 2M. A garden. Fee code F

Sir Fennimore Truscott, a retired Judge, sits under his mulberry tree and 'tries' his next-door-neighbour Tom Marjoriebanks for — allegedly — seducing Truscott's wife Margaret many years earlier. Is Tom the father of Edwin, Fennimore and Margaret's only son? Only Margaret knows the whole truth ... Barbed wit and a wealth of judicial felicities make this comedy a delight from swearing-in to verdict.
ISBN 0 573 12101 X

Effie's Burning. Play. Valerie Windsor
F2 (20s, 60s). A hospital room, a space. Fee code E

Effie, who has lived in mental institutions since the age of thirteen, has been admitted to hospital with severe burns. Treating her is Dr Ruth Kovacs, who finds in Effie's extraordinary story of injustice and official callousness the key to her own suppressed anger and power. Taut and powerful, tender and often funny, *Effie's Burning* is an emotional switchback of a play, with a searing anger at its heart.
ISBN 0 573 13236 4

Endgame. Play. Samuel Beckett
M3 F1. A bare interior. Fee code F

The world is coming to an end, and Hamm, a sightless despot, attended by Clov, his shambling slave, watch from their bleak cell. Hamm is flanked by two dustbins, inhabited by his legless parents, Nagg and Nell. Eventually Nell dies. In Beckett's vision, there is defeat and poetic despair but the whole is faintly illumined by a glimmer of salvation.

An Englishman Abroad. Play. Alan Bennett
M4 (20s, 50s) F1 (40s). A flat. Fee code F

Originally a television play, this forms part of the double bill *Single Spies* (see Section A) which was presented by the Royal National Theatre in 1988, winning the Laurence Olivier Award for Comedy of the Year. It is based on a true incident in the life of the actress Coral Browne and tells the witty, touching story of her meeting with Guy Burgess in Moscow in 1958.
ISBN 0 573 01891 X

Epitaph for a Hard Man. Play. Evelyn Hood
M1 (elderly) F2 (30s). A living-room. Fee code D

Ex-con Charlie McGhee wistfully prepares for his daughter Nan's weekly visit. Although alone in Nan's eyes, McGhee still shares his days with his dead wife Cathy, an ethereal presence which visits him. Threatened by a home for the aged, Charlie is forced to reveal a secret which will shatter Nan's life ... and his.
ISBN 0 573 12064 1

Ernie's Incredible Illucinations. Play for young people. Alan Ayckbourn
22 characters. Extras. Doubling possible. A bare stage, waiting-room at one side. Fee code E

Ernie Fraser has a vivid imagination, but his thoughts have a disturbing habit of turning into reality. After a number of embarrassing episodes, Ernie's parents consult a doctor. When Ernie fails to produce a brass band on demand, the doctor diagnoses group hallucination. However, 'Ernie's incredible illucinations' aren't to be dismissed quite so lightly!
ISBN 0 573 12063 3

The Escapologist. Play. David Henry Wilson
M2 (30s, middle-age) F1 (middle-age). A street. Fee code C

Joe, a passerby, becomes central in the act of Escalini, a street performer accompanied by a parrot-like wife. The show becomes a kaleidoscope of themes ranging from God to free will and, ultimately, death while the escapologist attempts to free himself from steel chains which — metaphorically — summarize man's fate.

B

The Evergreens. Play. David Campton
M1 (late 60s) F1 (late 60s). Simple settings. Fee code D

Brought together once more after more than forty years, He and Her must re-learn to accept their differences. Their encounter begins begins acrimoniously but progresses to their memories of a friendlier past, leading the pair arranging a date. Superb dialogue and imaginative sound effects suggest the setting with the minimum of props for this poignant love story and hilarious comedy of manners.
ISBN 0 573 12065 X

Every Picture Tells a Story. Melodrama. Harry Austin
M3 F1. Fee code B

Wicked Squire Ditchley hopes to appropriate Farmer Dodkins' farm and lovely daughter, Arabella, by unscrupulous methods and is nearly successful. However, his attempts to make Arabella tipsy have hilarious results and in the end everyone gains but the Squire. A short play suitable for inclusion in a Music Hall evening or similar compilation. Contained in *The Chinese Pendant and Other Plays*.
ISBN 0 573 00029 8

Everybody's Friend. Play. David Campton
F4 or M1 F3. Extras 5F optional (middle-age to elderly). Split set: two identical flats. Fee code D

Two ladies living next door to each other share a love of plants, but not of friendship. Mrs Roberts, 'Everybody's Friend' (and busy-body), tries to reconcile the two ladies who have quarrelled over one much-loved plant. However, the ladies become friends, united in their eventual hatred of Mrs Roberts.
ISBN 0 573 03378 1

Everyman. Morality play. Constance Cox
M7 F4 or F11. Extras optional. Choir. A market-place, dominated by a cross. Fee code A

A simplified version in modern English of the medieval morality play. Everyman, when he is summoned by Death, finds that, of all the friends, companions and possessions he has known on earth, not one will accompany him except Good Deeds and Knowledge. Period medieval
ISBN 0 573 06248 X

Everywoman. Verse drama. Hugh Steadman Williams, from the fifteenth-century morality play *Everyman* and Hugo von Hofmannsthal's *Jedermann*
M8 F4 or M7 F5. Simple settings on an open stage. Fee code D

Everywoman is a ruthless, successful careerist who has sacrificed everything for her own advancement. When Death appears, her successes fail her; only Faith, her deserted husband, and Crystal, her child, remain by her. Her eyes are opened, she repents, and is saved.
ISBN 0 573 06253 6

The Exception and the Rule. Play. Bertolt Brecht
Translations: Ralph Manheim, music by Dessau
                  Tom Osborn, music by Frank Wagland
                  Eric Bentley
M9 F1. Several simple interiors. Fee code G for play, code C for music

Crossing the desert, an unscrupulous merchant and his maltreated coolie run short of water. The coolie generously offers what water he has but the merchant, mistrusting the coolie, thinks he is about to attack and shoots him. The merchant is tried but is acquitted when it is decided that, in present day society, to murder one's oppressor is the Rule, and to repay cruelty with kindness is the Exception.

B

The Exiles. Play. Jeffrey Grenfell-Hill
M2 F4 (25, old). A shabby living-room. Fee code D

Countess Oriana, a penniless White Russian exile, has fled to Paris with her maid Nina and Nina's mother, Chita, where she continues to treat her servants like slaves. Eventually Nina kills her mistress. Chita pulls Oriana's body on to a mattress while Nina takes her place. When the doctor arrives he is told it is the servant who died. Period 1919
ISBN 0 573 02334 4

The Extraordinary Revelations of Orca the Goldfish. Comedy. David Tristram
M1 (middle-age) F1 (middle-age). Simple settings. Fee code E

For Henry Smith life was rarely dull. For Alice Smith life was rarely anything else. Enter Michel — French waiter — tall, dark, and available. Exactly what happened next, no-one's quite sure ... A virtuoso piece for two talented and versatile actors — one female and one male — requiring minimal props and scenery and therefore ideal for festivals.

Face the Music. A cautionary skit. Barry L. Hillman
F5 (20s-60s). A powder-room. Fee code D

It is the night of the 'Come Dancing' area finals, and the contestants in the ladies' powder-room are tough rivals. They are united, however, against Conchita Alvara — née Doreen Small — who proudly flaunts her professional status and is scornful of amateurs. They plot to cause Conchita's downfall, but their nefarious plan recoils on their own heads.
ISBN 0 573 03361 7

Failed Investments. Play. Lynn Brittney
M1 (60s) F4 (40s, 50s). A living-room. Fee code D

Carol and Anne host a residents' meeting for their block of flats and a number of human issues are aired. Anne is hounded by her ex-husband; Margaret has learned that her son is homosexual; Judith is coping with unemployment and a troublesome family — and Carol is revealed as a lesbian. Four strong parts for women in this adult social comedy.
ISBN 0 573 12141 4

Fallen Heroes. Play. Ian Armstrong
M3 (20s, middle-age) F3 (20s, old). Various simple settings including a trench. Fee code D

Mosey and Dom, friends since birth, are serving in the British Army in the First World War. Isolated from Brigade with Evans, their anti-Irish Corporal, they talk about their lives and their families and, when the question of desertion arises, it is a great test of their loyalty to each other and the Army. NB. Contains barrack-room language.
ISBN 0 573 12069 2

Family Voices. Play (from the triple bill *Other Places*). Harold Pinter
M2 (young, middle-age) F1 (middle-age). A bare stage. Fee code E

Written as a series of monologues featuring an exchange of letters between a mother and her absent son. The mother's desperate attempts to bring her son back to her from his lodgings in a sleazy London boarding house become more ill-attuned, serving only to accentuate the irreparable rift between them.
ISBN 0 573 12067 6

Fanny's Prayer, or, All Was Not Lost. Brian J. Burton
M4 (45, 65) F2 (18, 65). A farm labourer's cottage. Fee code B

A short melodrama for inclusion in a Music Hall evening. Little scenery is required and detailed production notes are given in the script. Contained with two other melodramas in *Cheers, Tears and Screamers*.

Fans or Don't Clap ... Just Throw Money. Play. Roy Eden
M7 (teenage, 38) F5 (teenage, 30s, 40s). Split stage: a theatre dressing-room, outside the stage door. Fee code D

Teenagers wait outside the stage door discussing the merits of the ageing rock star they have just seen. Inside the man himelf is questioning his lifestyle and threatening to pack it all in. A mother arrives to retrieve her daughter, and is persuaded to stay by reminders of her own youth.
ISBN 0 573 12074 9

The Fear of Heaven. Play. John Mortimer
M5 (young, middle-age) F2 (middle-age, elderly). A hospital ward. Fee code E

In a hospital housed in an old palazzo, two Englishmen recovering consciousness both see the ward ceiling, covered by a huge painting of Heaven, and imagine they have 'passed on'. In conversation it transpires that Fletcher, a rather rough type, has led the sort of Byronic life that scholarly Luby has only written about.
ISBN 0 573 12070 6

◆ **Festival Play**. Comedy. John Mayall
M4 (20s, mature) F8 (young, middle-age, mature, elderly) A stage and auditorium. Fee code D

Timid Richard Small finds himself catapulted into the leading role in his first ever amateur festival production, a modern morality play called *Mankind*. Problems abound — among them being the script itself — but the final performance is a triumph, though not in the category intended!
ISBN 0 573 12109 5

Field of Fashion. Minidrama. Richard Tydeman
F5-17. Fee code B

The field of fashion takes on rather more significance when a carriage full of models and their dresses become 'mixed up' with a football team and their kit, and the wrong basket arrives labelled 'Archways Fashion House'. Running time: 15-20 minutes

A Field of Olives. Play. Bryan Stocks. Based on a story by Guy de Maupassant
M2 (mid-20s, 58) F1. A veranda. Fee code D

The Abbé Vilbois returns home to find that a rough-looking fellow — a maoufatan — has called for him. The maoufatan is generously invited to supper, during which the Abbé speaks of a long-dead love affair which resulted in Rosetta having a child. With tragic results, the maoufatan reveals he is the child.

Fiesta Fandango. Minidrama. Richard Tydeman
M4 F6. Fee code B

Sweet Rosina, promised by her father, the not-so-sweet Don Lopez, to Don Carlos, infinitely prefers the much younger valet Rodrigo — who, of course, is not really a valet at all. Running time: 15-20 minutes
ISBN 0 573 12068 4

The Fifteen Minute Hamlet. Comedy. Tom Stoppard
M4 F2. An open stage. Fee code E

Following his success with *Rosencrantz and Guildenstern Are Dead*, Stoppard has taken the most well-known and best-loved lines from Shakespeare's play and condensed them into an hilarious version lasting approximately thirteen minutes, followed by an encore which consists of a two-minute version of the play! The vast multitude of characters is played by six actors with hectic doubling.
ISBN 0 573 02506 1

◆ **Figuring Things**. Play. Michael Fosbrook
M2 (middle-age) F2 (middle-age). Various simple settings. Fee code D

For Dennis, cricket averages are everything. When the Statisticians' Circle accepts Pat, its first female member, however, Dennis's life takes a sharp turn. Contrary to Dennis's assumptions, Pat excels in the craft. They plan a trip to the Caribbean but Dennis's wife doesn't know that Pat is female, so when they meet this highly original satire on male-female relations is set for an explosive ending.
ISBN 0 573 12205 9

A Fish in Her Kettle. A play for Coarse Actors. Edited by Michael Green

See the entry for *The Third Great Coarse Acting Show*.

A Fishy Business. Comedy. Margaret Wood
M6 (19, middle-age, elderly) F4 (19, middle-age). A sitting-room. Fee code C

After the cat has tasted Uncle Richard's salmon and all of George and Mary's dinner guests have eaten the fish, the cat is found dead on the doorstep. It is only as they are all on their way to hospital (and the stomach pump) that George and Mary discover what really happened to Tiddles!
ISBN 0 573 12077 3

The Flesh Game. Comedy. Rae Shirley
F6 (20s-50s). 1 male voice. A lounge. Fee code D

This lively comedy takes a light-hearted look at slimming. Set in a regimented Health Farm, presided over by the humourless and power-loving Nurse Burton, its guests respond to its structure like naughty schoolchildren. They all have their different reasons for being there, and there is plenty of fun and games as the different ways of cheating are sought.
ISBN 0 573 13242 9

Flowers for Mrs Hopkins. Play. Gladys M. Hogg
F4 (20s, 40s, 81). A living-room. Fee code C

On the happy occasion of Mrs Hopkins' eighty-first birthday, cards and presents arrive from family and friends, as well as an unknown Visitor, who brings a bunch of flowers. The trusting Mrs Hopkins immediately admits her, but as the Visitor's behaviour becomes increasingly erratic and sinister, the action builds to a frightening intensity.
ISBN 0 573 13239 9

Fluff. Comedy. John Scholes
M2 (30s, middle-age) F2 (young). A bedroom. Fee code D

Joe and Sally plan to steal some fur coats from party guests to finance a holiday. Sally falls for one guest, Nigel, who in turn pursues Sally, believing her to be an heiress. Nigel's girlfriend Alice arrives and it would appear that they too have designs on the furs. Joe determines to finish the job alone, but finds an unexpected accomplice in Alice.
ISBN 0 573 12072 2

For the Love of Norman. Play. Kay Jordan
M3 (young) F4 (young, 60s). A reception room. Fee code D

Mrs Grant-Williams, a stern, wealthy widow, rules her family with a rod of iron. They tolerate her in the expectation of inheriting her money, and are outraged when she becomes romantically involved with a young man. The young man will get her money, but not for the expected reasons as revealed in a neat final twist.
ISBN 0 573 12071 4

◆ Foreign Bodies. Play. Peter Nichols
M5 (25, middle-age, 60s) F2 (young, middle-age). Composite set: a study, a sitting-room. Fee code G

Swinging London meets bourgeois Shrewsbury in 1963 and the drinks are laced with cyanide. As the son of the household struggles to write his first play, a murder story is offered to him on a plate. Together with *A Game of Soldiers* this forms the double bill *Blue Murder* (see the entry in Section A).

The Form. Play. N. F. Simpson
M2 (23, 50s) F2 (20, middle-age). An art office. Fee code C

A parody of bureaucratic procedure occurs when a young man goes to be interviewed by a Mr Chacterson. When he approaches the secretary, it appears that she cannot help him until she takes on the persona of Mr Chacterson's receptionist, which will not be until Mr Chacterson rings for her. The interview takes place on consistently illogical lines.
ISBN 0 573 02076 0

Forty Winks Beauty. Minidrama. Richard Tydeman
M5 F7. Fee code B

A 'Potted Panto' with Beauty being awakened not by the prince, who's late, but by Charley Prince, a teddy boy. Luckily the day is saved, albeit unwittingly, by the wicked fairy Maud. Running time: 15-20 minutes
ISBN 0 573 06616 7

Forward to the Right. A play of Joan of Arc. Lily Ann Green
M1 F1. A gaol cell of a castle in Rouen. Fee code D

Joan of Arc, condemned to burn at the stake, is denied a rosary, cross or any form of service, but the guard becomes sympathetic and arranges for her to receive the last rites. In consequence he is imprisoned after Joan's death, refusing to acknowledge her powers as witchcraft.
ISBN 0 573 12057 9

FOUR PLAYS FOR COARSE ACTORS

Michael Green
M9 F3. Extras. Three living-rooms; a throne-room; a forest. Fee codes B and C

The number of characters given above would be sufficient to cover the presentation of all four plays by the same cast. Ages can vary from young to the practically senile.

The plays are presented as parodies of four dramatic styles, in the performance of which everything which can conceivably go wrong in a production does so. *Il Fornicazione* is a grim tale of operatic adultery, poison and mayhem. *Streuth* is a crime story which even Agatha Christie would never have dared to write. *A Collier's Tuesday Tea* combines the kitchen sink with the coal-mine, and with an irreverent glance at D.H. Lawrence. *All's Well That Ends As You Like It* ('from an idea by William Shakespeare' and set in 'the Forest of Solihull') pushes the genius of the Bard to its utmost limits, while managing to filch lines from most of his own plays. In all four, cues are missed, effects fail, props are lost or in the wrong place, furniture and scenery collapses — and one play, *Streuth*, gets itself into such confusion that it is doomed, apparently, to perpetual motion: but the Coarse Actors struggle gamefully on throughout. Apart from the essentials, the settings can be simple or elaborate, as facilities permit.
ISBN 0 573 00008 5

The Fourth Prisoner. Play. David Henry Wilson
M6 (20s, 40s, middle-age). 3 extras. Prison cell. Fee code C

Two veteran prisoners, Jack and Sean, are initiating newcomer Lamb into the cell routine. Each accepts his sentence in his own way. At night the cell is visited by Johnnie, the fourth prisoner, a sort of alter ego who gives them hope and strength to endure life behind the prison walls.

◆ **Frankenstein's Guests**. Comedy. Martin Downing
M5 (20s, 35, 40s) F4 (20s, 30s, 65) A castle hall. Fee code E

A shorter, re-worked version of *The House of Frankenstein!* in which the Baron tries to counsel and cure a motley crew of monsters he's invited to his castle, immediately regretting his action. When the Baroness hits the bottle, his guests reveal their true colours and all hell is let loose! A most amusing, finely tuned parody of the old Frankenstein movies.
ISBN 0 573 12150 8

From Five to Five-thirty. Comedy. Philip Johnson
F5 (36-40, 60s, 70). A living-room. Fee code C

Mrs Treetops' three middle-aged daughters find her charwoman, Mrs Boxer, insufferable. The daughters have decided it is time for their mother to go to a Home for Elderly Gentlewomen. Mrs Treetops, however, has some surprises in store for them, culminating in the revelation that they are really Mrs Boxer's children.
ISBN O 573 03240 8

B

From Here to the Library. Play. Jimmie Chinn
M2 (middle-age, 70s) F1 (30s). A living-room. Fee code D

Beryl, a librarian, is dominated by her elderly and irascible father; the library is her only escape. So when Beryl throws an uncharacteristic fit of temper at work and doesn't return, her boss visits her to find out why. He succeeds in showing Beryl that she both needs and is needed by the world outside.
ISBN 0 573 12058 7

The Frosted Glass Coffin. Play. Tennessee Williams
M3 (70s, 80s) F2 (old). The street façade of a low-priced Miami hotel. Fee code E

The old people staying at the hotel snobbishly regard the queue to enter a cafeteria across the street, which is cheaper than other restaurants. They sit, gossip and soliloquize, and when eventually a bell rings to indicate the queue is all in, they straggle slowly across to the cafeteria.

Fumed Oak. Comedy. Noël Coward
M1 (middle-age) F3 (14, 35, elderly). A drawing-room. Fee code C

For years Henry Gow has loathed his awful wife, their adenoidal child and his utterly repulsive mother-in-law. One evening Henry tells them all exactly what he thinks of them, announces he has saved £500 and that he is going to leave them. And off he goes, triumphantly slamming the door on three howling women. Period 1936
ISBN 0 573 02079 5

A Galway Girl. Drama. Geraldine Aron
M1 F1. Simple set: a table and two chairs. Fee code E

A married couple reminisce about their life together. The characters are young to begin with, then middle-aged, then old, then one of them dies. The anecdotes they relate are both humorous and tragic. At the end the wife's muted gesture of affection conveys the love that can endure through years of household bickering and incompatibility.
ISBN 0 573 62204 3

◆ **A Game of Soldiers.** Play. Peter Nichols
M5 (20s, middle-age, 60s) F2 (young, middle-age). An elegant room. Fee code G

A Game of Soldiers is a Whitehall farce set in St James's Palace in 1967. A young dramatist has brought his play to be censored but the Lord Chamberlain's Men have shameful secrets of their own to hide, including a priapic guardsman. With *Foreign Bodies* this forms the double bill *Blue Murder* (see the entry in Section A).

The Garden Room. Play. Don Roberts
F4 (25-35) A conservatory. Fee code D

Susanna returns home to recover after a traumatic experience. Her three sisters, except Constantia who thinks Susanna should be sent away, accept her. Constantia is finally forced by the others to accept Susanna and the unity of the family. A winner of the Drama Association of Wales 1992 Playwriting Competition, this is a moving portrayal of the emotional bonds between sisters.
ISBN 0 573 03383 8

A Gathering of Doves. Drama. Doris M. Day
F7 (young, 30s, middle-age, elderly). A living-room. Fee code D

A story showing the effects of brutal civil war on a group of women, and their forlorn hopes of ending it. The play is deliberately set in an anonymous country, for it is a situation that is paralleled wherever civil strife separates friends and family.
ISBN 0 573 03355 2

Genteel. Play. Evelyn Hood
M1 (middle-age) F2 (middle-age). A conservatory. Fee code D

Two sisters, Alice and Emily, share their home with an untidy, ill-mannered lodger, MacGillicuddy. Emily would prefer a more 'genteel' lodger and advertises for one. MacGillicuddy drinks a magic potion, reappears as he was thirty years ago and charms Emily, who believes he is answering her advertisement. But the effects of the potion soon wear off ...!
ISBN 0 573 12082 X

George. Comedy. Derek Hickman
M4 F5. A hospital ward. Fee code C

Who is George? To Mr Smith he is 'a proper gentleman', but to the hospital staff he is an embarrassment and a problem. For George is half of Mr Smith's split personality, and until he is disposed of Mr Smith is not likely to recover, nor can the hospital staff cease ministering to an invisible patient in the empty bed next to Mr Smith.
ISBN 0 573 02097 3

Getting Along. Comedy. Charles Mander
M3 (ageing, elderly) F2 (middle-age, ageing). An interior. Fee code D

Henry arranges a party holiday in France but finds the gîte below par. Unwilling to admit his mistake, he berates everyone, driving them to the brink of despair. Forever the victim, Henry believes his wife is unfaithful, the gîte is surrounded by gunmen, Marcia is demented, and Norman rabid. Finally, his faithful wife resolves the crisis, bringing the hilarity to its moving conclusion.
ISBN 0 573 12128 1

Getting and Spending. Comedy of Menace. David Campton
M2 F2. A room. Fee code D

See the entry under *The Lunatic View* in Section A.

Ghost of a Chance. Play. Brian J. Burton
F5 (20, 40, 50, elderly). A room. Fee code C

When Mrs Dean learns one of her ancestors haunts a deserted house nearby, she arranges to spend the night there alone. As she watches, dramatic events of 1860 are re-enacted and she leaves supposedly having found the reason for the reputed haunting.

The Gnädiges Fräulein. Tennessee Williams

See the entry under *Slapstick Tragedy* in Section A

God. Play. Woody Allen
M20 F8. Extras. An amphitheatre. Fee code F

Athens, approximately 500 BC. The Actor and Writer are trying to work out the ending of a play. Suddenly the Writer asks if the audience have any suggestions. Alarming abysses open. What if the audience are characters in another play, and somebody is writing *them*? In the ensuing mêlée of shifting realities time and space become inextricably mixed.
ISBN 0 573 62201 9

Going All the Way. Play. Michèle Bailey
M3 F2, doubling possible. A living-room, an office, a pub. Fee code D

Carol is middle-class, comfortably-off and sees herself as a caring person, writing letters on behalf of Amnesty International and arguing moral issues with her wise-cracking and seemingly callous boyfriend, Dave. But when Dave, acknowledging social guilt, gets a job in Africa and asks Carol to accompany him, her commitment is found sadly lacking.
ISBN 0 573 12083 8

Going Home. Play (from *Visiting Hour*). Richard Harris
M2 F4 (1 Black). A hospital ward. Fee code D

Taken from the full-length play *Visiting Hour* (see Section A), *Going Home* was seen in 1990 at the Duke's Head Theatre, Richmond, Surrey. It traces the lessons learned by a confrontation between a white woman patient and a black woman patient on the eve of their discharge from hospital.
ISBN 0 573 01925 8

◆ **Goodbye Iphigenia**. Play. George MacEwan Green
M3 F3. A military camp. Fee code D

The legend of Iphigenia, sacrificed by her father King Agamemnon to the goddess Artemis in order to free the becalmed Greek fleet in the port of Aulis is here made more accessible for contemporary audiences by dramatizing an 'eye witness' account of the events given by Andreas, the soldier, who guarded the royal tent that fateful day.
ISBN 0 573 12097 8

The Great Jowett. Play. Graham Greene
M17 F2, doubling possible. Composite set. Fee code E

The story concerns Benjamin Jowett and his rise to Master of Balliol College. Originally thwarted because of his outspoken religious views, Jowett sets out to win his students over, so that when they, in turn, become Fellows of the College they are able to elect him Master when the occasion arises. Period late-nineteenth century

The Green Eye of the Little Yellow Dog. Melodrama. Harry Austin
M6 F1 Fee code C

A stirring tale of true love, devotion to duty and stark staring stupidity on the part of Captain Quincey Hogg, newly arrived adjutant at the British fort just north of Katmandu, who falls foul of the curse of the green eye of the little yellow dog. Playing time approximately 20 minutes. Contained in *The Little Lights of Kimberley*.
ISBN 0 573 10023 3

B

Green Favours. Play. Frank Vickery
M1 (40s) F1 (50s). An allotment shed. Fee code E

As the first-ever woman in the gardening club, plain, practical Val is grateful to Tom for all his friendly help and advice. When Tom's attractive, glamorous wife becomes jealous, Val is stunned. Forced to acknowledge her true feelings Val is unwilling to betray her husband. Will love blossom in the allotment shed? This flourishing romantic comedy reaps warmth, humour and great delight.
ISBN 0 573 12103 6

Green Forms. Play. Alan Bennett
M2 (middle-age, 1 Black) F3 (30s, 40s). An office. Fee code F

Doris and Doreen are comfortably installed in an obscure department of a large organization. On a normal day the girls keep busy by flirting or pursuing their bitter feud over office supplies with the Personnel Department. Work is nowhere. However, a shadow falls across their tranquil lives. Is it redundancy?
ISBN 0 573 12087 0

Growing Pains. Play. Ian Armstrong
M2 (middle-age) F4 (middle-age); 3 roles either M or F, doubling possible. Various simple settings. Fee code D

Frank and Mary Shaw have each allowed their son Andrew to become the centre of their separate worlds. When Andrew is fatally injured in a motor-cycle accident, the world has ended for Mary and Frank, unless they can come together and draw strength and comfort from each other.
ISBN 0 573 12081 1

♦ **The Guilt Card**. Short play (From *Deckchairs II*). Jean McConnell
F2 (middle-age). A seafront. Fee code C

Marion discovers, by a cruel twist of fate, that her life has been blighted by the machinations and emotional blackmail of her sickly elder sister, Deborah.
ISBN 0 573 10004 7

The Gypsy Curse or The Flower of the Tribe. Melodrama. Brian J. Burton
M3 F3. One exterior. Fee code D

A gypsy romantic drama, telling the story, recounted by one of the gypsies in Maria Marten, of the events that were supposed to have occurred to William Corder before he met Maria and foully murdered her in the red barn. Contained in *Three Hisses for Villainy*.

Half an Idea. Comedy. Bob Larbey
M9 F18 (doubling possible). Composite set: three living rooms. Fee code G

The Writer types 'Curtain', completing his first play: a rage against life ... But when the script is enacted before his eyes it turns out to be a very funny piece. The hilarity must stop, the Writer commands, and so rewrites it as a funeral. But this, too, brought to life, becomes an hilarious comedy. The Writer vows he will re-cast!
ISBN 0 573 12132 X

B

The Hamelin Incident. Play. Graham Walker
M13 F2. 8 children. Extras. Simple interior and exterior settings. Fee code E

This adaptation of the Pied Piper tale centres on the figure of Blankenfeld, the one member of the Town Council to feel a moral obligation towards the Piper once he has rid the town of rats. He alone is exempt from the doom the town brings upon itself by ignoring the Piper's demands for his payment.
ISBN 0 573 12092 7

Hands Across the Sea. Comedy. Noël Coward
M5 (young, middle-age) F4 (30s, middle-age). A drawing-room. Fee code E

On their world tour, Piggie Gilpin and Lady Dalborough invited all their kind hosts to see them when they returned to England. An unassuming couple from Malaya stray into the Gilpin flat, only to find themselves bewildered by Naval officers, smart and totally meaningless chatter, and a hostess who has forgotten who they are. Period 1936
ISBN 0 573 02091 4

The Happy Journey. Play. Thornton Wilder
M3 (13, middle-age) F3 (15, 22, middle-age). No scenery. Fee code C

An ordinary American family journeys to visit a married daughter in a distant town. Their extremely amusing encounters and discussions are interwoven with a tender philosophy and sincere faith as expressed by the mother and a kindly common sense in the father — a combination which gives the play a most satisfying quality.
ISBN 0 573 02093 0

Harlequinade. Farce. Terence Rattigan
M10 (20s-middle-age, old) F5 (young, middle-age, old). A stage set for *Romeo and Juliet*. Fee code F

Arthur and Edna Gosport are opening a Shakespearian tour. During the dress rehearsal of *Romeo and Juliet*, a pallid spectre turns up out of Arthur's past, claiming to be his daughter. In a few moments before the curtain rises, the harassed Arthur makes wild attempts to solve this imbroglio.
ISBN 0 573 02094 9

Have a Nice Day. Play. Lynn Brittney
M2 F3. 1M, voice only. A hospitality suite. Fee code D

Carol presents a morning TV show, wearing pastel jumpers and a silly smile. But when the tabloids reveal that she will be sacked she is ready for a showdown with neurotic producer Marjorie and intellectual researcher Joe. Betrayed by her agent David, she explodes and goes on slightly scruffy, dressed in black. As ever, David turns her new-found determination to his advantage.
ISBN 0 573 12131 1

♦ **Heart's Desire**. Play. Caryl Churchill
M2 F4 with doubling. Child extras. A kitchen. Fee code E

A family await the return of their daughter after a long sojourn in Australia. The moments before the arrival are re-enacted over and over again with increasingly wild variations in the course of which a crazy selection of visitors bursts upon the scene. Together with *Blue Kettle*, this forms the double bill *Blue Heart* (see Section A).

The Hebrew Lesson. Play. Wolf Mankowitz
M4 (young, elderly). An attic. Fee code C

It is the time of the 'Troubles' (1921). An elderly Jew is trying to learn essential phrases in Gaelic. A young man breaks in seeking shelter from the Black-and-Tans. The Jew feeds and shelters him, finally dressing him unwillingly as a Jew to escape the Black-and-Tans. The man is saved and has learned a little of the character and philosophy of the Jews.

The Heir's Return. Burlesque. Michael Kilgarriff
M1 F1. Chairman. Fee code C

An hilarious burlesque in which the repetitive dialogue, mindless patriotism and fatuous plot of a typical Victorian dramatic sketch are mercilessly guyed. Intended for inclusion in an Old Time Music Hall evening the piece commences with the late arrival of the not-too-distinguished actor Mr D'Arcy Hilliard and his slightly inebriated wife. After apologies to the Chairman they disappear into the wings, determined to give the audience the thrill of a lifetime ... Full costume, setting and lighting plots are given, together with two original pieces of music and extensive production information by Michael Kilgarriff. Contained in *Three Comedy Sketches*.
ISBN 0 573 00028 X

Hello from Bertha. Play. Tennessee Williams
F4 (young, middle-age). A bedroom. Fee code E

Bertha, a prostitute, is ill, probably fatally, and her room is needed by the other prostitutes. Despite her friend Goldie's protestations, she refuses to leave. Goldie suggests that Bertha should write to Charlie, one of Bertha's erstwhile customers, and ask for money to help her. Bertha dictates the letter — her last message — but it seems unlikely that it will ever be sent.

Henry the Tenth. (Part Seven). A play for Coarse Actors. Michael Green

See the entry for *The Coarse Acting Show 2*.

♦ **Her Big Chance.** Monologue. Alan Bennett
F1 (early 30s). A room. Fee code F

Meet Lesley, an actress. She has just completed a video ('targeted chiefly on West Germany') in which she plays Travis, a career girl who enjoys life, spends a remarkable amount of time topless and shoots a man with a harpoon gun. She tells all, blind to the sinister undertones of her story as well as to her own self-delusions and gullibility.
ISBN 0 573 13241 0

Hi-Fi Spy. Minidrama. Richard Tydeman
M5 F6. Fee code B

What the Butler didn't see. A notorious gang of international suspects, compounded with intrepid policewomen in disguise, go to make a highly suspicious plot, until All is Revealed. Running time: 15-20 minutes
ISBN 0 573 12106 0

Hidden Meanings. Comedy. Michael Snelgrove
M4 (middle-age) F5 (young, middle-age). A sitting-room. Fee code D

Rodney and George are to provide the dramatic interlude at the Sherlock Holmes Society's Annual Congress. When George discovers Charles's blood-stained body (dressed as Moriarty), Rodney proudly acknowledges that he has murdered Charles, and is piqued when three others also make the claim. Charles staggers out, bleeding, with a suicide note, all to the accompaniment of *The Pirates of Penzance*!
ISBN 0 573 12098 6

Hiss the Villain! or Foiled and Counterfoiled. Melodrama. Adapted from *The Poor of New York* by A. R. Taylor and W. Ernest Cossons
M5 (young, middle-age, old) F2 (young, middle-age). One exterior, two interiors. Fee code B

Snaker has robbed Captain Noble of his life's savings. Later, when Snaker's clerk sees the plight of widowed Mrs Noble and the lovely Lucy, he repents of his wickedness and redeems himself and the villain. Period 1890
ISBN 0 573 02099 X

The Hitman. Comedy. J. C. W. Brook
M2 (25-40, 60-80) F2 (young, 60-80). A patio. Fee code D

This compelling comedy of plot and counter-plot adapted from a BBC Radio 4 play, begins with George and Alice, an elderly couple, bickering over cucumber sandwiches. Sinister undertones develop when George reveals he has a hankering for a dusky maiden and has retained Mr Romero, the Hitman, to take Alice for a final journey to a motorway construction site.
ISBN 0 573 12104 4

Hitting Town. Play. Stephen Poliakoff
M1 (20) F2 (18, 30). Composite setting. Fee code F
ISBN 0 573 11179 0

The Hole. Play. N. F. Simpson
M5 F2. Around a hole dug in the road. Fee code E

There is a hole in the road, where men are working. Watchers gather, curious folk who wonder what is going on below, obsessed with the need to categorize what is happening. Each one sees a fantastic significance in the hole. Their theories are ingenious but contradictory, and each tries to impose his own interpretation on everyone else.
ISBN 0 573 02100 7

Hot Fudge. Play. Caryl Churchill
M5 F5 or M2 F3. Simple interior settings. Fee code E

The play was given a performance reading at the Royal Court Theatre Upstairs in 1989 and performed as a double bill with *Icecream* in New York in 1990. In this brief series of vignettes we meet various couples in a completely amoral world where money is all that matters and lies are the only truth.
ISBN 0 573 62234 5

B

The House Plant. Play. Sally Warboyes
M2 (20s) F2 (20s, 60). 1F, voice only. Composite set: three rooms. Fee code D

Lee-Anne and Philip move into a converted Victorian house, happily accepting an ageing sitting tenant as they assume she'll be dead soon. But in the bitter domestic war that follows the tenant is more than a match for the young couple. Cynical and blackly amusing, this is a deadly comedy with many a devious twist in its tail.
ISBN 0 573 12117 6

A House Without Windows. Play. Joe Valentine
M2 (30s) F3 (20s, 30s). 1 boy (11), 1 girl (4). All characters age over 17 years. A living-room and hospital rest room. Fee code D

Father has raised Alan and Emily single-handedly. Now Father has left for a new life in America and Alan is at a loss as to what to do. Should he sell the house — and help pregnant Emily who needs money — or marry Rita and stay where he is?
ISBN 0 573 12108 7

Housekeeper Wanted. Farce. Philip King and Falkland L. Cary
M1 (young) F4 (young, middle-age). A lounge. Fee code C

After his wife leaves him, Victor holds interviews for a professional housekeeper. Applicant One turns out to be a dipsomaniac; Applicant Two a sex maniac; Applicant Three a homicidal maniac. When Victor's wife returns for some belongings he mistakes her for Applicant Four, a kleptomaniac. She decides to stay and Victor is left with a money maniac.
ISBN 0 573 12111 7

The Human Voice. Play. Jean Cocteau. New authorized English version by Anthony Wood
F1. A bedroom. Fee code F

A woman awaits and receives a phone call from her lover who has recently left her. 'The actress should give the impression that she is bleeding, losing her life's blood, like a wounded beast, finishing the play as if the bedroom is drenched in blood.'
ISBN 0 573 03381 1

Humour Helps. Play. Peter Barnes
M1 (any age) F1 (any age). A living-room. Fee code C

An actress hamfistedly tries to commit suicide, finally achieving her aim with the unwitting aid of a neighbour. May be presented as part of the full-length entertainment *Corpsing*. For details, see the entry in Section A.
ISBN 0 573 10006 3

B

Humphrey Pumphrey Had a Great Fall. Play. Alfred Greenaway
M3 F2. A bare stage. Fee code C

Humphrey, lately deceased, relives through flashbacks the events leading up to his being pushed off a cliff by his wife. He obviously provoked her, or did he? Perhaps she was the one who should have been dispatched to the other side? Why did the picnic hamper contain rope and a hammer? Who was having an affair with whom?
ISBN 0 573 12107 9

Hunting Pink. Play. William Norfolk
M3 (20s, 50s) F3 (20s, 50s). Extra. Composite setting. Fee code D

Stella, who picks up men by wearing her 'hunting pink', finds her son Alan is ashamed of her, and her daughter Gloria's marriage has failed, partly through Stella's pushing. Alan tells Stella how much she disgusts him and Stella is left to the bottle and her tears.
ISBN 0 573 02503 7

Husbands Are A Girl's Best Friend. Melodrama. Harry Austin
M4 F1. Fee code B

Clarissa manages to accumulate a fortune by bigamously marrying two rich men whilst playing the dual role of twin sisters. The husbands find out, do the 'decent thing' by shooting each other, and Clarissa is left with the money, managing to handle the law as well. A short play suitable for inclusion in a Music Hall evening or similar compilation. Contained in *The Chinese Pendant and Other Plays*.
ISBN 0 573 00029 8

Husbands Supplied. Farce. Falkland L. Cary
M1 F7 (young, middle-age). An office. Fee code A

Five ladies appear at the 'Husbands Supplied' bureau in search of a husband and, when a charming man appears, rivalry is intensified by the bids of the proprietress and her assistant. When it is discovered that one of the anxious rivals is in fact the man's lawful wedded wife, six very disappointed women call it a day.
ISBN 0 573 02109 0

Hyde Park. Play. Graham Swannell
M2 (40s) F2 (young, 40s). A garden. Fee code E

A hot summer's day, a good lunch and several bottles of wine conspire to make this Sunday a day of revelations for Yvonne, her husband Lawrence, and their friend, Fraser. Yvonne bemoans a lack of excitement in her life but when Fraser confesses to always having loved her, she shies away, scared of commitment. This moving and ironic study of three old friends is from the author of the acclaimed *A State of Affairs*.
ISBN 0 573 12105 2

I Can't Imagine Tomorrow. Play. Tennessee Williams
M1 (middle-age) F1 (middle-age). Various pieces of furniture on an open stage. Fee code E

Each of the two characters is the only friend of the other. Their conversation consists mainly of broken sentences varied by occasional long speeches by the woman. In one of them she describes the 'country of pain'; her speech might be taken as the theme of the play, with life at its lowest ebb, and little to look forward to except death.

I Never Thought It Would Be Like This. Play. Evelyn Hood
M2 (young, middle-age) F2 (middle-age). A tropical island. Fee code D

When Doreen and Arthur are wrecked together on a tropical island one might expect things to turn out pleasantly romantic. Doreen, however, is distinctly shocked when Arthur proposes building only one shelter. Unexpected complications arise when Doreen's mother appears, followed even more surprisingly by the as yet unborn Norman, their 'son'.
ISBN 0 573 12113 3

I Rise in Flame, Cried the Phoenix. Play. Tennessee Williams
M1 (40s) F2 (middle-age). A sun porch. Fee code E

This brief play, set at Vence in the Alps Maritimes, is an imaginary depiction of D. H. Lawrence's last moments, showing the intense love-hate relationship with his wife as, dying of consumption, he expresses his controversial views on art and sex, referring in particular to a recent exhibition of his paintings.

I Spy. Play. John Mortimer
M3 (middle-age) F2 (middle-age). Composite setting. Fee code C

Mr Frute, a private detective, is employed by Captain Morgan to trace his errant wife and the Other Man. There is, however, no Other Man; Mrs Morgan is a paragon. Hard pressed to produce results, Frute plays the Other Man himself. He sends Captain Morgan the necessary report, but success is bitter, for he has learnt to love Mrs Morgan.
ISBN 0 573 02110 4

If Yer Take A Short Cut. Play. David Henry Wilson
M4 (young, elderly) F1 (elderly). Truthseekers' home. Fee code D

This perceptive play, centred on an elderly couple afflicted by boredom and despair, brings to mind Beckett's *Waiting for Godot*. Set in a hypothetical future which resembles only too well the present day, it follows the painful search for truth of Archibald, an aged man who cannot communicate any longer with his estranged wife.
ISBN 0 573 62364

If You're Glad I'll Be Frank. Play. Tom Stoppard
M7 (middle-age) F5 (young, middle-age). An open stage. Fee code E

Frank recognizes the voice of the GPO speaking clock as that of his long-lost wife. Determined to get her back, he forces his way into the inner sanctum of the Authorities to demand her release. Underlying the light-hearted story is a satiric comment on man's servitude to the clock.
ISBN 0 573 12112 5

Il Fornicazione. A play for Coarse Actors. Michael Green

See the entry for *Four Plays for Coarse Actors*.

In by the Half. Play. Jimmie Chinn
M1 F4, or F5 (young, 40s, elderly). A living-room. Fee code E

Madam, once a distinguished actress, lives in seclusion looked after by her ex-dresser. Their peaceful routine includes visits from the doctor and the insipid Sylvia, who takes acting lessons from Madam. But the initial acerbic comedy of the play gives way to a poignant drama with the arrival of Madam's estranged daughter who nurses a bitter secret.
ISBN 0 573 12126 5

In Need of Care. Play. David E. Rowley
M2 (teenage) F2 (teenage). A farm outbuilding. Fee code C

Shirley and Rita, having run away from school, are hiding. They are surprised by two boys who know who they are from the newspapers. The play follows the developing relations among the four, Jeff and Rita becoming immediately attracted to each other. The encounter and the resulting delay alters all their plans.
ISBN 0 573 02322 0

In Room Five Hundred and Four. Play. Jimmie Chinn
M2 (20s) F2 (20s, 60s). A room in a boarding-house. Fee code D

Edie reminisces about herself and Harry on their wedding-day in February 1942. Together the couple discover life's big truths in the span of one night. The day after, Harry will leave for the front, never to return. The uncertainties of their relationship mirror the wider uncertainties of the forties, producing a finely balanced portrait of that period.
ISBN 0 573 12120 6

♦ **Indian Summer**. Play. Lucy Maurice
F2 (20s). A railway station café. Fee code F

'Look at this place! You know, in here, all the secrets of the world exist.' Laura and Steph work, talk, laugh and cry in the station café. People come and go, each one sharing a moment, a hope, or a fear over a hot cup of coffee. Laura and Steph realize it is not only the cappuccino machine that's broken. This attractive two-hander is easily staged.

Interior Designs. Play. Jimmie Chinn
M1 (40s) F3 (40s). A bare stage. Fee code D

Him, a brash, arrogant odd-job man, is offering his 'services' to three women. Although of very different backgrounds, the three women share a common fate of loneliness and frustration. *Interior Designs* follows their yearning to fill the emptiness of their lives and their various attempts to trap the eligible Him.
ISBN 0 573 12114

The Intruders. Comedy. Peter Horsler
M2 F2. A lounge. Fee code D

Bill is caught by Adrian while breaking into a suburban house. When Helen, Adrian's wife, appears, Bill calls in Linda, heavily pregnant, from the garden. Adrian shows them that the visible affluence is a façade for enormous debts. Bill urges Linda to be absolutely honest, whereupon she removes the cushion from her jumper. Later it appears Adrian and Helen are guilty of untruths, as they are not the actual houseowners.
ISBN 0 573 12115 X

Iron Hot Strikers. Minidrama. Richard Tydeman
F12 plus Extras. Fee code B

Laundry workers decide to go on strike, having been refused time off to go to the wedding of one of their colleagues. But the boss comes back from America and saves the situation — until the vicar goes on strike himself! Running time: 15-20 minutes

Is It Something I Said? Play. Richard Harris
M2 (50s) F1 (40s). A hotel reception area/landing/bedroom. Fee code E

Intending to kill himself, Wallace books into an hotel run by Arthur and Stella. Wallace's plans, however, are repeatedly thwarted and his determination wavers. After he and Arthur discuss their hatred for their respective wives, Wallace is fired with new determination to end it all, leaving poor Arthur contemplating a similar approach to escape from the unpleasant Stella.
ISBN 0 573 12119 2

♦ **Is There Anybody There?** Play. Lee Flewitt
M4 (young, middle-age) F4 (young, middle-age). A Victorian parlour. Fee code E

In Late Victorian London, Mrs Carrington, a blind clairvoyant, deceives her gullible customers with secret machinery. Tonight, however, when one of the party is possessed by the spirit of a murdered girl it is for real. Any of those present could be suspect. Who is the killer? The doors are locked, time stands still, and there are footsteps approaching ...
ISBN 0 573 12315 2

It's All in the Game. Play. Valerie Maskell
M3 (23, 40s) F3 (15, 30s, 40s). A living-room. Fee code D

Nat's family is preparing for the ritual of watching the Game, a government-sponsored super football. They are horrified when their son, a state employee who has been allowed into the stadium, declares the whole thing is a gigantic con — a computerized fraud. They settle down again to watch what they know is a contrived trick.
ISBN 0 573 12116 8

The Janna Years. Play. Gillian Plowman
M2 (late 30s, middle-age) F3 (20s-40s). One interior setting. Fee code D

Ruby's boarding house is home to an odd mix of characters in this moving and well-observed play about four lonely people: Abe, the middle-aged divorcee, Chas, the Northerner forced to find work in the South, Fleur, put there by her social worker and Holly, struggling to save enough money to move out.
ISBN 0 573 12125 7

Joggers. Play. Geraldine Aron
M2 (40s) F2 (28, 40s). A beach and the lawns of an hotel. Fee code E

Gus, on a package holiday with his wife, meets Wally, on a three-week honeymoon with his second wife. At first, Gus is envious of Wally, who seems to have everything — money, success, a beautiful young wife. Gus comes to terms with his life, however, and realizes that he'd rather be himself.
ISBN 0 573 12124 9

Joining the Club. Comedy. David Tristram
M1 F1. A living-room. Fee code C

Vicky is pregnant. Her husband Mark has been passed over for promotion and he's convinced it's because he's not a member of the 'baby club'. He has resigned from his job and roundly insulted his boss. When he hears Vicky's news Mark phones his boss to get his job back but Vicky, hearing him grovel, snatches the phone from him and reiterates Mark's original insult. They now face impending parenthood happily together!

B

A Jolly Sinister Jape. Play. Elliot Strange
M2 (young, 30s) F2 (young). An entrance hall. Fee code D

Lord Stubbs, Biffy Trubshaw and his actress wife Ophelia are stranded by a collapsed bridge in a mysterious house in a thunderstorm. As romance blossoms, someone locks the front door, trapping the three unfortunates. Who else is in the house? A fast-moving, madcap comedy, set in the 1920s, with a liberal sprinkling of hilarious period slang, along with mystery and thrills.

The Judge's Wife. Play. Caryl Churchill
M3 (young, 60s) F4 (20s, 50s, 60s). Various simple settings. Fee code D

A Judge passes a harsh sentence on a young man, Vernon Warren. Warren's brother kills the Judge. Caroline, the Judge's wife, explains her husband's reactionary behaviour, seeing his death as 'his way of committing suicide'; deliberately making himself a parody of a right-wing bigot, thereby giving his life for the oppressed, for the revolution.

Julius and Cleopatra. A play for Coarse Actors. Michael Green

See the entry for *The Third Great Coarse Acting Show*.

Just a Little Word. Play. Enid Coles
F6 (middle-age, elderly). The entrance hall of a seedy private nursing home. Fee code D

At this private nursing home, Matron seems to be taking an unusual amount of interest in the wealthy Miss Charlesworth, including escorting her to see her solicitor. Mrs Woods, the elderly speech-handicapped patient, knows the real reason for Matron's attention, but can she relay it to the Chairman of the League of Friends before it is too late?
ISBN 0 573 13268 2

Keeping Mum. Monologue from **Visiting Hour**. Richard Harris
F2 (middle-age). A hospital ward. Fee code D

First presented as a National Theatre Platform performance in the Cottesloe Theatre in 1987 and subsequently seen in a revised version at the Duke's Head Theatre, Richmond, Surrey in 1990, this poignant monologue sees Pauline sitting at the bedside of her dying mother. As she mulls over her own churning emotions she realizes a love that, it eventually transpires, is now too late to communicate.
ISBN 0 573 13291 7

Kids. Play. John Morgan
5 characters either M or F. A playground. Fee code D

A very amusing play based on the premise that all children are born highly intelligent, but by the time they can effectively communicate, they have either forgotten the information or had it knocked out of them! The end leaves you laughing — with a lump in your throat. The children's parts are taken by adults with suitably oversized playground equipment.
ISBN 0 573 12142 7

A Kind of Alaska. Play (from the triple bill *Other Places*). Harold Pinter
M1 (60s) F2 (40s). A room. Fee code G

Deborah was a lively 16-year old and part of a close-knit family when she fell victim to sleeping sickness. Twenty-nine years later, having been watched over throughout by the same doctor, she comes to life and gradually tries to adjust to the world around her.
ISBN 0 573 12129 X

A Kind of Vesuvius. Play. Gillian Plowman
M3 (mid 30s). An empty sitting-room. Fee code D

A sensitive treatment of the devastating effects of unemployment, both on individuals and their families. David, Derek and Ian attempt to preserve their everyday lives, warding off depression and the feelings of rejection, anger and aggression, their efforts ranging from the touching to moments of manic humour.
ISBN 0 573 04229 2

Knightsbridge. Play. John Mortimer
M2 (middle-age) F2 (19, middle-age). A sitting-room. Fee code E

Francesca brings her lover, Henry, to her mother's flat to announce their intention to get married. While waiting for Mrs Stokes, Francesca answers a mysterious phone call. From what he overhears, Henry concludes that Mrs Stokes is a member of the oldest profession. It is later revealed that Mrs Stokes deals in nothing more erotic than antique furniture.
ISBN 0 573 12130 3

Krapp's Last Tape. Play. Samuel Beckett
M1 (old). A room. Fee code F

Krapp is alone in his room. Slowly, and with much fumbling, he selects the spools of recording tape he needs. Crouched over the recorder, and in moods of exaltation, he listens like a drowning man to the record of his past as preserved on the magnetic tapes.

Lady Audley's Secret. Melodrama. Constance Cox. Adapted from Miss Braddon's novel
M4 (middle-age, elderly) F8 (20s, 30s, middle-age). A garden. Fee code D

A one-act version of the famous melodrama concerning the ambitious, unscrupulous Lady Audley who, when an unwanted husband returns, attempts to get rid of him in the garden well. But she is observed, and neither bribery nor attempted arson avail her. Nemesis overtakes her and tragedy ensues. Period 1860s
ISBN 0 573 02345 X

Lady Bracknell's Confinement. Monologue. Paul Doust
M1 or F1, 3M 2F voices only. A hall. Fee code F

In *The Importance of Being Earnest* Jack Worthing discovers every obstacle has been removed from marriage to Gwendolen. Or so he believes. Gwendolen's mother, Lady Bracknell, confesses her own bizarre family history, revealing she is not Gwendolen's mother, she is her father! Paul Doust has produced a perfect simulation of Wilde's characteristically epigrammatic wit in this splendid role for an actress — or actor!
ISBN 0 573 12504 X

The Lady of Larkspur Lotion. Play. Tennessee Williams
M1 F2. A windowless room. Fee code E

Mrs Hardwicke-Moore lives in an imaginary past in which she supposedly owned a Brazilian rubber plantation; the Writer dreams of an equally imaginary future as a great literary figure. Mrs Hardwicke-Moore has a furious row with the landlady and the Writer complains of the disturbance to his work — or possibly his drunken stupor. The landlady jeers at them and they resume their absurd dreams.

A Lady of Letters. Monologue from *Talking Heads*. Alan Bennett
F1 (middle-age). A bleak suburban room. Fee code F

Miss Ruddock writes letters — not, unfortunately, social communications filled with harmless news — but letters of complaint, comment and, occasionally, officious praise to various businesses and government departments. She complains about the lack of care she assumes the child living opposite is receiving and ends up in prison. There, ironically, Miss Ruddock finds freedom and is, for possibly the first time, happy.
ISBN 0 573 03384 6

◆ **The Last Bread Pudding**. Comedy. Nick Warburton
M3 (middle-age) F4 (young, middle-age) or M2 F5. A room. Fee code D

The committee of an amateur drama group is meeting to discuss a new play. We notice that, strangely, the presentation of the meeting to us is reflecting the ideas put forward by the committee, making the play a demonstration as well as a discussion of those ideas. A clever and entertaining piece, ideal for festivals.
ISBN 0 573 12145 1

Last Call For Breakfast. A play for Coarse Actors. Michael Green

See the entry for *The Coarse Acting Show 2*.

The Last Munro. Play. Dave Watson
M2 (20s, middle-age) F1 (20s). A mountain top. Fee code D

Mark and Sandra arrive at the peak of a Munro. Sandra is not keen on repeating the experience — but then the couple meet John, a widower who has just climbed his last Munro and regrets that his late wife cannot share his triumph. His story wins Sandra's sympathy and she changes her mind, leading Mark off to the next peak as the play ends.
ISBN 0 573 12147 8

Last of My Solid Gold Watches. Play. Tennessee Williams
M3 (35, 70s (1 Black)). A hotel room. Fee code E

Charlie, an old-fashioned travelling salesman, is visited by Harper, a salesman of the modern style. As they talk together of their trade it becomes apparent that Charlie's bravado hides a poignant consciousness of the changes that come to everyone with the approach of old age.

The Last of the Last of the Mohicans. Comedy. Hugh Leonard
M3 (40, middle-age) F2 (30s, middle-age). M1 or F1 voice only. Fee code F

See entry for *Suburb of Babylon* in Section A.

Last Panto in Little Grimley. Comedy. David Tristram
M2 F2. A bare stage. Fee code D

This is a long overdue sequel to the tremendously popular *Last Tango in Little Grimley* and features the same characters. Even though this is a stand-alone story, societies who haven't yet produced the original might care to check it out first. Indeed, running both plays together makes for a full and very entertaining evening. An excellent choice for a festival.

Last Scene of All. Play. Margaret Wood
M2 (elderly) F5 (elderly). Simple interior setting. Fee code D

Four retired actresses bicker and banter in a Home for Retired Artistes. Dame Anthea's dresser observes them and injects pithy comments into the actresses' small talk. Needing a man for their projected Christmas play, they enlist the help of newcomer Arthur Pendragon, but it is the dapper Antony Redfern who devises an entertainment ideally suited to their personalities.
ISBN 0 573 12133 8

Last Tango in Little Grimley. Comedy. David Tristram
M2 F2. A simple stage. Fee code D

Membership of the local amateur drama society has dwindled to four. Time for dramatic action. There's only one thing that sells tickets these days — sex. But how will the locals react to the promise of a sizzling sex comedy? All is revealed in this fast-paced comedy of an Am-Dram in trouble. David Tristram's hilarious play requires only the simplest of props and no scenery.

Last Things. Play. Peter Barnes (In a volume).
M1 (elderly) F1 (elderly). An empty space. Fee code C

An elderly couple of thespians awake in bed to find themselves dead. Troupers that they are, they decide to go into the next world with their famous husband and wife sketch — to the applause of the heavenly host. May be presented as part of the full-length entertainment *Corpsing*. For details, please see the entry in Section A.
ISBN 0 573 10006 3

The Last Wife. Play. Lynn Brittney
M2 F3. An open stage. Fee code D

Facing imminent death, Henry the Eighth needs a son to succeed him. His wife Catherine fails to fulfil his hopes and his Chancellor, Wriothesley, is told to remove her. Wriothesley plots to have her condemned to death. But the ghosts of previous murders haunt Henry's delirious mind, and he shows pity at last. A dramatic portrayal of courtly tyranny, based on historical facts.
ISBN 0 573 12134 6

Late Frost. Play. Jean McConnell
F2 (middle age). A seaside promenade. Fee code B

See the entry for *Deckchairs I.*

Leaving. Play. Don Woods
F3 (middle-age, elderly). A living-room. Fee code D

B

Auntie encounters a woman in the house. Can it be her niece, Lil? It is! Seven weeks ago, after both her husband Bill and Auntie had walked out on her, she made a choice between suicide and a new life. The woman with whom Bill left arrives to inform Lil he has had a massive stroke and needs her. All is not gloom, however ...
ISBN 0 573 13264 X

◆ **Leslie**. Play (from *A Different Way Home*). Jimmie Chinn
M1 (middle-age). A living-room. Fee code H

Leslie, who has lived with his mother all his life in a small, closely-knit, North of England town, narrates the events leading up to her death, unwittingly revealing the extent of his loss and his bitterness towards his sister Maureen who lives nearby but is not in touch. This deeply-moving and astutely observed monologue has a running time of approximately 55 minutes.
ISBN 0 573 11092 1

The Lesson. Comic drama. Eugene Ionesco. Translated from the French by Donald Watson
M1 (middle-age) F2 (18, middle-age). A study. Fee code E

The Professor's private lesson begins well: his pupil seems remarkably gifted. Suddenly he discovers she cannot subtract. The lesson gets more frenzied as he persists in forcing her to understand subtraction. Maddened by her insensibility, he stabs her. The maid clucks with dismay. This, she complains, is the fortieth to be stabbed today.

◆ **Lifelines**. Play. Amy Rosenthal
M1 (young) F1 (young). A split set; a bedroom, a kitchen. Fee code E

When Robert misdials, Annie is ready to hang up on what she thinks is a nuisance caller interrupting her indulgent sobbing. This accidental telephone call is the start of a distant, yet significant telephonic relationship. Both Robert and Annie are plagued by love troubles and enjoy the opportunity to let off steam, take a few tips and perhaps begin again.
ISBN 0 573 12139 7

Little Benjamin. Play. Enid Coles
F5 (40s, 50s, 70s). An attic. Fee code D

When Mrs Glenheriot and her daughter Edwina decide to move from their home, Susan, the youngest member of the family, returns to the house to help with arrangements. To escape the chaos below she retreats to the attic amongst the lumber and secrets of the past sixty years. However, not even she can guess at the secrets the attic holds. The climax is dramatic, moving and certain to shock.
ISBN 0 573 13267 4

Little Brother, Little Sister. Play. David Campton
M2 (teenage, old) F1 (teenage). A fall-out shelter. Fee code E

An atomic bomb many years previously made prisoners of a cook and two children, now teenage, who know nothing of the old world and must wait thirty more years before it is safe to venture outside. Cook inadvertently tells them of a door to the outside world. They trick him into revealing its whereabouts and they begin to turn the handle ...

The Little Lights of Kimberley. Melodrama. Harry Austin
M4 F1. Fee code B

A heart-warming tale of how young war widow Lulu Littlehampton is saved from the dishonourable designs of Captain Harvey Kneetrembler and Arkwright, the Pickled Onion King, by the timely return of her husband Walter, who is not only not dead, but also very rich, having stumbled upon a hidden diamond mine! Playing time approximately 16 minutes. Contained in *The Little Lights of Kimberley and Other Plays*.
ISBN 0 573 10023 3

Little Red Whittington. Minidrama. Richard Tydeman
M4 F4. Extras (M and F). Fee code B

A unique situation arises when two companies, each about to perform a different pantomime — 'Little Red Riding Hood' and 'Dick Whittington' — combine forces and do the two as one. Running time: 15-20 minutes
ISBN 0 573 06618 3

♦ LittleBro Morning and BigSis Afternoon. Play. Mike Tibbetts
M5 F5 or M4 F4, 1 boy 1 girl. Various simple settings. Fee code E

A father is driven by despair to abandon his family after the tragic death of his wife. He leaves his children to run successfully a family home, unknown to any authorities. When money eventually runs out, they have one day left together. This is a fascinating and ultimately moving story.
ISBN 0 573 12154 0

London Vertigo. Play. Brian Friel. Based on a play *The True Born Irishman,* or *The Irish Fine Lady* by Charles Macklin
M3 F2. A room. Fee code G

This is a superb satire on Irish Anglophiles. Nancy O'Doherty has been smitten by 'the London vertigo', a sudden, dizzy conviction that London is the only place for style, wit, good fortune and excitement. Her husband enlists the help of his brother-in-law to restore her to sanity and Irishness. Period eighteenth century

The Long Christmas Dinner. Play. Thornton Wilder
M5 F7. A dining-room. Fee code C

Ninety years are traversed in this play, which represents in accelerated motion ninety Christmas dinners in the Bayard household. Each member of the family ages with the passing years until finally they die and exit from the stage. We hear them comment on the development of the countryside, the enormous changes in manners and customs during this period of time.
ISBN 0 573 02144 9

The Long Goodbye. Play. Tennessee Williams
M7 (young) F2 (young, middle-age). A tenement apartment. Fee code E

While Joe waits for the moving men to cart away his furnishings, he talks to a companion, Silva, about his past life — his mother who suffered from cancer and killed herself, and about his sister, strong-willed and attractive. Silva's inclination is to look forward, but to Joe life is 'just a long, long goodbye'.

B

The Long Home. Play. Derek Bowskill
F5 (teenage, 20, 30, 50s). A women's remand home. Fee code D

Three inmates of a women's remand home are acting out the lessons their tutor has taught them. Both the Warden and the Tutor encourage them, believing them to be expressing themselves dramatically. But it is only when it is too late that they realize the deep and horrifying undertones to the girls' actions.
ISBN 0 573 03364 1

The Long Noon. Play. Patricia Chown
M2 (29, 50s) F5 (20s-60s). The veranda of a large country house. Fee code D

Seven guests sit and chat, gradually discovering that each has been invited for a totally different reason. Peter analyses the reasons for their presence: each is guilty of one of the seven deadly sins. Salvation arrives for four of them as the coach comes to take everyone home.
ISBN 0 573 12143 5

The Long Stay Cut Short, or The Unsatisfactory Supper. Play. Tennessee Williams
M1 F2. A porch and sideyard. Fee code E

Baby Doll and Archie Lee have had their senile Aunt Rose staying with them, and are at the end of their tether. They argue that she should be sent to stay with other relatives, and eventually in a fury Archie Lee bursts out at her. Nature takes a hand in settling the matter.

The Loophole. Play. N. J. Warburton
M4. An office, a room. Fee code D

Mr Overall, the Junior Under Minister for Justice, has a special knack for finding legal loopholes. When Prisoner 604 is sentenced to death all his talent is brought to bear. Aided by the prison chaplain, he finds a way, only to be defeated by his officious assistant and the prison officer. But Overall is not quite convinced that the game is over.
ISBN 0 573 04228 4

Lord Byron's Love Letter. Play. Tennessee Williams
M1 F3 (middle-age, elderly). A parlour. Fee code E

In New Orleans the Old Woman and her granddaughter try to alleviate their poverty by displaying a love-letter supposedly written to the former by Lord Byron. When a couple arrive, the two women tell their story. The visitors hear the Mardi Gras parade arriving and dash out without paying. The Old Woman angrily accuses her granddaughter of dropping 'her grandfather's' letter on the floor.

The Love Course. Drama. A. R. Gurney
M2 F2. One interior set. Fee code E

A woman professor has been teaching a course on 'the literature of love' with a younger male colleague. She has fallen in love with him through the books and the experience of the classroom. Now, in the last year of the class, she is attempting to bring the course and their relationship to a climax and a conclusion.

The Lover. Play. Harold Pinter
M2 (30s) F1 (early 30s). Composite setting. Fee code F

Richard and Sarah have created fictional lovers, Max and Sarah. They indulge in erotic wish fulfilment and thus keep the marriage refreshed. Then Richard begins to upset the *status quo* by refusing to allow the distinct halves of their relationship to remain separate. The afternoons have been for Max, the evenings for Richard. This evening, Max encroaches on Richard's preserves.
ISBN 0 573 02148 1

Lovesick. Play. Caryl Churchill
M4 (25, 40) F2 (30). Various simple settings. Fee code D

Hodge, a psychiatrist, has successfully developed an aversion therapy. Ellen, a depressive patient, loves Kevin, a homosexual, while Hodge is strongly attracted to Ellen. He decides to use his therapy on her and Kevin to make Ellen fall in love with him and turn Kevin from his homosexuality. Kevin's brother Robert despises Hodge and secretly alters the treatment so that Ellen becomes a lesbian and Kevin falls madly in love with Hodge.

A Lovesome Thing. Play. Jean McConnell
F8 (middle-age). A conservatory. Fee code D

Lady Cleveland has helped the Little Dowgate branch of the Women's Institute in the past, and four of its members are determined to repay her at all costs. When old Bates, Lady Cleveland's gardener, goes into hospital they see a perfect opportunity. Well-intentioned though they are, chaos ensues. Luckily for Lady Cleveland, Bates is coming back ...
ISBN 0 573 13269 0

Lunch Hour. Play. John Mortimer
M1 (40s) F2 (23, 40s). An hotel bedroom. Fee code E

Two lovers, a Man and a Girl, meet in a hotel room one lunch time for a hour. To preserve a façade of respectability he tells the Manageress he is expecting his wife, the mother of his three children. The Girl arrives and knowing nothing of the story is surprised by the sympathy of the Manageress but she soon comes to identify with the fictional tired mother and storms out.
ISBN 0 573 02149 X

Magic. Play (from *Visiting Hour*). Richard Harris
M2 (middle-age, elderly) F4 (early 20s (Black), 35, middle-age, elderly). A hospital ward. Fee code D

Brenda, a timid spinster awaiting a hysterectomy, suffers a visit from a crass work colleague and her appalling husband who performs very bad jokes and conjuring tricks. The play was seen as part of the full length play *Visiting Hour* (see Section A) which was presented in 1990 at the Duke's Head Theatre, Richmond, Surrey.
ISBN 0 573 01925 8

A Man of Letters. Play. Tim Firth
M2 (18, 54). A ledge. Fee code F

A truly outstanding, genuinely funny play, with a wry twist at the end, first seen at the Stephen Joseph Theatre in the Round Studio, Scarborough. Frank has erected signs for a commercial letterer for twenty-five years. With trainee Alan, he attempts to spell 'Forshaw's' — the letters collectively forming the play's third 'character'. He is nonplussed when the right letters do not appear and then realization dawns.
ISBN 0 573 04227 6

B

Mantrap. Thriller. Paul Reakes
M3 (30s-50s) F2 (17, 30s). A living-room. Fee code E

A taut thriller which begins when Trevor Wyatt lets a girl in to his house who says she has been the victim of an attack by a lorry driver. But that's nothing compared to what follows — petty larceny, manslaughter, bogus policemen and a devilishly elaborate form of blackmail.
ISBN 0 573 12167 2

Maria Marten. Melodrama. Harry Austin
M3 F1. Fee code B

The sad tale of Maria Marten is enlivened by the return of her sweetheart Jack (plus false beard) and, just when we think Maria is dead by the birth of her baby, there is a joyful reunion of the two innocents. A short melodrama suitable for inclusion in a Music Hall evening or similar compilation. Contained in *The Chinese Pendant and Other Plays*.

Maria Marten. Melodrama. Richard Dennis. Edited by Michael Kilgarriff
M2 F1. fee code A

A short — and very dramatic — rendering of the murder in the red barn, hindered by an over-enthusiastic stage-manager. for inclusion in a Music Hall evening. Contained in *Three Melodramas*. Music available separately.
ISBN 0 573 00018 2

Maria Marten or **The Murder in the Red Barn**. Victorian Melodrama. Constance Cox
M5 F9. A garden or green. Fee code C

This is a version of the famous nineteenth-century crime in which an innocent young country girl is murdered by a local squire who had earlier seduced her and is now anxious to marry an heiress. Partly through the agency of a gypsy, however, retribution overtakes the villain. Ingeniously telescoped in time and place into one simple setting.
ISBN 0 573 02325 5

Martyred Wives. Play. Margaret Wood
M5 (middle-age, elderly) F4 (young, 30s, 40s). Extra M or F. A cottage and courtroom. Fee code D

This is the story of the wives of the Tolpuddle Martyrs of 1834 whose husbands banded together to try to get a fair wage, and who were then left behind to manage as best as they could when the men were savagely sentenced to seven years' transportation. Easily staged, the simple scenes in cottage and courtroom are linked by a singer.
ISBN 0 573 12155 9

The Master and the Maid. A riotous routine for Music Hall. Michael Kilgarriff
M2 F2. Music Hall Chairman. Fee code A

A six-minute sketch in the mode of the silent movies wherein a film of husband, wife, lover and maid is first shown ordinarily, then backwards and finally forwards at double speed! Contained in *Music Hall Miscellany*.
ISBN 0 573 00013 1

♦ **Matchstick Dreams**. Comedy. Fiz Marcus
M3 (50s, 60s, any age) F1 (60s) or M2 F1 with doubling. A living-room. Fee code D

After forty-five years of marriage George Balmforth is determined to make his mark and create something original, but when his wife Dora discovers that he intends to build a model of Leeds Town Hall out of two hundred and fifty thousand matchsticks, the trouble starts!
ISBN 0 573 12157 5

♦ **Maureen**. Play (from *A Different Way Home*). Jimmie Chinn
F1 (middle age). A living-room. Fee code E

Maureen, living in a small, closely-knit, North of England town, relates how she felt rejected by family and friends because she married a Jew. She also feels betrayed for not being asked by her brother to help when their mother was dying. This astutely observed monologue conveys the need for families to communicate, and for love to transcend prejudice. Running time: approximately 35 minutes.
ISBN 0 573 11092 1

Mayhem at the Mill, or, **Fortune's Fate**. Brian J. Burton
M3 F1. A gloomy mill. Fee code B

A short melodrama for inclusion in a Music Hall Evening. Little scenery is required and detailed production notes are given in the script. Contained with two other melodramas in *Cheers, Tears and Screamers*.

Me and My Friend. Two one-act plays. Gillian Plowman
M2 and F2. Fee codes on application

The first act of this full-length play may be presented as a one-act play for men, the second as a one-act play for women. Please see the entry in Section A.
ISBN 0 573 01831 6

The Measures Taken (The Decision). Play. Bertolt Brecht
Translations: Carl Mueller
                      John Willett
M4 F1. A concert platform. Fee code G

Four Communist agitators have killed a comrade while on a mission to China. A 'Control Chorus' instructs them to describe how this came about, so that a verdict may be pronounced. Their reasons for the deed are re-enacted: the victim, though a true Communist, had committed several serious errors in Communist practice and therefore agreed to his own death. They are praised by the Control Chorus for their successful work.

Meat and Two Veg. Comedy. Paul Beard
M2 (elderly) F1 (elderly). A living-room. Fee code D

Margaret and Arthur, a retired couple, are preparing dinner for their neighbour, Albert, whose wife, Enid, left him abruptly two months ago. This light-hearted comedy takes a darker turn when Arthur, aware that Albert has an eye for Margaret, suggests their neighbour's smelly bonfires could indicate Albert has done away with Enid ...
ISBN 0 573 12165 6

B

Medea. One-woman play. Dario Fo and Franca Rame. Adapted by Olwen Wymark
F1. An open stage. Fee code B

See the entry under *Female Parts* in Section A.

♦ **Melons at the Parsonage**. Comedy. Nick Warburton
M4 F4, 1M or F. A village hall stage. Fee code D

Two amateur drama groups become joint winners of a play festival. A tie-break involves the groups performing an extract from their own entry and then an excerpt from the opposing team's play, but the pieces are very different. They compete again with hilarious results but the outcome is still a tie. This time a rugby scrum will decide the winner!
ISBN 0 573 12159 1

Memento Mori. Comedy of Menace. David Campton
M2. A room in an empty house. Fee code D

See the entry under *The Lunatic View* in the Section A.

Merry Regiment of Women. Comedy. Rae Shirley
M3 F6. A fragment from the old Globe Theatre. Fee code E

Shakespeare's great women and three extraordinary men meet and perform a totally contemporary play. Kate and Petruchio, Romeo and Juliet, daring Henry V, plus Lady Macbeth and Cleopatra, combine to produce a mad and merry, totally irreverent but particularly apt, tribute to the greatest writer of all! A triumph of irony in the iambic — yet warm of heart. Forsooth play on!

The Miasma in Mostyn Mews. Satirical comedy. Alan Ogden
M3 (20s, middle-age) F3 (20s, 40s). A sitting-room. Fee code D

When the Coopers discover a strange smell and rising mist in their council house they receive a visit from the Housing Inspector Mr Biddlecombe. However he blinds them with official procedure, pronounces the mist 'condensation' and silences his assistant when the cause of the miasma is discovered. However, the Coopers decide it's time for action and Biddlecombe is made to suffer the effects of his decision.
ISBN 0 573 12161 3

Mobile 4. Play. Stephen Jeffreys
M3 (20s-30s) F2 (20s-30s). A bare stage. Fee code E

Fallowfields, a self-supporting country community, is presenting an exhibition with a mobile by a member, Leo, as its centrepiece. As they assemble the mobile, tensions are brought to a head with a telephone call from Leo to say he is going to join another community. Duncan and Beth announce they too are leaving. It seems to signify the end of Fallowfields — or is it?
ISBN 0 573 02508 8

Moby Dick. A play for Coarse Actors. Michael Green

See the entry for *The Coarse Acting Show 2*.

The Molecatcher. A riotous routine for Music Hall. Realized by Malcolm Sircom. Edited by Michael Kilgarriff
M3. Chairman. Fee code A

B

A brief (ten-minute) rousing sketch with music showing three yokels and their trials and tribulations with moles. Contained in *Music Hall Miscellany*
ISBN 0 573 00013 1

Monmouth. Comedy. Charles Mander
M3 (young, elderly) F2 (young). Park. Fee code D

Malcolm, a young drop-out, hangs around the park. Today Sue, pregnant with his child, arrives with some ham butties. The park gardener tries to get Malcolm to move on as a civic event is about to take place. Malcolm's threat of rude gestures causes Sue to walk out on him but just in time his genuine feelings for her get the better of him and he follows her.
ISBN 0 573 12166 4

Moony's Kid Don't Cry. Play. Tennessee Williams
M1 (25) F1 (young). A kitchen. Fee code E

A dawn quarrel in the middle of a slovenly kitchen between the frustrated labourer and his ailing wife boils up until she strikes him and he catches her by the throat. She tells him to go if he wants to, she will return to work but she insists he take the child with him and places it in his arms.

Mortmain. Play. Richard Parsons
M1 (young) F1 (middle-age). A flat. Fee code C

When Diana found her dead husband's diary, all her previous assumptions about her marriage were threatened. She meets up with Steve, Toby's lover for almost three years, and, as they talk, bitterness is replaced by a realization of how much she and Steve do share. It seems that both are still in a dead person's control — both are to be forever held in *mortmain*.
ISBN 0 573 10001 2

Mountain Language. Play. Harold Pinter
M5 F2. Various simple settings. Fee code F

'Focusing on the brutalities of a society which forbids a minority of its population to speak in their own language, it is a play of few words which add up to an eloquent indictment of the banning of any human utterance.' Paul Taylor in the *Independent*. It was presented by the National Theatre at the Lyttelton Theatre in 1988 starring Eileen Atkins, Michael Gambon and Miranda Richardson.
ISBN 0 573 12163 X

Mrs Meadowsweet. Play. David Campton
F6 (young, 30s-50s). A lounge in a guest house. Fee code D

This bewitching little play centres on the animosity present between two siblings, Alice and Fleur. Mrs Meadowsweet and her homely guest-house, *Respite*, seem to mellow the ever garrulous Alice, much to Fleur's suspicion. The other guests, too, seem particularly amiable and pleasant — in fact, without a care in the world. What is the power that Mrs Meadowsweet has for enveloping other people's problems?
ISBN 0 573 13282 8

B

Mum's the Word. Play. Brian Miller
M2 (30s, 65) F3 (30s-50s). A sitting-room and patio, a police station. Fee code D

On a sunny afternoon Grantham, a retired army officer, cleans his service revolver. Jessica, his younger wife, arrives with tea. But this normal scene changes when the subject of divorce arises and Jessica shoots Grantham. Dotty Aunt Herbacia happily plans the funeral and when Amelia arrives from America she reassures Jessica. But Herbacia has her own plans ...
ISBN 0 573 12172 9

Murder Play. Play. Brian J. Burton
M2 F2. A living-room. Fee code D

Peter and Robyn wake up after a dinner party at the home of friends David and Jane Valentine. It now appears David is dead and they are forced to accept that Jane is the killer. To avoid implicating themselves they have to help dispose of the body. Stunned and bitter, they leave, but then it transpires that the 'murder' is really an elaborate practical joke.
ISBN 0 573 12171 0

The Music Lovers. Farce. Georges Feydeau. Adapted by Reggie Oliver
M1 F4. An apartment salon. Fee code E

Set in 1890s Paris and very typically Feydeau in style, this lively and fast-moving play revolves around the idea of mistaken identity. Lucille awaits her new music teacher but the man who walks into her apartment is Edouard, in the mistaken belief that he is attending a rendezvous with his mistress. A series of hilarious misunderstandings and *double entendres* ensues.
ISBN 0 573 12169 9

Mutatis Mutandis. Comedy of Menace. David Campton
M1 (young) F2 (young). A clinic waiting-room. Fee code D

Douglas arrives to collect Celia, his wife, after the birth of their child. But it appears the child is a mutation; physically changed as well as very advanced for its tender years. The parents agree to an adoption. But Celia hears the child cry. They cannot leave him and the three go home together to face a life of ostracism.

The Mutilated. Tennessee Williams

See *Slapstick Tragedy* in Section A

Nasty Things, Murders. Play. Arthur Lovegrove
F5 (55, elderly). A lounge. Fee code D

The four ladies in the Home for Retired Gentlewomen are very upset when their television set stops working just at the climax of a real-life murder drama. Conversation turns on the circumstances of the murder. To the horror of three of them, it appears that the fourth, the sweet and gentle Mary, may have been the actual murderess in the crime under discussion.
ISBN 0 573 03354 4

B

Neighbours. Play. James Saunders
M1 (young, black) F1 (young). A bedsitting-room. Fee code E

This is a psychological study of a Man who calls on a Woman late at night. Both are nervous and easily embarrassed. His defence against embarrassment is an insistence on her defining the terms of the relationship and she ends up as a defeated individual, quite convincing in her willingness to sleep with him after all that's passed between them.

Nellie's Nightlights. Comedy melodrama. Harry Austin
M4 F3. Fee code E

A Victorian/Edwardian comedy melodrama in which young Nellie Larkin becomes the 'face that flickers in a thousand bedrooms', thanks to her invention of 'Nellie's Nightlights'. Playing time approximately 42 minutes. Contained in *The Little Lights Of Kimberley*.
ISBN 0 573 10023 3

A New Leaf. Comedy. E. Eynon Evans
M4 (young, middle-age, elderly) F4 (young, middle-age). A living-room. Fee code D

Suddenly Tom Jones changes his ways — no more evenings at the club, perfect father and a considerate husband. But this only arouses suspicions in his wife, Mary. Scandal raises its ugly head but all is sorted in the end with Mary thankful to see him going off again as before — safe at the club.
ISBN 0 573 02333 6

The New World Order. Sketch. Harold Pinter
M2, 1M extra. A bare stage. Fee code A

Des and Lionel stand and discuss what they are going do with the prisoner who sits blindfolded on a chair before them. They taunt the silent victim with speculatory chit-chat that intimates the torture that is to follow. Lionel breaks down in tears because he loves his job so much, it makes him feel 'so pure'. Des replies he is 'keeping the world clean for democracy'.

Night Errant. Comedy. Michael Pilch. Adapted from *Feu la Mère de Madame* by Georges Feydeau
M2 (40s, elderly) F2 (20, 40s). A bedroom. Fee code E

A farcical comedy set in 1910. Lucien arrives home in the early hours dressed as Louis XIV. His late arrival and enraptured account of the ball invites the wrath of Yvonne, his wife and it isn't long before the maid, suffering with flu, and the bumbling, elderly manservant are dragged into the argument.
ISBN 0 573 12173 7

A Night Out. Play. Harold Pinter
M10 (28, 50, 65) F5 (25, 55). Composite setting. Fee code E

Albert finds himself dominated by his mother. At an office party he is mercilessly teased by his colleagues and arrives home, his temper rising. When his mother nags he attacks and leaves her, gets picked up by a girl and is able to reduce her to humble servility. Yet, when he arrives home his mother is there fully recovered and ready to reassert her dominance. (*Please specify author when ordering*)
ISBN 0 573 02176 7

A Night Out. Comedy. Frank Vickery
M2 (middle-age, late teenage) F2 (middle-age, late teenage). A living-room. Fee code D

Seizing the opportunity, while her parents are out, Doreen decides to invite round Eric, her boyfriend. However, the evening is doomed to failure for all concerned: Doreen tries to calm Eric's passions while Mam and Dad overcome a ruined hair-do, the losing of all-important tickets and the car's flat battery only to find that they have the wrong night. (*Please specify author when ordering*)
ISBN 0 573 12011 0

The Nightingale and Not the Lark. Play. Jennifer Johnston
M2 (young) F2 (young, late 60s). A room. Fee code D

Mamie spends most of her time in an alcoholic haze. Below her are a rehearsing theatre company. Strains of *Romeo and Juliet* filter up to Mamie who starts to rail at Owen, her husband, torn between loving and hating him. It is only when the ASM interrupts that we learn Owen was killed during the last war.
ISBN 0 573 12178 8

Night's Candles. Play. Hazel Wyld
M3 (young, elderly) F2 (young, 78). A rambling garden. Fee code D

Fizz and Frank, elderly actors who were deeply in love, have been divorced for many years. Amazingly, they find themselves in a rambling garden where two young people enact scenes from their past. A man appears, explaining they have entered the 'hereafter' but Fizz is not really meant to be there and must choose between life and her true feelings for her husband …
ISBN 0 573 12177 X

No Picnic. Play. George MacEwan Green
M3 (young) F3 (young). 1 voice. A hillside. Fee code D

Four English students gather for a picnic in Germany in 1938. Then Esther, a Jewess, appears, hunted by Karl of Hitler Youth. She is dragged away and thunder clouds form over what had previously been a fine day. A Narrator tells us of the fate of five of the party but we can only guess at Esther's fate.
ISBN 0 573 12181 8

No Why. Play. John Whiting
M4 (young, middle-age) F3 (middle-age). Extras. An attic. Fee code C

Jacob, a young child, has been banished to the attic and is then subjected to further verbal abuse as, one by one, the family visit him. Loathed by his father, resented by his mother, Jacob is once again left alone. While the music plays downstairs Jacob hangs himself.
ISBN 0573 02180 5

None the Wiser. Comedy. Anthony Booth
F7. A convent living-room. Fee code C

A gang of women posing as nuns are operating a successful shop-lifting racket. The trouble is that at home in their convent they have to look the part, and when two nuns seeking accommodation appear at the door they can't turn them away. However, the newcomers aren't what they seem either.
ISBN 0 573 13286 0

Not Bobby. Play. N. J. Warburton
M1 F4, doubling possible. A living-room. Fee code D

Anxious to complete yesterday's newspaper crossword, Frank finds the page missing. His mother, Pam, confesses to using it in the newly acquired rabbit's cage. Extracting the page Frank is astonished to find the crossword is now complete. Could the rabbit, Bobby, be responsible ... ? A quirky, well-observed satire from the author of *Don't Blame It on the Boots*.
ISBN 0 573 12179 6

Not Not Not Not Not Enough Oxygen. Play. Caryl Churchill
M2 (19, 60) F1 (30). A room. Fee code D

The time is 2010. Mick and Vivian live in a tower block, protected from the violence and pollution outside where groups of 'fanatics' roam, setting fire to themselves in protest against wars and famine. Mick hopes his rich son will give him money to escape, but when Claude arrives they learn he has given his money away and is to join the 'fanatics' outside.

Nothing Personal. Play. Hugh Leonard
M2 (30s, 40) F1 (30s). Fee code C

See entry for *Suburb of Babylon* in Section A.

Now and Then. Play. David Campton
F6 (middle-age). Extras. A room. Fee code D

For a brief while in an old house, time merges across four centuries. The Wise Woman, from Tudor times, is expecting a Customer who wishes to make use of her apparently extra-sensory powers. By chance two women from the present day happen to intrude on this event of long ago. An antique buckle provides an eerie link between the two widely-separated periods.
ISBN 0 573 03376 6

Nudes in Waning Light. Comedy. George Brockhill
M2 (60) F5 (18, 20, 40s, 50s). A living-room. Fee code D

Winner of the Geoffrey Whitworth Cup in 1984, this fast-moving comedy centres on Walter, hen-pecked husband, who, in his wife's absence, is led into debauched ways — including the painting of two nude women, one a model and the other his wife's cleaner. Eruptions arise when Molly, Walter's wife, unexpectedly arrives home.
ISBN 0 573 12182 6

♦ **Office Song**. Play. Nick Warburton
M1 (20s-40s) F2 (20s-40s). A cloakroom. Fee code D

Brian is attempting to escape his firm's Christmas party when he is waylaid in the cloakroom by Claire, who soon discovers a secret about her unassuming colleague: at home, he likes to sing Doris Day songs. Claire tries to persuade Brian to take part in a talent contest; with her friend Wendy she sets about training Brian to sing in public.
ISBN 0 573 12174 5

B

The Old One-Two. Drama. A. R. Gurney
M2 F1. Fee code E

A professor of Classics at an American university gets into an affair with a female student. Meanwhile the dean of the department has become involved in a sly relationship with the professor's mysterious wife. The play is saved from a tragic ending by a sudden surprising discovery.

Old Quebec. Play. William Norfolk
M2 (48) F3 (20s, 40s). An hotel foyer and restaurant. Fee code D

Mr Robinson is holidaying in Brussels with his 'son'. On a split level set we eavesdrop on two conversations: that of M. and Madame Lapin, hotel-owners, and Babette, the maid and that of Mr Robinson and his companion and their talk of the former's wife, now dead. Lapin, reading of a murder in England, finds convincing similarities between their guests and Dr Crippen and his lover ... Period 1910
ISBN 0 573 12190 7

Old Tyme Dancing and **The Whizzer**

Words by Joyce Grenfell. Music by Richard Addinsell
Fee code A for each sketch

Olive and Hilary. Play. Geraldine Aron
M2 (middle-age) F3 (30s-40s). A living-room. Fee code E

Olive and Hilary, relinquishing professional careers, have found true happiness living simply. Monica, Olive's sister and a marketing executive, arrives for a break from her husband Derek who has quit a pensionable job. Olive and Hilary sympathize with Derek, cheerfully resisting Monica's attempts to dissuade them from their chosen lifestyle and Monica's intolerance becomes her downfall in this amusing, very entertaining play!
ISBN 0 573 12186 9

On the Verandah. Play. Bryan Stocks
M2 (30s, elderly) F2 (young, late 20s). A verandah. Fee code D

Don José, a lawyer, visits his unmarried client Inez at her villa in Andalusia. An earlier love affair of hers with Miguel ended unhappily and he took holy orders. But after Don José has gone Inez sees a new young priest coming up the hill to see her — Miguel.

Once and for All. Play. Enid Coles
F6 (30s, 50s). A garden-room. Fee code D

A gentle, subtle play about two contrasting mothers and daughters — common, garrulous Mrs Painter and Patsy and genteel but poor Mrs Burnett and Charlotte. The mothers met 30 years previously in hospital at the birth of their daughters — but were they given each other's baby all those years ago?
ISBN 0 573 13287 9

B

◆ **One Careful Owner**. Play. H. Connolly
M2 (late 20s, 55) F2 (young, late 20s). A sitting-room. Fee code D

Percival is thinking of buying a car that Darren has advertised in the *Auto-Trader*. When Darren's wife, Jane, arrives, Percival is somewhat taken aback as he was under the impression she was *his* wife — Amanda! Jane's explanation does little to pacify the situation, and the appearance of her new lover, Tony, leaves both men wishing they could put the clock back.
ISBN 0 573 12160 5

One for the Road. Play. Harold Pinter (from the triple bill *Other Places*)
M2 (30s, 40s) F1 (30s) 1 boy (8). A room. Fee code F

This award-winning play about a torturer and the family he victimizes was premièred in 1984 and subsequently presented as part of the triple bill *Other Places* at the Duchess Theatre, London in 1985. 'It is a disturbing and brilliantly controlled little masterpiece of a play.' *Spectator.* ' ... dialogue that rings like a hammer blow.' *Guardian*
ISBN 0 573 12184 2

◆ **One Month Early**. Farce. Georges Feydeau, translated by Peter Meyer from *Lèonie est en Avance*
M2 (38, middle-age) F4 (young, middle-age). A dining-room. Fee code E

Léonie is eight months pregnant and, it seems, going into labour. Toudoux, her husband, is torn between supporting Léonie and trying to eat as much as possible of his dinner. His in-laws and the midwife arrive and he is berated by everyone, until the midwife makes a stunning announcement. Period 1910

One Month to Pay or **The Sailor's Return**. Melodrama. Brian. J Burton
M3 F3. One interior. Fee code D

The traditional battle between a wicked landlord and the wife of his impecunious tenant, with 'Jolly Jack Tar', village simpletons and 'saintly child' themes thrown in for good measure. Virtue, of course, triumphs in the end. Contained in *Three Hisses for Villainy*.

One Season's King. Play. George MacEwan Green
M3 (middle-age) F1 (middle-age). A graveyard. Fee code C

Eveline meets up with three men who courted her. It is a play of characterization and its successful presentation depends on the male actors being able to convey the tension which exists between them. This tension springs not only from their rivalry for Eveline's favours but also from their sense of class, and can perhaps be most effectively portrayed through voice inflection.

One-Sided Triangle. Play. Stephen Smith
M2 (young, middle-age) F1 (30s). An hotel garden. Fee code D

Mike offers Brian money to courier heroin from Thailand to London. Brian needs the money but is aware it means the death penalty if he's caught and goes for a walk to it think over. Meanwhile, the true nature of the game is revealed and the ending is sad and profound, its implications set to reverberate long after Brian's fate becomes known.
ISBN 0 573 12153 2

B

One Thing More or **Caedmon Construed.** Play. Christopher Fry
M10 F4 or M7 F3, with doubling. Extras. A bare stage. Fee code G

An account of the poet Caedmon isolated and silenced for thirty years by an immense personal grief. A person appears to him in a dream, makes him talk and tells him to sing. The miracle happens and Caedmon sings the 'Hymn Of Creation'. Fry's play was produced at Chelmsford Cathedral and broadcast on BBC Radio 4 in 1986.

The Orchestra. Play. Jean Anouilh. Translated by Miriam John
M1 F6. Extras 3M (2 of whom need not appear). A concert stage. Fee code F

As they play their little pieces of music, the ladies of the brasserie orchestra (and the solitary male pianist) reveal seething volcanoes under the placid exterior. Jealousy, gossip, boasting and thwarted emotions climax in one of them shooting herself in the toilets — but the music goes jauntily on.
ISBN 0 573 02343 3

Other People. Play. Geoff Saunders
M2 (early 20s, 30s) F2 (early 20s, mid-20s). A living-room. Fee code D

Neurotic Andrea, slobbish Stephen, efficient Hilary and meek Duncan share a flat and, given their very different characters, it is no surprise that they do not get on particularly well. *Other People* depicts half an hour in the life of this chaotic and argumentative household, in which tempers are lost, crockery is broken and tears are shed ...
ISBN 0 573 12183 4

Our Branch in Brussels. Play. David Campton
F6 (young, middle-age, elderly). A drawing-room. Fee code D

Outwardly respectable Mrs Bee does 'good work' on the Committee of the Bountiful Bequest, a charity for distressed females. However, unbeknown to the other Committee members, she is financing the charity, and feathering her own nest, by running a branch in Brussels where the younger and prettier girls are transported in dubious circumstances. Blackmail ensues ... Period nineteenth century
ISBN 0 573 13283 6

Our Man. Play. Daniel Clucas
M2, 4 either M or F. Inside Private Jones' head. Fee code E

This highly original play, first seen at the Lyric Studio, Hammersmith, has a very flexible casting and is easy to stage. The action takes place inside Private Jones' head. Sir orders the various parts of the body to get him up and ready for battle, organizing the senses as this 'lethal fighting machine' wakes on the last day of his life.
ISBN 0 573 12187 7

Out for the Count or How Would You Like Your Stake? Vampire yarn. Martin Downing
M5 (20s, middle-age) F4 (young, 19). A sitting-room. Fee code D

A highly amusing blood-chilling spoof, wherein Count Nolyard, newly arrived from Translyvania and visiting Dr Sewer's lunatic asylum in Whitby, attempts to seduce the women of the house, hungry as he is for more than Bridget's fruit cup or Constance's bloody Mary!
ISBN 0 573 12189 3

Out of the Flying Pan. Play. David Campton.
M2. A bare stage. Fee code C

Two diplomats meet to engage in a bout of international bargaining, with outlandish double-talk and windy pronouncements. They inevitably disagree and the treaty is torn up. A moment passes. A bird twitters, gentle music plays, the diplomats return and another round of pretentious gibberish begins while mankind holds its collective breath.

Overtime. Play. H. Connolly
M3 (20s, 40s, 50s) F2 (20s, 40s). A workshop. Fee code D

Albert's colleagues organize a retirement party for him. Albert appears, but seems oddly detached from the proceedings — as though he was not really there ... He 'freeze frames' the action to wryly observe the mayhem but the mood of the play suddenly shifts from the early comedy and we are unprepared for the startling climax which surprises and shocks us all.
ISBN 0 573 12193 1

Parcel. Play. David Campton
M5 (middle-age) F3 (middle-age, elderly) or M3 F5. Extras. Various scenes in a standing set. Fee code D

Grandma is the 'parcel' who is passed from one relative to another. One day, she disappears. When, belatedly, this is discovered, a hurried search involves a call to the police station. But Grandma has merely at last asserted her rights as an individual — she reappears, munching the last remnants of an enormous bag of crisps.
ISBN 0 573 12196 6

Parentcraft. Play. Stephen Smith
M1 (30s) F4 (20s, 30s, middle-age). A hospital room. Fee code D

Four expectant mothers and one father find themselves in a small hospital room awaiting the midwife who is to give them their first Parentcraft class. Differences in experience, outlook and class lead to some interesting and at times hilarious exchanges, as each of the five have to face, and come to terms with, the prejudices and foibles of their companions.
ISBN 0 573 12214 8

Parochial Problems. Play. Margaret Wood
M5 (young, middle-age) F3 (30s, middle-age). A parish hall. Fee code D

On this occasion of a Parochial Church Council meeting temperaments clash over such matters as the redecoration of the church and what to do about the cherubs. Meredith, builder and decorator, considers it is 'not a bad afternoon's work', however, with profitable repair bills in prospect, and even possible future happiness with the attractive Miss Jones.
ISBN 0 573 12199 0

Party Time. Play. Harold Pinter
M5 (20s, 40s-50) F4 (20s-30s, 70). A living-room. Fee code H

The streets are blockaded outside Gavin's upmarket flat, the result of a military occupation. Inside, Gavin hosts a party where the machinations between the guests are as potent and suffocating as any wider social upheaval. This play (first performed at the Almeida with *Mountain Language*) is sparse, but in typical Pinter style, it is bursting with confrontational contemporary themes.

B

Pastiche. Farce. Nick Hall
M2 (young, 50) F2 (young, 45). A sitting-room. Fee code E

Medford, a young servant, is setting an elegant supper table at which Sir Peter is shortly to entertain a young girl. However Sir Peter's wife Lady Alexandra unexpectedly arrives and with Medford's help hides under the table as Sir Peter and his guest arrive. This is only the start of fantastic plotting in which Medford and Lady Alexandra, in a variety of disguises, foil Sir Peter's plans for a quietly amorous evening.

The Patient. Play. Agatha Christie
M5 (26, 35, 45) F4 (20s, 38, middle-age). A consulting room. Fee code E

Mrs Wingfield fell over the balcony but no-one could be sure whether it was an accident, attempted murder or failed suicide. All her relatives are summoned to the nursing home and Mrs Wingfield is now unable to speak but with the aid of Dr Ginsberg's ingenious device the attempted murder is solved.
ISBN 0 573 02198 8

The Patio Window. Play. Norman Stubbs
M2 (25-40, mature) F2 (young, 60s). A sitting-room. Fee code D

Miss Croft, a retired teacher, has an Edwardian house with a wonderful garden. After six months in a nursing home, following a heart attack, she returns home for a visit, fearful that her health will force her to sell her beloved home. An unexpected visitor gives her new hope that the garden will continue to bloom and she may be able to return.
ISBN 0 573 12191 5

People Like Us. Play. Cherry Vooght
F4 (middle-age, elderly). A small garden outside a caravan. Fee code D

Independence and loneliness are the themes of this sensitive and wryly humorous play about three women on a caravan holiday.
ISBN 0 573 13293 3

A Perfect Analysis Given by a Parrot. Comedy. Tennessee Williams
M3 (2 non-speaking) F2 (40s). A tavern. Fee code E

Flora and Bessie are members of the Women's Auxilliary of the Jackson Haggerty Post of the Sons of Mars in Memphis and are in town for the National Convention. Having got separated from 'the boys' they await them in the tavern, where they chat and gossip. Things get tearful but luckily 'the boys' arrive and all ends in jubilation.

Perfect Partners. Play. Alan Richardson
M2 (20s) F2 (40s). An office. Fee code D

Edwina and Jonathan Lovelock are to divorce — hardly the best advertisement for 'Perfect Partners', the dating agency they run together. When a prospective client is revealed as a journalist looking to write a blistering exposé of dating agencies, the couple have a battle on their hands. Sparkily amusing, combining a satirical glimpse of the cynical yet romantic world of dating agencies with a witty, touching personal drama.
ISBN 0 573 12197 4

Permission to Cry. Play. David Campton
F5 or M1 F4 or M2 F3. A bare stage. Fee code D

Julia Gibbon, a junior minister, is thrown into turmoil by the conflict between private and public morality. Her affair with Penelope Wright, a frank and forthright journalist, very much a thorn-in-the-side of the Establishment, forces Julia to confront insecurities and doubts she never knew she had. This is a compassionate play about love and politics in our hypocritical age.
ISBN 0 573 12208 3

A Person of No Consequence. Play. Margaret Wood
F8 (young-middle-age). A drawing-room. Fee code D

Life does not hold out much pleasure for either Elizabeth or Elinor: Elizabeth is in love with a man of whom her overbearing mother does not approve, Elinor is in love with the man Mrs Hartley is determined Elizabeth shall marry. The prospects of both girls are made much brighter through the machinations of the quiet Miss Jane — whose surname is none other than Austen. Period Regency
ISBN 0 573 03369 2

Philip and Rowena. Play. Gillian Plowman
M3 (40, 70) F4 (30-40, 65, 70). Simple settings. Fee code D

Philip and Rowena are terminally ill. Philip seeks a divorce from his bitter wife, Lilian. Rowena longs for the unity of her family. Together they find friendship, romance, consolation and an amazing capacity for fun. In their hospice, they share an imaginary holiday in Florence. An acceptance of death is coupled with an extraordinary devotion to life.
ISBN 0 573 12195 8

A Phoenix Too Frequent. Play. Christopher Fry
M1 (young) F2 (young, any age). An underground tomb. Fee code F

Dynamene is ready to die from grief over the death of her husband and has immured herself, fasting, in his tomb. After a 'brilliant parade of poetry, paradox, wit, humour and intellectual discourse' she is diverted from her death-wish by the handsome soldier, Tegeus, and even offers her husband's body to save Tegeus' life.

Piccalilli Circus. Minidrama. Richard Tydeman
M6 F4. Fee code B

A pickled minidrama of the Big Top, with tightrope walkers, knife throwers, acrobats, lion tamers and clowns all poured into a pot-pourri of post performance perambulations. Running time: 15-20 minutes

Pity About Kitty. Play. Jimmie Chinn
M1 (middle-age) F3 (40s). Simple interior. Fee code D

Humorous, articulate and painfully observant of human nature, this is one of Chinn's most intriguing and sensitive plays. Against the background of a medical tribunal Kitty is carried along by events she hardly comprehends and we see the pattern of her life in flashbacks, using imaginative lighting and heightened dialogue.
ISBN 0 573 12203 2

B

Pizzazz. Play. Hugh Leonard
M2 F3. A reception area. Fee code F. (In a volume)

Whilst waiting to hire out cabin cruisers on the River Shannon, two apparent strangers play an elaborate game, which involves re-enacting a marriage on the rocks, with the other people in the reception area as a supporting cast. But this is a Chinese box of a play and all is not what it seems …
ISBN 0 573 01641 0

Plaster. Play (from *Visiting Hour*). Richard Harris
M1 F1 (middle-age). A hospital ward. Fee code D

Eric, hospitalized following a car accident, is visited with hilarious results by his canny wife! The play was seen as part of the full-length play *Visiting Hour* (see Section A) which was presented at the Duke's Head Theatre, Richmond, Surrey, in 1990.
ISBN 0 573 01925 8

Play for Yesterday or **The Little Hut of Enmity.** Play. James Saunders
M4 (young, middle-age, 80s) F3 (young, middle-age). Mountain hut. Fee code E

A blizzard is raging on a mountainside. Gradually various climbers — bickering Elspeth and Justin, Ilse and Young Kurt, Maisie in love with tough Mike and Old Kurt who has come to die — make their way to the hut. They eventually find themselves through playing the 'Truth' game — the whole play being full of film and theatre clichés.

Play the Game. Play. Bill Tordoff. Music by Paul Woodhouse
11 characters. Extras. A wasteground and TV studio. Fee code D

A starkly realistic play for young people with dark comic overtones which addresses the ever-prevalent social issue of youth unemployment. Entering a competition to win £100,000 Jason and his group find they have been exploited in a callous and elaborate hoax to amuse the richer members of society.
ISBN 0 573 12194 X

Poor Old Simon. Duologue. James Saunders
M1 (middle-age) F1 (middle-age). A living-room. Fee code B

Mother and Father, half of a string quartet, are cross with Daughter (violin) who has refused to sleep with her boyfriend (viola) and thus he has left the quartet. This is the third time this has happened. The parents have tried to encourage their daughter to be part of the permissive society but she is taking a *moral* stand. The problem is solved by the parents inviting the discarded boyfriend round to be *their* friend.

Portrait of a Madonna. Play. Tennessee Williams
M4 (young, middle-age, old) F2 (middle-age). A living-room. Fee code E

Lucretia has been described as a Blanche DuBois with variations. She has been living in a state of utter neglect and disorder with her mind steadily giving way. The play depicts her last moments before being taken away to a mental institution, whilst she chatters on about her extraordinary fantasies.

Post Mortem. Play. Brian Clark
F1. M4 F1 voices only. An office. Fee code E

Helen arrives at the office to find in the post a tape from her boss, L. K. Halpin, saying he will not be in. As one business crisis after another develops Helen is never off the telephone, Halpin himself remaining unreachable. Then we see Halpin on a projected slide, dead in his bed at nine a.m. ...

Present Slaughter. A play for Coarse Actors. Edited by Michael Green

See the entry for *The Third Great Coarse Acting Show*.

The Private Ear. Play. Peter Shaffer
M2 (20s) F1 (20). A bed-sitting room. Fee code F

Bob is a born loser: plain and shy he is no match for Ted whose facile charm impresses 'the birds'. Bob thinks he has found a different kind of girl and invites her to dinner. Ted bustles about, further reducing Bob's store of confidence. Doreen arrives. Her quiet poise is revealed as foolishness and she finds classical music as tedious as Bob's conversation.
ISBN 0 573 02215 1

Private View. Play. Václav Havel. Translated by Vera Blackwell
M2 F1. A living-room. Fee code E

Private View has the same irony and touch of comic absurdity as its two companion pieces in the Vanek trilogy. Invited by his ridiculous friends Michael and Vera, the mild-mannered writer, Vanek, endeavours to enthuse over their newly, pretentiously refurbished flat. But as the couple happily express the perfection of their marriage their tone gradually develops into a personal attack on Vanek.
ISBN 0 573 12212 1

Properly Processed. Play. Lynn Brittney
M2 (any age) F1 (40s), 1 M or F. An office. Fee code D

Carol Benson-Brown (Ms), a high-powered Chief Planning Officer, walks into Simkins's office to elicit help. But this is no ordinary office. Carol is dead, and the office processes applicants for the afterlife. Carol learns that the aim is to cause the maximum amount of discomfort for the individual. Offering a management review, she devises a system which will prolong the whole process.
ISBN 0 573 12201 6

The Proposal. A new version by Alfred Emmett (with acknowledgement to Constance Garnett) of the play by Anton Chekhov
M2 (35, 50) F1(30). A drawing-room. Fee code C

Lomov comes to seek the hand of neighbouring landowner Tchbukov's daughter, Natalya. But he is so nervous he gets sidetracked into a dispute over land. Natalya banishes him, but when she learns the reason he visited she calls him back. The two are soon engaged in battle with a desperate father screaming a toast to the happy couple.
ISBN 0 573 12213 X

Protest. Play. Václav Havel. Translated by Vera Blackwell
M2. A study. Fee code E

Part of the *Vanek Plays* trilogy *Protest* features the writer Vanek who visits a fellow writer, Stanek. During their conversation a debate raises interesting questions about loyalty and integrity under a totalitarian regime with Stanek battling with his conscience and self-interest.

The Public Eye. Play. Peter Shaffer
M2 (35, 40) F1 (22). An office. Fee code F

Charles and Belinda are an ill-assorted couple yet they were once in love. Insanely jealous, Charles engages a private eye, Julian, to follow her round London. Julian can only report that she is attached to someone. When the three meet it transpires that Belinda has fallen for Julian. Deciding to mend a marriage, rather than break it, Julian banishes Belinda to her wanderings but this time to be followed by Charles.
ISBN 0 573 12219 4

Pullman Car *Hiawatha.* Play. Thornton Wilder
M15 F9. Extras. No setting. Fee code D

In this composite picture of travellers in an American Pullman car, conversations and thoughts reveal their past lives and future hopes. Various characters representing the Weather, the Hours, the Planets and a Field bring to life the time and places through which the train is passing. There are even two archangels on the train, disguised as young men in serge suits.
ISBN 0 573 02220 8

The Purification. Play with music. Tennessee Williams
M6 F3. Chorus of M3 F3. A room. Fee code E

A play in verse, to be performed to guitar music. Set in the form of a trial, it tells of the death of a young girl, the love for her of her brother and the tragic act of a Rancher. The characters are Spanish Ranchers and American Indians. Period nineteenth century

The Push. Play. Alec Baron
M3 F2. Interior settings. Fee code D

This warm comedy introduces us to Maggie Greenwood who has spent twenty years as housekeeper to Elijah Watson and who is shocked when she is unexpectedly asked to leave. However, she is unable to claim income support as Elijah has omitted to pay National Insurance for her. He can only think of one way of getting out of trouble: marry Maggie. But Maggie isn't as simple as she first seems!
ISBN 0 573 12205 9

Puss in Slippers. Minidrama. Richard Tydeman
M4 F6. Extras. Fee code B

In this production Puss seems to have got tangled up with the Savoy operas, but when Little Buttercup becomes the Marchioness of Carrabas the time has come for some pretty neat sorting out to be done. Running time: 15-20 minutes
ISBN 0 573 16612 9

Put Some Clothes On, Clarisse! Farce. Adapted by Reggie Oliver from *Mais N'te Promène Donc Pas Toute Nue!* by Georges Feydeau
M4 (40s) F1 (30s). A Parisian apartment. Fee code E

The troubles of Ventroux, parliamentary deputy, begin when his wife Clarisse insists it is so hot that she can only wear a négligé around the apartment. Hochepaix, a former political enemy, visits; Clarisse is stung in a most unfortunate place and pleads with Hochepaix and her husband to suck out the sting for her. When a reporter from *Le Figaro* kindly administers first aid in full view of the President it seems doubtful that poor Ventroux's political career will survive!
ISBN 0 573 12211 3

Quake. Play. Anthony Booth
F5 (30-45). A bare, shabby room. Fee code D

Five wives of men working on a dam in South America are isolated by an earthquake while returning home. Their driver is killed and they find shelter, but their chances of being rescued are uncertain. Under this strain the differences in their characters and inter-relationships are brought into sharp relief. As they head for an unresolved future, two of them have learned mutual respect.
ISBN 0 573 03376 5

A Question of Attribution. Play. Alan Bennett
M5 (20s, 40s-50s) F1. An office, a corridor. Fee code G

This forms the second part of the double bill *Single Spies* (see Section A) which was presented by the Royal National Theatre in 1988, winning the Laurence Olivier award for Comedy of the Year. Anthony Blunt, Surveyor of the Queen's Pictures, tries to solve the riddle of an enigmatic painting and is himself the subject of a more official investigation. Period 1980s
ISBN 0 573 01891 X

The Railwayman's New Clothes. Play. Willis Hall
M3 (young, middle-age) F1 (middle-age). A shop. Fee code D

Mr Lumley, branch manager of a tailor's shop, is giving Hartigan, his assistant, a lesson on how to treat customers. When Henshaw comes in with his domineering wife to cancel an order, Lumley takes over, determined to land a sale. But at the moment of triumph he is defeated by his own over-confidence and overreaches himself.
ISBN 0 573 02335 2

Random Moments in a May Garden. Play. James Saunders
M3 F3. 2 girls. Extra 1M. A garden and sitting-room. Fee code E

This play is set simultaneously in the Victorian era where, in the garden, two little girls pose for their photograph, and in the present-day sitting-room of the house where David and Sophie have just moved in. A surveyor finds a scrap of the photograph and Sophie feels, behind the quietness, as if the other time is still going on. But she ruins the photo of the children, not wanting 'dead strangers in my house'.

Rape of Bunny Stuntz. Play. A. R. Gurney
M1 (40) F2 (young, 35). A table, a chair. Fee code E

An efficient suburban matron, chairing an evening meeting, finds that she has to cope with an offstage intruder. The meeting degenerates into a wild party, and the lady confesses to the lure of a liaison with this representative from the underside of society. The meeting ends by coming to order under a new woman but the implications are that she must also undergo some sort of expiation.

B

The Rats. Play. Agatha Christie
M2 (29, 38) F2 (30s). A flat. Fee code E

Sandra and her lover David arrive for a non-existent party followed by Alec. A Kurdish knife attracts attention and is dropped over the balcony after Sandra and David have handled it. Alex leaves, locking them in the flat with the body of Sandra's husband and they realize that this is Alec's revenge for the death of a man for whom he had a crazed homosexual devotion.
ISBN 0 573 02223 2

Rattling the Railings. Play. Peter Terson
M3 (middle-age, old) F2 (40s). A living-room. Fee code E

Alec and Brenda have looked after Alec's lively but trying dad for fifteen years. Alec's sister Pauline, leaving her flat for a bungalow, is now in a position to take her turn to look after Dad. She has no intention of doing this but after a visit from Dad appears to be having a change of attitude!
ISBN 0 573 12230 X

◆ **The Reading Group.** Play. Fay Weldon
M2 (30, middle-age) F5 (50, middle-age). A front parlour. Fee code E

A witty, astutely observed study of sexual politics in contemporary society which centres on an all-female reading group. Oriole wants to study contemporary authors, while Anne prefers well-known classics. Pondering the relative merits, the women reveal themselves, their personalities echoing the literary heroines. But not everyone is there for literature. Nefarious designs are uncovered and tensions rise to a dramatic climax.
ISBN 0 573 12227 X

The Real Inspector Hound. Play. Tom Stoppard
M5 (young, middle-age) F3 (20s, young, middle-age). A sitting-room with auditorium behind. Fee code H

Moon and Birdboot, two drama critics, arrive to watch the performance of a new detective play, a parody of the conventional stage thriller. However the private lives of the critics become inextricably mixed with those of the play's characters until Moon is shot dead and the real Inspector Hound proves to be ...?
ISBN 0 573 02323 9

Receive This Light. Play. N. J. Warburton
M3 (30s, any age) F1. Interior setting. Fee code D

A modern morality play wherein Michael and Tom, petty thieves, are interrogated by a Man and and a Woman who wish to be rid of a certain man. They send the thieves to spy on him but Michael runs away rather than betray him. Tom informs but later regrets his action. Both are taken out to die on either side of the man.
ISBN 0 573 06254 4

Red Hot Cinders. Minidrama. Richard Tydeman
M5 F3. Extras M and F. Fee code B

The story of Cinderella is condensed into a 'Potted Panto' which, unlike the others, follows more closely, though just as quickly, the original story. Running time: 15-20 minutes
ISBN 0 573 06615 9

◆ **Red Hot in Amsterdam.** Play. Patricia Robinson
M4 F3. 1M or F. A parlour. Fee code D

Running from Amsterdam police, diamond thieves Frank and Mickey find an open window, clamber inside, and discover they are in a brothel! They hide the diamonds and escape, planning to return later. Two working girls, Corrine and Kora, find the diamonds and move them to a vase, but their boss, Madame Celestine, finds them in turn and vows to keep them. Chaos ensues!
ISBN 0 573 12218 0

Red Peppers. Comedy with music. Noël Coward
M4 (young, 30s, middle-age) F2 (30s, middle-age). A theatre dressing-room/front-cloth. Fee code C

The Red Peppers — George and Lily — have a music hall act which is going none too well. They make a bad exit in the first house and have a row with the MD and Manager. Going on for the second house, Lily ends up throwing her hat at the MD because he is playing a number impossibly fast. Period 1936
ISBN 0 573 64242 9

Relics. Play. David Campton
F4 (middle-age). A bedsitting-room. Fee code D

With the best of all possible motives, needless to say, Winifred and Una come to 'sort through' Aunty Dorothy's things after the funeral, and they find that they have been forestalled! The self-righteousness tinged heavily with greed, and the pretensions and pretences that afflict families at such times are perceptively portrayed in this amusing and touching family play.
ISBN 0 573 13302 6

A Resounding Tinkle. Play. N. F. Simpson
M1 (young) F2 (young). A living-room. Fee code E

Bro and Middie Paradock are quite unperturbed by the presence of an elephant in their suburban front garden, but they are annoyed at being sent the wrong *size* of elephant. Uncle Ted arrives causing momentarily raised eyebrows as he has become an elegant 'she'. The Paradocks' talk satirizes suburbia, and amidst its anarchic comedy turns a ribald eye on us all.
ISBN 0 573 02229 1

A Respectable Funeral. Play. Jimmie Chinn
M1 (50s) F3 (50s). A living-room. Fee code E

Three middle-aged sisters are gathered at the house of their dead mother. Surprisingly, Charlie, their brother, who looked after their mother, has failed to turn up. From the sisters' gossip it appears that Mother was no saint. They have plans for Mother's money but then Charlie suddenly arrives with a request that will put paid to all their plans … A sharp and often funny play.
ISBN 0 573 12232 6

The Return. Play. Tony Edwards
M4 (20s, middle-age, old) F2 (20s, middle-age). A living-room. Fee code D

Newlyweds Penny and Tom are entertaining when Harry, a character from Tom's past, arrives to offer Tom a job. But why should Tom be alarmed at the offer and what gives Harry the power to threaten Tom if he refuses? A tense drama building to an unusual twist in the tail.
ISBN 0 573 12224 5

Rialto. Play. Richard Parsons
M1 (45) F1 (elderly). Simple exterior settings. Fee code D

Bruce, a debonair and attractive ex-actor, is employed by elderly dying ladies to help them make the most of their last days. Together he and his latest client, Clemmie, are visiting Venice. Clemmie, rich and widowed, apparently presents the perfect opportunity for a bit of extra cash on the side. However, Clemmie is more than a match for Bruce's financial craftiness.
ISBN 0 573 10001 2

The Rialto Prom. Play. Angela Wye
F5 (20s-30). A street, a cloakroom. Fee code E

Four friends meet at the Rialto Ballroom to go to the Saturday dance. One of them introduces a shy, gauche newcomer to their hardbitten world. They initiate her into the tough, not to say unscrupulous code of conduct of the dance hall, dressing her up to turn her from her usual retiring self into a sex-symbol — they hope. Period 1960s
ISBN 0 573 03358 7

The Right Place. Play. David Campton
M6 F3. Extras. A bare stage. Fee code D

Adam is walking determinedly to the Right Place where everyone is a king. A band of followers join him in his quest but find his pace relentless and drop by the wayside. When Adam arrives at the golden city he finds his followers already there. They stopped long enough to see what was around them — Adam was trying too hard.

Ringing For You. Play. Norman Stubbs
M5-7 (young, middle-age, ageing) F3 (young, middle-age). Various interior settings. Fee code D

Ageing and remembrance of ordinary people are explored with startling originality in this award-winning play. Man, a retired manager, is lying in bed, contemplating his past. His thoughts are lost in dreams depicting people who have steered the course of his life, those he cared about, those who hated him, and those he was forced to betray.
ISBN 0 573 12226 1

Ritual for Dolls. Play. George MacEwan Green
M2 F2. An attic. Fee code D

A golliwog, a toy soldier, a doll and a monkey with a drum lie forgotten in an attic. Each night they enact the story of the brother and sister who owned them long ago — a story that bursts with violence through the straitlacing of Victorian society.
ISBN 0 573 12231 8

The River. Play. Charles Mander
M2 (17, 50s) F1 (18). A sea wall. Fee code D

Bert is one of the last fishermen netting salmon on the Somerset flats. Richard, a dreamer, thinks he wants to join Bert rather than work in a factory. His sister is sent to persuade him to leave the riverbank. '…encapsulates the pollution versus nature, and employment versus the environment, issues in a a neat parable … ' *Guardian*
ISBN 0 573 02509 6

Roman Fever. Play. Hugh Leonard, based on Edith Wharton's story
M1 F2. A terrace. Fee code D. (In a volume)

On a restaurant terrace in Rome, Mrs Slade and Mrs Ansley are reminiscing about a Roman holiday they had together many years before. Mrs Slade, envious of the other's daughter's engagement to a rich marchese cannot resist a spiteful jibe which demolishes a cherished memory. But in the end it is Mrs Slade's illusions that are shattered. Period 1930
ISBN 0 573 01641 0

The Room. Play. Harold Pinter
M4 (young, 40s (black), 50s, elderly) F2 (young, 60). A bedsitting-room. Fee code E

Rose and Bert rent a room that might almost be a paleolithic cave; the outside is terrifying and unknown. Rose never goes out, Bert only goes to drive his van with furious aggression. A young couple call, and then a blind black man. Bert comes home, massive with triumph at smashing every car that challenged his van. Finding the stranger he kicks him to death and Rose goes blind.
ISBN 0 573 02236 4

Same Old Story. One-woman play. Dario Fo and Franca Rame. Adapted by Olwen Wymark
F1. An open stage. Fee code D

See the entry under *Female Parts* in Section A.

Sandcastles on the Beach. Play. John McColl
M2 (middle-age, elderly) F2 (young, elderly). A living-room. Fee code D

A bizarre tale which challenges the everyday concept of grief, making this a unique, yet poignant play. Marge and Butter are awaiting the arrival of their son, Weston, and his new wife. Butter is dying and Marge plans to have him stuffed and mounted in a drinks cabinet from MFI to counteract her foreseen loneliness.
ISBN 0 573 12237 7

Save My Child! or, **Trapped by the Bottle**. Brian J. Burton
M2 (35, middle-age) F2 (12, 30). A wretched attic room. Fee code B

A short melodrama for inclusion in a Music Hall evening. Little scenery is required and detailed production notes are given in the script. Contained with two other melodramas in *Cheers, Tears and Screamers.*

Savoury Meringue. Play. James Saunders
M2 F1. Extra M or F. An empty stage. Fee code D (In a volume)

Hessian, a woman of undisclosed age, addresses the audience. A man, who may be her brother, enters and they begin a semi-Music Hall act. Ferdinand, who stays mute during the play, scuttles to a corner to watch them. Speeches are interrupted by a telephone which may, or may not, be answered. We perceive we may be in some kind of home, looking inside Hessian's mind.

Say Something Happened. Play. Alan Bennett
M1 (60s) F2 (20s, 60s). A hallway and living-room. Fee code F

Eager but green June is despatched by the Council to register elderly people in the area. Mam and Dad are elderly and therefore must be in need of registering — but the able-bodied, street-wise couple have no intention of being registered. Increasingly desperate, June resorts to Mr Farquharson's notes on Conduct of Interviews while no-nonsense Mam sorts her out!
ISBN 0 573 12246 6

School Ties. Play. George Brockhill
M3 (teenage,40s) F3 (young, 40s). Fee code D

There is entertainment and laughter in every line of this fast-paced comedy which explores the influence of the past through characters whose relationships with each other are complex. It begins with Stella and Derek awaiting prospective buyers to view their house. When one turns out to be more than an old school friend of Stella the situation is ripe for development.
ISBN 0 573 12238 5

Sea Side Trippers. Minidrama. Richard Tydeman
M or F16. Fee code B

The action takes place on an organized coach trip to the seaside and is filled with stirring questions as, who pinched the sandwiches? And was George really stuck on the top of the rock? Running time: 15-20 minutes
ISBN 0 573 13305 0

Seagulls. Play. Caryl Churchill
M1 (young) F2 (middle-age). Simple exterior setting. Fee code D

Valery is to let off a firework at a public function—by power of thought. When the firework fails to ignite, Valery is afraid her extraordinary powers are waning. She is comforted by a fan who relates the Chinese parable of the seagulls who come to a man every time he goes to the beach, but on the one occasion he needs a seagull to come to him, none approach.

The Second Easter. Play. Norman Holland
F7 (young, 30s, middle-age). An inn. Fee code D

On the first anniversary of the Crucifixion, Mary, the Mother of Jesus, Mary Magdalen and Salome, return to Jerusalem to renew their faith by visiting the sacred places. At an inn near Calvary they fear for their lives when approached by a Roman woman. But it is Pontius Pilate's wife, now a confirmed Christian, come to ask their forgiveness and blessing for her troubled husband.
ISBN 0 573 06229 3

Secrets. Play. Giles Cole
M2 (30s-50) F2 (30s). A living-room. Fee code F

This disturbing play captures all the suspicion and paranoia that living with lies engenders, and explores the nature and inherent iniquities of marriage, loyalty and love. Hannah has been forced to accept that her husband is quite possibly a traitor and a spy. The action shifts back and forth in time to enact Hannah's encounters with a government agent and her recaptured husband.
ISBN 0 573 12235 0

Señora Carrar's Rifles. Play. Bertolt Brecht. Translated by Wolfgang Sauerlander
M6 F3. Extras. Simple interior. Fee code G

Widow Carrar observes neutrality by refusing to let her sons join the Spanish Republican Army, or to let her brother have the rifles which were concealed by her husband before his death. When the elder son is killed by the rebels, mother and son decide to take the hidden rifles and leave with her brother for the front. (The play is a modern version of J. M. Synge's *Riders to the Sea*.)

A Sense of the Ridiculous. Play. Rae Terence
M2 (60s) F2 (30s, 60s). Fee code D

Mary lives with Mother and Uncle Henry. In Mary's dream, her mother and uncle have murdered twenty-three people and now the Devil arrives to exact retribution. He puts an idea into Mary's head, and when she wakes to her hellish reality, she carries out his suggestion with startling effect. But is she going to hell for her crime, or has she just left it?
ISBN 0 573 12243 1

A Separate Peace. Play. Tom Stoppard
M2 (40s) F4 (young, middle-age). A nursing-home ward and reception office. Fee code E

Mr Brown arrives at an expensive nursing home, apparently in no need of treatment. He takes a room, treats the place like a hotel, spends his time painting a vast mural but all the time remaining courteous. It is only the young nurse Maggie who can make contact with him.
ISBN 0 573 12254 7

September Revisited. Play. Enid Coles
F4. Two benches, denoting a park and a living-room. Fee code D

Unemployed Carlene, her friend Val and the homeless Woman share their mornings in the park. They indulge in mockery of Nanny, another park regular. In Val and Carlene, Nanny recognizes traces of her own past that trouble her conscience. Val and Carlene enact a dramatic flashback to forty years before, in which Nanny dismisses her nursery maid Rosie for 'immoral' behaviour.
ISBN 0 573 13310 7

Sequence of Events. George MacEwan Green
M3 (20s, middle-age) F2 (young, middle-age). Three acting areas. Fee code C

A hangman, a prostitute, a murderer and murderer's stricken parents are the ingredients in this taut drama. In a fascinating chopped time sequence they spin a strange web of sex and death. Period Edwardian
ISBN 0 573 12239 3

Set a Thief To Catch A Thief. Melodrama. Peter Ventham and Michael Kilgarriff
M5 F1. Fee code C

A short melodrama for Music Hall. Contained in *Three More Melodramas*.
IBN 0573 00019 0

B

Sexual Perversity in Chicago. Comedy. David Mamet
M2 (20s) F2 (20s). Various simple settings. Fee code H

The play opens with a duologue between the two men in which they discuss various sexual adventures and then proceeds to further scenes in which their attitudes and those of the women are investigated. The scenes are brief, the settings very simply staged and may be indicated largely through effective lighting changes. Running time is approximately 90 minutes

Shadows of the Evening. Play. Noël Coward
M2 (28, 50s) F2 (45, 50). A private suite in a luxurious hotel. Fee code F

Linda, George's mistress and Anne, his estranged wife decide to settle their animosities for George's sake as he has now only a few months to live. He has to accept that he will go back with Anne, not only because he wants to see his children again but also because he has still continued to love her just as he will continue to love Linda.
ISBN 0 573 02309 3

Shindig. Play. Arthur Aldrich
F5 (30-40). An office. Fee code D

The usual high jinks are promised at the Christmas party at Harrison Hosiery. However events take a downward spiral when Julia appears with a black eye and Barbara, hiding a pregnancy, is discovered in a pool of her own blood. But a helping hand is extended from a most unexpected quarter.
ISBN 0 573 03382 X

Shop for Charity. Comedy. Charles Mander
M1(50s, 79) F4 (middle-age, 60s, 79). A charity shop. Fee code D

Are charity shops really there to help the Developing World or are they just a sop to the consciences of the middle-class people who run them? Easy to stage, thought-provoking and full of 'characters' this is a very amusing play about the nature of charity.
ISBN 0 573 12247 4

Shoppers. Comedy. Jean McConnell
F2 (middle age). A seaside promenade. Fee code B

See the entry for *Deckchairs I*.

◆ **Short Changed**. Short play (From *Deckchairs II*). Jean McConnell
F2 (50, 80s). A garden. Fee code C

Miss Westlake, a retired headmistress, tries to retire peacefully to the prestigious residential home of Merrywinds, but finds that her earlier misdemeanours as a headmistress still haunt her. Julia, a social service official and ex-pupil of Miss Westlake has the ideal opportunity for revenge and justice.
ISBN 0 573 10004 7

Showbusiness. Play (from *Visiting Hour*). Richard Harris
M5 F9, may be played by M2 F4 (1 black). A hospital ward. Fee code D

We follow the satirical vagaries of a TV crew filming a documentary on the world's first quadruple transplant — until they discover they are pipped at the post by a transplant operation in another hospital! The play forms part of *Visiting Hour* (see Section A) which was presented at The Duke's Head Theatre, Richmond, Surrey, in 1990.
ISBN 0 573 01925 8

Silver Wedding. Play. John Bowen
M1 (51) F1 (49). Extras 1M or F (voice only). A kitchen. Fee code D. Typescript on hire

This one-act play is the longer version of the play of the same title which forms part of *Mixed Doubles*. On the evening of their silver wedding Margaret and David have an argument which develops into a frank discussion about their failed marriage, acknowledging they have stayed together because it was easiest. The marriage, as it is, will continue.

Singing in the Wilderness. Play. David Campton
6 characters. A wood. Fee code D

The well-known fairies from *A Midsummer Night's Dream* and *Peter Pan* are under continuous attack from the hazard of waste brought by humans. Unexpectedly they stumble on a copse which promises to be a safe haven and yet it seems all is not well. The fairies soon find themselves faced with the prospect of living their lives in public view. Can they escape before it is too late?
ISBN 0 573 12233 4

Sins of the Father. Play. Leo Smith
M1 F2. A bedroom representing two locations. Fee code D

Kevin, an upwardly mobile family man, is manipulated into an affair by the glamorous Kitty who then manoeuvres the pliable Kevin into confessing the affair to his wife. After an acrimonious scene, she takes the children and leaves. Each of the characters shows their true persona in revealing monologues, with the dark undertones of Kitty's real nature only surfacing at the play's climax.
ISBN 0 573 12253 9

Sister Mary Ignatius Explains It All for You. Play. Christopher Durang
M2 (30s) F3 (30s, 50s). 1 boy (8). A lecture platform. Fee code J

See the entry in Section A.

The Skip. Play. Mary Rensten
F5 (40s, 60s-70s, elderly). A street. Fee code D

Five women gather round a skip on a suburban street. Two of them, antiques dealers scavenging for saleable items, become embroiled in a dispute over a reproduction Victorian chamber-pot and a genuine Regency chair, their opponents being two genteel but quietly determined bag-ladies. Watched over by a tramp, the ladies fight to the (metaphorical) death in this warm and witty comedy.
ISBN 0 573 13304 2

A Sleep of Prisoners. Play. Christopher Fry
M4. Church interior. Fee code F

An anti-war verse drama in the form of a modern Passion play. Four English soldiers are locked up for the night in a church turned into a prison camp. Privates King and Able fight and are separated by the other two. All four dream of the row, interpreting it in different Biblical ways.

B

A Slight Accident. Play. James Saunders
M1 F2 plus offstage voices. A drawing-room. Fee code D

After shooting her husband Harry, Penelope invites Camilla and Rodger up to her drawing-room where there is some conventional thriller-type suspense — will they find the body? Just as we learn that Harry was much the same kind of man as Rodger, we see Rodger destroying himself in the same way that Harry did — by putting the revolver in his wife's hands, confident that she won't shoot.

A Slight Ache. Play. Harold Pinter
M2 (middle-age) F1 (middle-age). Composite setting. Fee code E

Flora and Edward invite the matchseller into their home. The matchseller is silent; faced with this silence, Edward destroys himself while Flora gains strength, until finally Flora turns Edward out with the tray of matches. The midsummer's day which began with Edward having a 'slight ache' ends in his total disintegration.
ISBN 0 573 02249 6

A Small Affair. Comedy. Bob Larbey
M5 F12. A rehearsal room. Fee code G

The television drama department is short of performing space. Director Guy's drama is shunted into a small room and he is beset with problems. The cast come to loggerheads but after a 'calming' break return to find their space double-booked by would-be contestants on an idiotic panel show. When the Head of Drama drops into the rehearsal the drama turns into a farce ...
ISBN 0 573 12135 4

A Smell of Burning. Comedy of Menace. David Campton
M2 F1. A living-room. Fee code D

See the entry under *The Lunatic View* in Section A.

Smile. Play. David Campton
F5 (20s, 50s, 70s). A garden. Fee code D

In thirty years Grandmamma has not allowed any man to enter her house, forcing seclusion on Mamma and her twin girls. A young man comes into their lives and Grandmamma is made to face her repressed feelings of guilt and both twins are thwarted in their plan to elope with the young man. Mamma finally asserts herself, offering the twins new freedom and some sound advice. Period late nineteenth century.
ISBN 0 573 13306 9

Snow White Special. Minidrama. Richard Tydeman
M10. Extras 2F. Fee code B
A faulty magic mirror and an inept and hard-of-hearing Wizard's Assistant land the laundry maid — Snow White — in a lot of trouble and she is driven to take refuge in the house of seven of the largest dwarfs you've ever seen. Running time: 15-20 minutes
ISBN 0 573 16608 0

Sold to the Gypsies, or, **The Wicked Stepmother**. Melodrama. Brian J. Burton
M2 F7. A poor cottage. Fee code B

A mini melodrama for inclusion in a Music Hall Evening, with the emphasis on comedy with a difference. Contained in *Foiled Again!*

The Soldier and the Woman. Play. Elaine Morgan
M3 (26, 30s) F1 (24). A stable. Fee code E

Herod sends his soldiers to slaughter the innocents and Rachel's son is slain. Finding an officer in the stable she determines to kill him. Then a soldier enters. Revolted by his orders, he had mutinously attacked the officer. His rough, kindly wisdom overcomes Rachel's hysteria. Wearily she leans against the manger and suddenly all bitterness is drained from her, and in its place is charity. Period Biblical
ISBN 0 573 06234 X

Soldiering On. Monologue from *Talking Heads*. Alan Bennett
F1 (50s). A room. Fee code F

Muriel's husband Ralph has just died, leaving her rather well off — until, that is, her son Giles gets his hands on the money and Muriel comes out the loser. Eventually, neglected by Giles and no longer needed by her disturbed daughter Margaret — whose state may well have been caused by Ralph himself — Muriel ends the play alone and poor.
ISBN 0 573 133115

Something Unspoken. Play. Tennessee Williams
F2 (40s, 60). A living-room. Fee code E

Between two spinsters, one, Cornelia, a grand, imperious, wealthy Daughter of the Revolution, and the other, Grace, her pale, fragile little secretary, there is a mysterious tension. As the play opens on a crucial afternoon, Cornelia upbraids Grace for having to impersonate her on the telephone — because she was asleep. Grace compares herself bitterly to a 'cobweb' but refuses to discuss what must 'remain unspoken'.

The Sound of Silence (*Le Bel Indifférent*). Play. Jean Cocteau. Translated by Anthony Wood
M1 F1 (middle-age). An hotel room. Fee code F

A modern, accessible translation of this monologue which combines black humour and tragedy. The woman awaits the return of her lover, a notorious gigolo. As the hours tick by she becomes increasingly frustrated. When Emile finally arrives he calmly ignores her outburst, preparing to leave again as the woman rushes to the window.
ISBN 0 573 12266 0

Sour Grapes and Ashes. Play. N. J. Warburton
M2 (30s, 40s) F3 (teenage, 30s). A hillside. Fee code D

Bernard is fulfilling his dead father's wishes to scatter his ashes over his favourite fell. After a trail of misunderstandings and clashes in the family's relationships Bernard realizes the part his father has played and some sort of understanding is reached; Father, of course, has the last word.
ISBN 0 573 12244 X

B

The Space Between the Years. Farce. John Scholes
M2 (young, 40s) F2. A reception area in an hotel. Fee code D

A visitor from Jupiter has mistakenly been sent to what he expects to be the Elizabethan era. Dressed in full Tudor regalia he arrives at the *Ye Olde Spotted Cow*. At first Doris and Mellissanda are puzzled but Doris soon realizes that with his apparently inexhaustible supply of gold Elizabethan coins he is worth cultivating and what follows is a succession of hilarious events.
ISBN 0 573 12251 2

Spacewoman. Minidrama. Richard Tydeman
F17 or F4. Fee code B

Have you ever noticed how all the sci-fi stories concerning outer space never seem to figure ordinary, down-to-earth (if you'll pardon the expression) women? Well, here's an all-women, inter-planetary minidrama to redress the balance. Running time: 15-20 minutes
ISBN 0 573 13312 3

Sparrows. Comedy. Charles Mander
M2 (50s) F2 (young, ageing) A seaside esplanade. Fee code D

Harold Makepiece gets involved with Joyce whose main preoccupation is feeding sparrows. He then meets up with the freakish Edward and seaweed-eating Sandra. It turns out that they all are planning to bomb a large power station nearby because of the pollution it causes. They try to rope in Harold as an accessory, until events are taken out of all of their hands in a totally unexpected way.
ISBN 0 573 12258 X

Speeches and Cream. Minidrama. Richard Tydeman
F10. Extras. Fee code B

Speech day at St Nancy's School for Girls gets off to an inauspicious start when the secretary muddles the owner of some dog kennels with the headmistress of another school and invites the former to come and give a speech at the annual prizegiving. Running time: 15-20 minutes
ISBN 0 573 13309 0

Split Ends. Comedy. Frank Vickery
M2 F2 (young, middle-age). A living-room. Fee code D

A very funny comedy, written with Frank Vickery's usual panache and style. Nancy and Cyril are to meet their son's girlfriend, Susan. Cyril, naturally bald, goes into hiding when his wig disappears, and reappears in disguise. But there are further problems when Susan loses a contact lens in the salad — Cyril is soon on his way to hospital wearing a dead kitten on his head!
ISBN 0 573 12264 4

Spring Song Singers. Minidrama. Richard Tydeman
M or F7-15. Fee code B

A rehearsal for a concert just prior to the performance turns out to be, to the consternation of many, a rehearsal twenty-four hours in advance. Running time: 15-20 minutes
ISBN 0 573 12234 2

Stalag 69. A play for Coarse Actors. Edited by Michael Green

See the entry for *The Third Great Coarse Acting Show*.

B

The Stanley Parkers. Play. Geraldine Aron
M2 (middle-age). A bedroom. Fee code E

Written in a clear and unpretentious blank verse, this play tells the story of Stanley and Dimitri, two middle-aged men who have lived together and loved each other for seventeen years. They speak directly to the audience, sharing their story with insight, humour and very obvious affection. The story ends sadly but our overriding impression is of the tenderness and warmth of a happy, unselfish relationship.
ISBN 0 573 04230 6

Still Life. Play. Noël Coward
M6 (30s) F5 (young, 30, middle-age). A station refreshment room. Fee code E

Laura, a married woman, starts a love affair with Alec Harvey. For several months they try to enjoy their love while they can but find they can't go on. Alec takes an appointment in South Africa and leaves with only a handshake. Period 1936
ISBN 0 573 02255 0

Stop the Nightmare. Play. George MacEwan Green
M2 (middle-age) F2 (30s (oriental), middle-age). Temple forecourt. Fee code D

Maxwell and Joanne are American tourists visiting a far-eastern country. There Maxwell relives a horrifying scene from his army days and he considers the futility of war. They then meet an innocent napalm victim. The play is a wryly humorous examination of the way prejudice and ignorance protect us from the truth about ourselves.
ISBN 0 573 12241 5

The Strangest Kind of Romance. Play. Tennessee Williams
M3 (35) F1 (40s). A room. Fee code E

The Little Man moves into lodgings where he finds an alley-cat which had been rescued from the street by a previous tenant. The lonely lodger finds warmth and comfort in this equally lonely animal. However on losing his job, he is forced to leave. Later he returns to ask for the cat. It is still alive but the result is not as he expected.

Streuth. A play for Coarse Actors. Michael Green

See the entry for *Four Plays for Coarse Actors*.

Stuttgart. Play. Graham Swannell
M1 F1. A bedroom. Fee code D

See the entry for *A State of Affairs* in Section A.

Suddenly Last Summer. Play. Tennessee Williams
M2 (young) F5 (young, middle-age). A patio and garden. Fee code H

Mrs Venables, in order to protect her dead son's reputation, wants Catherine, who witnessed the death, to be lobotomized. The doctor administers a truth serum and Catherine pours out the whole appalling story of the young man's homosexuality and corruption, of his being pursued by starving, naked young people and of the finding of his mutilated and partly eaten body.

The Summoning of Everyman. Morality play. Herbert W. Payne
M9 F7. Two platforms dominated by a cross. Fee code C

A modern version of Medieval Morality. That all is vanity, that we can take nothing but our characters with us when we die, is the theme of *Everyman* and it is not for one age but for all time. Perhaps it is not too presumptous to hope that performances in present-day speech and costume will serve as an introduction to the glories of the original.
ISBN 0 573 06237 4

Sunbeams. Play. Rosemary Mason
M1 (middle-age) F2 (20s, 30s). A bedroom. Fee code D

Frances, a social worker, calls on the downstairs flat to find she is interrupting the end of a caller's session with a prostitute, Louise. Later she and Louise have a lengthy discussion where each states and develops her views on Louise's trade. Frances leaves her own job to 'help' Louise. It seems that trying to apply her own kind of philosophy might not always have the best results.

Sweet Caroline Sweet. Play. Tony Edwards
M1 or 2 (middle-age) F2 or 3 (young, middle-age). Two flats. Fee code D

Middle-aged Percy writes to a Lonely Hearts column and Caroline Sweet turns up on his doorstep. But Percy realizes he has been the easy victim of a con trick and there is only one way he knows of expressing his hurt … There are one or two unexpected twists in the plot of this fast paced and easily staged play.
ISBN 0 573 12260 1

♦ **Take Your Medicine Like a Man**. Farce. Georges Feydeau, translated by Peter Meyer from *On Purge Bébé*
M3 (30s, any age) F3 (30s, any age), 1 boy. A study. Fee code E

Follavoine, attempting to impress his guests with his unbreakable chamber pots, contends with his wife, Julie, who is panicking because their son, Toto, has constipation and won't take his medicine. Julie insults the guests, Follavoine is challenged to two duels and Toto cunningly avoids taking his laxative. Period 1910

Talk to Me Like the Rain and Let Me Listen. Play. Tennessee Williams
M1 (young) F1 (young). Child's voice. A room. Fee code E

It is a Sunday morning, for the Man a 'morning after' a drunken debauch. After he describes what he went through the Woman tells him she wants to leave him, and in a long reverie describes her vision of a perfect peace by the sea. He begs her to come back to bed with him and, as the curtain falls, she responds.

The Tea Dance. Play. Margaret Bower
F7 (middle-age). An hotel sitting-room. Fee code D

In the summer of 1936, Jean, Barbara and Olive hope for some excitement as they holiday in South Devon. It is Barbara who first spots the mysterious woman who wants to remain incognito, and Jean who overhears 'Mrs Chisholm' plotting a murder. Easy to stage and costume, this delightful play has a twist or two up its sleeve and a neat ending.
ISBN 0 573 13322 0

Teddy Bear's Picnic. Play. Paul King
M1, 3 others. 1 voice. A bedroom of a small boy. Fee code D

Two robots, Tran and LCD find themselves in a small boy's bedroom. They find Teddy behind the chest of drawers and interrogate him about his exact role. The robots decide to forcibly take control. It is only the fast thinking of Action Man that saves the day. A seemingly simple play but with more than a hint of a warning in it.
ISBN 0 573 12267 9

Temptation Sordid or Virtue Rewarded. Melodrama. Winifred Phelps
M2 (25, 50s) F3 (18, 30, 50). Two interiors, One exterior. Fee code C

Sir Jasper, of the black heart, is out to win Lady Lucre's fortune via the hand of the lovely Arabella; and Clarence, of the pure heart, is out to thwart him and also win Arabella. Through valleys of iniquity they all travel, the journey being enlivened by the wiles of the voluptuous Fanny, who of course aids and abets Sir Jasper. Virtue is triumphant at the last and Clarence and Arabella are united. Period Victorian
ISBN 0 573 02265 8

Terrace Talk. Play. George MacEwan Green
F6 (young, middle-age). A terrace. Fee code D

The fictitious pleasantries that two maid-servants imagine are passed in the usual course of tea on the terrace are not at all what goes on — once the servants have been dismissed. In an off-hand manner that shocks her hostess, Caroline announces she is terminally ill. Her subsequent revelations only serve to draw the two women closer together. Period Edwardian
ISBN 0 573 13316 6

♦ **Theatrical Digs**. Short play (From *Deckchairs II*). Jean McConnell
F2 (elderly). A seafront. Fee code C

Pascaline Holbein, a glamorous and conceited actress, who is playing in the end of pier show, meets her challenge in the elderly and eccentric Maggie Festoon. When Pascaline discovers that Maggie Festoon is also an actress, the result is a comical and farcical battle of work, agents and mobile phones.
ISBN 0 573 10004 7

Then. Comedy of Menace. David Campton
M1 F1. Fee code D

See the entry under *The Lunatic View* in Section A.

B

♦ **There's None So Blind.** Play. Gillian Plowman
M4 (20s, 40s) F3 (30, 30/40, 40). A treatment room and reception area. Fee code D

A letter to Geoffrey, a reflexologist who is blind, informs him that his wife is having an affair with a work colleague. His trip to the leisure centre where Alice works changes both their lives as he confronts the other man. Geoffrey's friend Anton also has an illuminating experience at the leisure centre where he meets Amaryllis, his longed-for ideal woman.
ISBN 0 573 12270 9

Thermal Underwear. Black comedy. Andrew Davies
M3 (30s, 60) F3 (30s, 60s). A living-room. Fee code E

Family and relations arrive to celebrate Mr and Mrs Hubb's ruby wedding anniversary. As the celebrations progress the tangled web of their lives is skilfully revealed and the day becomes memorable for all the wrong reasons. This acerbic comedy is both amusing and touching in its shrewd characterization.
ISBN 0 573 12273 3

Think the Beautiful Thoughts. Play. Rae Shirley
F5 (middle-age, elderly). A living-room. Fee code D

Having packed her mother, Mrs Morgan, off to a neighbour's house, Bessie and two friends await the arrival of Madame Maria, fortune-teller *par excellence*. Visited by royalty, consulted by princes and doing house-calls at fifty pence a time, Madame Maria is a rather surprising apparition. However, Mrs Morgan's sudden reappearance is not as disconcerting as Bessie had expected!
ISBN 0 573 13321 2

THE THIRD GREAT COARSE ACTING SHOW

Michael Green
ISBN 0 573 00030 1

M9 F5. Extras. Various interior and exterior settings

The number of characters given above would be sufficient to cover the presentation of all four plays by the same cast. Ages can vary from young to the practically senile. Fee codes: A Fish in Her Kettle: C; Present Slaughter: B; The Vagabond Prince: B and B (for music); Stalag 69: C; Julius and Cleopatra: C.

In this third volume of Coarse Plays, Michael Green defines a Coarse Acting Show as a 'closely observed imitation of stage disaster', and these five plays cover a range of disasters appalling enough to turn any show into a Coarse one. They are, also, of course, extremely entertaining. In **A Fish In Her Kettle**, it is the simple lack of a door handle which causes the disaster, as most of the cast find themselves trapped on stage when the door jams. The second play, **Present Slaughter**, collapses because of one unlucky slip by the leading man, who cuts his wrist when he collides with a tableful of glasses. **The Vagabond Prince** is an all-purpose Coarse Musical, with a roistering chorus of gypsies and earthy tavern men and women. The fourth play, **Stalag 69**, is, according to the director, 'a seminal investigation into the relationship between man and war', a noble concept somewhat marred by the fact that the set is upside down for the first run-through, and collapses completely during the second, revealing the stage staff enthusiastically producing a startling range of live sound effects. The final play, **Julius and Cleopatra**, a Roman spectacular, illustrates two of the Laws of Coarse Acting — one, that every person in a Coarse crowd is hideously deformed or crippled for some reason, and two, that when stabbed, all pain is always felt in the bowels, no matter where the wound is!

'This Desirable Cottage … ' Farce. Anthony Booth
M4 (24, middle-age) F3 (20s, 30). A cottage living-room. Fee code C

Three honeymooning couples accidentally arrive at the same holiday cottage at the same time and all are waving their agreements at each other. Woody, the shy fisherman, arrives and takes charge. Then along comes Fred with a demolition order. Five of the occupants escape leaving Woody to his fate.
ISBN 0 573 02271 2

This Property is Condemned. Play. Tennessee Williams
M1 F1 (13). A railroad embankment. Fee code E

Willie tells Tom, in what is virtually a monologue, the story of her upbringing in a house that took in railroad men. She speaks with pride of his sister Alva, now dead. All the clothes Willie now wears she inherited from Alva. As she leaves he hears her singing 'You're the only star in my blue Heaven'.

Thor, with Angels. Play. Christopher Fry
M9 F3. A Jutish farmstead. Fee code F

At the time of St Augustine's mission to Britain, a young Christian soldier, Hoel, is captured by the Jutes. He is threatened with death, and later crucified, but others are converted through these events to Christianity, forsaking the Norse gods such as Thor. As the play ends the voices of Augustine's men are heard singing in the distance. Period AD 596

Three More Sleepless Nights. Play. Caryl Churchill
M2 F2. A double bed. Fee code E

Three couples are viewed in bed in three successive scenes. The first, Margaret and Frank, have been married for ten years and row constantly. The second, Pete and Dawn, have muted exchanges as she drifts to eventual suicide while he recounts the plot of *Alien*. The third scene shows Pete and Margaret together, starting out happy but gradually falling into the same patterns of non-communication they experienced before.

A Time of Wolves and Tigers. Play. Hugh Leonard
M1 (40s). M1 or F1 voice only. Fee code D

See the entry for *Suburb of Babylon* in Section A

Tippers. Play. Gillian Plowman
M3 (20s-40s) F2 (20s, 30s). A rubbish tip. Fee code D

In this grim world of poverty there is little room for finer feelings. The tippers mistrust one another and each sex blames the other for the mess they are all in. The only escape from unendurable reality is football. Maybe with the birth of Annette's baby, trust and affection will be born amongst them ...
ISBN 0 573 12262 8

Too Hot to Handle. Play. Jim Hawkins
M1 F2 (30s). Split setting: a kitchen, a lounge, a bedroom. Fee code D

Suzanne, neat, houseproud, and conventional, is astonished and horrified when she finds a collection of hard porn photos and magazines in her bank manager husband Peter's wardrobe. The shock leads to a vital discussion and examination of their whole attitude towards each other. It seems that a more satisfying, understanding and realistic future of intimacy may await them both.

B

Too Long an Autumn. Play. Jimmie Chinn
M3 (middle-age, elderly) F4 (middle-age, elderly). Various simple interior settings. Fee code E

Long Autumn is a retirement home for theatricals. Maisie May, a former music-hall star, arrives and initially copes with the rigours of Long Autumn in her ever-cheerful, irrepressible style. She becomes increasingly depressed, however, until a breezy impresario arrives with big plans for Maisie ...
ISBN 0 573 12274 1

Top Table. Satirical comedy. Margaret Wood
M8 or F8 or mixed cast. Extras. A conference room. Fee code D

The delegates from many governments arrive in an atmosphere of suspect bonhomie. The two cleaners, backed by the troops and ordinary people, take over and announce a slight amendment to international law: in future a formal declaration of any war shall be by the public execution of all members of governments concerned.
ISBN 0 573 12275 X

◆ **The Train**. Play. Carl Slotboom. Translated by Dr Louis I. Leviticus
M2 (young, elderly) F2 (young, elderly). 1 male voice, 1 voice. 2 train compartments. Fee code D

Two elderly Jewish people, David and Clara, sit in a 1990s train whilst their younger selves are seen in a converted cattle wagon in the 1940s. The modern train has halted unexpectedly and the enforced wait sends David's thoughts back to that earlier train, also stationary, and the war memories it evokes ... Period 1995 and 1943
ISBN 0 573 12332 2

The Tram-Track Tragedy. A riotous routine for Music Hall. Edited by Michael Kilgarriff
M3 F3. Music Hall Chairman. Fee code D

A twenty-five minute sketch in the best melodrama fashion, without music, but with the provision of a tram! Contained in *Music Hall Miscellany*.
ISBN 0 573 00013 1

The Trial. Play. Anthony Booth
F5 (20s-50). A cellar. Fee code C

A frightened young girl is tried by three women. One is a captain in an armed resistance organization, another is a witness and the third is the informer in the 'trial'. The girl is acquitted of betrayal but led away to be punished for fraternization. The proceedings have, however, uncovered the guilt of another woman present — the informer herself.
ISBN 0 573 13324 7

The Trial of Joan of Arc at Rouen, 1431. Play. Bertolt Brecht. Translated by Ralph Manheim and Wolfgang Sauerlander
M25 F9. Extras, children. Interior and exterior settings. Fee code G

Brecht's play is an adaptation of a radio play by Anna Seghers based on the original records of the trial of Joan of Arc. The play emphasizes the destruction of Joan as a common interest to both the occupying power and the collaborationist clergy, and the clash of interests between them.

The Trial of Lucullus. Radio play. Bertolt Brecht
Translations: Frank Jones
             H. R. Hays
Fee code G

The great Roman General Lucullus is judged in the underworld by representatives of the living future. The figures from his triumphal frieze are called as witnesses to his victories but only his introduction of the cherry tree into Europe speaks for him. Thus his bloody hands are not entirely empty, but 80,000 dead is a high price to pay. Set in classical Rome.

A Trouble Shared, or, **Two to the Rescue**. Melodrama. Brian J. Burton
M2 F2 Simple exterior setting. Fee code B

A mini melodrama for inclusion in a Music Hall Evening, with the emphasis on comedy. Contained in *Foiled Again!*

♦ **Tryst**. Play. Colin Crowther
M1(40-60) F2 (40-60), or M2 F1. Various simple settings. Fee code E

Tom, suffering from heart disease and aware that he does not have long to live, commissions Jan, an artist, to paint a picture that Tom can leave to his wife Brenda. From this simple premise Colin Crowther has created a many-layered, thoughtful play exploring illness, grief and the difficulties of caring for the dying, threaded with a lucid discussion of the redemptive power of art.
ISBN 0 573 12211 X

Tunnel Vision. Play. Sheila Hodgson
M2 (20s, 50s) F3 (teenage, 20s, late 40s). An Underground station. Fee code D

A family await a late-night train in a London Underground station, deserted but for Liz, a teenage runaway. Strange and unsettling things happen, footsteps echo, shadows alive with malice appear, and Liz has designs of her own ... Soon, a connection between the present ghostly phenomena and poignant past events becomes obvious. A tense, dramatic play, ideal for festival work.
ISBN 0 573 12269 5

The Twelve-Pound Look. Play. J. M. Barrie
M2 (50s) F2 (30s, 40s). A study. Fee code D

Sir Harry Sims hires a typist, who turns out to be his former wife, Kate. She was so oppressed by his pretensions that she secretly learnt to type and left him when she had earned £12, the price of a typewriter. Later the second Lady Sims makes a bold request — the price of a typewriter! Period 1910
ISBN 0 573 02281 X

Twenty-Five Not Out. Play. Hazel Wyld
M2 (20s, middle-age) F3 (20s, middle-age). A bedroom. Fee code D

Diane and Harold Blott give a party for their silver wedding. Harold becomes sulkier and sulkier, and Diane finally realizes that the cause of Harold's behaviour is the presence at the party of his current lover. Diane faces a dilemma: either to wound Harold's ego, or carry on with her 'pretending-not-to-know' farce.
ISBN 0 573 12278 4

B

27 Wagons Full of Cotton. Comedy. Tennessee Williams
M2 (middle-age, 1 Latin) F1 (middle-age). A cottage porch. Fee code E

Jake, owner of a Mississippi cotton gin, burns down the mill of a competitor. Silva Vicarro, the man whose gin he destroyed and who is suspicious of the circumstances surrounding the fire, seduces and rapes Jake's wife. Finally, however, they all tacitly accept the position in the name of good neighbourliness.

◆ **Two Fat Men**. Light-hearted drama. Gillian Plowman
M3 F5. A room. Fee code D

Duncan and George feel far from comfortable attending a Weight Busters meeting, surrounded as they are by women. Waiting for the meeting to start, they meet an old flame of George's — who bore him a child many years earlier — and Duncan strikes up an affecting romance with a sign language teacher. Line dancing and snatches of Gilbert and Sullivan enhance the jolly mood of this touching comedy-drama.
ISBN 0 573 12313 6

Two Summers. Play. Gillian Plowman
M4 (30s, 70s) F2 (30s, 70s). Two sitting-rooms. Fee code D

Stifled by army life, the Colonel's Wife falls in love with the Sergeant sent to play the piano at her dinner parties. Towards the end of the play we realize that the Old Man and Old Woman on stage are the Sergeant and the Colonel's Wife forty years on: she had sacrificed her lifestyle to marry the Sergeant. Period 1932 and 1972
ISBN 0 573 12285 7

Umjana Land. Play. Gillian Plowman
M3 (20s, 40s) F4 (20s-40s, any age). A living-room/study. Fee code D

Leah discovers her author husband Gordon is having an affair with Ursula. Meanwhile, Gordon remembers Umjana Land, the childhood dream world he inhabited with his sister Agnes, and determines to write. When Agnes appears, having written a Booker Prize-nominated book about Umjana Land, Gordon is left strangely alone as his daughter, Leah, Ursula and Agnes find a common bond.
ISBN 0 573 12140 0

Under the Twelfth Sign. Play. Enid Coles
M1 (middle-age) F4 (50s). A sitting-room. Fee code D

Mary has many visitors, and whenever she leaves the room they 'freeze' into whichever action they are performing. Mary's mother has passed on to her the extraordinary ability to imagine something and persuade others it was true. However, at the end of the play we find it is not Mary, but her sister Marjorie who has this ability.
ISBN 0 573 12276 8

Unhand Me, Squire! Minidrama. Richard Tydeman
M4 F8. Fee code B

Or 'Much Ado About Sweet Fanny Adams'. The usual melodramatic plot of the villain versus hero and heroine suffers a reversal when the hero proves to be less than heroic and the villain gets the girl! Running time: 15-20 minutes
ISBN 0 573 13327 1

The Upstairs Cuckoo. Farce. Peter Horsler
M2 F2. A kitchen/dining-room. Fee code D

A witty, fast-moving, acutely observed, riotous farce with a human heart. Having separated from her husband Steve, Claire now lives with boyfriend Derek. Her daughter, Libby, tells Steve that Claire is advertising for a lodger, so, while Claire is absent, unsuspecting Derek lets the room to Steve. Old animosities quickly appear and finally Claire and Libby move out, leaving Derek and Steve to share as bachelors.
ISBN 0 573 12283 0

Urban Cycles. Play. Michael Snelgrove
M6 (30s-60s) F5 (30s-60s). A shopping piazza. Fee code D

Robin is organizing a sponsored exercise-bicycle ride. The assorted participants are gathered in the early hours, ostensibly to support each other, but feelings get out of hand. Robin argues with Wolf, slaps down Derek and blackmails Gerard into taking his turn. The event falls apart after the security guard's dog attacks the do-gooders!
ISBN 0 573 12279 2

Us and Them. Play. David Campton
Any number of characters. A bare stage. Fee code D

This play was written to be performed by a company of almost any size, of any age and of either sex. Two parties enter, A and B, from East and West. Each party plans to settle down, then sees each other. Instant suspicion. A dividing wall is built. After mutual spying war ensues and the wall is broken down.
ISBN 0 573 02346 8

Vacant Possession. Play. Don West
M2 (middle-age) F2 (young, middle-age). A kitchen. Fee code D

Alice and Ben have been paid compensation to leave their flat — the last sitting tenants blocking the sale of the property. They leave, but immediately move back. Warren endeavours to oust them, but it appears they cannot leave because of the cellar. Warren goes to investigate and becomes one more reason why they cannot leave.
ISBN 0 573 12280 6

The Vagabond Prince. A play for Coarse Actors. Edited by Michael Green

See the entry for *The Third Great Coarse Acting Show*.

Victoria Station. Play (from the triple bill *Other Places*). Harold Pinter
M2. A car, an office. Fee code D

The Controller of a radio-cab firm is trying to contact Driver 274 and get him to pick up a fare at Victoria Station. The Driver doesn't know where he is and professes not to know where Victoria Station is. 'Brilliantly funny' *Daily Telegraph*
ISBN 0 573 04225 X

The Victory of the Cross. Passion play. M. Creagh-Henry
M3 F4. A room. Fee code A

Set in the room in the house in which the Last Supper took place, this play relates the events surrounding the Easter passion. The story begins with news of the arrest of Jesus on Holy Thursday, and continues through to the final scene on Easter morning. Period Biblical
ISBN 0 573 06250 1

A View from the Obelisk. Hugh Leonard
M2 F1. A hilltop. Fee code D. (In a volume)

Owen insists on showing Rosemary the view from a hilltop near Dublin. He is exhausted after the climb and Rosemary goes off to summon a car. While she is gone a boy appears, and Owen strikes up a casual conversation with him. The boy goes, and it is only when Rosemary returns that Owen realizes why the boy seemed so familiar ...
ISBN 0 573 01641 0

Vigil. Play. Emlyn Williams
M3. The hall of a manor house. Fee code D

Issaiah, a slow-witted boy, waits for the morning when the Master's bell will summon him. A newcomer, Atherton, keeps an appointment with Richman, the Permanent Guest. It seems that no one can leave the Manor once lured there. Atherton and Richman plot to kill the Master but cannot do the deed. But Issaiah has been slowly poisoning the Master. The other two escape, leaving Issaiah in an empty house...

Vin Extraordinaire. Play. Stella Ross
M4 (young, middle-age, elderly) F3 (young, middle-age). A study. Fee code D

When an apparent miracle occurs in the village and a fountain statue of Jesus starts pouring wine instead of water, it appears that both villagers and monastery will benefit. However, the village becomes a show-place of greed, strife and commercialism. As the Cardinal points out, God moves in a mysterious way, and is quite capable of rectifying his own mistakes.
ISBN 0 573 12290 3

A Visit from Miss Prothero. Play. Alan Bennett
M1 (60s) F1 (middle-age). A living-room. Fee code E

Mr Dodsworth has recently retired. Sitting at home he is contemplating his life and achievements with quiet satisfaction when there is a sharp ring at the door: his former secretary has come to ruin it all.
ISBN 0 573 12286 5

The Visitor. Thriller. Maureen Lee
F4 (30s, middle-age). A lounge. Fee code D

Ex-secretary and ex-mistress of a wealthy businessman who committed suicide, the unpleasant Laura complains to her neighbour that she would have inherited much more than her cottage if a certain will had not disappeared. The arrival of a strange woman with threats of blackmail results in Laura being deprived of her cottage — and more as she receives her full deserts.
ISBN 0 573 03372 2

B

The Wages of Sin. Melodrama. Andrew Sachs. Edited by Michael Kilgarriff
M3 F1. Fee code A

The seduction of two husbands by a beautiful and unscrupulous adventuress leads to a stage as body-strewn as the last act of *Hamlet*. For inclusion in a Music Hall evening. Contained in *Three Melodramas*
ISBN 0 573 00018 2

Waiting. Play (from *Visiting Hour*). Richard Harris
M1 (elderly) F1 (black). A hospital ward. Fee code D

A moving depiction of lonely old age which was seen as part of the full-length play *Visiting Hour* (see Section A) in 1990 at the Duke's Head Theatre, Richmond, Surrey. An old man sits in hospital awaiting visitors that never come and falls back on distant memories of his boyhood and the ups and downs of his married life.
ISBN 0 573 01925 8

Waiting for a Bus. Play. Peter Barnes
M2 F1. A bedroom. Fee code D. (In a volume)

A pair of lovers are interrupted in bed by the arrival of the husband — or are they actors rehearsing a new comedy *Waiting for a Bus* about a pair of lovers disturbed by the husband's arrival ...? May be presented as part of the full-length entertainment *Corpsing*. For details, please see the entry in Section A.
ISBN 0 573 10006 3

Waiting for Alec. Play. Frank Eccles
M1 (40s) F8 (young, 30s-50s, 80), or M2 F7. Simple interior settings. Fee code D

A perceptive study of two patients in a mental home. Mrs Wainright, well on her way to recovery relapses when visited by her insensitive husband and sister, while Ethel, a long-term inmate, awaits her son Alec who appears in her dreams but who is long dead. Well-written and imaginatively set, this provides a challenge for any drama group.
ISBN 0 573 12297 0

The Waiting Room. Play. John Bowen
M3 (20s) F2 (30s). A waiting room, a corridor. Fee code E

Harriet is shown into a waiting room. Paul is also shown in. They fall into conversation, and appear to already know one another. Though hatred is the natural emotion between them, the strange reason for their meeting forms a bond, and as they leave together after their purpose here is accomplished, she offers him her hand.
ISBN 0 573 02327 1

Waking Up. One-woman play. Dario Fo and Franca Rame. Adapted by Olwen Wymark
F1. An open stage. Fee code D

See the entry under *Female Parts* in Section A.

B

The Walking Dead! Thriller. Michael Lambe
M2 (30s) F3 (30s, elderly). A cottage room. Fee code D

Geoffrey and Joanna look forward to a quiet weekend in a remote cottage, but a chain of eerie events turns the holiday into a nightmare! Mark, a walking corpse, is claiming his yearly share of love, but the object of his desire is now no longer his shabby sister ... Will Geoffrey succeed in protecting Joanna against Mark's other-worldly lures?
ISBN 0 573 12295 4

The Wall. Play. David Henry Wilson
M2 (20s, elderly) F1 (20s). A wall. Fee code B

Chalked on a huge wall are the words: 'The Wall'. John-John and Doll pass by and try their best to replace the two words with more pregnant ones ranging from 'Shakespeare' to 'Sex'. An old man hobbles on stage: he is lonely and in need of help, but the big words on the wall stress the inexorability of his loneliness.
ISBN 0 573 62364 3

Way Out West. Minidrama. Richard Tydeman
M6 F4. Extras M and F. Fee code B

When a Bad Man (Jake) marries a squaw and tells her his name is Joe (a Good Man) all manner of misunderstandings occur. Particularly when Running Water and Big Jake come looking for the errant bridegroom. Running time: 15-20 minutes
ISBN 0 573 12288 1

Ways and Means. Comedy. Noël Coward
M5 (young, 30s) F4 (young, middle-age). A bedroom. Fee code E

Toby and Stella find themselves as guests in a house on the Riviera with no money and an outstayed welcome. A burglar breaks in and Stella offers to direct him to a rich guest's stash if he will go halves. He agrees, obtains and hands over the loot, then leaves them bound and gagged to allay suspicion. Period 1936
ISBN 0 573 02291 7

Wendlebury Day. Play. David Henry Wilson
M1. A bare stage. Fee code C

A monologue by Tom Wendlebury, a middle-aged man, who presents five different accounts of his life stressing that companionship is the only key to survival.
ISBN 0 573 62364 3

What Are You Doing Here? Play. David Campton
M5 F5. Extras 1M or 1F. A bare stage. Fee code D

A large jeering crowd appears on stage. A Narrator tries to analyse why ordinary people can suddenly be turned into an ugly mob. He describes a series of everyday events that upset people who in turn upset someone else. He asks who upset the first man in the chain. It was the Narrator himself.
ISBN 0 573 12296 2

What Brutes Men Are. Comedy. Constance Cox
F4 (20s-60s). An hotel lounge. Fee code D

Janet and Carol converse casually in an hotel lounge. Carol has left her husband, Godfrey, and tells Janet how he was always comparing her with his first wife. Janet realizes Godfrey is her own ex-husband and says *she* was always being compared with Godfrey's mother. When Godfrey's mother arrives, it transpires that Godfrey has had this unfortunate habit of comparison all his life!
ISBN 0 573 13337 9

What Ho Within! Minidrama. Richard Tydeman
F4. Extras M and F. Fee code B

A damsel in distress, a worthy son of the soil, a knight named Sir Loin of Beef in a suit of rusty armour and a dragon who's nothing more than a Baroness, combine in this romp through Merrie England. Running time: 15-20 minutes
ISBN 0 573 12292 X

What Shall We Do With The Body? Comedy. Rae Shirley
M1 F2. A cottage sitting-room. Fee code E

Pauline Temple, an author of popular detective fiction, is dictating to her secretary, Miss Worthington. Miss Temple hears spine-chilling feminine screams which Miss Worthington doesn't hear. Then an oddly-dressed man turns up with a bizarre tale of an escaped lunatic from a nearby asylum. There is indeed a homicidal maniac loose — but which of the three is it?

What the Dinosaur. Minidrama. Richard Tydeman
M3 F3. Extras M and F. Fee code B

In a stone-age studio, outside of which a dinosaur has eaten three parking meters, two traffic wardens and a partridge in a pear tree, a compère narrates an everyday story of domestic bliss — neolithic style. Running time: 15-20 minutes

What's for Pudding? Comedy. David Tristram
M3 (middle-age) F2 (middle-age). A living-room. Fee code D

Mary and Jack's dull Saturday evening is interrupted by the arrival of Maureen, Ted and Dennis. The occasion rapidly dissolves into a drunken gathering as Ted's intellect is likened to that of a paper clip, Maureen, his wife, reveals a liking for Jack, and Jack rapidly cultivates a taste for pouring whisky over his head.
ISBN 0 573 12305 5

Whence. Play. Leo Smith
M1 (young) F1 (middle-age). Underground. Fee code D

A play set in the distant future but very much for our time. Driven underground by the greenhouse effect of CFCs on the earth's atmosphere, a 'baby factory' earth-mother and a genetically engineered survivor eke out an existence in a wary partnership. At the end we realize all hope is not lost as a baby cries in the darkness.
ISBN 0 573 12300 4

B

The White Liars. Play. Peter Shaffer
M2 (young) F1 (47). A fortune-teller's parlour. Fee code E

Two pop singers, Frank and Tom, visit Sophie, a fortune-teller, for consultation. Frank says Tom is trying to lure away his girl; Tom says Frank's attitude rests on lies. Tom leaves Frank and reveals to Sophie the secret of his true relationship with his friend. Sophie herself reveals that her supposed high connections are lies. Lies surround the seedy trio.
ISBN 0 573 12302 0

Who Calls? Play. David Campton
F6 (30-60). A kitchen. Fee code D

Four servants sit solemnly in the kitchen of a large Victorian house. Their Mistress has died suddenly and the cook, discovering that the housekeeper and personal maid have stolen some of her jewellery, demands a share. Reluctantly they agree. Then the bell rings in the Mistress's room ... everyone is in the kitchen, so who calls?
Period late-nineteenth century
ISBN 0 573 03345 X

Who Was Hilary Maconochie? Play. James Saunders
F3 (middle-age, elderly). A drawing-room. Fee code E

This play, written in the Absurdist style, opens on Mrs Brute who has seen an 'In Memoriam' notice in *The Times*, supposedly from herself, mourning the death of Hilary Maconochie, an unknown name. The maid supplies information on the household in asides to the audience and when Mrs Drudge, a friend, arrives to play strip cribbage, the ladies discuss various possibilities surrounding 'Hilary Maconochie'.

Who Will Man The Lifeboat? A riotous routine for Music Hall. Devised by Michael Kilgarriff
M3 F3. Music Hall Chairman. fee code A

A six minute sketch, set on a beach, with music. Contained in *Music Hall Miscellany*.
ISBN 0 573 00013 1

Who's Bean Stalking? Minidrama. Richard Tydeman
M7 F4. Extras (M and F). Fee code B

Jack is living in affluence with his mum until Fetchit and Keepit, the broker's men, appear on the scene. But with the aid of Scarlet Runner the Beanstalk fairy, he defeats the Giant and escapes with restored wealth back down the Beanstalk. Running time: 15-20 minutes
ISBN 0 573 06620 5

Whose Wedding is it Anyway? Play. Margaret Bower
F5. A living-room. Fee code D

Middle-aged Myra and Mavis return home for their mother's second marriage to a young waiter Ricardo, insisting on a low-key register office ceremony. But Mother is having none of this and makes her own arrangements helped by the charlady and they both have the last laugh.
ISBN 0 573 03389 7

The Winter of 1917. Play. David Campton
6 characters. A room. Fee code D

Seemingly lost without a compass, the six members of the group stumble across a large country house. Taking refuge, they find one room with a roaring fire. Truepenny explores, finding desolation and decay, but upon returning to the room encounters another era and takes on the persona of one of the characters. Clegg, too, feels the emotions of that winter of 1917.
ISBN 0 573 12299 7

Woman Alone. One-woman play. Dario Fo and Franca Rame. Adapted by Olwen Wymark
F1. An open stage. Fee code D

See the entry for *Female Parts* in Section A.

A Woman of No Importance. Monologue from *Talking Heads*. Alan Bennett
F1 (middle-age). A hospital room. Fee code F

At work Peggy has carved herself a comfortable niche. Once in hospital, she loses no time in establishing herself as Queen Bee, taking on several responsibilities. Persistently cheerful, blind to the feelings of others and, at heart, terribly lonely, Peggy is at once a richly comic and desperately moving creation, providing a rewarding challenge for a mature actress.
ISBN 0573 03390 0

Womberang. Comedy. Sue Townsend
M1 (30s) F6 (young, middle-age, elderly, with doubling and trebling). A hospital outpatients' waiting-room. Fee code F

It is the afternoon gynaecology clinic and an assortment of patients sit in a grim hospital room. Rita Onions breezes in. Her verve and energy, combined with a complete lack of respect for authority, gradually spreads an infectious, joyous anarchy throughout the patients as she demolishes officious hospital staff and generally sorts out the patients' personal problems.

World Première. Comedy. Charles Mander
M3 (middle-age, ageing) F4 (young, middle-age). A village hall. Fee code D

A fast-paced comedy about an amateur dramatic society gathering for the technical rehearsal of a play by their producer Gordon. Minus the set, director and stage crew, new-recruit Val frantically tries to improvise. Matters become increasingly frenetic with the arrival of Gordon's dypsomaniac wife Ruth, and an assortment of people totally unconnected with the drama group!
ISBN 0 573 12284 9

Yes and No. Comedy. Graham Greene
M2 (young, middle-age). A bare stage. Fee code D

The Director calls the Actor for an early rehearsal of a Pinter-type play. The Director pours forth advice in a stream of admonitions, instructions and statements about this great opportunity for the Actor. The Actor replies either 'Yes' or 'No' throughout, causing some misunderstanding when the words turn out to be from the play script.

Young Guy Seeks Part-Time Work. Play. John Bowen
M3 (16, middle-age) F1 (39). A kitchen, an hotel room. Fee code E. Typescript on hire

While Philip and Joan's teenage son Steve is out, they receive phone calls from 'clients'. Philip discovers that Steve is advertising personal massage. Steve returns, answers the phone and goes out. Upon Philip and Joan's interrogation, Steve quits the personal massage business — it isn't worth the hassle with your parents when you get home!

Zartan. Play. N. J. Warburton
M6 (20s, middle-age, elderly) F3 (20s, elderly), doubling possible. Extras. Various simple settings.
Fee code D

Lord Greycoat lost his son when the boy's carrycot dropped from a plane over the African jungle. An expedition is mounted to find the adult Zartan, who suffers from a split personality and doubts about his extraordinary size in comparison to his ant 'parents'. Through Greycoat's secretary, Jane, Zartan discovers his true identity — and love.
ISBN 0 573 12304 7

The Zoo Story. Play. Edward Albee
M2 (middle-age). Central Park. Fee code E

To escape his wife, two daughters and two parakeets Peter sits on a bench in Central Park, reading and thinking. Jerry joins him, having just been to the zoo. He draws the unwilling Peter into conversation and extracts information from him. In return Jerry supplies Peter with a curious medley of information about his wanderings in New York. The outcome of the meeting is a willing death for one of them.
ISBN 0 573 04222 5

Revue Sketches

B

B

Beyond the Fringe. Alan Bennett, Peter Cook, Jonathan Miller and Dudley Moore
Fee code for each sketch code A

A madhouse of hilarity in both London and New York. Their skits include one about an impassioned preacher whose emotion carries him so far from the text that he can't find his way back. There's a delicious spoof on Shakespeare in beautifully faked speech and a couple of panel scenes. A lucky dip of highly intellectual fun.

Steppes in the Right Direction. M4
Royal Box. M2
Man Bites God. M3
Fruits of Experience. M1
Bollard. M4
The Heat Death of the Universe. M1
Deutscher Chansons. M2
The Sadder and Wiser Beaver. M2
Words ... and Things. M3
T.V.P.M. M1
And the Same to You. M1
Aftermyth of War. M4
Civil War. M4
Real Class. M4
Little Miss Britten. M2
The Suspense is Killing Me. M4
Porn Shopping. M1
Studio 5. M4
Sitting on the Bench. M1
Bread Alone. M4
Take a Pew. M1
So That's the Way You Like It. M4
The End of the World. M4
Home Thoughts from Abroad. M4
The English Way of Death. M1
The Well Song. M1
The Great Train Robbery. M2
One Leg Too Few. M2
Portraits from Memory. M2
Death of Lord Nelson. M1
Interviews (Studio 5). M4
The Minor. M1

INTIMACY AT 8.30

David Climie, Peter Myers and Alec Grahame. Music by John Pritchett, Ronald Cass and Norman Danatt

Fee code A for each sketch. ISBN 0 573 07012 1

Knit Yourself a Lost Weekend. M2 F2
It's not the drink that intoxicates but the determined jollity of one's fellows, so, substitute a wool shop for the pub and what have you? Strong men going down like ninepins under the influence of a couple of sweaters and a pair of socks.

Coach and Five.* M2 F3
Mum, Dad, their offspring and Auntie decided to give Morecambe a miss and join a Poly Holiday Tour. They had great fun 'doing' Europe although they were stranded in France and Auntie had to sell her souvenirs to get them all home again.

Fit to be Tied.* M1 F1
A Spiv falls in love with the girl on a hand-painted tie and remains faithful to her even when she is chipped beyond recognition.

Siren Song.* F1
Frustrated in her ambition to be a *femme fatale* a young woman becomes an announcer on a railway station and the result is that a simple call like 'Have your seasons ready' brings male passengers to their knees.

Sustained Objection.* M1 F1
A learned judge complains that all the juiciest cases go to his brothers while he is fobbed off with the disputed Rights of Way — but when a certain lady QC disturbs his reverie he thinks of the juicy case that's coming in which he will be playing the lead.

Earliest Edition.* M1 F2
Three Babies review the modern trend to offer children junior editions of newspapers and they see no reason why the vogue should not spread to all papers and periodicals and possibly culminate in *The Daughter of Amber* or *The Son of Miss Blandish.*

Business in Great Waters.* M3
Three old sea dogs turned literary sailors pay tribute to the Cruel, Cruel Sea which has helped them to draw such splendid dividends from their publishers.

Soft Shoe Shuffle.* M1 F1
A Man and a Woman indulge in a little Edwardian nostalgia for the gay old Swanee tunes which have been ousted by be-bop.

We Come up from Mummerset. M3 F3
The Starchers, that homely farming family who have delighted millions in their serial, are in reality played by a set of very strange theatrical types. Mum drips with furs and diamonds, Hilary, who plays the old farmhand, is sick at the thought of his dialogue and young Phil is played by an octogenarian who collapses before he can reach the mike.

Peter Patter.* M1 F1
When a young lady thinks she has met a friend from her past nothing will stop her tongue except perhaps a visiting card — and even then she can't understand how a stranger could sit there listening to her amorous reminiscences without saying a word.

Music is available separately for this sketch

LISTEN TO THIS

Sketches and monologues by Michael Frayn
Fee code A for each sketch. ISBN 0 573 69179 7

A collection of seventeen monologues, dialogues and parodies, one written for *The Secret Policeman's Ball*, some culled from his *Observer* column and some written for Eleanor Bron's TV series, *Beyond a Joke*. This volume is a delight to read and offers a wonderful repertoire of comic performance pieces.

B

> **An Occasion of This Nature.** Monologue
> **At the Sign of the Rupture Belt**. M2 F2
> **Blots.** Monologue
> **Confession**. Monologue
> **Glycerine**. M1 F1
> **Head to Head**. Monologue
> **Heaven.** M1 F1
> **Listen to This**. M1 F1
> **A Little Peace and Quiet**. M1 F1
> **The Messenger's Assistant**. M2 F1
> **Never Mind the Weather**. Monologue
> **A Pleasure Shared**. Monologue
> **The Property Speculators**. M2 F1
> **Sons and Customers**. M2 F1
> **Through the Wilderness**. M3 F1
> **Value for Money**. Monologue
> **Who Do You Think You Are?** M1 F1

LIVING FOR PLEASURE

Arthur Macrae. Music by Richard Addinsell
Fee code A for each sketch. ISBN 0 573 07013 X

Jollijaunts. F2
Mavis Davis and her friend Doreen wrestle with the problems of a travel agency — soon, who knows, they may be selling trips to the moon and, when everyone is going there, they may be able to get into *My Fair Lady*.

Under Your Hat. M1 F3
The latest fashion in hats is all very well, especially, if you are one of the social set, but when the hat covers the face like an extinguisher it can lead to some embarrassing mistakes of identity.

No Ball. F2
The modern Cinderella is not at all keen to avail herself of her godmother's offers to send her to the ball; she is more enthusiastic when an escort is to be arranged until she learns that the subject of this spell is to be the cat — he has already been arranged.

Getting Away With It. M2 F3
With their play in full swing the actors are finding it difficult to progress with the story because of frequent interruptions from the censor — there is only one way to get round that problem — play it *à la* Shakespeare.

Low Finance. M1 F2
Mrs Meadows has been having trouble with her nerves, as she explains on her last visit to Mr Slater, the grocer, before leaving the district. Unfortunately Mr Slater is bothered in the same way and before the shopping is complete they are both in a state of collapse.

Friends. F3
Hilda and Mabel are enjoying a cup of coffee and a character-shredding session — the subject is Daphne, a mutual friend. Just when Daphne is characterless she appears and is welcomed with smiles.

B

Shepherding Sheep.* M1 F2
Hyde Park isn't what it used to be: at one time they imported a flock of sheep complete with a shepherd to add colour in the spring. As he sits amidst the Scottish mists, the Shepherd laments the loss of the happy life he led in and around Hyde Park.

Neuroses in Bloom.* F1
The Lady in the Powder Room of a Paris hotel is nostalgic for her life in other European capitals; what with constant crises and expensive vices Paris is not for her.

Leave It on the Tray.* M2 F2
What has become of the newsvendors now that one helps oneself and drops the money in a tray? — they are living in luxury at the Ritz on the proceeds of public honesty.

Love You Good, Love You Right.* M1 F1
The Boy and the Girl are so much in love that, whatever the circumstances, their verdict on each other is that they can each have 'the lot'.

No Better than She Should Be.* M1 F1
The Lady who just can't get attention, not even from the waiter, feels her past hasn't been worth it. Considering she's no better than she should be she should have done much better than she has.

The Horse's Aspirations.* M2
Herbert is in a fix; he is the front portion of a very successful horse but, alas Charlie, the rear, has classical aspirations. Fortunately Charlie realizes that one does not reach Stratford via the back legs of a horse and the situation is saved.

The Pretty Miss Brown.* M2 F2. Chorus
The pretty Miss Brown gets all the bouquets but the other Miss Brown knows what a man can live with and gets a husband.

Music is available separately for this sketch

ONE TO ANOTHER

John Mortimer, N. F. Simpson and Harold Pinter
Fee code A for each sketch. ISBN 0 573 07021 0

Triangle. M2 F1
The Waitress studies her two regulars — one timid and uncertain, the other forceful and decisive. They both have powers to charm and as she serves them she dreams of life in their respective homes — the only snag is they are quite unaware of her aspirations.

Gladly Otherwise. M2 F1
Into the lethargy of the Brandywine household comes the Man, a high-powered salesman. Within minutes he has them tied in knots, but when he removes his personality they sink back into domestic gloom.

The Black and White. F2
Two old women, down-and-outs from London's Embankment and back streets, regale themselves with bread and soup in the early hours of the morning.

Trouble in the Works. M2
Fibbs interviews Wills from the works and tries to plumb the mental depths of his engineering workers. After cutting his way through a jungle of technical jargon he discovers what they really want to make is brandyballs.

Cleaning Up Justice. M1 F1
The court usher and the charwoman deplore the shocking goings-on of their betters who are brought to court — how differently and how happily they themselves have lived since they committed bigamy.

Collector's Piece. M6 F4
When young Albert caught a Goat Moth in his father's garden it changed his life — in future he would study Nature. Unfortunately his life passes and death comes too quickly, for, at the end, all he has discovered is the Goat Moth.

Conference. M3
The Tycoon interviews Jones, but he is such a popular fellow and so tied up with his telephones that a frustrated Jones retreats to a call box and winds up their meeting by phone to his own if not to the Tycoon's satisfaction.

Can You Hear Me? M2
Crob and Hud are staying in a reputable hotel but find the amenities leave much to be desired. When Crob feels the urge to have a speaking tube it is some time before it is supplied and then he finds it difficult to control.

Three Sketches from

A SLIGHT ACHE AND OTHER PLAYS

Harold Pinter
Fee code A for each sketch

B

Request Stop. M3 F4
At a request stop the woman complains loudly about the insulting reply the little man gave her when she asked him if she could get a bus to Shepherd's Bush. Left alone at the stop with another man she asks him if she can get a bus from here to Marble Arch.

Last to Go. M2
At a coffee stall an old newspaper seller and the barman discuss the fact that tonight the *Evening News* was the last to go, although another night one of the others might be last.

Applicant. M1 F1
Lamb is given a rigorous interview by Miss Piffs, who finally announces 'We'll let you know'.

SECTION C
Plays for Children and Young People

CONTENTS

Classified Index

Longer Plays

Plays which have an approximate running time of more than one hour

Non-Musical Plays

Adventures of Bear Called Paddington
Alice's Adventures in Wonderland (Pearn)
Alice in Wonderland (S. S. B)
Alien Stole My Skateboard
Angel of the Prisons
Babe, the Sheep-Pig
BFG
Big Noise at Fort-Issimo
Bug-Eyed Loonery
Callisto Five
Card Play
Champion of Paribanou
Children's Crusade
Christmas Carol (Way)
Christmas Crackers
Crowns, the King and the Long Lost Smile
Curse of the Egyptian Mummy
Dandelion Time
Discovery and Survival
Do We Ever See Grace?
Evil Eye of Gondôr
Gargling With Jelly. The Play!
Good King Wenceslas and the Chancellor
   of Bohemia
Grinling Gibbons and the Plague of
   London
Hans, the Witch and the Gobbin
Horse and His Boy
Hundred and One Dalmatians
Idiot King
Incredible Vanishing!!!!
Invisible Friends
Jump for Your Life
Jungle Book
Khalid the Dreamer
Kidnapped at Christmas
Land of Kerfuffle
Lion, the Witch and the Wardrobe
Little Victories
Lords of Creation
Magical Voyage of Ulysses

Magician's Nephew
Monster That Ate 3B
More Adventures of Noddy
More Grimm Tales
Mr A's Amazing Maze Plays
Mr Macaroni and the Exploding Pizza Pie
My Very Own Story
Noddy
Old King Cole
Oliver Twist (Way)
Only a Game
Perkin and the Pastrycook
Peter Pan
Phantom Tollbooth
Pinocchio
Play of the Royal Astrologers
Puss in Boots
Railway Children
Rainbow's Ending
Right Christmas Caper
Scatterbrained Scarecrow of Oz
Sleeping Beauty (Way)
Snatching of Horrible Harold
Snow Queen
Speak the Speech I Pray You
Stags and Hens
Storytellers
Struggle
Tale of the Red Dragon
Telling Wilde Tales
13 Clocks
This Is Where We Came In
Three Musketeers
Thwarting of Baron Bolligrew
Treasure Island (Way)
Two Weeks with the Queen
Utter Garbage
Voyage of the Dawn Treader
Whale
Wind in the Willows (Morley)
Winnie-the-Pooh
Witches
Wizard of Oz
Zigger Zagger

Musical Plays

Adventures of a Bear Called Paddington
Aesop's Fables
Alan and the King's Daughters
Alice in Wonderland and Through the
  Looking Glass
Babe, the Sheep-Pig
Bad Day at Black Frog Creek
Beowulf
Big Al
Burston Drum
Call of the Piper
Christopher Columbus
Curious Quest for the Sandman's Sand
Dazzle
Dinosaurs and All That Rubbish
Down-Going of Orpheus Hawkins
Dracula Spectacula
Dream Date
Dreams of Anne Frank
First Time
Flibberty and the Penguin
Frankenstein Monster Show
Gingerbread Man
Giraffe and the Pelly and Me
Golden Masque of Agamemnon
Grimm Tales
Helen Come Home
Hiawatha
Hijack Over Hygenia
I Was a Teenage Jekyll and Hyde
Ideal Gnome Expedition
Jennings Abounding!
Jenny and the Lucky Bags
Joshua's Egg
Little Princess
Make-believe
Meg and Mog Show
Mothers and Daughters
Nightingale and the Emperor
Nutcracker Sweet
Old Father Time
Old Man of Lochnagar
Our Day Out
Owl and the Pussycat Went to See…
Papertown Paperchase

Peter and the Wolf
Peter Pan (Chater-Robinson)
Pied Piper
Plotters of Cabbage Patch Corner
Quest for the Whooperdink
Robin Hood
Rockafella
Rockasocka
Rupert and the Green Dragon
Sammy's Magic Garden
Save the Human
See Saw Tree
Selfish Shellfish
Seven
Seven Golden Dragons
Shake, Ripple and Roll
Share and Share Alike
Siege
Snow White and the Seven Dwarfs
Some Canterbury Tales
Space Junk
Summer in the Park
Surgical Sensation at St Sennapod's
Sweeney Todd Shock 'n' Roll Show
There Was an Old Woman
Think of the Magic
Tinder Box
Toad of Toad Hall
Tom Kitten and His Friends
Treasure Island (Hall)
Ulysses
United We Stand
Voyage of the Jumblies
Water Babies
Where the Rainbow Ends
Wind in the Willows (Bennett)
Wind in the Willows (Hall)
Wizard of Wobbling Rock
Worzel Gummidge

Shorter Plays

Plays which have an approximate running time of less than one hour

Non-Musical Plays

Adventure Faces
Alice in Wonderland (Marvin)
All the World's a Stage
Arabian Nights
Balloon Faces
Bell
Birthday of the Infanta
Boy with a Transistor Radio
Came a Dealer in Dreams
Captain Blackboot and the
  Wallamagrumba
Captain Blackboot's Island
Cinderella (Marvin)
Clown
Crossroads
Crowning Glory
Dawn on our Darkness
Decision
Do It Yourself
Do-Gooders
Domby-Dom
Dreamjobs
Emperor's New Clothes
Ernie's Incredible Illucinations
Firebird
Ghost Writer
Hat
Horatians and the Curiatians
I Read the News Today
In Need of Care
Island
Jack, the Giant and the Jiggery Plot
Key
Ladder
Lantern
Legend of Scarface and Bluewater
Littlest Tailor
Magical Faces
Mirrorman
Mr Easter Bunny
Mr Grump and the Clown
On Trial
Opposites Machine
Our Day Out (shorter version)
Pantomime Play
Papa Panov's Magic Christmas
Percival the Performing Pig

Pied Piper (Marvin)
Pinocchio (Marvin)
Primula the Non-Sheep Dog and the
  Great Grey Wolf
Rabbit
Rainbow Box
Real Spirit of Christmas
Red Dragon
Round the World with Class 6
School Play
Sleeping Beauty (Marvin)
Stone Soup
Teddy Bear's Picnic
Terraces
True Story of Good King Wenceslas
Ugly Duckling
Valley of Echoes
Wheel
You, Me and Mrs Jones

Musical Plays

Dragon for Dinner
Play the Game
River Witch
Tickle

C

Authors' Index

Entries in italics refer to novels by well-known authors which have been dramatized either under their own name or under another title which is given in parenthesis

C

Aesop
Fables (see Aesop's Fables)

Andersen, Hans Christian
Nightingale and the Emperor
Snow Queen
Tinder Box

Ayckbourn, Alan
Callisto 5
Champion of Paribanou
Ernie's Incredible Illucinations
Invisible Friends
Mr A's Amazing Maze Plays
My Very Own Story
This Is Where We Came In

Baker, Edna
True Story of Good King Wenceslas

Barrie, J. M.
Peter Pan

Barton, Tony and Richards, Peter
Khalid the Dreamer, or, The Magic Almond

Baum, Frank L.
Wizard of Oz

Bennett, Alan
Wind in the Willows (adapt.)

Berwick, Liz
Call of the Piper

Bishop, Brian L.
Bug-Eyed Loonery

Blythe, Richard
Jack, the Giant and the Jiggery Plot

Blyton, Enid
Noddy stories

Bogdanov, Michael
Hiawatha

Bolt, Robert
Thwarting of Baron Bolligrew

Bond, Michael
Paddington Bear stories

Bradley, Alfred
Adventures of a Bear Called Paddington
   (adapt.)
Nightingale and the Emperor (adapt.)

Scatterbrained Scarecrow of Oz
Tale of the Red Dragon
Wizard of Oz (adapt.)

Brecht, Bertolt
Horatians and Curiatians

Browning, Robert
Pied Piper

Buckeridge, Anthony
Jennings Abounding!

Burnett, Frances Hodgson
Little Princess

Campbell, Ken
Old King Cole

Collodi, Carlo
Pinocchio

Carroll, Lewis
Alice's Adventures in Wonderland
Through the Looking Glass and What Alice
   Found There

Chater-Robinson, Piers
Peter Pan (adapt.)

Chaucer, Geoffrey
Canterbury Tales (see Some Canterbury Tales)

Clarke, David
Down-Going of Orpheus Hawkins
River Witch

Coffey, Denise
Incredible Vanishing !!!!

Conville, David and Gooderson, David
Curse of the Egyptian Mummy (adapt.)

Crocker, John and Hampton, Tim
Frankenstein Monster Show

Cullen, Alan
Hans, the Witch and Gobbin

Dahl, Roald
BFG
Giraffe and the Pelly and Me
Witches

Dane, Clemence
Alice's Adventures in Wonderland and
   Through the Looking Glass (adapt.)

Dickens, Charles
Christmas Carol
Oliver Twist

Dowsett, Kevin
Dream Date

Dryden, Ellen and Taylor, Don
Burston Drum
Summer in the Park

Duffy, Carol Ann
Grimm Tales (adapt.)
More Grimm Tales (adapt.)

Dumas, Alexandre
Three Musketeers

Ellison, Les
Space Junk
Utter Garbage

Farrow, G. E.
Wallypug of Why (see Land of Kerfuffle)

Foreman, Michael
Dinosaurs and All That Rubbish

Foster, Kirk and Gardiner, John
First Time

Foxton, David
Card Play
Crowns, the King and the Long Lost Smile
Perkin and the Pastrycook
Rabbit

Gardiner, John
Big Al
Dazzle
Dracula Spectacula
Rockasocka

Gardiner, John and Coleman, Fiz
Bad Day at Black Frog Creek
Mr Macaroni and the Exploding Pizza Pie
Snatching of Horrible Harold
Surgical Sensations at St Sennapod's, or Dr
   Scalpel's Missing Bit

Gavin, Bill
Land of Kerfuffle (adapt.)

Gleitzman, Morris
Two Weeks with the Queen

Goss, Bernard
Big Noise at Fort-Issimo

Grahame, Kenneth
Wind in the Willows
(see also Toad of Toad Hall)

Greig, Noël
Do We Ever See Grace?
Rainbow's Ending

Grimm, Brothers
Tales (see Grimm Tales, More Grimm Tales)

Hall, Willis
Christmas Crackers
Kidnapped at Christmas
Play of the Royal Astrologers
Right Christmas Caper
Treasure Island (adapt.)
Water Babies (adapt.)
Wind in the Willows (adapt.)

Hartoch, John
Jungle Book (adapt.)

Harter, J.
Seven

Holliday, Graham
Primula the Non-Sheepdog and the Great Grey
   Wolf

Holman, David
Whale

Horitz, Tony
Good King Wenceslas and the Chancellor of
   Bohemia
You, Me and Mrs Jones

Howarth, Donald
School Play

H.R.H. The Prince of Wales
Old Man of Lochnagar

Hutchins, Pat
Curse of the Egyptian Mummy

Ireland, Vicky
Giraffe and the Pelly and Me (adapt.)

Jackson, Douglas
Pantomime Play

Jones, Graham
Do-Gooders
Dreamjobs

C

Juster, Norton
Phantom Tolbooth

King, Paul
Teddy Bear's Picnic

King-Smith, Dick
(see Babe, the Sheep-Pig)

Kingsley, Charles
Water Babies

Kipling, Rudyard
Jungle Book stories

Kops, Bernard
Dreams of Anne Frank

Lewis, C. S.
Horse and his Boy
Lion, the Witch and the Wardrobe
Magician's Nephew
Voyage of the Dawn Treader

Lewton, Randall
Alien Stole My Skateboard
I Was a Teenage Jekyll and Hyde
Monster That Ate 3B
Seven Golden Dragons
(see also Miller, Peter)

Lowe, Frank
13 Clocks (adapt.)

Macalpine, Joan
Christopher Columbus

Magee, Wes
Real Spirit of Christmas

Marvin, Blanche
Alice in Wonderland (adapt.)
Arabian Nights (Sinbad the Sailor)
Birthday of the Infanta
Cinderella
Crowning Glory
Emperor's New Clothes
Firebird
Legend of Scarface and Bluewater
Littlest Tailor
Mr Easter Bunny
Peter and the Wolf (adapt.)
Pied Piper (adapt.)
Pinocchio (adapt.)
Red Dragon
Sleeping Beauty

Miller, Peter and Lewton, Randall
Sweeney Todd Shock 'n' Roll Show

Mills, Clifford and Ramsay, John
Where the Rainbow Ends

Milne, A. A.
Make-believe
Toad of Toad Hall
Ugly Duckling
Winnie-the-Pooh

Mitchell, Adrian
Pied Piper (adapt.)
Siege
Tom Kitten and His Friends (adapt.)

Morley, John
Wind in the Willows (adapt.)

Morris, Mary
Two Weeks with the Queen (adapt.)

Morrow, Geoff
Share and Share Alike

Murdoch, Helen
Alan and the King's Daughters
Dragon for Dinner
Jenny and the Lucky Bags

Nanus, Susan
Phantom Tolbooth (adapt.)

Nesbit, E.
Railway Children

Nicol, Ron
Snow Queen (adapt.)

Nicoll, Helen and Pienkowski, Jan
Meg and Mog books

Owen, Brian
Evil Eye of Gondôr

Owen, Dilys
Percival the Performing Pig

Patten, Brian
Gargling With Jelly. The Play!

Pearn, V.A.
Alice's Adventures in Wonderland

Pethybridge, David C.
Do It Yourself

Pickering, Kenneth
Some Canterbury Tales (adapt.)

Pickering, Kenneth and Cole, Keith
Beowulf
Mothers and Daughters
Ulysses

Pirotta, Saviour
Idiot King

Poskitt, Kjartan
Sammy's Magic Garden

Potter, Beatrix
Tom Kitten stories

Prendergast, Shaun
Little Victories

Robbins, Glyn
Horse and his Boy (adapt.)
Hundred and One Dalmatians (adapt.)
Lion, the Witch and the Wardrobe (adapt.)
Magician's Nephew (adapt.)
Voyage of the Dawn Treader (adapt.)
Winnie-the-Pooh (adapt.)

Rodgers, Frank
Think of the Magic

Rowley, David E.
In Need of Care

Russell, Willy
Boy with the Transistor Radio
I Read the News Today
Our Day Out (musical and non-musical version)
Stags and Hens
Terraces

S.S.B.
Alice in Wonderland (adapt.)

Sayer, Philip Freeman
Voyage of the Jumblies

Scott, Les and Oakes, Roy and Bolam, Ken
Rockafella
United We Stand

Scott, Noel
Came a Dealer in Dreams

Simpson, Dave
Railway Children (adapt.)

Smith, Dodie
Hundred and One Dalmatians

Shapiro, Jacqui
Joshua's Egg

Stevenson, Robert Louis
Treasure Island

Supple, Tim
Grimm Tales (dram.)
More Grimm Tales (dram.)

Tasca, Jules
Telling Wilde Tales (adapt.)

Taylor, Jeremy James
Helen Come Home or Achilles the Heel

Teacey. A. H.
Quest for the Whooperdink

Terson, Peter
Aesop's Fables (adapt.)
Zigger Zagger

Thompson, Paul
Children's Crusade

Thain, Paul
Papa Panov's Magic Christmas (adapt.)
Stone Soup

Thurber, James
13 Clocks

Tordoff, Bill
Play the Game

Toksvig, Jenifer
Curious Quest for the Sandman's Sand
Shake, Ripple and Roll

Todd, Barbara Euphan
Worzel Gummidge characters

Tolstoy, Leo
Papa Panov's Magic Christmas

Tourtel, Mary and Bestall, Alfred
Rupert stories

Tydeman, Richard
Dawn on Our Darkness

Vivis, Anthony
Horatians and Curiatians (trans.)

C

Warburton, Nick
Domby-Dom
Ghost Writer
Round the World with Class 6

Waterhouse, Keith and Hall, Willis
Worzel Gummidge (adapt.)

Way, Brian
Adventure Faces
Angel of the Prisons
Balloon Faces
Bell
Christmas Carol (adapt.)
Clown
Crossroads
Decision
Discovery and Survival
Grinling Gibbons and the Plague of London
Hat
Island
Key
Ladder
Lantern
Magical Faces
Mirrorman
Mr Grump and the Clown
Oliver Twist (adapt.)
On Trial
Opposites Machine
Pinocchio (adapt.)
Puss in Boots
Rainbow Box
Sleeping Beauty
Speak the Speech I Pray You
Storytellers
Struggle
Three Musketeers (adapt.)
Treasure Island (adapt.)
Valley of Echoes
Wheel

Whelan, Peter
Tinder Box (adapt.)

White, Jesse Braham
Snow White and the Seven Dwarfs

Whitmore, Ken
Jump for Your Life

Wild, Michael
Little Princess (adapt.)

Wilde, Oscar
Seven Fairy Tales (see Telling Wilde Tales)

Wiles, John
Golden Masque of Agamemnon
Lords of Creation
Magical Voyage of Ulysses

Wilson, David Henry
All the World's a Stage

Wood, David
Babe, the Sheep-Pig (adapt.)
BFG (adapt.)
Dinosaurs and All That Rubbish (adapt.)
Flibberty and the Penguin
Gingerbread Man
Hijack Over Hygenia
Ideal Gnome Expedition
Meg and Mog Show (adapt.)
More Adventures of Noddy (adapt.)
Noddy (adapt.)
Nutcracker Sweet
Old Father Time
Old Man of Lochnagar (adapt.)
Papertown Paperchase
Plotters of Cabbage Patch Corner
Rupert and the Green Dragon (adapt.)
Save the Human
See-Saw Tree
Selfish Shellfish
There Was an Old Woman ...
Tickle
Witches (adapt.)

Wood, David and Arthur, Dave and Toni
Pied Piper (adapt.)
Robin Hood

Wood, David and Ruskin, Sheila
Owl and the Pussycat Went to See ...

Wood, Patricia
Captain Blackboot and the Wallamagrumba
Captain Blackboot's Island
Dandelion Time
Wizard of Wobbling Rock

Younghusband, Carol
Only a Game

C

Plays for Children and Young People

The plays are listed alphabetically with marginal marks to indicate the playing time of the individual titles and whether they are for performance by children, young people or adults to children. Please note the classifications are only suggestions and the playing times are approximate.

Key to symbols

C

A = Adults
C = Children
Y = Young people

S = playing time of under 60 minutes approximately
L = playing time of over 60 minutes approximately

Example margin marks:

A
L

= adults to perform to children; playing time longer than 60 minutes (approx.)

C
/
Y
S

= to be performed by children or young people; playing time shorter than 60 minutes (approx,)

A
+
C
L

= to be performed by adults and children; playing time longer than 60 minutes (approx.)

Adventure Faces. Play. Brian Way
M2 F2. Fee code E

A large corporation is evicting Charles the Carnival King to make way for a new amusement park. When Nicky, a former protégé, returns to perform in the final production of 'Carnival of the Seasons' everyone learns it is he that is evicting Charles and his family and the tension mounts.

The Adventures of a Bear Called Paddington. Play for children. Alfred Bradley from the stories of Michael Bond
M5 F3. Extras 6M 3F but can be played by 2M and 2F. Composite setting. Fee code K

The stories of the lovable bear, Paddington, who was found on Paddington Station by the Browns and adopted by them, have been favourites with children for years and this series of playlets woven together to make a full-length play have delighted young (and old!) audiences alike. ISBN 0 573 05035 X

Aesop's Fables. Play. Peter Terson with music by Jeff Parton
21 characters, some doubling possible. A bare stage. Fee code H for play, code B for music

The captive Aesop must go to almighty Zeus to gain his liberty, learning from the animals as he goes. Aesop sets out on his long journey and finds that, as he observes the creatures he meets and learns from their example, the links in his chains gradually drop off. Once free, he passes on to other men the lessons he has learnt in the form of fables. ISBN 0 573 05078 3

Alan and the King's Daughters. Children's play. Helen Murdoch. Music by Ethel McCracken
M11 F8 or M10 F9. 6 Dancers. Simple composite setting. Fee code H

The seven young Princesses have been put under a spell by Winnie the Witch. Her spell requires the hairs of a black cat. She finds one and imprisons it, but a young forester hears it crying and comes to the rescue. Together they set out to defeat the wicked witch. ISBN 0 573 05028 7

Alice in Wonderland. Play. S.S.B.
M8 F7. Three interiors. Fee code A

An abridged version of Lewis Carroll's well-loved story. Playing time about 75 minutes. ISBN 0 573 05003 1

Alice in Wonderland. Play. Blanche Marvin
12 characters. Various simple settings. Fee code B

In the Commedia dell'arte style. The chessboard is the floor and Carroll's well-known characters move, dance and sing their way through Wonderland in the tradition of the Italian street players.

C / Y L

Alice's Adventures in Wonderland. Play. V. A. Pearn
Any number of characters. Composite setting. Fee code C

This longer adaptation of Lewis Carroll's story is designed for children of a slightly older age group. Playing time about 90 minutes

A / C L

Alice's Adventures in Wonderland and Through the Looking Glass. Musical play. Clemence Dane. Music by Richard Addinsell
Any number of characters. Composite setting. Fee code H

The first act tells of Alice's adventures in Wonderland, of the people she meets there, including the White Rabbit, Mad Hatter and March Hare, and of her escape into the Looking Glass land of the second act, where she finds the rest of Lewis Carroll's well-loved people.
ISBN 0 573 05001 5

C

C L

An Alien Stole My Skateboard. Comedy. Randall Lewton
22 speaking characters. Extras. Various simple settings. Fee code L

On Wuldor, a Tolkien-type planet, King Fruma instructs his wizard, Dwimor, to protect his son Prince Erfa from the evil Snithan. Dwimor transposes Bryn, a schoolboy from England, and Erfa, using Bryn as a decoy on Wuldor. How Erfa, with the help of schoolboys Don and Shaun and Don's hippy-type parents, rescues Bryn and brings about Snithan's downfall is the subject of this fast-moving, fun-packed comedy. This play is ideal for schools and youth groups and the staging is very flexible.
ISBN 0 573 05097 X

Y S

All the World's a Stage. Morality play. David Henry Wilson
Any number of characters. An empty stage. Fee code B

The children assemble on the stage and are given neither script nor plot. The parts chosen include a nurse, a shop assistant, a mother, a policeman, a politician and a rich man. The Producer's instructions are explained but fighting breaks out. The Producer's son tries to persuade everyone to play a better part. He is killed but returns to give his advice.

Y L

Angel of the Prisons. Play. Brian Way
M15 F9 or M4 F4 with doubling. Fee code K

An engrossing, moving drama of the life and achievements of the English prison reformer Elizabeth Fry. A very popular play imaginatively presented in a cinematic form.

Y S

Arabian Nights (Sinbad the Sailor) Play. Blanche Marvin
13 characters, 1 voice. Extras. A throne room. Fee code B

In Kabuki style this tells the story of *Scheherezade*, who in turn spins her tales to save her life. Animals and birds are interchanged with humans. Symbolic use of scenery, as well as dance movement, defines the style. Sinbad the Sailor's adventure is told through the curse of the three oranges.

◆ **Babe, the Sheep-Pig**. Play. David Wood. Based on the book by Dick King-Smith
10 actors, with doubling. Various simple settings. Fee code M (play) code D (music — optional)

This is a tale of high adventure in the farmyard; of humble beginnings and courageous triumphs. This is the story of one piglet's rise to become the world famous "sheep-pig", hero of the Grand Challenge Sheep-dog Trials. The play is suitable for everyone from 5 years upwards. Incidental music by Peter Pontzen is available separately on hire.

Bad Day at Black Frog Creek. Musical play. John Gardiner and Fiz Coleman
M5 F4. Extras. A saloon. Fee code E

C

One Christmas Eve, the Muldoon Mob arrive in Black Frog Creek, bent on retrieving the diamond which saloon-keeper Lil has had cemented into one of her teeth. They get the diamond, only to be foiled yet again by Filthy Frank. The play may be adapted quite simply to suit any period of celebration — not just Christmas. Approximate playing time 90 minutes.
ISBN 0 573 05249 2

Balloon Faces. Play. Brian Way
M2 F2. Fee code E

All the world's balloons, including Eileen's magic balloon Face, are slowly losing their air. Some way must be found to save them. Efforts of the audience and players lead them to the Land of Balloons on the dark side of the moon, where they discover the special moon-reed whose song saves the balloons. Theme play: Faces

The Bell. Play. Brian Way
M2 F2. Fee code E

Tom the Bellman and his friend Wag, an enormous bear, sell bells every day in the market-place. A strange, deeply worried man comes to them asking if they could possibly make the 'Bell of Happiness'. The exciting efforts of Tom, Wag and the audience to make the Bell involve the fascinating utilization of the five senses.

Beowulf. Anglo-Saxon epic drama. Kenneth Pickering and Keith Cole
M9 F4. Chorus. Extras. An open stage. Fee by arrangement. Vocal score available separately

The play tells the story, in the form of a rock musical, of the great hero of Viking times, Beowulf. The first half concentrates on his battle with the loathsome monster, Grendel, and his marriage to Hygd, daughter of the Danish King Hrothgar. The climax of the second part recounts his assault on a fearsome dragon, which results in Beowulf's death. The play ends with the lighting of Beowulf's funeral pyre. Period AD fifth century.
ISBN 0 573 08052 6

The BFG (Big Friendly Giant). Play. Roald Dahl, adapted for the stage by David Wood
30 roles may be played by M4 F4. A playroom/bedroom, a cave, Dream Country, Buckingham Palace. Fee code M

Roald Dahl's book about a twenty-four-feet-high giant and a little girl is recreated faithfully for the stage by David Wood. The play begins in Sophie's playroom at her birthday party when family and friends act out the story of The BFG using props, objects and puppets to tell the tale in an improvisatory manner.
ISBN 0 573 05094 5

Big Al. Musical play. Book and lyrics by John Gardiner. Music by Andrew Parr
M57 F57, can be played by M10 F10. Composite setting. Fee by arrangement

This lively musical, originally written for teenagers and young people, is based on the life and times of Al Capone, the infamous Chicago gangster. Although there are 114 characters appearing in this musical the parts can be divided between a minimum cast of twenty. The set comprises a standing construction of scaffolding which is used to represent different areas in Chicago.
ISBN 0 573 08048 8

The Big Noise at Fort-Issimo. Play for children. Bernard Goss
M10 F9. Extras. Various simple settings on an open stage. Fee code L

The Soldiers have been swept away — no longer toys cared for and played with. Encouraged by Mr Busker and led by the redoubtable Sergeant-Major Bumble, they set off to discover their lost fort. *En route* they meet other discarded toys — dolls and animals — and after a brave fight against the terrible Oogly Googlies, they recapture their fort and return to the happy days when 'toys were *toys*'.
ISBN 0 573 15009 5

The Birthday of the Infanta. Play. Blanche Marvin
7 characters. Extras. A palace ballroom with simple insets. Fee code D

Based on Oscar Wilde's fairytale which in turn is based on a true Spanish story, its theme is the corruption of power possible even in a child. It is also about the rigidity of structures and authority as it destroys regardless of motive. The adaptation is straightforward — a Spanish story in classical sixteenth-century Spanish style in design, music and movement.

Boy with the Transistor Radio. Play. Willy Russell
M7 F3. Extras. Simple settings. Fee code D

Terry is leaving school with few prospects in his native Liverpool. His father finds him a job in a local warehouse, but Terry has other ideas. Living in a dream world promulgated by a radio DJ to whom he listens constantly, Terry is convinced there is something better and he makes an angry escape bid. This compelling, compassionate play was transmitted on Thames Television.

Bug-Eyed Loonery. Play. Brian L. Bishop
30 named speaking parts. Chorus. Various simple interior and exterior settings. Fee code H

Imagination, Queen of the Land of Nursery Rhyme and of the Land of Childhood, reveals that children are under a spell and that she has been usurped by the monster HE, whose wicked minions (including the Bug-Eyed Loons) ensure Imagination remains exiled. But then some of the evil ones swap sides and the struggle for the Land of Childhood is on with a vengeance! This play, a delight for performers and audiences alike, can involve up to seventy or more young people.
ISBN 0 573 05075 9

The Burston Drum. Musical for young people. Book by Ellen Dryden, lyrics by Don Taylor, music by Charles Young
M14 F11. Children. Extras. Three simple settings. Fee by arrangement

On the 1st April, 1914, in the village of Burston, a group of children went on strike to protest at the unfair dismissal of their teachers, Kitty and Tom Higdon. This musical play tells the story of the events leading up to this historic event and of Kitty's battle to provide a comprehensive and enjoyable education for all the village children and Tom's fight to organize the villagers into a more democratic rural community.
ISBN 0 573 08082 8

The Call of the Piper. Musical for children. Book by Liz Berwick. Music by Dorothy Everhart 36 named parts. Extras. Various simple settings. Fee by arrangement

Seven lonely children from differing backgrounds in Victorian London find themselves transported to the Kingdom of Scholastica, once a musical country, but now a tyrannical state under the rule of the Sum King. The Staff, former ministers of the deposed High C, explain to the children that they have been sent for a specific purpose and cannot return home until they have found the missing Golden Triangle which will end the reign of slavery and terror. The children set about the task encountering many exciting adventures ...
ISBN 0 573 08078 X

Callisto 5. Play. Alan Ayckbourn
M3 (17, 30s, any age) F1 (30s) or M2 F2, 2 M or F voices. A space station interior. Fee code M

Jem is alone on space station Callisto 5 with Damaris, a babysitting robot, and Iris, the all-powerful computer, as his only company. Jem is bored with the childish amusements provided by the computer and despairs increasingly at Damaris's instability. Jem has to do battle with The Thing, a marauding alien that can only be seen through a video camera, and finds his efforts rewarded in a very surprising way ...
ISBN 0 573 05107 0

Came a Dealer in Dreams. Play. Noel Scott
M7 F1 (variable). Extras. A castle courtroom. Fee code D

In the Kingdom of Wide Awake the trial is in progress of the mysterious 'Sleep', who has been casting spells on people. The advantages and disadvantages of his power are given. Even the King senses some advantages — in regard to his ceaselessly talkative queen. Sleep is condemned to have his head cut off — but he sends the executioner and everyone else off to Slumber.
ISBN 0 573 15211 X

Captain Blackboot and the Wallamagrumba. Play. Patricia Wood
M15 F9. A desert island. Fee code D

The sequel to *Captain Blackboot's Island* opens with the Captain and his crew puzzling over the whereabouts of their octopus, Oliver. Luckily James, Sally and Victoria arrive, overhear some wreckers plotting and discover that Oliver is to be made into an octopus stew! A happy ending is assured, however, following their victorious battle with the wreckers, and when Oliver appears from the sea, it seems that the Wallamagrumba may not be so bad after all.
ISBN 0 573 15223 3

Captain Blackboot's Island. Play for children. Patricia Wood
Mixed cast of children. A desert island. Fee code D

Captain Blackboot and crew have been living on the desert island for months and he has worked out a Treasure Trail hoping his island will become famous. Three young seekers arrive followed by Wicked Pirates and even the Captain's wife and children. Real treasure is found and a battle results.
ISBN 0 573 15208 X

Card Play. Play for young people. David Foxton
16 characters. Two simple settings. Fee code H

A funny, truthful, fast-paced play about — a pack of cards! But there the two-dimensional world ends, as each card has a character of its own (moaning, greedy, caddish, funny) and the seniority very strictly depends on your face value. The most greedy and knavish of the cards hatch up a plan to steal the trophies and gate money from an event at the stadium. Their plot is overheard by some of the minor cards, who hasten to plot their downfall ...
ISBN 0 573 15005 2

◆ The Champion of Paribanou. Play. Alan Ayckbourn
M7 F3 with doubling. Various simple settings. Fee code M

Murganah loves Ahmed, the Sultan's youngest son, but feeling herself rejected, she invokes the help of dark supernatural forces to regain him. When she finally loses him to another she seeks a terrible revenge. Alan Ayckbourn writes: 'For the first time in a children's play, I've strayed into the grey area of individual choice. Are any of us ever born good or bad? Or do we only grow that way as a result of the circumstances we face and the choices we make?'

The Children's Crusade. Play. Paul Thompson
May be performed by 57 boys and 8 girls. Various simple interior and exterior settings. Fee code M

The action is based on the mythology surrounding the two Children's Crusades of 1212. A German boy, Nicholas, declares that God has commanded him to lead an army of children to Jerusalem to bring back the Cross. Thousands set off with him on the perilous journey. The mime sequences and the opportunities for improvisation make it an exciting experience for both the audience and the cast. The music is included in the text.
ISBN 0 573 05069 1

A Christmas Carol. Play. Brian Way
M50 F30 or M16 F8 with doubling. Fee code K

A moving adaptation of the Dickens' classic tracing the gradual conversion of Scrooge from the loathsome ogre to warm-hearted soul. This innovative rendition was commissioned by the Victoria Theatre, Stoke-on-Trent.

Christmas Crackers. Children's play. Willis Hall
M7 F2. An empty stage. Fee code M

This is the hilariously funny sequel to *Kidnapped at Christmas*. Crosby and Gilbert, our two convict friends are spending a lonely Christmas Eve eating baked beans on the stage of an empty theatre when they encounter their old enemies — Detective Constable Grummett (and his wife and horrible son) and Constables Mullins and MacBain. Add a failed beauty queen, some pantomime costumes, and a green skeleton and an evening of fun is assured for all.
ISBN 0 573 05040 6

Christopher Columbus. Play. Joan Macalpine. Music by Peter Durrent
18 named parts. Large cast can be involved. Various locations. Fee code G

A thrilling play concerning itself with Columbus's early days — the perils and excitement of a great discovery and a sense of what might go wrong if the discovery is not handled with care and imagination. The times, dates and places Columbus visited are historical facts and his comments on them come from his reports on the voyage.
ISBN 0 573 05102 X

Cinderella. Play. Blanche Marvin
7 characters. A drawing-room, a ballroom foyer. Fee code D

A comedy of manners à la Oscar Wilde's *The Importance of Being Earnest*. The ugly sisters are played by men who take one or two lumps of sugar in their tea. The Fairy Godmother is Britannia, who rules the waves but who is only a part-time Fairy Godmother with part-time magic, although she's cousin to Columbia the Gem of the Ocean. There's a prince and the class struggle of snobbery and élitism as Cinderella rises from rags to riches.

The Clown. Play. Brian Way
M2 F2. Fee code E

Y
S

A more serious, biographical approach to the clown's story. The play depicts the clown's many years of hard work before establishing a famous act with Jock, the Ringmaster, and the loss of his laugh when Jock is killed in a civil war. His laugh returns when he is chosen to take Jock's place. Theme play: The Clown

Crossroads. Play. Brian Way
M3 F3. Fee code E

Y
S

An indecisive, care-free Tramp at the crossroads must help resolve the conflicts between the Scientist of the South, the Monster of the West, the Great Bird of the East, and the Cold Queen of the North. Through his experiences the Tramp discovers a more meaningful purpose for living.

C

The Crowning Glory. Play. Blanche Marvin
13 characters, doubling possible. 3 acting areas. Fee code B

Y
S

Definitely a classical Biblical style this is the story of Esther and how she became Queen of Persia. By her growing courage, she saved the life of her uncle Mordecai and all the Jews of Persia. Eventually the celebration of Purim was created to honour that event.

The Crowns, the King and the Long Lost Smile. Play for children. David Foxton
M7 F3. Extras. Various simple settings. Fee code L

A
L

The play tells the story of how the Crown Troupe — Thomas, Ben, Will and Sally, a strolling band of entertainers — help the Princess Dulcinea find her father the King, who has been kidnapped by the wicked Baron Drax, and thus regain her long-lost smile. The easily staged settings encourage plenty of audience participation.
ISBN 0 573 05050 3

♦ **The Curious Quest for the Sandman's Sand**. Children's Musical. Book and lyrics by Jenifer Toksvig. Music by David Perkins
11 principals. Chorus. Various simple settings. Fee by arrangement

C
L

Three children embark on an eventful journey into the mysterious world of silver-tongued Harry, the Sandman, to retrieve the magical sand. Along the way they meet extraordinary creatures — Snoodle Werps, the Trash Trump, Litter Bugs to name but a few — before their final showdown with Jewels, the Witch and the awesome Gump Grump. A colourful, fun-packed adventure musical for children between the ages of 7 and 13. Running time: approximately one hour.
ISBN 0 573 08109 3

The Curse of the Egyptian Mummy. Pat Hutchins, adapted for the stage by David Conville and David Gooderson
12 adults, M7 F5 or M6 F3 with doubling. 8 or more children. Simple settings. Fee code K

A
+
C
L

A fast-moving, hilarious adventure, adapted from Pat Hutchins' children's book, first seen at The Open Air Theatre, Regent's Park, London. The 15th Hampstead Cub Scouts are looking forward to their weekend in the country, but before they even reach the campsite strange things start to happen ... What exactly is the Curse of the Egyptian Mummy?
ISBN 0 573 05100 3

C
L

Dandelion Time. Fantasy. Patricia Wood
43 characters, doubling possible. Extras. Composite setting. Fee code J

Three modern-day children suddenly find themselves dressed in Edwardian costume. It seems that Father Time has been kidnapped and the world is out of time. Together with Hickory Dickory Dock and Rekelen, a moth-eaten raven, and with the help of dandelion clocks, the children set off to rescue Father Time. They meet with many varied and interesting characters and situations before they are finally successful in their quest.
ISBN 0 573 05043 0

C/
Y
S

Dawn on our Darkness. Play. Richard Tydeman
M9 F1. Extras. An acting area. Fee code C

An unusual treatment of the nativity story, designed for performances in church or hall, by actors of any age. Richard Tydeman's skill in conveying the true meaning of Christmas is here exploited to the full.
ISBN 0 573 16603 X

C

C
+
Y
L

Dazzle. Musical Space-tacular! Book and lyrics by John Gardiner. Music by Andrew Parr
M5 F4. Chorus. 12 named parts plus extras and chorus. Simple settings. Fee by arrangement

With brilliantly funny parodies of *Star Trek*, *Dazzle* charts a voyage of the starship Sunburster One on its highly important first mission under the control of the dashingly handsome (and doesn't he know it!) Captain Sam Galactic. The musical has flexible casting, settings and costumes are easily achieved and extensive notes are given in the text for these, together with suggestions for lighting, sound and special effects.
ISBN 0 573 08088 7 — Libretto
ISBN 0 573 08591 9 — Vocal Score

Y
S

The Decision. Play. Brian Way
M2 F2. Fee code E

The people of beautiful, isolated Xavia, content with the simplicity of their way of life, are faced with the decision (dependent on audience choice) of whether they should alter their society and join the world of materialistic nations.

A
+
C
L

Dinosaurs and All That Rubbish. Musical play. David Wood and Peter Pontzen. Based on the book by Michael Foreman
Flexible casting. Various simple exterior settings. Fee code F

Man destroys his own world through misuse and disrespect, only to search for a replacement in the stars. In his absence the Dinosaurs restore the Earth to its former beauty. Ironically when man returns he tries to lay claim to this new blooming planet, but is reminded that it is the same decaying Earth he had abandoned. The final note of this lively play is that Earth belongs to everyone and should be respected.
ISBN 0 573 15205 5 — Libretto
ISBN 0 573 08584 6 — Vocal Score

Y
S

Discovery and Survival. Play. Brian Way
M4 F2. Fee code K

A wonderful exploration of how discoveries and adversities have influenced the growth of man. Various episodes include a refugee escape story, a drought scene set in the Third World, the creation of braille, and the first telegraph. Smooth, fast-paced development enhances this awareness drama.

Do It Yourself. David C. Pethybridge
M6 F5. A suburban side-road. Fee code C

A group of children decide to earn some money for themselves by giving advice on how to 'do it yourself'. Business isn't very good until they catch a pickpocket, and win a reward, but at the end of the play they are no better off than they were at the beginning.
ISBN 0 573 05204 2

Do We Ever See Grace? Play. Noël Greig
Large ensemble playing many roles. A bare stage. Fee code J

This play is presented as a 'clown show' in which most of the actors wear clown-style costumes, creating a kaleidoscope of impressions around the central character of Grace, representing all those people who are scorned in this world but who develop a resistance to such injustice. An intelligent and searching contemporary play of ideas, ideal for school groups and young people.

Do-Gooders. Play. Graham Jones
M4 F2. A bare stage. Fee code D

This play concentrates on the pollution of our environment. The water of the local caves is suspected of being contaminated by a local factory. Nora investigates but her father is a director in the factory. After a friend dies in the water, Nora's investigation meets opposition. Excitement and tension mount at a confrontation in the caves when Nora threatens to drink the water unless she is allowed to continue her investigation.
ISBN 0 573 12054 4

♦ **Domby-Dom**. Comedy. Nick Warburton
Flexible, minimum of 12 actors. A stage. Fee code D

Some children decide to put on a play. It must be about football, says one. It must be set in Space, says another. There must be adventure. So begins the production of *Indiana Smith and the Cup Final of Doom*, or *The Return of the Tedi*, in which Teddy and Jemima battle against Timmy and Popkins who are intent on destroying the Inter-Galaxy Cup Final at Wembley.
ISBN 0 573 12221 0

The Down-Going of Orpheus Hawkins. Play for children. David Clarke with music by Mavis Dunston
Cast of children, 16 main speaking parts. A bare stage. Platform settings. Fee code J

The play starts with two rival storytellers relating the drama of the ill-starred lovers, Pyramus and Thisbe. A quarrel ensues, and the script is obviously going sadly awry. Young Orpheus Hawkins is in the audience. In a moment of inspiration he decides to improvise the story of Orpheus and Eurydice; and despite the protests of Mrs Hawkins and the interference of Pyramus and Thisbe, he most successfully and beautifully does just this.
ISBN 0 573 05039 2

The Dracula Spectacula. A spooky musical. Book and lyrics by John Gardiner. Music by Andrew Parr
24 characters. Large supporting cast. Various interior and exterior settings. Fee by arrangement. Vocal score available separately

In this bubbling modern extravaganza for the young the immaculate Miss Nadia and her three pupils are swung into riotous Transylvanian happenings with the irrepressible Count and his gruesome acolytes. Plenty of good parts, a sizzling score and a fresh hilarious script make this an attractive enterprise for a young company.
ISBN 0 573 18013 X

A Dragon for Dinner. Musical play for children. Book and lyrics by Helen Murdoch. Music by Ethel McCracken
M4 F5. Extras. A palace garden. Fee code D

The Princess, tired of the lonely life within the Royal Palace and Gardens, is delighted when she hears that someone new is coming to dinner. Unfortunately, the guest is a dragon, and the Princess is going to be his dinner. But the Dragon is found a hobby to take his mind off Princess-eating for good.
ISBN 0 573 15203 9

Dream Date. Book and Lyrics by Kevin Dowsett. Music by James Osborne
17 principals. Extras. Various interior and exterior settings. Fee by arrangement

Dream Date is a teenage comic strip magazine which crams its pages, and the heads of some of those who read it, with glamorous fantasies of romance, pop stars and boyfriends. Contrasted with this is the central character, Kathy, a sixteen-year-old who has turned her back on her own life and friends in search of a fantastic Mr Right, as personified in the feature articles of *Dream Date*.
ISBN 0 573 08065 8 — Libretto
ISBN 0 573 08569 2 — Vocal score

Dreamjobs. Play. Graham Jones
F5. A waiting-room. Fee code D

While waiting for interviews with Youth Employment Service, five teenage girls dream of the romantic, exciting jobs they would like to do. The dreams are enacted by all the girls together. Each has a rude awakening. Beverly eventually brings them down to earth. They are only fit for the drabbest of jobs.
ISBN 0 573 03379 X

Dreams of Anne Frank. Play. Bernard Kops
M4 (16, middle-age) F4 (13, 18, middle-age). Simple set. Fee code H for play, B for music

Bernard Kops's play, with music by David Burman, was premièred at the Polka Theatre, London, in 1992 and won the *Time Out* award for best children's production. Using a cinematograph approach with minimal scenery, it tells the famous story of how two Jewish families hid from the Nazis for two years in a cramped Amsterdam attic and the fantasy world the adolescent Anne Frank created to escape her incarceration.
ISBN 0 573 05101 1

The Emperor's New Clothes. Play. Blanche Marvin
6 characters. A throne room. Fee code C

Written as a parody of a medieval morality play ranging from an elaborate madrigal mocking the Emperor to the imaginary weaving of cloth in front of a hypocritical Court. The French traditions of comedy are incorporated from Molière to Giraudoux.

Ernie's Incredible Illucinations. Play for young people. Alan Ayckbourn
22 characters, doubling possible. Extras. A bare stage, waiting-room at one side. Fee code E

This bright comedy based on the extraordinary powers of Ernie Fraser, a daydreamer with a difference, shows his thoughts having a disturbing habit of turning into reality. After some embarrassments, Ernie's parents consult a doctor. Many of Ernie's adventures are acted out in flashback. When Ernie fails to produce a Brass Band, group hallucination is diagnosed. Ernie's 'illucinations' aren't to be dismissed quite so lightly ...
ISBN 0 573 12063 3

The Evil Eye of Gondôr. Play. Brian Owen
20 main speaking parts (all male or mixed). Extras. Various settings on a bare stage. Fee code G

An exciting adventure story for performance by, or to, children, revolving around the age-old battle between good and evil, but with many inventive twists. The Valley has been dominated by the Guardians of the Castle of Gondôr, whose power comes from the Eye, since ancient times. One day a Stranger comes into their midst and gives them the strength to throw off their chains of oppression ...
ISBN 0 573 05066 X

The Firebird. Play. Blanche Marvin
7 characters. A garden. Fee code C

This is written to be produced as a Japanese Noh play, all of its movement choreographed in order to stylize the piece. Since The Firebird must not be captured or she would die, it is a perfect fairytale for the Noh style. The setting in Japan enhances the story and the exotic make-up and costumes, the sword fights, the set of six screens fascinate the children.

First Time. Book by Kirk Foster and John Gardiner. Music by Kirk Foster and Paul Sabey
Large number of characters, much doubling possible. Various simple settings on an open stage. Fee by arrangement

This original and hugely enjoyable show is best described as a musical revue which takes a light-hearted look at the first time experiences and feelings all of us have or will come up against. Each song and sketch is associated with the word 'first' in one way or another — First Child, First Job, First Glance, First Family Christmas, First Bite(!).

Flibberty and the Penguin. Musical play for children. David Wood
M10 F2, some M characters can be played by F. Five exterior, two interior simple settings. Fee code J

Young Penguin has come from Iceland to find his father and mother. This must be done before the spring weather gets too warm. He falls in with Flibberty, a genial goblin, who helps him in his search. They incur the wrath of Krafty Kingfisher, who accuses the Penguin of stealing a fish from him. The parent penguins are eventually discovered in the Zoo. Flibberty and Young Penguin manage to set them free, and to put Kingfisher in his place.
ISBN 0 573 05033 3

The Frankenstein Monster Show. Book by John Crocker and Tim Hampton. Music by Ken Bolam. Lyrics by Les Scott
M10 F3. Extras. Various simple settings. Fee by arrangement

This inventive and exuberant musical brings the old Frankenstein story bang up-to-date — right into the computer age in fact. When Frank Enstein arrives at Enstein hall from the USA, he continues the reanimation experiments of his deceased great-great uncle. Frank's expertise in computer robotics and the timely arrival of Burke and Hare, two rather suspicious undertakers, soon have remote-controlled monsters rolling off the production line.

Gargling With Jelly. The Play! Play. Brian Patten. Based on poems from his book *Gargling With Jelly*
11 characters, doubling possible. Various simple settings. Fee code L

Sadly, everything in Jimmy's world is grey and boring, because of the evil Doctor Sensible and her terrible medicine which inoculates people against fun. The doctor is poised to sell her medicine worldwide, with only one condition: she must get Jimmy, the last child in Britain to resist her, to take it within four days. He refuses, and as the deadline approaches Dr Sensible becomes more and more cunning ...
ISBN 0 573 05092 9

Ghost Writer. Play. N. J. Warburton
M13 F8, doubling possible. The writer's study and the Colonel's lounge. Fee code D

Jeffrey and Belinda are just about to type the last word of their new play when a full range of characters come to life and start to enact parts the authors can no longer control. A ghost writer lends a hand. As the play draws to a close, the writers find themselves totally embroiled in the action and only the ghost's ironical laughter is left for a grand finale!
ISBN 0 573 15216 0

The Gingerbread Man. Musical play. Book, music and lyrics by David Wood
M4 F2. A kitchen dresser. Fee code M. Vocal score available separately

While the 'Big Ones' are asleep plenty of activity is taking place on the kitchen dresser. The cuckoo clock has lost his voice and might be threatened with the dustbin in the morning if he doesn't recover it. The efforts of the salt cellar and the pepper-mill to help him regain it involve them in confrontation with the Old Tea-Bag ... but all is resolved by morning.
ISBN 0 573 05042 2

The Giraffe and the Pelly and Me. Play with music. Adapted by Vicky Ireland from the story by Roald Dahl
M5 F1, 1 boy (12). Various simple settings. Fee code H

Billy and a strange trio of animals, the Giraffe, the Pelly and the Monkey, known as 'The Ladderless Window-Cleaning Company', set off to clean the many windows at the Duke of Hampshire's house, and have a tense encounter with cat burglar 'Cobra' Clive. For performance to children aged five to nine, with music and a host of special effects! (NB. The music is available separately from The Polka Theatre.)
ISBN 0 573 05109 7

The Golden Masque of Agamemnon. Play. John Wiles
40 singing or speaking parts. A bare stage. Fee code M

This play tells the story of the blood curse on the House of Atreus from its beginning to its end, through the lives of Agamemnon and his children. This is not a straight re-telling of Greek legends but a new creation — a Masque with speech, songs and movement. Neither is it restricted to being specifically Greek. The casting is very flexible and the text contains extensive production and rehearsal notes by the author.
ISBN 0 573 15008 7

Good King Wenceslas and the Chancellor of Bohemia. Play. Tony Horitz
M5 F2, 8M or F (minimum). Interior and exterior settings. Fee code F

Please see the entry in Section D.

Grimm Tales. Play with music, adapted from the Brothers Grimm by Carol Ann Duffy, dramatized by Tim Supple
Large cast may be played by M4 F3. Various simple settings. Fee code M

Eight stories from the Brothers Grimm, presented in different and exciting styles with an emphasis on the horror, grotesquerie and savage farce of the originals:*Hansel and Gretel*; *The Golden Goose*; *Ashputtel; A Riddling Tale; The Mouse, the Bird and the Sausage; Iron Hans; The Lady and the Lion*; and *The Magic Table, the Gold-Donkey and the Cudgel in the Sack*.

Grinling Gibbons and the Plague of London. Play. Brian Way
M30 F10 or M8 F4 with doubling. Extras. Fee code K

An exciting, swashbuckling costume drama of a struggling young woodcarver attempting to gain recognition and support in seventeenth-century London. The story is related as a mother's folk tale to her son during the Blitz of World War II. There are exceptional opportunities for audience participation and recreating the atmosphere of London during the Great Plague and the Fire of the 1660s.

Hans, the Witch and the Gobbin. Play. Alan Cullen
M7 F6. Composite setting. Fee code H

The story of Hans, a young medical student, and his search for the Princess who has lost her memory to a witch called Daisy. Hans, who is aided by the Gobbin — a gormless kind of Goblin with magical powers — goes through many adventures before he wins his Princess.
ISBN 0 573 05010 4

The Hat. Play. Brian Way
M2 F2. Fee code E

Peter and his mother are hat-makers who make very rare and extraordinary hats. The most special hat of all is one made by Peter's mother for Mr Hump — a strange hat that creates many an adventure for all. And the biggest problem can only be solved by Peter's remarkable dog.

Helen Come Home or **Achilles the Heel**. Jazz musical. Jeremy James Taylor
21 boys or girls (11-15). Extras. A swimming-pool, a seashore, inside Troy. Fee code L

The story of the choice of Paris (set as a holiday camp competition complete with compère), the abduction of Helen, the Trojan War and the Wooden Horse, is told in modern jazz terms, but in this version no-one is hurt — except Achilles in the heel — and all ends happily! Period BC 3050 and 3040. ISBN 0 573 15004 4

Hiawatha. Play. Michael Bogdanov

Please see the entry in Section A.

Hijack Over Hygenia. Children's play with music. David Wood
M8 F4, with doubling. An aeroplane interior, a roof, a throne room, a bedroom. Fee code K

Hygenia is the cleanest kingdom in the world. Disease is unknown, but one day a villainous Measle enters illegally and starts bringing the inhabitants out in spots. It is all the plot of Doctor Spicknspan who, owing to prevailing healthiness is always out of work. Things look serious, but the plot is foiled by the gallantry of the Royal staff: peace, health and cleanliness are restored.
ISBN 0 573 05034 1

The Horatians and the Curiatians. A didactic play for children. Bertolt Brecht. Translated by Anthony Vivis
Fee code G

The Curiatii decide to attack the city of the Horatii; both sides organize their armies. Thanks to better weapons the Curiatii win the bowmen's and pikemen's engagements, and in the engagement between the swordsmen the Horatii run away. But the pursuit splits up the Curiatii, so that the Horatian swordsmen can engage them singly and beat them.

The Horse and his Boy. C. S. Lewis. Adapted by Glyn Robbins
M23 F3 or M11 F2 with doubling. Extras. Various simple settings. Fee code M

This enthralling adaptation of one of C. S. Lewis's Chronicles of Narnia blends drama, fantasy and humour. To escape the clutches of the evil warlord Rabadash, the horse, Bree and the boy, Shasta, run away together from the cruel land of Calormen. When they discover that Rabadash has plans to invade Narnia and neighbouring Archenland, they race ahead to warn the people of Narnia. The play can be very simply staged.
ISBN 0 573 05095 3

◆ **The Hundred and One Dalmatians**. Play. Dodie Smith. Adapted by Glyn Robbins
20 characters, extras. May be played by a cast of 9, plus extras. Simple interior and exterior settings. Fee code M

Pongo, a Dalmatian dog, and his Missis are expecting their first litter. They become jittery when obsessive fur collector Mrs Cruella de Vil arrives. When Missis produces fifteen puppies, Cruella is enraptured and has the Badduns kidnap the litter. Distraught, Pongo and Missis enlist support on the Twilight Barking and encounter many adventures before rescuing their own pups — and a great many more!
ISBN 0 573 05114 3

I Read the News Today. Play. Willy Russell
M4, 3M or F. Split set: radio station and police station. Fee code D

This telling tale from the author of *Educating Rita* relates the night that the local radio station's late-night broadcast is interrupted by the arrival of Ronnie, who has escaped from police custody. Ronnie's act of 'vandalism', for which he has been convicted, was in reality a one-man stand against the lies told by advertisers and DJs. Ronnie is led away for psychiatric tests, but who is disturbed — Ronnie or the dream merchants?
ISBN 0 573 15222 5

I Was a Teenage Jekyll and Hyde. Musical play. Book and lyrics by Randall Lewton. Music by Peter Miller
11 main speaking parts, large supporting cast. Various simple interior and exterior settings. Fee by arrangement. Vocal score available separately

Eustace Crucible, crazed chemistry teacher, has found a formula to enhance his appearance and intelligence. But courage fails him and he persuades downtrodden Sylvester Jekyll to drink the potion, transforming him into Hyde, a super-cool, handsome, laid-back youth. Between momentary flashbacks to his real self Hyde learns of people's true feelings for Sylvester and in the end decides to 'be himself'.
ISBN 0 573 18009 1

The Ideal Gnome Expedition. Musical play. David Wood
6 characters M or F. A back yard, an alley, an adventure playground, a street, a traffic island. Fee code M

After rescuing a toy duck from the dustbin in their back yard, Mr Fisher and Mr Wheeler, two temporarily nomadic garden gnomes, decide to venture into the big wide world. Their object is to find a holiday island, just like the 'Big Ones', but being unused to the hazards of the town, they almost don't make it. Although nothing turns out quite as expected, they all agree that it is the best holiday they've ever had.
ISBN 0 573 05061 9

The Idiot King. Play. Saviour Pirotta
21 characters, may be played by M4 and F3 (Arabs). Various interior and exterior settings. Fee code G

This play, set in the fifteenth century, shows how a cruel and thoughtless tyrant is transformed. The Sultan of Arabia conquers Malta and refuses its people the freedom to practise their religion, or maintain a national identity. The people resist. By magical means the Sultan is reduced to a King of fools. Through suffering humiliation he learns the true meaning of kingship.
ISBN 0 573 15218 7

In Need of Care. Play. David E. Rowley
M2 F2. A derelict barn. Fee code C

Two girls on the run from an approved school take shelter in an old barn where they are discovered by two boys of their own age. The resulting delay prevents their escape from their followers, but one of the girls, at least, has benefited from the encounter.
ISBN 0 573 02322 0

The Incredible Vanishing!!!! Play. Denise Coffey
M7 F2. Extras. Composite setting. Fee code J

Written especially for the Young Vic and intended principally for eight to twelve-year-olds, the play tells how a barrow-boy, a meter-maid and an intrepid police constable descend into the underworld of the Marsh Goblins to investigate an 'incredible vanishing' — the spiriting away of countless children by Her Marshesty, the Monarch of the Drains. Needless to say, our brave heroes (and heroine) save the day — but not without the co-operation of the audience.

Invisible Friends. A play. Alan Ayckbourn
M4 F3. Composite setting. Fee code M

Lucy is a very ordinary, straightforward teenager. With her father glued to the telly, her mother preoccupied with gossip and her brother enclosed in his ear-phones, no-one wants to know about her place in the swimming team. Lucy revives her childhood fantasy friend, Zara. However, Zara materializes, bringing with her an idealized father and brother. The moral of this cautionary tale is clearly spelt out — that when you get what you want it's not what you wanted: Lucy's dream family is a nightmare.

The Island. Play. Brian Way
M2 F2. Fee code E

Army forces, in preparation for a mainland invasion, take over an island whose population has only known peace. Prescribed rules and regulations set up by the commanding officer are finally withdrawn when the islanders prove their peaceful intent.

Jack, the Giant and the Jiggery Plot. Play. Richard Blythe
13 characters, or M6 F2 with doubling. Various simple settings. Fee code F

The Prime Minister and the General plot to kill the Princess so that the King will die of a broken heart. They recruit Jack as part of their plan but he turns good. He rescues the Princess and his own long-lost father and kills the giant. The plotters are banished and Jack becomes Prince, allowing true love to blossom.

Jennings Abounding! Musical based on the 'Jennings' books. Anthony Buckeridge. Music by Hector Cortes and William Gomez. Additional music and arrangement by Nigel Carver
M4 (young, middle-age, elderly) F1 (young). Extras 4 boys 3 girls. A main hall and dormitory. Fee by arrangement

Mr Wilkins, the unpopular master of Jennings' boarding school, is rumoured to be leaving. When Mr Wilkins is asked to play the King in the end-of-term performance of *Henry V*, the result is near to chaos. However, the last-minute arrival of a 'real' actor saves the day.
ISBN 0 573 05048 1

Jenny and the Lucky Bags. Musical play for children. Book and lyrics by Helen Murdoch. Music by Ethel McCracken
M4 (boys, middle-age) F5 (young, middle-age, elderly). Extras. A street, a shop, an open space. Fee code K. Vocal score available separately

Jenny's sweet shop is very popular, but she cannot get any sweets to sell. However, with the help of PC Spearmint and Jenny's pretty niece, following a magic trip and a thrilling encounter with the wicked Sugar Sorceress, Jenny's sweet stock is marvellously multiplied in time for the local fair.
ISBN 0 573 05059 7

♦ **Joshua's Egg**. Play. Jacqui Shapiro, music by Andrew Dodge
M3 F4, may be played by M1 F2 with doubling. Various simple settings. Fee code G (play), code B (music)

Joshua is about to become a brother, isn't happy at the prospect, and doesn't want to stay with Uncle Ronnie and five-year-old Lucy. Then Joshua finds a dinosaur egg and a magical adventure begins as they travel back in time to return the egg. Written for adults to perform to children aged from five to seven it is also successful with audiences up to age eleven. Running time: approximately one hour.
ISBN 0 573 05119 4

Jump for Your Life. A dangerous play for children. Ken Whitmore
M6 F2, with doubling. Composite setting. Fee code L

Young Frederick has a difficult task — to persuade all of us, in the world and in the audience, to jump into the air at a given moment, or the world will crash to pieces. Frederick explains urgently how he has tried desperately to persuade the government and the television broadcasters. But will he succeed in overcoming the general scepticism and saving all of them — and us — in time?
ISBN 0 573 05049 X

The Jungle Book. Play. John Hartoch. Adapted from stories by Rudyard Kipling
Minimum 13 with doubling. Various simple jungle settings. Fee code M

Mowgli, the 'man-cub', lost in the jungle, is rescued from the clutches of the fearsome tiger, Shere Khan, by Baloo the bear and Bagheera the black panther. Brought up with a family of wolf-cubs, the time eventually comes for Mowgli to return to the world of Man. But Mowgli is not finished with the jungle, for one day he returns to settle the score with Shere Khan ...
ISBN 0 573 05077 5

The Key. Play. Brian Way
M2 F2. Fee code E

A drought-ridden community can only save itself by journeying across the mountains to a land where rain falls in abundance. A mysterious stranger takes charge of the people with ruthless discipline, commanding that all travelling water be stored under lock and key. The journey involves active participation of the entire audience for three-quarters of the play. Theme play: A Key

Khalid the Dreamer, or, The Magic Almond. Play for children. Tony Barton and Peter Richards
M8 F4. Extras 4M or F. Large supporting cast. Various interior and exterior settings. Fee code K

A young gardener, Khalid, rises to the position of Captain of the King's Guard. We see him fight the bear set on him by the fierce King of the Forest, and the comic antics of the dwarfs and the long-suffering King's troubles with the obstinate Princess Zayda. In the end Khalid wins the love of the Princess — despite the disgust of the crotchety dwarf at such soppy romance!
ISBN 0 573 05071 6

Kidnapped at Christmas. Play. Willis Hall

For a full synopsis please see the entry in Section D.

The Ladder. Play. Brian Way
M2 F2. Fee code E

At the top of the mountain stands a ladder and the Keeper of the ladder briefly fulfils the dream of those who climb the mountain — a combat-weary soldier who seeks new adventures; a peasant girl who wants to be a dancer; an unpleasant and powerful merchant who has bought the mountain and claims ownership of the magic ladder.

The Land of Kerfuffle. Play for Christmas. Bill Gavin. Loosely adapted from *The Wallypug of Why* by G. E. Farrow

For a full synopsis please see the entry in Section D.

The Lantern. Play. Brian Way
M2 F2. Fee code E

To an old lighthouse come several people to investigate what happened one hundred years ago when a storm wrecked many ships. The magic power of the old lighthouse lantern stimulates three remarkable visions — a future world that is run totally by machinery and gadgets; a noisy and polluted city standing at the side of the lighthouse; and a vision of the past revealing how the ships were destroyed.

The Legend of Scarface and Bluewater. Play. Blanche Marvin
17 characters. An Indian village. Fee code D

Written and originally produced as an end-of-term project for St Paul's Way School, London, this play based on a North American Indian legend should be performed preferably by children in schools, with an age range from primary up to 14 years. There is no set style, only place and period and music, movement, costume, scenery and props are selected to suit the American Indian culture.

A + C L

The Lion, the Witch and the Wardrobe. Play by Glyn Robbins. Adapted from the book by C. S. Lewis
M8 F5, with doubling. Extras. Various simple settings. Fee code M

Peter, Susan, Edmund and Lucy embark on a magical mystery tour to the Land of Narnia through the wardrobe. There they encounter the wicked White Witch, representing the forces of evil, and the King of the Beasts, Aslan the lion, representing all that is good and right. The White Witch is destroyed, allowing good to triumph over evil in the time-honoured way.
ISBN 0 573 05081 3

A+ C L

C

A Little Princess. Musical play. Michael Wild, from the novel by Francis Hodgson Burnett
M10 F16. Extras. Various settings on an open stage. Fee by arrangement. Vocal score on hire

From the authoress of *Little Lord Fauntleroy*, this is the story of Sara, left by her widowed father in the care of the formidable Miss Minchin's school. She is pampered there at first because of her father's wealth, but when he dies, penniless, Sara is demoted to slavery. Her goodness shines through her troubles and everything turns out right in the end. Period nineteenth century
ISBN 0 573 05047 3

A L

Little Victories. Play. Shaun Prendergast
M2 F2. Extras. Various interior and exterior settings. Fee code J

Tony's father has died and his mother, Debs, has taken up with a 'plonker' called Gordon. Gordon gives Tony Death-Dealer, a game that takes the player to strange and exciting places; then Gordon also takes Tony and Debs to France, where they meet Josie, a no-nonsense girl who is is dying of cancer, and the final Death-Dealer game may be the hardest of all … This play, part fantasy, part rite-of-passage tale, is funny, heart-rending and very, very theatrical.
ISBN 0 573 05103 8

Y S

The Littlest Tailor. Play. Blanche Marvin
6 characters. A veranda and garden, a swamp. Fee code C

In the comic minstrel style, using the shuffle and soft dances, the Mr Bones routine, the post-Civil War period of America, the Southern swamps and plantations, to tell the story of the little tailor who by killing seven flies at one blow is led to the conquest of the Giants. But who are the Giants in this version? That's where the fun lies.

Y L

Lords of Creation. Play for young people. John Wiles
75 parts, doubling possible. A jungle clearing. Fee code M

The story of God's request to Tangaroa to find six species that deserve to survive the destruction of all other life is presented in the form of a Balinese folk-tale. The action takes place in a jungle clearing, which can be as elaborate or as simple as conditions dictate. There is also plenty of scope for the cast to make their own accompanying oriental music with the aid of finger xylophones, gongs and bells.
ISBN 0 573 05082 1

Magical Faces. Play. Brian Way
M2 F2. Fee code E

Mayor and Mrs Gravity have banished all laughter and smiling from their town, and signs are posted all over saying so. Paul and his magical friend Tickle-laff decide the only way to change things is to get the cheerless couple to laugh, with the help of the audience, of course! Theme play: Faces

The Magical Voyage of Ulysses. Play. John Wiles
25 characters. A bare stage. Fee code M

Troy has fallen ... The captains and the kings depart, some like Nestor to a happy homecoming, others like Agamemnon to a bloody one. Ulysses is condemned to ten years' exile for offending the gods during the siege. The story of his wanderings is well known from Homer's *Odyssey*, here providing a marvellous stimulant to the youthful imagination. *The Magical Voyage of Ulysses* is an exciting and energetic play. The casting is very flexible and the text contains extensive production and rehearsal notes by the author.
ISBN 0 573 05093 7

The Magician's Nephew. Play. Glyn Robbins. Adapted from the book by C. S. Lewis
M9 F4, with doubling. Various simple interior and exterior settings. Fee code M

Digory is concerned about his ill mother and about his Uncle Andrew, who seems very strange indeed. When Digory and his friend are tricked by Uncle Andrew into embarking on a series of magical adventures, they are brought into contact with the forces of both evil and good. Digory is set a task, which he completes successfully, and the safety of Narnia and the restored health of his mother are thereby ensured.
ISBN 0 573 15013 3

Make-believe. Musical play. A. A. Milne
18 characters. Extras. Six interiors, two exteriors. Fee code F

Owing to the difficulties of actually writing it down, a group of children imagine their play in which there are scenes from a fairy tale — *The Princess and the Woodcutter* — a pirate story and a Christmas episode which includes many pantomime and nursery rhyme characters.
ISBN 0 573 05014 7

Meg and Mog Show. Book, music and lyrics by David Wood. Based on Meg and Mog books by Helen Nicoll and Jan Pienkowski
15 characters, may be played by F1 and 6 or 7 M or F. Extras optional. Various simple settings. Fee code M

Ingeniously combining stories from five of the books we see Meg, Mog and Owl set off on an adventure to find the ingredients for a getting-rid-of-Steggy spell — an adventure that takes them to a medieval castle, zoo, and the moon! Lively songs and plenty of audience participation ensure a production to enchant all ages!
ISBN 0 573 05065 1

The Mirrorman. Play. Brian Way
M2 F2. Fee code E

The Toymaker has created a most unusual doll that, with the audience's help, can walk and talk. They are swept into a series of adventures by the Toymaker's reflection in the mirror — the Mirrorman — who needs help to protect his book of spells and magic from a Witch who could conquer the world beyond the mirrors.

The Monster That Ate 3B. Play for schools and youth groups. Randall Lewton
About 25 speaking parts. Many extras. Various simple settings. Fee code K

When the pupils of 3B arrive in Italy on a cultural exchange visit, they contend not only with a strange language, foreign food and a gang of Italian boys intent on re-running World War II, but also a sea-monster which has been terrorizing the town! The boys of 3B destroy the monster and even manage to reach a sort of *détente* with the local youths.
ISBN 0 573 05084 8

◆**More Adventures of Noddy**. Enid Blyton. Adapted for the stage by David Wood
17 characters may be played by 10 actors. Simple settings. Fee code M (full length play), code G for each separate part

This is David Wood's second adaptation of Enid Blyton's classic children's stories. In two acts it may be performed as a full length play or each act may be performed separately as a one-act play. 'David Wood, the country's top children's dramatist has adapted some of Enid Blyton's charming Noddy stories and created another delightful, colourful show packed with fun, excitement and plenty of audience participation.' *What's On in London*
ISBN 0 573 05115 1

◆**More Grimm Tales**. The Brothers Grimm. Adapted by Carol Ann Duffy. Dramatized by Tim Supple and the Young Vic Company
Large cast, may be played by 9 actors. Simple settings. Fee code M

Funny, magical, cruel and wondrous, the folk classics *Little Red Riding Hood*, *Snow White*, *Rumpelstiltskin* and others from the brothers Grimm are presented here in acclaimed poet Carol Ann Duffy's enchantingly fresh adaptation, with a beguiling and vigorous dramatization by Tim Supple. 'The best demonstration all year of the living power of theatre, the children squealed with delight and so did I.' *Observer*

Mothers and Daughters. Books and lyrics by Ken Pickering. Music and lyrics by Keith Cole
6 to 200 characters. A bare stage. Fee by arrangement. Libretto and vocal score on hire

'It is a characteristic of the human race that the most satisfactory relationships are those in which mother and daughter relationships achieve the transition into friendship ...' This highly entertaining musical presents mother/daughter relationships in a pastiche of situations which encompass school, exams, driving tests, budding romance, dreams, disillusionment, unemployment and employment.

Mr A's Amazing Maze Plays. Play. Alan Ayckbourn
M6 F2. Various simple settings. Fee code L

An ingeniously constructed play in which Suzy's mother buys her a small puppy to keep her company while she works hard to earn a living for them. A strange man— Mr Accousticus — moves into the empty house opposite their cottage; he charms Suzy's mother but frightens Suzy and her puppy Neville. Odd things start to happen ... Suzy is convinced that Mr Accousticus is responsible. She and Neville have to find out and how they do this depends on decisions taken by the audience aided by the Narrators!
ISBN 0 573 05098 8

Mr Easter Bunny. Play. Blanche Marvin
5 characters. A sitting-room and garden. Fee code B

Two children uncover the real basis of Easter, the rites of Spring, as pagan as ever was, and manage to convert their parents with the help of Mr Easter Bunny.

Mr Grump and the Clown. Play. Brian Way
M2 F2. Fee code E

With the help of costumes from a box, the cast become characters in the story of a clown who lost his laugh, the amazing adventures in recovering it, and the eventual return of laughter and gaiety to Grump Castle, which has been a miserable place ever since Mr Grump lost his laugh.

Mr Macaroni and the Exploding Pizza Pie. Play for children. John Gardiner and Fiz Coleman
16 characters, doubling possible. Various simple settings on an open stage. Fee code K

This fun-filled play revolves around the antics of three waiters sacked by Mr Macaroni, the money-minded owner of the Pizza Pie Palace. They devise various schemes to get their jobs back, and are steered through their adventures with the help of the audience. After bangs, flashes, songs, dances, talking snakes and even exploding pizza pies, all ends happily with a double wedding.
ISBN 0 573 05062 7

My Very Own Story. Play. Alan Ayckbourn
M8 F5, with doubling. A stage. Fee code M

Time for Percy Parton's Very Own Story, a gothic tale about a young man called Rupert who, in the midst of a deep, dark and snow-laden wood, comes across a mysterious family whose lives have been made wretched by the terrible spell that hangs over them. But wait a moment, this tale can't be Percy Parton's because Peter Patchett claims it's his! But it can't be Peter Patchett's, for according to Paul Peel, it's his! As the three story-tellers squabble a macabre, darkly humorous morality tale is brought to life.
ISBN 0 573 05105 4

The Nightingale and the Emperor. Play for children. Alfred Bradley, after the story by Hans Christian Andersen
M6 (young, middle-age, elderly) F2 (young, middle-age). A palace throne-room, a kitchen, a wood. Fee code G

In this adaptation of the famous story the time scale has been altered so that the action is continuous. The story-teller's songs, which are included in the text, can be sung by the doctor or, the author suggests, could be played as Hans Andersen himself telling the story from a position outside the main acting area.
ISBN 0 573 05079 1

Noddy. Enid Blyton, adapted for the stage by David Wood
18 characters may be played by M5 F3. Various simple settings. Fee code M

Exploiting the excitement of live theatre with imaginative staging, music, light, puppetry and lots of audience participation, this play will be a hit with all, whether they know Noddy or not. The plot may be familiar enough — Noddy and his friends pitched against the sneering goblins and a greedy witch — but the treatment is fresh, funny and inventive.
ISBN 0 573 05104 6

Nutcracker Sweet. Family musical. David Wood
M3 F3. Extra 1M or F. Fairground booths on an open stage. Fee code M

The Nuts, led by the imposing Kernel Walnut, decide to show that Nuts need not be 'nutty'. Unfortunately William the Conker seems to prove the opposite and falls under the spell of the wicked Professor Jelly, who is always on the look-out for nuts to 'glaze'. Together they almost succeed in glazing all our hero nuts, but the day is saved when Professor Jelly is imprisoned in his own glaze and turned into a large chocolate.
ISBN 0 573 15002 8

Old Father Time. Musical play. Book, music and lyrics by David Wood
Up to 30 characters but can be played by a cast of 12 with doubling and trebling. Four simple settings. Fee code M

Old Father Time lives in Big Ben and makes sure things happen on time. One day the inconceivable happens and Big Ben stops! The action of the play chases across the centuries through prehistoric times and near and far history until, with the help of some not-too-bright buskers and a wicked sorceress, Big Ben is started once more.
ISBN 0 573 05046 5

Old King Cole. An entertainment. Ken Campbell
M6 F2. Faz's office, Wembley Stadium, the hall of Buckingham Palace. Fee code M

This play is a pioneer of the irreverent, knockabout style of children's theatre that has become the norm. The Old King Cole of the nursery rhyme hardly gets a look in, since the action is dominated by a couple of likeable villains straight out of *The Beano*. Their attempts to wreck the wedding of Princess Daphne Cole to sporty Cyril the Fiddler are aided by an audience whose vociferous participation can be guaranteed.

The Old Man of Lochnagar. Musical play by David Wood, based on the book by H.R.H. The Prince of Wales
16 characters, may be played by 12 actors with doubling. Various settings. Fee code M

The Gorms are responsible for spraying the Highland heather purple so why is there only white heather? The Gorms have gone to ground because Giant Gormless (a not very big giant) is trying to capture them for his performing circus. So, the Old Man of Lochnagar sets off determined to save the Gorms and bring the colour back to the Highlands!

Oliver Twist. Play. Brian Way
M18 F3 or M5 F3 with doubling. Fee code K

A straightforward version of Dickens's classic. An honest, loving and exciting adaptation.

On Trial. Play. Brian Way
M2 F2. Fee code E

A frightening epidemic threatens a whole community. The long, exhausting search for a special herb that can stop the disease results in several deaths and one member of the community stands accused of being responsible.

Only a Game. Play. Carol Younghusband
20 characters, may be played by 9 actors with doubling. Various simple settings. Fee code G

Ben finds himself transported to the Land of Dotties. He discovers he can only return home if he lights up the Five Magic Stones. The Rhythmic Dice, the Joker, the Master crossword and Jig-saw each present Ben with a puzzling test which he must complete in a time set by the King. This delightful play by Carol Younghusband is a funny and exciting tale with a moral, for performance to children aged 4 to 9.
ISBN 0 573 05111 9

The Opposites Machine. Play. Brian Way
M2 F2. Fee code E

With the audience's help the Professor builds an opposites machine. Although the creation is intended to benefit humanity, something goes drastically wrong and man and machine attempt world domination. After a series of amusing — and trying — adventures a helpful magician saves mankind by getting the key and de-activating the machine. Theme play: A Key

Our Day Out. Play. Willy Russell
M10 F4. 7 boys. 3 girls. Extras. Various simple interior and exterior settings. Fee code H. In the volume *Act I*

This play by award-winning Willy Russell was first seen on BBC2 in 1977 and has now been specially edited for practical use by schools, colleges and groups. Sad, humorous and true to life, it tells the story of a bunch of underprivileged, remedial Liverpool schoolchildren who are taken on a day's outing by their teachers.

Our Day Out. Book by Willy Russell. Songs and music by Bob Eaton, Chris Mellor and Willy Russell
M6 F3 (may be played by M3 F2). 16-20 children. Various simple interior and exterior settings. Fee by arrangement

Some underprivileged schoolchildren are taken on a day's outing by their teachers. The children boisterously rampage through a roadside café, a zoo, Conway Castle and a beach. A joyous celebration of the joys and agonies of growing up, but also a sharp pointer to the depressing present and empty future, for a day out is as much as these children can expect.
ISBN 0 573 08058 5

The Owl and the Pussycat went to See ... Musical play for children. David Wood and Sheila Ruskin
M9 F5. Extras. One basic setting. Fee code M

The story based on the adventures of Lear's Owl and Pussycat who went to sea in a beautiful pea-green boat; of the Pig with a Ring through its Nose; of the villainous Plum Pudding Flea and others. These are interlinked with songs and mimed interludes. After many adventures, the Plum Pudding Flea is foiled and the two protagonists are married and live happily ever after.
ISBN 0 573 05027 9

The Pantomime Play. Play. Douglas Jackson

M1 F1. 19 other characters could be played by children: 5 girls, 14 either sex. A living-room (curtains), a wood, a bedsitter (curtains). Fee code D

On her way through the woods Red Riding Hood meets various well-known fairy-story characters, and the grim, greedy Wolf. The Wolf arrives first at the Grandma's bedsitter, tricks Grandma, then eats her. Later he eats Red also. A quick-witted Rabbit raises the alarm and Red and Grandma survive.
ISBN 0 573 05229 8

Papa Panov's Magic Christmas. Play. Paul Thain. From a story by Leo Tolstoy

Please see the entry in Section D.

The Papertown Paperchase. Musical play for children. David Wood
12 characters, doubling possible. Extras. Nine simple settings. Fee code J

The Salamander is in trouble with the Fireflies because he is unable to breathe fire. To redeem himself he is sent on a mission to burn down Papertown. The townspeople gather their resources to meet the threat: even the two petty criminals, Blotch and Carbon, are released to join forces. In the end Salamander, who has fallen for timid little Tishoo, helps to thwart the Fireflies, and Papertown is saved from destruction.
ISBN 0 573 05032 5

Percival the Performing Pig. Play. Dilys Owen
21 characters, doubling possible. Extras. A bare stage. Fee code C

On old MacDonald's farm there lived a pig with a truly wonderful voice. Animals came from miles around to hear him sing; and so did Hiram J. Potter who bought him and took him off to London for a career in Grand Opera. But Percival wasn't keen on London so he planned to get home to the farm.
ISBN 0 573 15224 1

Perkin and the Pastrycook. Play for children. David Foxton
14 characters. Extras. Various simple settings. Fee code H

This delightful comedy of errors follows the fortunes of Perkin and Wat. Perkin is royal odd-job man to the court of the Emperor. His friend, Wat, has recently been demoted from court pastrycook following a disastrous batch of cakes (Wat swears he was framed by the head cook). Wat is the comic focus, meaning well, but repeatedly foiled. Our heroes triumph at the last, Wat regaining his status and Perkin winning the heart of Princess Sophie.
ISBN 0 573 15031 1

Peter and the Wolf. Play. Blanche Marvin
7 characters. A forest, a library. Fee code B

A parody of Chekhov's *Cherry Orchard*. It shows the child's confusion when faced with the adult world, particularly the selling of their house at auction. In Act II one proceeds to retell the story, but in terms of the child's point of view. Adults become the animals, matching their colours and disposition from human to animal. The Prokofiev score is kept in its entirety throughout the second act.

Peter Pan. Fantasy. J. M. Barrie

For a full synopsis please see the entry in Section D.

Peter Pan. Book, music and lyrics by Piers Chater-Robinson. Adapted from the play by J. M. Barrie
30 named parts. Extras. Fee by arrangement

The everlasting classic account of the children who follow Peter Pan and the fairy Tinker Bell into Never Land where children never grow old and where Captain Hook is outwitted, is here set to a delightful score. The addition of such songs as 'The Darlings', 'What Happens When you're Grown Up', 'Rich, Damp Cake' and 'You've Gotta Believe' enhances the play and will win new audiences everywhere.
ISBN 0 573 08059 3

The Phantom Tollbooth. Children's play. Susan Nanus. Based on the book by Norton Juster
Maximum of 37 roles for 19 performers. Several simple settings. Fee code K

Milo's adventures begin when he opens a large package and drives his small toy car through the tollbooth into a new world. He learns of the great argument between King Azaz of Dictionopolis and his brother the Mathe-magician of Digitopolis. Milo also has to rescue the Princesses Sweet Rhyme and Pure Reason, from the Land of Ignorance. Milo realizes his attitude toward learning will never again be the same.

The Pied Piper. Play. Blanche Marvin
8 characters, doubling possible. A palace courtyard. Fee code D

This is the well-known tale of the Pied Piper written with the added Elizabethan play characteristics such as soliloquies, comics, song and dance, disguised hero, tragedy involving deep emotions, and multi scenes within the acts.

The Pied Piper. Play with music. Adrian Mitchell, devised by Alan Cohen. Music by Dominic Muldowney. From the poem by Robert Browning
M8 F4, with doubling. Children. Various interior and exterior settings. Fee code H for play. The music rights are leased by Karlin Music. Ask Samuel French Ltd for details

Hamelin is infested with rats and the town's avaricious Mayor employs the Pied Piper, who solves the problem. But when cheated of his reward, the Piper spirits away the children, guiding them through a mountainous region of fearsome monsters and lonely knights until they reach a children's paradise.

The Pied Piper. Musical play. David Wood and Dave and Toni Arthur
M5 F3 (minimum). 20 children. A street. Fee code M

The Piper, as a modern busker, delights the childen with his music. Their parents soon put a stop to the energetic dancing. Music has been banned on this street for hundreds of years. The townsfolk act out the story of the Pied Piper, but the Piper once again enchants the children with his music. It is only when the Piper receives his fee promised by the medieval townsfolk that he frees Hamelin from the curse.
ISBN 0 573 15007 9 — Libretto
ISBN 0 573 08587 0 — Vocal Score

Pinocchio. Play. Blanche Marvin
4 characters. A bare stage. Fee code B

Based on Pirandello's *Six Characters in Search of an Author*, as Pinocchio is in search of becoming a *real* boy. A group of actors turns up. They cast the parts in front of the children, then with only a few decorations of costume transform themselves into the different characters before the children's eyes, going into a series of adventures.

Pinocchio. Play. Brian Way
M7 F5 plus minor roles, doubling possible. An open stage. Fee code L

One of the most popular children's plays in Britain and the subject of broad-based critical acclaim, this stimulating interpretation reaches out and captures youthful audiences with unprecedented spirit. The timeless story of the wooden puppet who must earn the right to fulfil his longing to be a real boy brilliantly conveys lessons of responsibility and respect for the feelings of others. A charmingly innocent, powerfully believable play.

The Play of the Royal Astrologers. Play. Willis Hall
20 characters, doubling possible. Extras. Various simple settings. Fee code M

When the lazy Father Mole-Cricket decided to become an astrologer to make an easy living, little did he know that the Emperor's gold would be stolen on the very same day. Ordered by the Emperor to find the gold 'in the skies' and aided by his equally lazy son, they have just four days in which to recover it. They succeed but only after an accidental discovery of the thieves, a trip on the high seas with pirates and a fortunate case of mistaken identity.
ISBN 0 573 05091 0

Play the Game. Play with music. Bill Tordoff. Music by Paul Woodhouse
11 characters. Extras. Wasteground, a TV studio. Fee code D

A starkly realistic play with dark, comic overtones, for young adults, which addresses the ever-prevalent social issue of youth unemployment. The plot revolves around a group of unemployed youths, led by Jason, who, full of incentive, encourages them to enter a competition to win £100,000 with which they can escape from a life of no hope.
ISBN 0 573 12194 X

The Plotters of Cabbage Patch Corner. Musical play for children. David Wood
M6 F4. 1M 1F voices only. A garden. Fee code M

The insects in the garden are overshadowed by humans — the Big Ones. Infuriated by constant 'spraying', Slug, Greenfly and Maggot call for rebellion and ruination of the garden. The others oppose this, and war is declared. The garden goes to ruin, and the Big Ones decide to build a garage on it. The insects combine forces to restore the garden to its original beauty and thus preserve their home.
ISBN 0 573 05030 9

Primula the Non-Sheepdog and the Great Grey Wolf. Play. Graham Holliday
8 parts may be played by M2 F4. A hillside. Fee code D

This fast-paced verse play requires only the minimum of props and staging facilities. Primula is quite definitely a non-sheepdog, frightened by everything she meets. This is unfortunate because she has to safeguard three very naughty, headstrong sheep from the great grey wolf.
ISBN 0 573 15226 8

Puss in Boots. Play. Brian Way
M7 F4. Fee code K

A free-spirited adaptation of the classic fairy tale. A family of minstrels, along with their cat, find Jasonland in a state of despair. The old King Jason is unable to rule and his eldest son and heir, Marcus, cannot be found. Will the ruthless younger son, Boris, soon be the new king? Through the cat's magic and the audience's assistance the mystery of Marcus's disappearance is solved and Boris is overthrown.

Quest for the Whooperdink. Play with music. A. H. Teacey
M3 F2, 4 others M or F. Extras. Various simple settings. Fee code H

The Whooperdink is a rare fantastical bird with magic powers, seen only by the Urgles. When Professor Potterton is informed of a sighting in Urgleland he eagerly sets off. Along the way he encounters Salmonella, a wicked witch, and the Snowflake maker, doomed to create snow while dreaming of sun-kissed sandy beaches. When the Whooperdink's magic is discovered, all ends happily: the Snowflake Maker transforms the snowflakes into wishes and Salmonella is reformed.
ISBN 0 573 05070 8

Rabbit. Play. David Foxton
15 characters (M and F). Simple settings on a bare stage. Fee code D

This perceptive play, set ten years 'after the Bomb', portrays with frightening clarity the destruction of the human character, as compassion and social standards become lost in the struggle for power and survival. Fifteen teenagers struggle to make sense of their world's desolation. Ironically, they soon begin to repeat their parents' mistakes, with the play ending in a thought-provoking clash of personalities.
ISBN 0 573 15240 3

The Railway Children. E. Nesbit. Adapted by Dave Simpson
M5 F5. 5 girls. 5 boys. Extras. A country railway station, a cottage, a railway tunnel. Fee code M

Set in and around a country railway station at the turn of the twentieth century, the plight of the Railway Children grappling with their new environment is imaginatively brought to life for a modern audience while losing nothing of the original spirit of humour, tension, adventure and the final triumph of good over evil.
ISBN 0 573 05083 X

The Rainbow Box. Play. Brian Way
M2 F2. Fee code E

Four rainbow makers make their final and most magnificent beauty of the day, only to have it ruined by clumsy but well-meaning Smudge. By solving riddles behind each of the seven coloured doors, the audience and performers rescue and preserve the beauty of the rainbow just in time to save the fading Rainbow Queen.

Rainbow's Ending. Play. Noël Greig
Large ensemble playing many roles. A bare stage. Fee code J

This is a modern fable which tells the story of a world in the grip of two giants whose insatiable appetite is driving it, apparently inevitably, to utter devastation. How a society and its individuals react to such a threat is the subject of this multi-faceted play, whose 'storytelling' style encourages inventive and imaginative approaches to dramatic work with the performer acting as both character and narrator.

The Real Spirit of Christmas. Christmas play for children. Wes Magee

See the entry in Section D.

The Red Dragon. Play. Blanche Marvin
5 characters. A sitting-room and garden. Fee code B

A contemporary drama based on a miracle at Christmas through St George. No fairytale, only a credible miracle centred on a one-parent family and a handicapped boy.

A Right Christmas Caper. Play. Willis Hall

For a full synopsis please see the entry in Section D.

The Attack Upon and Defence of the Old Elvish Kingdom of Vassia Against **The River Witch** and Her Grim Horde. A play. David Clarke
28 speaking parts. Extras. An open space. Fee code G

The peace-loving Elves of Vassia are disturbed by rumours that the River Witch is planning an attack. As the Warmorgs, Vorps and Krills advance the Elves have no choice but to plan their defence in this crucial battle of survival ... A simple fable of the power of good over evil.
ISBN 0 573 15241 1

Robin Hood. Musical celebration. David Wood and Dave and Toni Arthur

For a full synopsis please see the entry in Section A.

Rockafella. Musical play. Les Scott, Roy Oakes and Ken Bolam
M10 F7. Extras (M and F). Various interior and exterior settings. Fee by arrangement. Vocal score available separately

At the disco Angela desperately wants to be accepted as part of 'The Gang' and following her Godfather's advice she turns up one Friday night and bowls them all over. The DJ, Tazz, a popular Prince Charming, falls for her and sweeps her off her feet, and when she starts flirting with Burker it needs all of the Godfather's influence and skill to get the disco hopping and bopping in tune again!
ISBN 0 573 08094 1 — Libretto
ISBN 0 573 08592 7 — Vocal score

Rockasocka. Musical play. Book and lyrics by John Gardiner. Music by Andrew Parr
M9 F9. Minimum of 25 for other parts. Extras. Simple settings. Fee by arrangement

An hilarious musical comedy about the hapless City F.C. and their attempts to win the World Cup Six-a-Side Championship. With a whole host of comic characters this is sure to be a winner, offering plenty of opportunities for flexible casting and staging: it can be played on a proscenium stage, in the round or on a thrust stage to give your audience a real football atmosphere!
ISBN 0 573 08094 1 — Libretto
ISBN 0 573 08590 0 — Vocal score

Round the World with Class 6. Play for children. Nick Warburton
7 children or more. A classroom. Fee code D

Class 6 are well-behaved, hard-working ... and bored. Every day is much the same — and then Mr Parker, the supply teacher, sets them an interesting project: to re-enact Sir Francis Drake's circumnavigation of the world in 1577. Within minutes the room is transformed into an Elizabethan sailing ship and the brave adventurers set sail!
ISBN 0 573 15239 X

♦ **Rupert and the Green Dragon.** Musical play. David Wood
Based on the *Rupert* stories by Mary Tourtel and Alfred Bestall
16 characters. May be played by M5 F5. Various simple settings. Fee code M

Edward Trunk wishes for a sunny day for his birthday, but Nutwood is currently experiencing only winter weather. Rupert goes to see the Clerk of the Weather. The friendly Green Dragon is a great help but Zita, the Ice Maid, has to be foiled first! Songs take the place of rhyming couplets and there is a chance for the audience to help in the adventure.
ISBN 0 573 05113 5 — Libretto
ISBN 0 573 08598 6 — Vocal score

Sammy's Magic Garden. Play with music. Kjartan Poskitt
10 characters, doubling possible. Extras. Various interior and exterior settings. Fee code L

An enormously entertaining and funny musical comedy/ghost story. Sammy has just moved into a new house, overseen by 'housekeeper' Miss Nettles and a bumbling gardener, Compost. Weird things start happening! Sammy and his friend Alice find proof that Miss Nettles is a witch and that the garden is filled with enchanted Flower-children put under a spell by her. But it's Sammy and Alice, with some help from Compost, who save the day and the children are released.
ISBN 0 573 15015 X

Save the Human. Play with music. Based on the story by Tony Husband and David Wood. Book and lyrics by David Wood. Music by Peter Pontzen and David Wood. Lyrics for 'Rock 'n' Roar' by Tony Husband
Large flexible cast, minimum of 8 or 11 actors possible. Various simple settings. Fee code M

'It seems that long, long ago human beings ruled the world but made a terrible mess of it. They kept having wars and polluting the earth. They nearly succeeded in killing themselves off completely ... ' Now the animals are in charge. A worldwide campaign is started to SAVE THE HUMAN from extinction.
ISBN 0 573 05090 2

The Scatterbrained Scarecrow of Oz. Play for children. Alfred Bradley
M10 F5, or a mixed cast of 9 with doubling. An open stage. Fee code F

In the sequel to *The Wizard of Oz,* the Wicked Witch has stolen the Scarecrow's brains, the Lion's courage and the Tinman's heart. So off Dorothy and her old friends go to the Mountain of Darkness to get them back. Many hazards and dangers are encountered on the journey but they eventually manage to retrieve everything and, with the help of Glinda the Good Witch, the Wicked Witch is whisked off in a whirlwind.
ISBN 0 573 05057 0

School Play. Play for young people. Donald Howarth
Any number and sex of characters. A classroom. Fee code D. (In *Playbill One*)

School Play is a play specially written for use in schools. It is a scripted play with opportunities for improvisation in the classroom. It has moments of humour, and also of suspense. In tackling this experimental play and bringing it to life, students will be experiencing some of the problems of actors and producers in the modern theatre.

The See-Saw Tree. Musical play. David Wood
16 characters, doubling possible. Various simple settings. Fee code M

An ancient Oak stands on ground which is ear-marked for development into a children's playground by Mr Jay. A public meeting is held to discuss his proposals, which include cutting down the three-hundred-year-old tree. The members of the council are then seen inside the tree in their equivalent animal forms to show us the devastating effect such plans would have on the inhabitants of the tree. In the end, the audience is asked to vote whether the See-Saw Tree should be saved or not.
ISBN 0 573 15017 6 — Libretto
ISBN 0 573 08583 8 — Vocal score

The Selfish Shellfish. Play with music. David Wood
7 characters. A rockpool. Fee code M

In this play, the serious contemporary issue of oil pollution is looked at from the point of view of shellfish directly involved. The fight of Urchin, Mussel, Starfish, Seagull and the shellfish himself, H. C., to avoid becoming the innocent victims of pollution caused by the collison of two ships at sea, is delightfully told, with the audience being encouraged to participate in the battles with Sludge and The Great Slick.
ISBN 0 573 05069 4

The Seven. Sweet rock musical. Charles Harter
M7 F9. Extras. Singers. Dancers. A living-room, a chapel, hall. Fee on application. Music on hire

Six Deadly Sins, Greed, Lust, Envy, Anger, Sloth and Gluttony have come to Lady Penelope's 'Half-Way House for Sinnerholics' in the hope of achieving redemption. They do their best under her formidable and Draconian rule, but finally become aware that she herself is perhaps the worst Sin of all — Pride. Even Lady Penelope, however, is not wholly to be condemned; as the play ends all Seven join in a final plea for tolerance and understanding.
ISBN 0 573 08047 X

Seven Golden Dragons. Play with music. Book and lyrics by Randall Lewton. Music by Peter Miller
34 named characters. Extras. Various simple interior and exterior settings. Fee code L

A fast-moving, fighting musical fantasy for a cast of between 30 and 60. The Elflings lead peaceful, beautiful lives, until threatened by the Orcs and the leader, Znakbar, who intends killing an Elfling a day until they relinquish the magic. The Elflings mistake the 'Golden Dragons' football team for the Seven Gold Dragons who would assist them, and the seven lads find themselves transported to Dungeons and Dragons land.
ISBN 0 573 05089 9

◆ **Shake, Ripple and Roll**. Musical for young people. Book and lyrics by Jenifer Toksvig. Music by David Perkins
13 principals. Chorus. An ice-cream parlour. Fee by arrangement

C / Y L

Another hectic day at Angelo's New York ice cream parlour when suddenly the phone rings — Angelo is dead! In walks glamorous Deanna la Domme, claiming to be his only living relative and announcing she's going to sell to Crazy Flavours. It is time to call Dirk Manley — private detective — to find the will double quick. An exuberant musical, with a glitzy rock'n'roll score, and a running time of approximately one hour. Period 1950s
ISBN 0 573 08112 3

Share and Share Alike. Book, music and lyrics by Geoff Morrow
M3 F9. Extras. Various simple settings. Fee by arrangement

Y L

C

Class 6C are given a hypothetical sum of £100 to invest on the Stock Exchange by the patronizing local bank manager. However Class 6C play it for real and nobody can believe their luck when they manage to make a profit of several thousand pounds — and that's only the beginning of their problems. 'What a production! … quite simply one of the best children's musicals I have ever seen … could easily become the girls' school answer to *Joseph and the Amazing Techicolor Dreamcoat*'. *Times Educational Supplement*

◆ **The Siege**. Play with songs. Book by Adrian Mitchell. Music by Andrew Dickson
Large flexible cast. Various simple settings. Fee code K (for play) code C (for music)

Y L

Adrian Mitchell has created a vibrant and topical text with songs. War breaks out and the town of Arden is under siege. On their sixteenth birthday and liable for military call-up, Betsy and Arlo Swados decide to flee to a neutral country but on the journey Arlo is killed. Betsy and the townspeople rebel against the racist gangster who has taken over the town and Arlo's funeral turns into a celebration for peace.

The Sleeping Beauty. Play. Blanche Marvin
16 characters, doubling possible. Optional extras. 3 acting areas. Fee code C

Y S

A Restoration Comedy with a shy and absent-minded Prince who is browbeaten into marrying the Sleeping Beauty, 100 years his senior. The children in the audience lend him a hand while good and bad fairies deal with the politics of the day and the gossips of the Court vie with each other in telling scandal.

Sleeping Beauty. Play. Brian Way
M15 F6, M8 F4 with doubling. Fee code K

Y L

A lively, creative version of the famed story featuring such diverse characters as the good and wicked godmothers, Prince Simple, an hilariously wild foreign chef and an entire sleeping kingdom! Script includes a beautiful 'candle dance' sequence and wild sword fight on a pirate ship.

A + C L

The Snatching of Horrible Harold. Play for children. John Gardiner and Fiz Coleman
M4 F5. Extra 1M or F. Composite setting. Fee code K

Horrible Harold, an oversized 'baby' with disgusting habits and a liking for Guinness and heavy rock music, falls prey to Mr Slickerbotham. After a near miss with the Dry Cleaning Emporium he is saved by his mum and reunited with his long-lost father. Plenty of audience participation combined with hilarious properties and easy staging make this an appealing play for children of all ages, especially when dirt triumphs over cleanliness!
ISBN 0 573 05074 0

C L

♦ **The Snow Queen**. Play. Ron Nicol. Based on the story by Hans Christian Andersen
Large mixed cast. Much doubling and trebling possible. Various simple settings. Fee code K

Please see the entry under Christmas Plays in Section D.

C

C L

Snow White and the Seven Dwarfs. Musical play. Jesse Braham White
M15 F11. Extras. Three interiors, one exterior. Fee code F

The story of the Princess with hair as black as ebony, skin as white as snow and lips as red as blood, whose stepmother sends her into the forest to die. In this version the stepmother is rewarded, with an enormous nose, for her sins, while Snow White wins her Prince. The music is included in the copy.
ISBN 0 573 05024 4

Y L

Some Canterbury Tales. Freely adapted from Geoffrey Chaucer by Ken Pickering. Music by Derek Hyde
Variable cast, 7 named roles. Extras. Flexible settings. Fee by arrangement

Six of Chaucer's best known Canterbury Tales — the Knight's, the Wife of Bath's, the Pardoner's, the Franklin's, the Nun's Priest's and the Miller's — are here freely adapted for the stage. Original and adapted music to suit the period has been added. The style of the play is that of a spontaneous telling of a story by a group of strolling players, with all the Company taking various parts in enacting the different tales.
ISBN 0 573 08077 1

C + Y L

♦ **Space Junk**. Play. Les Ellison
Large mixed cast. Various simple settings. Fee code G (play), code B (music)

Following their adventures in *Utter Garbage*, Dumpster, an idealistic young rat, and his sensible Uncle Binlid live happily in a clean city park, until the reappearance of Lord Vermin and his vile helpers. But Dumpster wants to look at the stars and soon the good rats are building a spaceship from rubbish. Propelled into space by the child-people in the audience, they meet Volga Ratskaya, a space laboratory rat. But they must battle with Lord Vermin before they can return safely.
ISBN 0 573 05121 6

Y L

Speak the Speech I Pray You … Play. Brian Way
M4 F2. Fee code K

This stimulating introduction to Elizabethan theatre brings to life Shakespeare's Heminge, Kempe, Burbage and a boy apprentice as they recreate famous scenes and stage techniques for a twentieth-century time-traveller. The selection of scenes is highly flexible and can involve substantial audience participation.

Stags and Hens. Comedy. Willy Russell
M6 (one non-speaking) F5. The Ladies' and Gents' toilets in a dance hall. Fee code M

Dave gets legless on a mix of drinks, while his mates demonstrate a combination of fear, lust and bravado. Linda's chums, alternately sentimental and sceptical about marriage, turn nasty when the bride starts dancing with an ex-lover, Peter. Whether Peter's worldly wisdom persuades Linda to flee an unsuitable marriage or merely makes her more prepared for the drudgery to come, is left unsaid.
ISBN 0 573 01609 7

Stone Soup. Play. Paul Thain
Mixed cast of 16. Extras. A bare stage. Fee code E

The wise Sophia enters a starving village and declares she will feed everyone with her magical stone soup, thereby gradually encouraging the villagers to share their own hoarded goods for the benefit of the community. She is labelled a subversive by the autocratic government figure, General Mayhem, who attempts to nationalize the pot of soup and place it under government control. The play ends with the cast and audience alike dancing merrily, however.
ISBN 0 573 15242 X

Storytellers. Play. Brian Way
M22 F12 or M8 F4 with doubling. Extras. Fee code K

Within a framework using the characters of the Mirrorman and the Toyman are woven imaginative adaptations of *The Princess and the Pea, The Elves and the Shoemaker, The Giant and the Golden Hairs* and *The Nightingale*. A sensitive and perceptive play for children.

The Struggle. Play. Brian Way
M4 F2. Fee code K

An energetic, modern adaptation of Bunyan's *The Pilgrim's Progress*. Adam leaves his peers to strike out on his own and is immediately confronted with worldly temptations, against which he desperately defends his right to be himself. He is led to the city of Vanity Fair — the epitome of depravity — and is tried for opposing city officials. Adam's impassioned defence sways the decision of the city in his favour.

Summer in the Park. Musical. Book by Ellen Dryden, lyrics by Don Taylor, music by Charles Young
Large, flexible cast. Secluded area in a park. Fee by arrangement

A derelict park is threatened by developers and a group of young people try to rescue it by writing and performing a play. But the project soon falters: the developers hover, the cast bicker and the hot weather breaks with a violent storm. But the park exercises a strange hold over them. A subtle, touching story combining an accurate, amusing account of producing a play with lively, realistic characterization and a memorable score.
ISBN 0 573 08089 5

Y
L

Surgical Sensations at St Sennapod's, or Dr Scalpel's Missing Bit. Play with music. John Gardiner and Fiz Coleman. Music arranged by James R. Pearson
19 characters, doubling possible. Extras. A hospital ward. Fee code K

A top surgeon has disappeared from St Sennapod's Hospital leaving young Dr Boldly in charge of Ward 10. Sinister Dr Scalpel arrives, trying to corner the market in spare-part surgery by snipping off spare parts wherever he can. However, Orderly Jim Pill and the hospital staff succeed in foiling Scalpel's dastardly plans and all ends happily. This fun-filled, fast-moving play for children is easily staged and allows plenty of opportunity for audience participation.
ISBN 0 573 05087 2

Y
L

C

The Sweeney Todd Shock 'n' Roll Show. Musical play. Peter Miller and Randall Lewton
20 main speaking parts, large supporting cast. Various interior and exterior settings. Fee by arrangement. Vocal score available separately

Billy and Tommy encounter the Demon Barber and his murderous accomplice Mrs Lovett. When Billy decides he needs a shave before travelling home to give his Susan a string of pearls the scene is set for musical mayhem with plenty of blood, pies and horrible murder thrown in for good measure!
ISBN 0 573 18030 X

C
L

The Tale of the Red Dragon. Play for children. Alfred Bradley
M3 F3, with doubling. An open stage. Fee code F

Told in the style of a Chinese play, with a Property Master who supplies whatever is necessary, the play is made up of stories from many different countries. It tells the tale of a poor young girl who goes out to seek the formidable Red Dragon and rescues both him and the Nightingale — who has lost her song — from the clutches of the Queen of Midnight. Playing time about 90 minutes

A
/
Y
S

Teddy Bear's Picnic. Play. Paul King
M1, 3 others, plus voice. Bedroom of a small boy. Fee code D

Two robots find themselves deposited in a small boy's bedroom and reconnoitre their new environment. They question Teddy about his role and the purpose of the other toys in the nursery. Poor Teddy is unable to conceive what exactly his role is! From here a sinister element enters the play. A seemingly simple play but with more than a hint of warning in it!
ISBN 0 573 12267 9

A
L

Telling Wilde Tales. Seven Fairy Tales of Oscar Wilde. Adapted for the stage by Jules Tasca
Flexible cast. An open stage. Fee code L for complete play. Individual plays are each on fee code B

If all seven plays are performed together they can be played by M4 F3 (minimum) although each play can be performed separately

Jules Tasca offers brilliant adaptations of some of the most endearing fairy tales ever written. This full evening's entertainment includes *The Birthday of the Infanta, The Star Child, The Happy Prince, The Nightingale and the Rose, The Devoted Friend, The Fisherman and his Soul, The Young King.*

Terraces. Play. Willy Russell
M6 F6. 2 children. Simple settings. Fee code D

The local football team has reached the final and when Danny facetiously remarks on painting the street in support his friends take up the idea with fervour and paint their terraced houses yellow — the team's colour. But Danny refuses and when the family are ostracized by the community Danny's wife leaves him. Is he just stubborn and awkward or is he right to assert his independence?

There Was an Old Woman … Family musical. David Wood
6 main characters. Children. A glade, a hilltop. Fee code M

Happily crowded to the laces of the shoe they live in, Mother Shipton and her family are faced with eviction as the Giant, whose shoe it was originally, has now come looking for it. The Great Boon arrives and attempts to save the family from the Giant. However, after a lot of adventures, muddles and magic all ends happily. There is even a circus — with all the acts provided by Mother Shipton's clever children.
ISBN 0 573 05051 1

Think of the Magic. Book, music and lyrics by Frank Rodgers
M14 F10, with doubling. Extras. Various simple interior and exterior settings. Fee by arrangement

This chirpy, cheeky, exuberant musical has everything from rock 'n' roll to punchy pop as well as a glut of evil, scheming characters, a street gang led by an irrepressible ten-year-old tomboy, lovesick teenagers and a local housing officer whose shattering news that the Carrs' family home is to be demolished sets the ball rolling or rather a Genie to appear from an old electric kettle!
ISBN 0 573 08069 0

The 13 Clocks. James Thurber. Adapted for the stage by Frank Lowe
M13 F2, with doubling. Extras. Various simple interior and exterior sets. Fee code K

Prince Zorn, weary of his frivolous life, disguises himself as a ragged minstrel and travels the land learning the life of the lowly, and perhaps slaying a dragon or two. He hears of the matchless beauty of Princess Saralinda who is held captive by the evil Duke and resolves he must win her hand despite the staggering perils imposed on her suitors. The Golux arrives to help the Prince and eventually with the aid of a magic rose the Prince and Princess emerge victorious over the Duke.

This Is Where We Came In. Play. Alan Ayckbourn
M6 (young, old) F4 (young, old). A bare stage. Fee code M

Fred sits ... somewhere or other ... next to a sign which reads 'Stories told here today'. A group of actors, the StoryPlayers, arrives. They are followed by the ageing StoryTellers, who create characters and the plots for the StoryPlayers to act out. What the StoryPlayers would really like, however, is to make up their own stories and they enlist Fred's help to free them.
ISBN 0 573 05106 2

Three Musketeers. Play. Brian Way
M11 F3. Fee code K

This adaptation of Dumas' novel maintains clarity by following a single main storyline. The plot involves the Cardinal's attempt to discredit the Queen, and the eventual saving of the situation by the heroic Three Musketeers.

The Thwarting of Baron Bolligrew. Comedy for children. Robert Bolt
M16. Extras M and F. Composite settng. Fee code M

Oblong is far too conscientious for the Duke and the rest of his knights, who want a rest from succouring the poor and needy. So he is persuaded to go on a mission to the Bolligrew Islands to subdue the wicked Baron who tyrannizes the peasants and pulls down churches. Eventually, of course, Right triumphs, the Baron departs to hunt dragons in the North, and Oblong rules in his place.
ISBN 0 573 05020 1

Tickle. Play with music. David Wood
Minimum cast of 6 players, of either sex. A bare stage. Fee code E

A workman sneezes violently. The 'tickle' is ejected — and arrives, pathetic as a new born baby, on the stage. He is only anxious to find a friend and a home. He becomes involved with three wicked Germs and causes chaos but finally finds his friend and a safe home — with a laughing hyena.
ISBN 0 573 05247 6

The Tinder Box. Play with music. Peter Whelan, adapted from a story by Hans Christian Andersen
M5 F5. Extras. Various simple interior and exterior settings. Fee code L

Peter Whelan's fine play adaptation (with songs) of Hans Christian Andersen's famous story is intelligent, funny and witty, ideal for performance to children by adults or young people. A common soldier meets varied fortunes as he gains and then loses a vast wealth, is sorely tested by many evils and finally marries the King's daughter and finds the peace and happiness he has sought.
ISBN 0 573 05108 9

Toad of Toad Hall. Musical play. A. A. Milne. Music by H. Fraser-Simson
Any number of characters. Six interiors, four exteriors. Fee code M. Band parts on hire

A dramatization of Kenneth Grahame's *Wind in the Willows*, with the kindly Rat, wise Badger, gentle Mole, and conceited, foolish Toad, who is always in trouble. His addiction to firstly caravanning, and then cars, his subsequent imprisonment, and the fight with the weasels and stoats are all included.
ISBN 0 573 05019 8

♦ **Tom Kitten and His Friends**. Play with songs. Book by Adrian Mitchell. Music by Stephen McNeff. Based on stories by Beatrix Potter
May be played by a cast of 9. Various interior and exterior settings. Fee code G (for play) code C (for music)

A delightful adaptation of four Beatrix Potter stories suitable for the entertainment of younger children: *The Story of Miss Moppet, The Tale of Two Bad Mice, The Story of a Fierce Bad Rabbit* and *The Tale of Tom Kitten*.
ISBN 0 573 05116 X

Treasure Island. Book and lyrics by Willis Hall. Music by Denis King. Adapted from the book by Robert Louis Stevenson
M18 F1, with doubling. Extras. Various interior and exterior settings. Fee by arrangement

All the characters that have captivated the imagination of readers for generations are vividly presented here — the rascally one-legged sea-dog Long John Silver, Billy Bones, Blind Pew, Ben Gunn and of course, young Jim Hawkins the 'rare bright spark' who sets the Treasure Island adventure in motion. There are many delightful songs and musical numbers, with plenty of scope for imaginative staging.
ISBN 0 573 08068 2

Treasure Island. Play. Brian Way
M21, M13 with doubling, F1. Fee code K

This straightforward, faithful adaptation of the Stevenson classic follows the adventures of young Hawkins in his fast-paced, breathtaking encounters with Long John Silver. The action includes fights with swords and muskets, and a challenging fight scene in the crow's nest and rigging of an old ship.

The True Story of Good King Wenceslas. Comedy. Edna Baker
M7 F2. A throne-room. Fee code C

A light-hearted exposition of what may have really happened between the Good King and Yonder Peasant.
ISBN 0 573 06611 6

Two Weeks with the Queen. Play. Mary Morris, adapted from the novel by Morris Gleitzman
Large cast may be played by 6 actors. Various simple settings. Fee code M

Colin from New South Wales is dispatched to relatives in London where it is discovered that his younger brother Luke has terminal cancer. Resourceful Colin has a mission; he wants to speak to the Queen in the hope that she can send him home with a good doctor. Cousin Alistair would like to help but stress brings on his dandruff. Colin takes the lock off the back door and goes out alone ...

The Ugly Duckling. Comedy. A. A. Milne
M4 F3. A throne-room. Fee code C

To prevent the Princess growing vain, her fairy godmother has withheld the gift of beauty from her — until the day she falls in love.
ISBN 0 573 05238 7

Ulysses. Rock musical. Ken Pickering and Keith R. Cole
10 main speaking parts, large supporting cast. A bare stage. Fee by arrangement, vocal score available separately

For Ulysses on his rock odyssey through myth and time it's trouble all the way home! Can he resist Calypso? What is in store for the crew when they meet the liberated Circe and her Sauna Girls? And who will have the strength to bend the great bow? Armed with a native cunning and a dazzling score Ulysses rocks home with plenty of youthful verve and nerve!

Y
L

United We Stand. Musical Play. Book, lyrics and music by Ken Bolam, Roy Oakes and Les Scott
M10 F8, large supporting cast. Various simple interior and exterior settings. Fee by arrangement. Vocal score available separately

Merton United FC reach the FA Cup Semi-Final. For the Merton males football becomes their total obsession, to the fury of the Merton female population who feel themselves taken for granted and so announce they are going on strike! 'A good working team has come up with a superb example of an end of term musical.' *Stage*
ISBN 0 573 08054 2

A
L

Utter Garbage. Play. Les Ellison
7 characters, 5 extras. A rubbish dump. Fee code G (play) Fee code A (song)

C

Dumpster, an idealistic young rat who lives in a rubbish dump, dreams of a brighter, better world. But his dreams are dashed daily by His Ignoble Ratship The Lord Vermin, Ruler of the Refuse, Defender of the Dump and Guardian of the Garbage, who has plans to turn every park and every garden into Utter Garbage! A delightful play about our environment for performance to children, with plenty of opportunities for lively audience participation!
ISBN 0 573 05112 7

C
S

The Valley of Echoes. Play. Brian Way
M2 F2. Fee code E

To recover his laugh, the clown must journey to the Valley of Echoes, obtain a magic glove and return it to the Echo King. During the adventurous trek, the clown is chased through the Forest of Fear by the Shadow People, makes the difficult climb over the Mountain of Memories, and meets head-on with the chilling Icicle Queen. Theme play: The Clown

A
L

The Voyage of the Dawn Treader. Play. Glyn Robbins. Adapted from the book by C. S. Lewis
M11 F2, with doubling. Various simple interior and exterior settings. Fee code M

This enthralling adaptation of one of C. S. Lewis's Narnian stories tells the adventures of the *Dawn Treader,* a dragon-ship led by Caspian, King of Narnia. The story is a traditional quest and the marvels include dragons, invisible islanders and a lake that turns everything to gold. The play can be very simply staged with few scenic requirements and no elaborate props.
ISBN 0 573 05085 6

C
L

The Voyage of the Jumblies. Play with music. Philip Freeman Sayer
19 characters, doubling possible. Extras. Various simple settings. Fee code H

An original, highly-imaginative and stimulating entertainment for children, whether as actors or members of the audience. Based on the classic characters created by Edward Lear in his nonsense poetry the two-act play, with a running time of ninety minutes, has simple settings, offers excellent, flexible casting opportunities for children, and is complemented by Edward Lear's verse set to music adapted from traditional folk tunes.

The Water Babies. Play with music. Willis Hall. Songs by John Cooper. Based on the story by Charles Kingsley
19 characters, can be played by M3 F6. Extras. Various simple settings. Fee by arrangement

Charles Kingsley's well-loved story of the Water Babies is enchantingly brought to life in this adaptation by Willis Hall. The tale of young Tom, apprentice to the unpleasant chimney sweep Mr Grimes, and his underwater journey to the End-of-Nowhere, is interspersed with delightful songs by John Cooper.
ISBN 0 573 08076 3

Whale. Play. David Holman
51 characters, doubling possible. Various interior and exterior settings. Fee code M

In October 1988 three grey whales were trapped under the spreading ice-cap of an Arctic winter in Alaska. The story of Pitu, Siku and K'nik aroused international sympathy and support for the rescue operation which brought together the Americans, Russians and Inuits. Legend has it that the whales are trapped in Sedna's hair and only when she combs it will they be free. 'The juvenile audience gave every sign of being enthralled and it would be a hard-hearted adult who wasn't moved too.' *Sunday Telegraph*

The Wheel. Play. Brian Way
M2 F2. Fee code E

A fantastic wheel with a magical attendant spins three charming stories for its owner who is going blind. Designed specifically to help youngsters and teachers to see how easily they can act out their own stories.

Where the Rainbow Ends. Play with music. Clifford Mills and John Ramsay
18 characters. Dancers. Extras. One interior, six exterior settings. Fee code H

Since their mother and father were shipwrecked, Crispian and Rosamund Carey have been living with their aunt and uncle. Rosamund discovers in a book that all lost loved ones are to be found in the land where the rainbow ends. Together with a Genie of a magic carpet found in the library and two friends, the children set out on their search.
ISBN 0 573 05021 X

♦ **The Wind in the Willows**. Kenneth Grahame. Adapted for the stage by Alan Bennett. Music by Jeremy Sams
24 characters. Extras. Various settings. Fee code M (play) code C (music)

For a full synopsis please see the entry in Section A.

The Wind in the Willows. Family entertainment by John Morley, adapted from the novel by Kenneth Grahame

For a full synopsis please see the entry in Section A.

The Wind in the Willows. Musical play based on Kenneth Grahame's novel. Book and lyrics by Willis Hall. Music by Denis King
15 characters. Extras. Various settings. Fee by arrangement

A delightful dramatization, with enchanting songs, of Kenneth Grahame's classic tale of river-bank animals. Toad finds himself in prison but manages to escape, but not before Toad Hall, his pride and joy, has been overrun by the wicked Weasels. Thanks to the efforts of his kind and concerned friends, however, all ends happily, after an exciting battle to regain Toad's home.
ISBN 0 573 08070 4

Winnie-the-Pooh. Play. Glyn Robbins. Adapted from the novel by A. A. Milne
M7 F4. A nursery, a wood. Fee code M

We are introduced to all A. A. Milne's well-loved characters — Christopher Robin, Kanga, Roo, Piglet, Tigger, Eeyore and Owl, not forgetting the Bear of Very Little Brain himself, Pooh — and follow their adventures involving bees, balloons, boats and birthdays in the 100 Aker Wood. ' ... hard to imagine a more faithful adaptation ... translates so effortlessly you could almost imagine you were reading it.' *Oxford Mail*
ISBN 0 573 05086 4

◆ **The Witches.** Roald Dahl. Adapted for the stage by David Wood
21 characters, may be doubled by M4 F6 plus 15 witches (extras) doubling as Diners. Various interior and exterior settings. Fee code M

Roald Dahl's story is magically adapted for the stage by David Wood. It toured extensively before a successful West End season at the Duke of York's Theatre. ' ... while the kids will be thrilled by the dazzling illusions and the complex puppetry, their parents will be no less engaged by the sly humour that lurks within this ostensibly frivolous confection.' *What's On*
ISBN 0 573 05099 6

The Wizard of Oz. Alfred Bradley. From the story by L. Frank Baum
M6 F7, doubling possible. An open stage. Fee code K

This version can be produced very simply. It needs no stage and may be performed on the floor of a school hall. Alternatively a more ambitious production could use back-projection, flash-boxes, and all the magic of a proscenium stage, provided all the settings are kept simple. By doubling, the cast can be reduced to a total of nine players.
ISBN 0 573 05058 9

The Wizard of Wobbling Rock. Play with music. Book and lyrics by Patricia Wood. Music by Christopher Lummis
37 characters. Various interior and exterior settings. Fee code J. Vocal score available separately

Wicked Wizard of Wobbling Rock has taken over the Isle of Dippy, forcing the Islanders to emigrate. On the way, Princess Poppy is kidnapped by two Warlocks and chained up in the Wizard's cave with Duke Devastation. But of course all ends happily with the help of the Bookworms, three lesser-spotted Ding-Dings and some of the Wizard's Shrinking Spray! Simple settings and charming songs combine to give an evening of enchantment for all.
ISBN 0 573 05068 6

Worzel Gummidge. Book and lyrics by Keith Waterhouse and Willis Hall. Music by Denis King. Based on the characters created by Barbara Euphan Todd
M12, doubling possible, F4. 1 boy, 1 girl. Extras. Various interior and exterior settings. Fee by arrangement

All the familiar characters of the television series are brought to life again in this stage adaptation. Worzel creates havoc and farce wherever he goes in his frenzied efforts to win Aunt Sally's unwilling hand until he finds himself before the scarecrow court on a very serious charge. But the final resolution is a happy one with a birthday cake enormous enough to satisfy even Worzel's appetite!
ISBN 0 573 18031 8

You, Me and Mrs Jones. Comedy. Tony Horitz
M10 F9, doubling possible. Various simple settings. Fee code E

This comedy centres on two unemployed teenagers, uncertain about themselves and the world around them. They are sent on a mission to find 'heroes to save the day'. They encounter a hotchpotch of humanity from violent street gangs to a family of vagrants. And surprisingly it is in this final encounter that they find their 'heroes'. This is a fast-moving comedy yet it makes a serious statement too.
ISBN 0 573 12272 5

Zigger Zagger. Play. Peter Terson
M34 F5, doubling possible. Extras. Composite setting. Fee code J

Against the background of football is the author's concern at the emptiness and futility facing so many youngsters today when they leave secondary school only to find themselves in a series of dead-end jobs, if they are employed at all. Harry and Zigger Zagger are shown against a wide background of contemporary urban society. The play may indeed be called an important social document, but its essential appeal lies in its exhilarating theatrical life.

C

SECTION D
Pantomimes and Christmas Plays

CONTENTS

Pantomimes Full Length

Pantomimes by Betty Astell

Vocal scores available separately.

These pantomimes have all been successfully presented by Betty Astell and her husband Cyril Fletcher at various professional theatres. Against a background of traditional music Miss Astell has written her own compositions, and with an average cast number of 12 plus chorus, these pantomimes will be ideal for the average amateur theatre company.

Aladdin
12 Principals. Chorus. 8 Interiors. 5 Exteriors. Fee code K

Cinderella
16 Principals. Chorus. 8 Interiors. 4 Exteriors. Fee code K

Dick Whittington
13 Principals. Chorus. 4 Interiors. 5 Exteriors. Fee code K

Mother Goose
17 Principals. Chorus. 4 Interiors. 4 Exteriors. Fee code K

Queen of Hearts
12 Principals. Chorus. 5 Interiors. 6 Exteriors. Fee code K

The Sleeping Beauty
15 Principals. Chorus. 6 Interiors. 5 Exteriors. Fee code K

Pantomime by Julia Banks

◆ **Hercules — the Panto!**
M4 F8, 1M or F. Large chorus. Various settings. Fee code L
ISBN 0 573 16440 1

Pantomimes by Simon Brett

◆ **Sleeping Beauty**. Book and lyrics by Simon Brett. Music by Sarah Travis. M4 F4, 2M or F. Extras. Fee by arrangement, ISBN 0 573 08110 7 (libretto). Piano/vocal score on hire

◆ **The Tale of Little Red Riding Hood**. A Untraditional Pantomime. Simon Brett (book and lyrics), Sarah Travis (music). 8 principals. Chorus. Various simple settings. Fee by arrangement. ISBN 0 573 08106 9 (libretto). Piano/vocal score on hire. Optional violin score

Pantomimes by Alan Brown

Alan Brown's pantomimes recreate those of Victorian times, blending traditional elements — including Harlequin interludes and suggestions for period songs — with subtle updatings to suit modern young audiences.

Aladdin and His Wonderful Lamp
Mixed cast of 21. Various interior and exterior settings. Fee code M
ISBN 0 573 06486 5

The Babes in the Wood
Mixed cast of 25. Extras. Various simple exterior and interior scenes. Fee code M
ISBN 0 573 16432 0

Cinderella
17 Principals, with doubling. Extras. Various interior and exterior settings. Fee code M
ISBN 0 573 06475 X

Dick Whittington
Mixed cast of 22. Extras. Various interior and exterior settings. Fee code M
ISBN 0 573 06478 4

Puss in Boots
Mixed cast of 17. Extras. Various simple interior and exterior settings. Fee code M
ISBN 0 573 06466 0

Sleeping Beauty
Mixed cast of 23. Various interior and exterior settings. Fee code M
ISBN 0 573 06491 1

Basic Pantomimes

Specially written for those who want to build their own show. The traditional story is told in modern prose dialogue and provision is made for the inclusion of local and topical material, songs and musical numbers. At the same time each pantomime is complete as published, and can be performed, if desired, without any alteration. The fee for each pantomime is code E, unless otherwise stated.

The Babes in the Wood. S. A. Polley and Conrad Carter
17 Principals. Chorus. 2 Interiors. 6 Exteriors
ISBN 0 573 06408 3

Cinderella. P. H. Adams and Conrad Carter
8 Principals. Chorus. 3 Interiors. 2 Exteriors. Fee code F
ISBN 0 573 06415 6

Dick Whittington. Trudy West
16 Principals. Chorus. 2 Interiors. 4 Exteriors
ISBN 0 573 06420 2

Humpty Dumpty. Trudy West
19 Principals. Chorus. 2 Interiors. 2 Exteriors
ISBN 0 573 06426 1

Jack and the Beanstalk. P. H. Adams and Conrad Carter
9 Principals. Chorus. 1 Interior. 4 Exteriors
ISBN 0 573 06428 8

Mother Goose. Trudy West
18 Principals. Chorus. 1 Interior. 4 Exteriors
ISBN 0 573 06437 7

Puss in Boots. Conrad Carter and Trudy West
16 Principals. Chorus. 2 Interiors. 4 Exteriors. Fee code F
ISBN 0 573 06444 X

Sinbad the Sailor. Pauline Stuart
17 Principals. Chorus. 1 Interior. 5 Exteriors
ISBN 0 573 06451 2

Pantomimes by David Cregan with music by Brian Protheroe

These pantomimes were written for the Theatre Royal, Stratford East, and combine all the traditional elements with original characterizations, imaginative and innovative staging ideas and witty, melodic songs.

Aladdin
15 Characters. Various interior and exterior settings. Fee code K
ISBN 0 573 16404 5

Beauty and the Beast
12 Characters. Various simple interior settings. Fee code K
ISBN 0 573 06481 4

Cinderella
13 Characters. Various simple interior and exterior settings. Fee code K
ISBN 0 573 06488 1

Jack and the Beanstalk
19 Characters. Various interior and exterior settings. Fee code K
ISBN 0 573 06477 6

Red Riding-hood
M7 F5, with doubling. Various interior and exterior settings. Fee code K
ISBN 0 573 06474 1

Sleeping Beauty
12 Principals. Extras. Various simple settings. Fee code K
ISBN 0 573 06472 5

Pantomimes by Crocker and Gilder
Books by John Crocker, music and lyrics by Eric Gilder

These are full length pantomimes, entirely traditional with lots of humour. Each has its own original and delightful score which is available separately. The large number of both amateur and professional groups who present Crocker and Gilder pantomimes regularly every year is unmistakable proof of their success.

Aladdin
14 Principals. Chorus. 8 Interiors. 4 Exteriors. Fee code L
ISBN 0 573 06471 7

Babes in the Wood
13 Principals. Chorus. 5 Interiors. 5 Exteriors. Fee code L
ISBN 0 573 16409 6

Cinderella
15 Principals. Chorus. 7 Interiors. 4 Exteriors. Fee code L
ISBN 0 573 16457 6

Dick Whittington
12 Principals. Chorus. 4 Interiors. 8 Exteriors. Fee code L
ISBN 0 573 06465 2

Humpty Dumpty
15 Principals. Chorus. 4 Interiors. 7 Exteriors. Fee code L
ISBN 0 573 16413 4

Jack and the Beanstalk
14 Principals. Chorus. 6 Interiors. 7 Exteriors. Fee code L
ISBN 0 573 16454 1

Mother Goose
16 Principals. Chorus. 4 Interiors. 6 Exteriors. Fee code L
ISBN 0 573 16424 X

Puss in Boots
16 Principals. Chorus. 5 Interiors. 5 Exteriors. Fee code L
ISBN 0 573 16446 0

Queen of Hearts
14 Principals. Chorus. 5 Interiors. 6 Exteriors. Fee code L
ISBN 0 573 16438 X

Red Riding Hood
13 Principals. Chorus. 5 Interiors. 5 Exteriors. Fee code L
ISBN 0 573 16433 9

Robinson Crusoe
12 Principals. Chorus. 2 Interiors. 7 Exteriors. Fee code L
ISBN 0 573 06473 3

Sinbad the Sailor
15 Principals. Chorus. 3 Interiors. 8 Exteriors. Fee code L

The Sleeping Beauty
12 Principals. Chorus. 3 Interiors. 4 Exteriors. Fee code L
ISBN 0 573 16411 8

Pantomimes by Richard Lloyd

The Christmas Cavalier
M7 F5, Children. Various simple settings. Fee code K

All the traditional elements are intact in this new pantomime which is set just after the English Civil War, when the Puritan Witchfinder General is trying to stamp out Christmas jollifications and meeting spirited opposition.
ISBN 0 573 06510 1

Smut's Saga or Santa and the Vikings
M14 F4. Various interior and exterior settings. Fee code K

Smut's Saga is a tale of war, pillage and raucous innuendo set in the days when Vikings plundered the Scandinavian coastline, stealing booty, kidnapping women and generally causing havoc, with a scandalous disregard for personal hygiene.
ISBN 0 573 16502 5

♦ Treasure Island, the Panto
19 characters. Extras. Various simple settings. Fee code K

A swashbuckling tale of skulduggery upon the high seas, treasure on desert island, a Guatemalan crimson parakeet going by the name of Cap'n Haddock, Dame Ladd's fisherman's pies and — death by chocolate.
ISBN 0 573 06496 2

Pantomimes by Verne Morgan

Verne Morgan's pantomimes are clear and straightforward, following the traditional stories closely. Choice of music for songs and dances is left to the director, except in the case of *Jack and the Beanstalk*, for which several original numbers have been written by the author.

Babes in the Wood
M12 F4. Extras. Several simple sets. Fee code H
ISBN 0 573 16414 2

Dick Whittington
12 Principals. 6 Small Parts. Chorus. Dancers. Children. 5 simple settings. Fee code H
ISBN 0 573 16422 3

Jack and the Beanstalk
M6 F4. Extra 2M or F. Chorus. Children. Dancers. Various simple settings. Fee code H
ISBN 0 573 06467 9

Mother Goose
13 Principals. 3 Small Parts. Chorus. Dancers. Children. 5 simple settings. Fee code H
ISBN 0 573 06461 X

Old King Cole or King Cole in Space. Pantomime space oddity
13 Principals. Extras. Children. Dancers. Chorus. Various simple settings. Fee code H
ISBN 0 573 06470 9

Pantomimes by John Morley

John Morley's pantomimes are full of fun and originality and can be produced very lavishly or simply, depending on the company's resources, without in any way affecting the comedy routines or the telling of the story. The choice of music is left to the director.

Aladdin
19 Principals. Dancers. Chorus. Extras. Various front-cloth and full-stage sets. Fee code K
ISBN 0 573 06462 8

Dick Whittington
12 Principals. 5 Small parts. Chorus. Dancers. Children. Various simple settings. Fee code L
ISBN 0 573 16435 5

Goldilocks and the Three Bears
10 Principals. Dancers. Chorus. Various simple settings. Fee code L
ISBN 0 573 06464 4

Jack and the Beanstalk
14 Principals. Extras. Singers. Dancers. Various interior and exterior settings. Fee code K
ISBN 0 573 06463 6

Robinson Crusoe
16 Principals. Chorus. Various simple settings. Fee code K. (Revised version 1997)
ISBN 0 573 06468 7

Sinbad the Sailor
11 Principals. 8 Small parts (all M or F). Chorus. Simple outdoor settings. Fee code L
ISBN 0 573 16441 X

Pantomimes by Ronald Parr

These pantomimes can be performed with comparatively small casts, and only modest scenery is required. The songs are mostly to Sir Arthur Sullivan's music for the Savoy Operas. The fee for each is code H

The Story of Cinderella
9 principals. Extras. Chorus. 3 Interiors. 3 Front scenes
ISBN 0 573 06418 0

The Story of Jack and the Beanstalk
13 Principals. Chorus. 1 Interior. 1 Exterior
ISBN 0 573 06431 8

Pantomimes by Paul Reakes

Paul Reakes' pantomimes include many original twists to the familiar stories, with plenty of audience participation. They can be staged as simply or as elaborately as desired.

Babes in the Wood
14 Principals. Chorus. Extras. Various interior and exterior settings. Fee code K
ISBN 0 573 06487 3

Dick Turpin
14 characters. Extras. Various interior and exterior settings. Fee code K
ISBN 0 573 06494 6

◆ **King Arthur**. A pantomime adventure in Camelot. M6 F4, plus children, chorus and dancers. Various simple settings. Fee code K. ISBN 0 573 06498 9

Little Jack Horner
13 Principals. Chorus. Children. Fee code K
ISBN 0 573 06484 9

Little Miss Muffet
13 Principals. Chorus. Children. Various simple settings. Fee code K
ISBN 0 573 06480 6

Old Mother Hubbard
19 Principals. Chorus. Children. Various simple settings. Fee code K
ISBN 0 573 06492 X

Santa in Space
14 Principals. Chorus. Children. Various settings. Fee code H
ISBN 0 573 06509 8

Sinbad the Sailor
17 Principals. Chorus. Children. Various interior and exterior settings. Fee code K
ISBN 0 573 06482 2

Pantomimes by Norman Robbins

Norman Robbins' fun-packed pantomimes tell the traditional stories in a clear fast-moving style and can be staged simply or elaborately, as required. The choice of music is left to the director.

Aladdin
Mixed cast of 10. Children. Extras. Various simple interior and exterior settings. Fee code K
ISBN 0 573 16442 8

Ali Baba and the Forty Thieves
13 Characters. Chorus. Various simple interior and exterior settings. Fee code L
ISBN 0 573 06485 7

Babes in the Wood
M11 F3. Extras. Chorus. Various simple settings. Fee code L
ISBN 0 573 06493 8

Cinderella
12 Characters. Chorus. Various simple settings. Fee code L
ISBN 0 573 16417 7

Dick Whittington
12 Principals. Extras. Chorus. Dancers. Junior Chorus. Various simple settings. Fee code K
ISBN 0 573 06483 0

The Grand Old Duke of York
M8 F5. Chorus. Various simple interior and exterior settings. Fee code K
ISBN 0 573 16423 1

Hickory Dickory Dock
M10 F8 (some interchangeable). Extras. Various simple settings on an open stage. Fee code J
ISBN 0 573 06460 1

Humpty Dumpty
M9 F5. Chorus. Various simple settings. Fee code J
ISBN 0 573 16430 4

Jack and the Beanstalk
M5 F3. Extras. Chorus. Various interior and exterior settings. Fee code L
ISBN 0 573 06490 3

Puss in Boots
13 Principals. Extras. Various interior and exterior settings. Fee code L
ISBN 0 573 06489 X

◆ **Red Riding Hood**. M7 F4. Chorus. Dancers. Children. Various simple settings. Fee code L.
ISBN 0 573 06499 7

Rumpelstiltzkin
M9 or 10, F2 or 3. Extras. Various simple settings. Fee code L
ISBN 0 573 06459 8

Sing a Song of Sixpence
M8 F9. Extras. Various simple settings. Fee code J
ISBN 0 573 06458 X

The Sleeping Beauty
11 Principals. Chorus. Various simple interior and exterior settings. Fee code K
ISBN 0 573 06479 2

Snow White
15 characters. Chorus. Various simple settings. Fee code L
ISBN 0 573 06495 4

Tom, the Piper's Son
17 Principals. Extras. Chorus. Various simple settings. Fee code K
ISBN 0 573 06469 5

The Wonderful Story of Mother Goose
11 Principals. Extras. Chorus. Various simple settings. Fee code K
ISBN 0 573 06476 8

Pantomimes by K. O. Samuel

In these pantomimes the old stories have been re-written for modern audiences. They are equally suitable for performance by adults or older children. The fee in each case is code E

Aladdin and His Wonderful Lamp
10 Principals. Chorus. 3 Interiors. 2 Exteriors
ISBN 0 573 06405 9

Alibaba and the Forty Thieves
10 Principals. Chorus. 2 Interiors. 3 Exteriors
ISBN 0 573 06407 5

Robin Hood and the Babes in the Wood
10 Principals. Chorus. 1 Interior. 3 Exteriors
ISBN 0 573 06447 4

Pantomime by Janet Stanford

◆ **Snow White — the Purdiest Gal in the West**
Music by Carol Gulley. Variable cast: minimum M2 F2, maximum M1 F2, 9 M or F. Various simple settings. Fee code G (to include optional music). ISBN 0 573 01874 X

Pantomime by David Tristram

◆ **Cinders: The True Story**
9 Principals. Chorus. Various simple settings. Fee code L

Pantomimes for the Young

These are less sophisticated than the foregoing and are particularly suitable for the entertainment of children. Many of the parts can also be taken by the younger players.

By Margaret Carter

The fee for each of these pantomimes is code C

Aladdin
20 Principals. Chorus. 5 Interiors. 4 Exteriors
ISBN 0 573 06402 4

Dick Whittington
19 Principals. Chorus. 3 Interiors. 4 Exteriors
ISBN 0 573 06421 0

The Sleeping Beauty
20 Principals. Chorus. 3 Interiors. 1 Exteriors
ISBN 0 573 06453 9

Snow White and the Seven Dwarfs
23 Principals. Chorus. 3 Interiors. 2 Exteriors
ISBN 0 573 06456 3

By P. J. McLoughlin

Cinderladdin
7 Boys or Girls. 7 Extras. Chorus. Standing set: 2 Interiors. Fee code E
ISBN 0 573 06614 0

In this simply staged pantomime the stories of Cinderella and Aladdin are ingeniously combined.

Pantomime One Act

Potty Pantomime. Book by John Crocker. Lyrics and music by Eric Gilder
M8 or F8. With doubling may be played by M2 F1. A bare stage. Fee code B

A delightful, potty panto which is a pithy pot-pourri of popular pantomime plots!

Potted Panto-Parodies in Rhyme by C. R. Cook

Three one-act pantomimes on well-known themes — with a difference. The fee for each of the panto-parodies is code C.

Ali the Barber
9 Principals. Chorus. 5 Scenes
ISBN 0 573 06601 9

Beastie and the Beaut
12 Characters. 1 Interior. 1 Exterior
ISBN 0 573 06604 3

Cinderalfred or The Silvern Boot
M9 F4. 4 Scenes
ISBN 0 573 06607 8

Minidramas by Richard Tydeman

All of these plays last 15-20 minutes, need little or no rehearsal, and use only the simplest of costumes and properties. There is no reason why they should not be performed entirely by men or entirely by women, if a mixed cast is not available. For full synopses see the entries in Section B.

Albert Laddin. M4 F6	ISBN 0 573 06617 5
Ali's Barbara. M6 F7	ISBN 0 573 12006 4
Cock Robin Hood. M10 F3	ISBN 0 573 12027 7
Forty Winks Beauty. M5 F7	ISBN 0 573 06616 7
Little Red Whittington. M4 F4. Extras M and F	ISBN 0 573 06618 3
Puss in Slippers. M4 F6. Extras M and F	ISBN 0 573 16612 9
Red Hot Cinders. M5 F3. Extras M and F	ISBN 0 573 06615 9
Snow White Special. M10. Extras M and F	ISBN 0 573 16608 0

Family Musicals by David Wood

David Wood has adapted these fairy tales into musical plays rather than conventional pantomimes. Comedy, adventure and lively original songs combine to make these unusual plays sure-fire hits with family audiences.

D

Aladdin
15 Principals (doubling possible). Children. Various interior and exterior settings. Fee code M
ISBN 0 573 16403 7

Babes in the Magic Wood
Mixed cast of 12. Various interior and exterior settings. Fee code M
ISBN 0 573 06506 3

Cinderella
16M or F (variable). Extras. Various interior and exterior scenes. Fee code M
ISBN 0 573 16427 4

Dick Whittington and Wondercat
Flexible cast, minimum of M8 F5. Extra 1M or F. Chorus of adults or children. Several interior and exterior settings. Fee code M
ISBN 0 573 06507 1

Jack and The Giant
Mixed cast of 12. Various simple settings. Fee code M
ISBN 0 573 05080 5

Mother Goose's Golden Christmas
M6 F6, with doubling. Fee code M
ISBN 0 573 06504 7

Old Mother Hubbard
M10 F10, doubling, and some M and F interchangeable. A street, a forest, a well, a cave. Fee code M
ISBN 0 573 06504 7

Christmas Plays
Full Length

Bad Day at Black Frog Creek. Musical play. John Gardner and Fiz Coleman

For a full synopsis see the entry in Section C.

A Child's Christmas in Wales. Christmas musical. Jeremy Brooks and Adrian Mitchell. Based on the poem by Dylan Thomas
M15 F7. Extras. Various simple settings. Fee code M

This enchanting play with music uses a variety of carols and well-known Welsh songs to conjure up the pure magic of Christmas for the enjoyment of an audience of all ages. The main course of events takes place on Christmas Eve itself, when the Thomas family are host to their relatives. Apart from a potentially major hiccup when the turkey catches fire, the traditional yuletide celebrations are enjoyed by all.

A Christmas Carol. Musical play. Book by Christopher Bedloe, adaptation and lyrics by James Wood, music by Malcolm Shapcott from the story by Charles Dickens
39 characters, with doubling can be staged by a cast of 18-20. Extras. Fee by arrangement. Vocal score available separately

A wealth of pretty, singable music, witty lyrics and plenty of scope for dancing and colourful staging make this musical version of a well-loved story a real piece of Christmas cheer. Period nineteenth century

A Christmas Carol. Play. Adapted by John Mortimer from the story by Charles Dickens
Large mixed cast, doubling possible. Various simple settings. Fee code M

Charles Dickens' famous tale of Ebenezer Scrooge's transformation from embittered skinflint to generous benefactor has been dramatized by John Mortimer with typical flair and wit in this definitive adaptation, first performed by the Royal Shakespeare Company. Retaining Dickens' own ironic point of view through the use of a Chorus, Mortimer has created a panoramic view of Victorian London with all the much-loved characters in place. There is plenty of scope for imaginative doubling, and the staging requirements are flexible. Period nineteenth century
ISBN 0 573 01733 6

A Christmas Carol. Christmas play. Shaun Sutton. From the story by Charles Dickens
M24 F15. Composite setting: an office, a street, a parlour. Fee code K

This version of the famous story contains nearly forty characters, but with reasonable doubling it can be performed by a cast of twenty — 10 men, 6 women, 2 boys and girls. The story of Scrooge's conversion from miserliness to benevolence contains scenes that elaborate a Christmas play into a simple form of Christmas pantomime. Period nineteenth century
ISBN 0 573 01070 6

Christmas Crackers. Children's play. Willis Hall
M7 F2. An empty stage. Fee code M

This is the hilariously funny sequel to *Kidnapped at Christmas*. Crosby and Gilbert, our two convict friends, are spending a lonely Christmas Eve eating baked beans on the stage of an empty theatre when they encounter their old enemies — Detective Constable Grummett (and his wife and horrible son) and Constables Mullins and MacBain. Add a failed beauty queen, some pantomime costumes, and a green skeleton and an evening of fun is assured for all.
ISBN 0 573 05040 6

The Christmas Story. Nativity play. David Wood
Large cast. Various simple settings. Fee code G

David Wood writes: 'This version of the nativity story was written at the request of several teachers who wanted a play which revealed the human side of the great event. I have tried to combine the traditional elements of the holy story with reverent humour'. Christmas carols and hymns are used to further the story and there are many opportunities for good acting parts as well as middle-sized parts and walk-on parts for younger children.

Good King Wenceslas and the Chancellor of Bohemia. Play. Tony Horitz
M5 F2, 8M or F (minimum). Various interior and exterior settings. Fee code F

On the Feast of Stephen, the Chancellor of Bohemia is preparing a surprise for the King — a golden statue. The King, however, is beginning to have doubts about the difference between his wealth and the poverty of his subjects, a difference created, without his knowledge, by his Chancellor's cruelly hard taxes. The King leaves the palace in disguise and discovers the true nature of his Chancellor's actions on his behalf.
ISBN 0 573 16501 7

The Great Santa Kidnap. Christmas Play. Roy Chatfield
12 named characters. Extras. Various interior and exterior settings. Fee code J

It is Christmas Eve and Fergus, Santa Claus's Chief Forebrownie, is bustling about preparing Santa's sleigh. However, three goblins — Sneergripe, Snottle and Bug — are plotting to kidnap Santa Claus and hold him to ransom! The goblins stage the kidnap and it is up to Tommy and Anna to find Santa and safeguard Christmas for the children of the world. Playing time 90 minutes.
ISBN 0 573 06623 X

Kidnapped at Christmas. Play. Willis Hall
M7 F2. Six simple settings. Fee code M

Convicts Gilbert and Crosby are fed-up at the thought of another Christmas in prison, especially with the prison Christmas dinner. They manage to escape and their adventures on the run, in various disguises, dodging a host of amazing characters, are all tremendous fun.
ISBN 0 573 05037 6

The Land of Kerfuffle. Play for Christmas. Bill Gavin. Loosely adapted from *The Wallypug of Why* by G. E. Farrow
M9 F5 or M5 F9. Extras optional. Various settings on an open stage. Fee code K

It is Christmas Eve. Penny hears the Snowman in her garden speak, and this is the start of a night of magical adventures.The Christmas Tree Fairy comes to life and, with the help of the Fairy's wand, the room tidies itself up, and then Penny is whisked off to the magical Land of Kerfuffle. After a night she will never forget she is magically returned home on Christmas morning.
ISBN 0 573 06505 5

Land of the Christmas Stocking. Musical play for children and adults. Henry D. G. Foord and Mabel Buchanan. Music by Mabel Buchanan
19 characters. Dancers. Extras. Two interiors, three exteriors. Fee by arrangement

When Father Christmas comes to visit Tom and Tilly on Christmas Eve he overhears them talking with their Nurse and saying that they do not believe in Father Christmas. He is very distressed and decides to teach all three a lesson by taking them to Rhymeland. While they are there Tom and Tilly are brought to realize exactly what the Spirit of Christmas is.
ISBN 0 573 05012 6

Laughter in the Dark. Comedy. Victor Lucas

For a full synopsis see the entry in Section A.

The Merry Gentleman. Book and lyrics by Dorothy Reynolds and Julian Slade. Music by Julian Slade
M12 F8. A drawing-room, the roof tops, Christmasland. Fee by arrangement

Julian Slade writes: 'The intention behind this show is to present as many of the aspects of Christmas as possible, warmth, nostalgia and at times magic or absurdity or both.' Confusion arises when the real Father Christmas drops in on a Christmas night party in 1910. The guests soon find themselves in Christmasland on a very special treasure-hunt — a search for true happiness. The show has many enchanting and delightful songs and ends happily in the best of traditions.

The Nativity. Medieval miracle play. Adapted by Angela Black
M17 F5. A bare stage. Fee code H

The various changes of setting, in this medieval telling of the nativity story, are made by two guildsmen sceneshifters, and are mainly effected by the turning about of two benches and the draping of a dais, so that presentation is exceedingly simple.
ISBN 0 573 06010 X

An O. Henry Christmas. O. Henry. Adaptation, music and lyrics by Peter Ekstrom

Please see the entries for *The Gift of the Magi* and *The Last Leaf* under Christmas Plays One Act in Section D.

Peter Pan. Fantasy. J. M. Barrie
25 characters. Nursery, The Never Land, a ship. Fee code M

The everlasting classic account of two boys and a girl who follow Peter Pan and the invisible fairy, Tinker Bell, into The Never Land where children never grow old and where Captain Hook and his pirates are outwitted. Samuel French handle this play on behalf of the Hospital for Sick Children, Great Ormond Street. Restricted availability for amateurs. Please enquire before commencing rehearsals.
ISBN 0 573 05041 4

Peter Pan. Book, music and lyrics by Piers Chater-Robinson. Adapted from the play by J. M. Barrie

Please see the entry in Section C.

Pinocchio. Family entertainment. John Morley
Flexible casting: 9 to 14 Principals, adult and/or junior Chorus. One permanent set with three or four frontcloths. Fee code L

This delightful dramatization of Collodi's story Pinocchio has all the charm of the original. The story is simple to stage with many music and production suggestions, and the cast is flexible for both large and small companies.
ISBN 0 573 11345 9

Quest for the Whooperdink. Play with music. A. H. Teacey

For a full synopsis see the entry in Section C.

A Right Christmas Caper. Play. Willis Hall
M7 F2. Four simple settings. Fee code L

This is the third Christmas Eve spent in the company of convicts Gilbert and Crosby (the first two being *Kidnapped at Christmas* and *Christmas Crackers*). Our lovable heroes are back in prison again with Warders Mullins and MacBain. However, they intend to escape to find a Christmas tree, and when they do are pursued again by Detective Constable Grummett (who is closely followed by his horrid son and wailing wife).
ISBN 0 573 05044 9

D

Robin Hood — The Truth Behind the Green Tights. Play. David Neilson
M7 F2, with doubling. Various interior and exterior settings. Fee code L

For a full synopsis see the entry in Section A.

♦ **The Snow Queen**. Play. Ron Nicol. Based on the story by Hans Christian Andersen
Large mixed cast. Much doubling and trebling possible. Various simple settings. Fee code K

Skilfully adapted from the famous original story by Hans Christian Andersen, this is the story of Gerda, a little girl who seaches for her friend Kai when he is bewitched and imprisoned by the Snow Queen in her ice palace. Gerda's innocence charms all good people and animals she meets on the way. They help her to the royal court, and on to Lapland, where good conquers evil and the children are reunited.
ISBN 0 573 16503 3

Snow White and the Seven Dwarfs. Fairy tale play based on the story by the Brothers Grimm, for adults and children. Jessie Braham White. Music by Edmond Rickett
26 characters. Extras. Three interiors, one exterior. Fee code F

The famous story of Snow White, threatened with death by her jealous stepmother Queen Brangomar and cared for by the Seven Dwarfs, is excitingly and charmingly brought to life in this dramatization.
ISBN 0 573 05024 4

The Thwarting of Baron Bolligrew. Comedy for children. Robert Bolt

Please see the entry in Section C.

◆ **The Wind in the Willows**. Kenneth Grahame. Adapted for the stage by Alan Bennett. Music by Jeremy Sams
24 characters. Extras. Various settings. Fee code M (play) code C (music)

For a full synopsis please see the entry in Section A.

The Wind in the Willows. Family entertainment by John Morley, adapted from the novel by Kenneth Grahame

Please see the entry in Section A.

Worzel Gummidge. Book and lyrics by Keith Waterhouse and Willis Hall. Music by Denis King

Please see the entry in Section C.

Christmas Plays
One Act

'As With Gladness ...' Nativity play. Charles H. Sellars
M15 F6, Children. Various simple settings on an open stage. Fee code E

For a full synopsis see Section B.

At the Changing of the Year. Play. Malcolm Young
M3 F3. 1M voice. A sitting-room. Fee code D

For a full synopsis see Section B.

Christmas Incorporated. Satirical comedy. Peter Horsler

For a full synopsis see Section B.

Dawn on Our Darkness. Play. Richard Tydeman
M9 F1. Extras. An acting area. Fee code C

An unusual treatment of the Nativity story, designed for performances in church or hall, by actors of any age. Richard Tydeman's skill in conveying the true meaning of Christmas is here exploited to the full.

The Gift of the Magi. Christmas play. O. Henry. Adaptation, music and lyrics by Peter Ekstrom
M1 (young) F1 (young). A shabby one-room flat. Fee by arrangement

This tells the classic O. Henry short story, through music and lyrics, of the young couple in New York on Christmas Eve 1905, who loved each other so much that each sold his most prized possession to buy the other a Christmas present. Their special gifts bring a touching reaffirmation of their unselfish love.
ISBN 0 573 68132 5

The Last Leaf. Christmas play. O. Henry. Adaptation, music and lyrics by Peter Ekstrom.
M2 (30s, elderly) F2 (20s). A garret/studio. Fee by arrangement

This tells of two impoverished young women, Sue and Johnsy, struggling to become established artists in Greenwich Village, New York, in 1905 and how their aspirations are threatened when one is stricken with pneumonia. A combination of faith, prayer and strong chicken broth turns the tide, but not before a life allows itself to be selflessly given up in place of another.
ISBN 0 573 69572 5

The Pantomime Play. Children's play. Douglas Jackson
M1 F1. 19 other characters could be played by children: 5 by girls, 14 either sex. A living-room (curtains), a wood, a bedsitter (curtains). Fee code D

On her way through the wood Red Riding Hood meets various well-known fairy-story characters and the grim, greedy Wolf. The Wolf arrives at Grandma's first, tricks Grandma, then eats her. Later he eats Red also. The Wolf is eventually vanquished and Red and Grandma are rescued.
ISBN 0 573 05229 8

Papa Panov's Magic Christmas. Play. Paul Thain. From a story by Leo Tolstoy
21 characters. Extras. A workshop. Fee code C

This adaptation of a story by Leo Tolstoy, narrated by a Storyteller and involving an unlimited
cast of children, is a perfect play for Christmas. In a small Russian village an old shoemaker, now
almost too blind to thread a needle, has a dream that Jesus will visit him on Christmas Day.
ISBN 0 573 06622 1

The Real Spirit of Christmas. Play for children. Wes Magee
48 children (M or F). An open stage. Fee code D

Alfie Ruffcutt is a spoil-sport and a bully, who does not believe in Father Christmas, so his brothers
and sisters ask Father Christmas to bring Alfie 'the real spirit of Christmas'. Two spirits duly take
Alfie on a star-ship trip, showing him a variety of Christmas wonders which transforms him into
a happy, lovable boy.
ISBN 0 573 06613 2

The Soldier and the Woman. Play. Elaine Morgan
M3 (26, 30s) F1 (24). A stable. Fee code E

Rachel, whose baby son has been killed in the massacre of the innocents, is filled with hatred for
the wounded officer she finds in her stable. Simon, her husband, is frightened of the consequences
should the officer die; Rachel, eventually, is unable to watch him die. Period Biblical
ISBN 0 573 06234 X

The True Story of Good King Wenceslas. Edna Baker
M7 F2. A throne-room. Fee code C

A carol singer, delivering himself of *Good King Wenceslas*, is interrupted by 'Yonder Peasant'
who proceeds to recount what he alleges to be the true story of the ancient legend. Yonder Peasant
helped King Wenceslas to lose a long-lasting bout of hiccups and defrosted the royal pipes; he
was offered the hand of the Princess. The singer is sceptical about this story...
ISBN 0 573 06611 6

SECTION E
Musical Plays

This section of the Guide gives brief details of the Musical Plays controlled for performance by Samuel French Ltd. Full details — casting, orchestration, etc. — can be found in the catalogue of Musical Plays, published separately. Information about individual titles can, of course, be given by letter or over the telephone.

Please also see under the relevant headings in Section C (Children's Plays and Plays for Young People) and Section D (Pantomimes and Christmas Plays) of this Guide for full details of other Musical Plays and Plays with Music that are available for performance.

All for Your Delight. Book, music and lyrics by Roger Parsley.

And So to Bed. J. B. Fagan. Lyrics and music by Vivian Ellis.

Andy Capp. Book by Trevor Peacock. Music by Alan Price. Lyrics by Trevor Peacock and Alan Price.

Anne of Green Gables. From the novel by L. M. Montgomery. Adapted by Donald Harron. Lyrics by Donald Harron and Norman Campbell. Additional lyrics by Mavor Moore and Elaine Campbell. Music by Norman Campbell.

Annie Get Your Gun. Music and lyrics by Irving Berlin. Book by Herbert and Dorothy Fields.

The Arcadians. Book by Mark Ambient, A. M. Thompson and Robert Courtneidge. Lyrics by Arthur Wimperis. Music by Lionel Monckton and Howard Talbot.

Balalaika. Book and lyrics by Eric Maschwitz. Music by George Posford and Bernard Grun.

Bashville. Book by David William and Benny Green. Music by Denis King. Lyrics by Benny Green. Adapted from *The Admirable Bashville* by Bernard Shaw.

The Belle of New York. Book by Hugh Morton. New book by Bernard Dunn and Emile Littler. Music by Gustave Kerker.

The Best Little Whorehouse in Texas. Book by Larry L. King and Peter Masterson. Music and lyrics by Carol Hall.

Big Al. Book and Lyrics by John Gardiner. Music by Andrew Parr.

The Biograph Girl. Book by Warner Brown. Lyrics by Warner Brown and David Heneker. Music by David Heneker.

Bitter Sweet. An operetta by Noël Coward.

Bless the Bride. Book and lyrics by A. P. Herbert. Music by Vivian Ellis.

Blossom Time. Adapted by Sydney Box. Music arranged and derived from Franz Schubert by G. H. Clutsam. Lyrics by G.H. Clutsam, John Drinkwater and H. V. Purcell.

Bob's Your Uncle. Austin Melford. Music by Noel Gay. Lyrics by Frank Eyton.

The Boy Friend. Book, music and lyrics by Sandy Wilson.

The Buccaneer. Book, music and lyrics by Sandy Wilson.

The Burston Drum. Book by Ellen Dryden. Lyrics by Don Taylor. Music by Charles Young.

La Cage aux Folles. Book by Harvey Fierstein. Music and lyrics by Jerry Herman. Based on the play by Jean Poiret.

Careless Rapture. Ivor Novello. Lyrics by Christopher Hassall.

Carissima. Book and lyrics by Eric Maschwitz. From the story by Armin Robinson. Music by Hans May.

Chess. Lyrics by Tim Rice. Music by Björn Ulvaeus and Benny Andersson.

Chicago. Book by Fred Ebb and Bob Fosse. Music by John Kander. Lyrics by Fred Ebb. Based on the play *Chicago* by Maurine Dallas Watkins.

Chrysanthemum. Book and lyrics by Neville Philips and Robin Chancellor. Music by Rob Stewart.

Chu Chin Chow. Book by Oscar Asche. Music by Frederick Norton.

Cole. An entertainment based on the words and music of Cole Porter. Devised by Benny Green and Alan Strachan.

Cowardy Custard. An entertainment devised by Gerald Frow, Alan Strachan and Wendy Toye featuring the words and music of Noël Coward.

◆ **The Curious Quest for the Sandman's Sand.** Book and lyrics by Jenifer Toksvig. Music by David Perkins

Dames at Sea. Book and lyrics by George Haimsohn and Robin Miller. Music by Jim Wise.

The Dancing Years. Devised, written and composed by Ivor Novello. Lyrics by Christopher Hassall.

The Dancing Years. A revised version for the theatre by Cecil Clarke and Tom Arnold of the original musical by Ivor Novello and Christopher Hassall.

Dazzle. Book and lyrics by John Gardiner. Music by Andrew Parr

Divorce Me Darling! Book, music and lyrics by Sandy Wilson.

◆ **Dreams from a Summer House**. Words by Alan Ayckbourn. Music by John Pattison

The Dubarry. Adapted by Eric Maschwitz from the play by Paul Knepler and J. Welleminsky. Lyrics by Rowland Leigh. Additional lyrics by Eric Maschwitz. Music by Karl Milloecker. Arranged by Theo Makeben. Adapted and augmented by Bernard Grun.

The Duenna. Adapted by Lionel Harris from the operetta by Richard Brinsley Sheridan. Music by Julian Slade.

Elegies for Angels, Punks and Raging Queens. By Bill Russell. Music by Janet Hood.

The End of the Pier Show. Book, music and lyrics by Roger Parsley.

The Farndale Avenue Housing Estate Townswomen's Guild Operatic Society's Production of *The Mikado*. By David McGillivray and Walter Zerlin Jnr. Based on *The Mikado* or *The Town of Titipu* by W. S. Gilbert and Arthur Sullivan. Music arranged by Sue Van Colle.

◆ **Fawkes—The Quiet Guy**. Kjartan Poskitt

Fings Ain't Wot They Used T'Be. Book by Frank Norman. Music and lyrics by Lionel Bart.

First Impressions. Book by Abe Burrows. Music and lyrics by Robert Goldman, Glenn Paxton and George Weiss.

First Time. Book by Kirk Foster and John Gardiner. Music by Kirk Foster and Paul Sabey.

Follow That Girl. Book and lyrics by Dorothy Reynolds and Julian Slade. Music by Julian Slade. Adapted by Bernard Dunn from the original production by Dennis Carey.

Free As Air. Book and lyrics by Dorothy Reynolds and Julian Slade. Music by Julian Slade.

Gay's the Word. Book and music by Ivor Novello. Lyrics by Alan Melville.

The Geisha. Book by Owen Hall. Lyrics by Harry Greenbank. Music by Sidney J. Jones.

Glamorous Night. Book and music by Ivor Novello. Lyrics by Christopher Hassall.

Godspell. Conceived and originally directed by John-Michael Tebelak. Music and new lyrics by Stephen Schwartz.

Goodnight Vienna. Book and lyrics by Eric Maschwitz. Music by George Posford. Additional material by Harold Purcell and Sydney Box.

The Grand Tour. Jerry Herman, Michael Stewart and Mark Bramble, based on S. N. Behrman's adaptation of Franz Werfel's play *Jacobowsky and the Colonel*.

Grease. Book, music and lyrics by Jim Jacobs and Warren Casey.

The Great American Backstage Musical. Book by Bill Solly and Donald Ward. Music and lyrics by Bill Solly.

Henry the Tudor Dude. A musical play by Kjartan Poskitt.

The Hired Man. Book by Melvyn Bragg. Music and lyrics by Howard Goodall.

◆ **The Hunchback of Notre Dame.** Book and lyrics by Gary Sullivan. Music by John Trent Wallace. Based on *Notre Dame de Paris* by Victor Hugo

I'm Getting My Act Together and Taking It on the Road. Gretchen Cryer and Nancy Ford.

Jack the Ripper. Book and lyrics by Ron Pember and Denis de Marne. Music by Ron Pember.

King's Rhapsody. Devised, written and composed by Ivor Novello. Lyrics by Christopher Hassall.

◆ **Kiss of the Spiderwoman**. Book by Terrence McNally. Music by John Kander. Lyrics by Fred Ebb. Based on the novel by Manuel Puig

Little Mary Sunshine. Book, music and lyrics by Rick Besoyan.

A Little Princess. Michael Wild. Adapted from the novel by Frances Hodgson Burnett.

Lock Up Your Daughters. Adapted from Henry Fielding's comedy *Rape Upon Rape* by Bernard Miles. Lyrics by Lionel Bart. Music by Laurie Johnson.

Love from Judy. Music by Hugh Martin. Book by Eric Maschwitz and Jean Webster. Lyrics by Hugh Martin and Jack Gray.

Love Off the Shelf. Book by Roger Hall. Lyrics by A. K. Grant. Music by Philip Norman.

Lust. Book, music and lyrics by The Heather Brothers, based on William Wycherley's *The Country Wife*.

♦ **Mack and Mabel**. Book by Michael Stewart. Music and lyrics by Jerry Herman. Based on an idea by Leonard Spigelglass.

Magyar Melody. Adapted by Eric Maschwitz and George Posford from the play by Eric Maschwitz, Fred Thompson and Guy Bolton. Music by George Posford and Bernard Grun.

Maid of the Mountains. Book by Frederick Lonsdale, with revisions by Emile Maschwitz, Fred Thompson and Guy Bolton. Music by George Posford and Bernard Grun.

Make Me an Offer. Book by Wolf Mankowitz. Music and lyrics by David Heneker and Monty Norman.

The Matchgirls. Book and lyrics by Bill Owen. Music by Tony Russell.

Me and My Girl. Book and lyrics by L. Arthur Rose and Douglas Furber. Music by Noel Gay. Book revised by Stephen Fry, contributions to revisions by Mike Ockrent.

The Merry Gentleman. Book and lyrics by Dorothy Reynolds and Julian Slade.

Moll Flanders. Book by Claire Luckham, lyrics by Paul Leigh. Music by George Stiles. Based on the novel by Daniel Defoe

The Musical Importance of Being Earnest. A musical adaptation of Oscar Wilde's classic by John Sean O'Mahoney.

♦ **Nine**. Book by Arthur Kopit. Music, adaptation and lyrics by Maury Yeston. Adapted from the Italian by Mario Fratti.

♦ **Noël and Gertie**. Devised by Sheridan Morley. Words and music by Noël Coward. Arrangements by Jonathan Cohen.

Nunsense. Dan Groggin.

An O. Henry Christmas. A Christmas Musical. Adaptation, music and lyrics by Peter Ekstrom.

Oh, Brother! Book and lyrics by Donald Driver. Music by Michael Valenti.

Joan Littlewood's musical entertainment **Oh What a Lovely War.** By Theatre Workshop, Charles Chilton, Gerry Raffles and members of the original cast. Title suggested by Ted Allan

Old Chelsea. Walter Ellis. Music by Richard Tauber. Additional numbers by Bernard Grun. Lyrics by Fred S. Tysh and Walter Ellis.

On the Twentieth Century. Book and lyrics by Betty Comden and Adolph Green. Music by Cy Coleman.

Perchance to Dream. By Ivor Novello.

Peter Pan. Adapted from the play by J. M. Barrie. Book, music and lyrics by Piers Chater-Robinson.

The Phantom of the Opera. Based on the novel by Gaston Leroux. Book and lyrics by Ken Hill. Arrangements and incidental music by Alasdair MacNeill.

Pickwick. Based on *Posthumous Papers of the Pickwick Club* by Charles Dickens. Book by Wolf Mankowitz, lyrics by Leslie Bricusse, music by Cyril Ornadel.

Pink Champagne. Adapted by Eric Maschwitz and Bernard Grun from *Die Fledermaus* by Johann Strauss.

Poppy. Book and lyrics by Peter Nichols. Music by Monty Norman.

Pump Boys and Dinettes. Conceived and written by John Foley, Mark Hardwick, Debra Monk, Cass Morgan, John Schimmel and Jim Wann.

The Quaker Girl. (Original version) Book by James T. Tanner and Emile Littler. Lyrics by Adrian Ross and Percy Greenbank. Music by Lionel Monckton.

The Quaker Girl. Freely adapted and arranged by Andrew Nicklin and Philip Beeson, from the original version.

The Revenge of Sherlock Holmes. Book, music and lyrics by Leslie Bricusse. Based on characters created by Sir Arthur Conan Doyle.

The Rink. Book by Terence McNally. Music by John Kander. Lyrics by Fred Ebb.

Rio Rita. Book by Guy Bolton and Fred Thompson. Lyrics by Joseph McCarthy. Music by Harry Tierney.

Robert and Elizabeth. Book and lyrics by Ronald Millar. Music by Ron Grainer. From an original idea by Fred G. Morrit. Based on *The Barretts of Wimpole Street* by Rudolph Besier.

Rockasocka. Book and lyrics by John Gardiner. Music by Andrew Parr

Rose Marie. Book and lyrics by Otto Harbach and Oscar Hammerstein. Music by Rudolf Friml and Herbert Stothhart.

Rumpelstiltskin Racket. Book, music and lyrics by Kjartan Poskitt.

Runaways. Elizabeth Swados.

Salad Days. Book and lyrics by Dorothy Reynolds and Julian Slade. Music by Julian Slade.

◆ **Scrooge — the Musical**. Book, music and lyrics by Leslie Bricusse. *Restrictions apply*.

The Secret Life of Walter Mitty. Book by Joe Manchester. Lyrics by Earl Shuman. Music by Leon Carr. Based on the story by James Thurber.

Seesaw. Music by Cy Coleman. Lyrics by Dorothy Fields. Book by Michael Bennett. Based on the play *Two for the Seesaw* by William Gibson.

◆ **Shake, Ripple and Roll**. Book and lyrics by Jenifer Toksvig. Music by David Perkins

◆ **Sleeping Beauty**. Book and lyrics by Simon Brett. Music by Sarah Travis

A Slice of Saturday Night. Book, music and lyrics by The Heather Brothers.

Some Canterbury Tales. Freely adapted from Chaucer by Ken Pickering. Music by Derek Hyde.

Something's Afoot. Book, music and lyrics by James McDonald, David Vos and Robert Gerlach. Additional music by Ed Linderman.

Songbook. Music by Monty Norman. Lyrics by Julian More. Book by Monty Norman and Julian More.

Strider. Adapted from Leo Tolstoy's story.

Suburban Strains. Book and lyrics by Alan Ayckbourn. Music by Paul Todd.

Summer in the Park. Book by Ellen Dryden, lyrics by Don Taylor, music by Charles Young

Summer Song. Book by Eric Maschwitz and Hy Craft. Lyrics by Eric Maschwitz. Music by Bernard Grun, from themes of Anton Dvorák.

♦ **The Tale of Little Red Riding Hood**. An untraditional pantomime. Book and lyrics by Simon Brett. Music by Sarah Travis

A Tale of Two Cities. Adapted from Charles Dickens' novel by Dave Ross, Michael Mullane, Neil Parker and Vivienne Carter.

Tarantara! Tarantara! Book, music and lyrics by Ian Taylor, using songs by Gilbert and Sullivan.

Teller of Tales. A Musical Adventure from the life of Robert Louis Stevenson. Book and lyrics by Neil Wilkie. Music by Neil Wilkie and David Stoll.

1066 — And All That. Book and lyrics by Reginald Arkell, from the memorable history of the same name by W. C.Seller and R. J. Yeatman. Music by Alfred Reynolds.

They're Playing Our Song. Book by Neil Simon. Music by Marvin Hamlisch. Lyrics by Carol Bayer Sager.

Tom and Huckleberry. Music and lyrics by Mike Carter. Book by John Lazenby and Mike Carter.

Treasure Island. Adapted from Robert Louis Stevenson by Willis Hall. Music by Denis King.

Trelawny. Book by Aubrey Woods. Music and lyrics by Julian Slade. Adapted from Sir Arthur Pinero's *Trelawny of the 'Wells'* by Aubrey Woods, George Rowell and Julian Slade.

Two Bouquets. Eleanor and Herbert Farjeon. Music arranged and orchestrated by Ernest Irving.

The Vagabond King. Book and lyrics by W. H. Post and Brian Hooker from Justin Huntly McCarthy's romance *If I Were King*. Music by Rudolph Friml.

Valmouth. Book music and lyrics by Sandy Wilson.

Waldo and Sons. Book and Lyrics by Andrew McGregor. Music by David Pickthall.

Walking Happy. Roger O. Hirson, Ketty Frings, Sammy Cahn and James Van Heusen. Based on the play *Hobson's Choice* by Harold Brighouse.

Waltz Without End. Eric Maschwitz and Bernard Grun. To music from the works of Frederick Chopin.

The Water Babies. A play by Willis Hall with songs by John Cooper. Based on the story by Charles Kingsley.

Water Gypsies. Book and lyrics by A. P. Herbert. Music by Vivian Ellis.

Wedding in Paris. Vera Caspary. Lyrics by Sonny Miller. Music by Hans May.

White Horse Inn. Adapted by Hans Muller and Erik Charell from a play by Blumenthal and Kadelburg. Original lyrics by Robert Gilbert. Music by Ralph Benatsky and Robert Stolz. English book and lyrics by Harry Graham. The whole adapted by Eric Maschwitz and Bernard Grun.

The Wind in the Willows. A musical based on Kenneth Grahame's novel. Book and lyrics by Willis Hall. Music by Denis King.

The Wiz. The new musical version of *The Wonderful Wizard of Oz* by L. Frank Baum. Book by William F. Brown. Music and lyrics by Charlie Smalls.

♦ **A Word from our Sponsor**. Words by Alan Ayckbourn. Music by John Pattison

Worzel Gummidge. Keith Waterhouse and Willis Hall. Music by Denis King. Based on the book by Barbara Euphan Todd.

Zip Goes A Million. Book and lyrics by Eric Maschwitz. Music by George Posford. Based on an idea by Winchell Smith and Byron Ongley.

SECTION F
Technical Books

CONTENTS

AUDITION MATERIAL

All on Stage. Selected by Mary Greenslade
Book one: group scenes for young players (aged 9-13 years)
ISBN 0 573 19011 9

Book two: group scenes for students (aged 14 years upwards)
ISBN 0 573 12012 7

An exciting collection of extracts for group performance in classroom drama lessons, concerts, festivals and examinations at all levels, chosen by Guildhall examiner Mary Greenslade from some of the best plays available. Each excerpt is introduced to set it in context and to provide a challenging springboard for group production work.

Scenes for Two. Book 1. Mary Greenslade and Anne Harvey

A collection of duologues from thirty-eight plays by authors including Eugene O'Neill, Mark Twain, Michael Redgrave, Carson McCullers, Enid Bagnold and Nicholas Stuart Gray, for use by children in school and at play.
ISBN 0 573 09032 7

Take Two. Anne Harvey

In this exciting book there are over sixty duologues for two boys, two girls, or one boy and one girl, chosen by Anne Harvey from the very best of the world's plays and novels.
ISBN 0 573 19027 5

MAKE-UP

The ABC of Stage Make-Up for Men. Douglas Young   ISBN 0 573 09132 3

The ABC of Stage Make-Up for Women. Douglas Young   ISBN 0 573 09133 1

An up-to-date guide to the practical application of stage make-up. 20 cards bound together and illustrated in full colour showing 12 different make-ups as well as cards on hair and wigs, period hair styles and general principles of make-up. Suitable for any brand of make-up, the materials being listed in such a way that they will not go out of date.

MUSICAL INTEREST

Four Bars of 'Agit'. Incidental Music for Victorian and Edwardian Melodrama. David Mayer and Matthew Scott. With a preface by Sir Peter Hall

This is a unique collection of original incidental music for Victorian and Edwardian melodrama. The majority of the works come from the folio of Alfred Edward Cooper, which was found by chance and purchased for the nation by the Theatre Museum, London. A fascinating introduction by David Mayer sets the scene for these fifty-nine original melos. Matthew Scott has faithfully reproduced the music, adding his own transposition, into a minor key, of several pieces. With notes on the use and meaning of the melos this book is not only a wonderful insight into Britain's theatrical heritage but also a work of great importance to all concerned with theatre and history — a working book for today stepping straight from the pages of history.
ISBN 0 573 09010 6

SHAKESPEARE

Performing Shakespeare. A guidebook by J. W. Aykroyd. Costume illustrations by Lindy Swanson

The information collected in this book will be of invaluable use to English teachers and drama groups in schools and colleges, to student actors and to local amateur societies. Aspects of staging, acting, music, clothes, props and furniture which are relevant to Shakespeare production are outlined; suppliers, sources and books for further reading are listed and a short account of each play in terms of minimum and maximum castings, basic props and effects is given in Chapter 9. The plays are approached, as they were written, as blueprints for performance. The author shows how the text contains implicit and explicit directions to the performers. Exploring these directions and putting them into practice in a way that Shakespeare's own actors may have done is by far the most interesting and rewarding way for young people to learn about Shakespeare.
ISBN 0 573 19035 6

SPEECH TRAINING

Anthology of British Tongue Twisters. Ken Parkin

The first collection of the best traditional and new tongue twisters, divided into sections according to the oral exercise they are best suited to. Practical and instructive, but amusing too.
ISBN 0 573 09028 9

Ideal Voice and Speech Training. Ken Parkin

How often teachers of speech must long to discover some fresh exercises — here is a book of exercises which have been proved in the author's classes.
ISBN 0 573 09013 0

THEATRE

The Art of Coarse Acting. Michael Green

Newly revised and updated to take account of changes in the amateur theatre world in the thirty years (heavens — that long!) since it was first published, Michael Green's work is consistently funny and required reading for all devotees of theatre, amateur and professional!
ISBN 0 573 19007 0

It Gives Me Further Pleasure. Further Ruminations upon the Art of the Music Hall Chairman, plus over Six Hundred Ready-Made Song Introductions. Michael Kilgarriff

An invaluable source book for music hall chairmen and a fascinating historical insight into the genre. Six hundred song titles of the period are given, together with their lyricists, composers, dates of first performance or publication and the artistes who made them famous. Introductions and back announcements are given for each — some straightforward, some funny and some downright saucy!
ISBN 0 573 19007 0

It Gives Me Great Pleasure. The Complete *Vade Mecum* for the Old Time Music Hall Chairman. Michael Kilgarriff

The author has many years of experience in the world of Old Time Music Hall and this book is a distillation of his notes and records. It provides a guide for both amateur and professional companies with little or no experience of the genre to the production of Music Hall including song titles and over 600 patter entries, all of which have been tried out in performance.
ISBN 0 573 09036 X

Title Index
Sections A-F

Title Index

C

G

M

Wendlebury Day 432
Whale 497
Whale Music 290
What Are Little Girls Made Of? 291
What Are You Doing Here? 433
What Brutes Men Are 433
What Every Woman Knows 291
What Ho Within! 433
What I Did in the Holidays 291
What Shall We Do with the Body? 433
What the Butler Saw 291
What the Dinosaur 433
What's for Pudding? 433
Wheel 497
When Did You Last See Your Trousers? 291
When I was a Girl, I Used to Scream and
    Shout 292
When She Danced 292
When the Barbarians Came 292
When the Cat's Away 292
When the Wind Blows 292
When We Are Married 293
Whence 434
Where the Rainbow Ends 497
White Horse Inn 533
White Liars 434
Who Calls? 434
Who Goes Bare? 293
Who Killed Santa Claus? 293
Who Saw Him Die? 293
Who Was Hilary Maconochie? 434
Who Will Man the Lifeboat? 434
Whodunnit 293
Whoops-a-Daisy 294
Who's Afraid of Virginia Woolf? 294
Who's Bean Stalking? 434
Who's Under Where? 294
Whose Life Is It Anyway? 294
Whose Wedding Is It Anyway 435
Why Me? 294
Why Not Stay for Breakfast? 295
Widows 295
Wife Begins at Forty 295
Wild Duck 295
Wild Goose Chase 295
Wild Honey 296
Wildest Dreams 296
Will You Still Love Me in the Morning? 296
Wind in the Willows
    Grahame/Bennett 296, 497, 520
    Grahame/Morley 296, 497, 520
    Grahame/Hall/King 498, 533
Wind of Heaven 297
Wings 297
Winnie-the-Pooh 498
Winslow Boy 297
Winter Glory 297

Winter Guest 297
Winter of 1917 435
Winter Wife 298
Witches 498
Witness for the Prosecution 298
Wiz 533
Wizard of Oz 498
Wizard of Wobbling Rock 498
Wolf at the Door 298
Wolfsbane 298
Woman Alone 435
Woman in Mind 298
Woman in White 299
Woman of No Importance 435
Womberang 435
Women 299
Women on the Verge of HRT 299
Wonderful Story of Mother Goose 511
Word from Our Sponsor 299, 533
World Première 435
Worzel Gummidge 499, 520, 533
Woyzeck 299
Wuthering Heights 300

Y

Yard of Sun 300
Year After The Fair 300
Yerma 300
Yes and No 436
You, Me and Mrs Jones 499
You Say Tomatoes 300
You Should See Us Now 301
Young Guy Seeks Part-Time Work 436

Z

Zack 301
Zartan 436
Zigger Zagger 301, 499
Zip Goes A Million 533
Zoo Story 436

Classified list of Advertisers

Drama Training

Drama Studio London   page iv

Furniture and Properties

Howorth Wrightson Ltd   page vi

Insurance

First Night   page xxiv

Lighting

White Light   page x

Make-Up

Charles H. Fox   page xviii

Merchandising

Global Marketing   page xvi

Organizations

Amdram   page xxii
Drama Association of Wales   page xx
National Drama Festivals Association   page xiv

Printing

Cowdall's Printing Company   page viii

Publication

The Stage   page xxx

Reference

Theatre Record   page xiv

Special Effects

Hi-Fli   page xxviii

Wigs

Derek Easton (Hair and Wigs)   page xxviii